GEOMETRY TRIGONOMETRY

MAT 121

D1373569

**Dale Downs, Melinda Fox, Ed Gallo
Bill Graesser, Paul Hessert, Dan Ledsome
Susan Newman-Bourne, Kathie Potter**

Ivy Tech State College

Taken from:
Essentials of Geometry for College Students
by Margaret L. Lial, Arnold R. Steffensen, and L. Murphy Johnson

Essentials of Geometry for College Students, Student Solutions Manual
by Margaret L. Lial, Arnold R. Steffensen, and L. Murphy Johnson

Basic Technical Mathematics, Seventh Edition
by Allyn J. Washington

Student's Solutions Manual to Accompany Basic Technical Mathematics
by John R. Martin

Pearson
Custom
Publishing

Addison
Wesley

Cover Art: *Probability*, by Angela Sciaraffa.

Excerpts taken from:

Essentials of Geometry for College Students
by Margaret L. Lial, Arnold R. Steffensen, and L. Murphy Johnson
Copyright © 1990 by Margaret L. Lial, Arnold R. Steffensen, and L. Murphy Johnson
Published by Addison-Wesley Publishing Company
A Pearson Education Company
Boston, Massachusetts 02116

Essentials of Geometry for College Students, Student Solutions Manual
by Margaret L. Lial, Arnold R. Steffensen, and L. Murphy Johnson
Copyright © 1990 by Margaret L. Lial, Arnold R. Steffensen, and L. Murphy Johnson
Published by Addison-Wesley Publishing Company

Basic Technical Mathematics, Seventh Edition
by Allyn J. Washington
Copyright © 2000, 1995, 1990, 1985, 1978, 1970, 1964 by Addison Wesley Longman, Inc.

Student's Solutions Manual to Accompany Basic Technical Mathematics
by John R. Martin
Copyright © 2000 by Addison Wesley Longman, Inc.

Printed in the United States of America

10 9 8 7 6 5

Please visit our web site at www.pearsoncustom.com

ISBN 0–536–67407–8

BA 994134

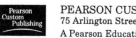

PEARSON CUSTOM PUBLISHING
75 Arlington Street, Suite 300, Boston, MA 02116
A Pearson Education Company

Right Prism

h = height; P = perimeter of base;
B = area of base
Lateral area: $LA = Ph$
Surface area: $SA = 2B + LA$
Volume: $V = Bh$

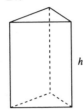

Rectangular Solid (Prism)

ℓ, w, h = edges
Surface area: $SA = 2\ell h + 2wh + 2\ell w$
Volume: $V = \ell wh$
If $\ell = w = h$, the solid is a *cube*.

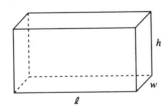

Cube

e = edge
Surface area: $SA = 6e^2$
Volume: $V = e^3$

Right Circular Cylinder

r = radius; h = height
Surface area: $SA = 2\pi rh + 2\pi r^2$
Volume: $V = \pi r^2 h$

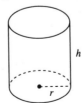

Sphere

r = radius
Surface area: $SA = 4\pi r^2$
Volume: $V = \dfrac{4}{3}\pi r^3$

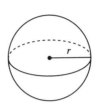

Regular Pyramid

h = height; p = perimeter of base;
ℓ = slant height; B = area of base

Lateral area: $LA = \dfrac{1}{2}p\ell$

Surface area: $SA = B + \dfrac{1}{2}p\ell$

Volume: $V = \dfrac{1}{3}Bh$

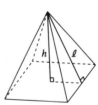

Right Circular Cone

r = radius; h = height
Lateral area: $LA = \pi r\sqrt{r^2 + h^2}$
Surface area: $SA = \pi r\sqrt{r^2 + h^2} + \pi r^2$

Volume: $V = \dfrac{1}{3}\pi r^2 h$

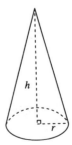

GEOMETRY

Geometry–Trigonometry

Preface

Introduction

For many years, Ivy Tech State College has offered a course in Geometry-Trigonometry for technical majors such as Heating, Ventilation, and Air Conditioning (HVAC), Construction Technology, and Design Technology. Although the topics of geometry and trigonometry are related, it is difficult to find a single textbook that covers both of these subjects. For this reason, faculty members from Ivy Tech State College worked with Pearson Custom Publishing to produce a book specifically designed for our Geometry-Trigonometry course.

In developing this custom textbook, our main goal was to be sure to include material that covered all of our Geometry-Trigonometry course objectives. The material in the book was not written anew; it was taken from *Essentials of Geometry for College Students* by Lial, Steffensen and Johnson and from *Basic Technical Mathematics* by Allyn J. Washington. In addition, material from the Student's Solutions Manuals for these two textbooks was included in our custom textbook.

Geometry

The first three parts of the book contain material mostly from *Essentials of Geometry for College Students*. This book takes a somewhat formal approach to geometry by introducing concepts in the form of definitions and postulates. Formal proofs of various geometric theorems are also included. There are, however, enough material and exercises on each topic so that instructors may give little or no emphasis to the proofs.

While most of the geometry comes from Lial et. al., we have also included material from Washington's book. The major difference between these two texts is that Washington does not include formal proofs. It is also worth mentioning that Washington introduces radian measure early while Lial et. al. does not include radian measure at all. Therefore, we chose to include radian measure from Washington in section 2.5 of the custom textbook in order to support its use later in the trigonometry section.

Trigonometry

Parts 4-8 of this custom textbook cover the trigonometry portion of the course. All of the trigonometry material comes from *Basic Technical Mathematics* by Allyn Washington. This text includes numerous applications throughout. In Part 7 (Graphs of the Trigonometric Functions), some material and exercises make use of graphing calculators. However, graphing calculator usage is not overly emphasized. Therefore, graphing calculators are not required for an effective presentation of graphing these trigonometric functions.

Appendices

The appendices include topics intended to supplement the text, as well as to provide course objectives and a cross-reference from this custom textbook to the Lial et. al. and Washington textbooks.

Appendix A is an introduction to the metric system and unit conversions. Appendix B covers ratio and proportion and variation. Appendix B material may be a useful review before discussing trigonometric ratios. Appendix C includes a table of values of the trigonometric functions of angles for each 10-minutes, as well as for the equivalent radian measure.

Appendix D provides a list of the eighteen "General Course Objectives" that are contained in the Ivy Tech State College course outline/syllabus. And, finally, Appendix E contains a cross-reference between the custom textbook section number and title, the Ivy Tech State College general course objective, and the source textbook section number.

Organization of the Custom Textbook

Since this textbook was custom published from two different textbooks and two different student solutions manuals, there are differences in the "look" of the pages in the different chapters, sections, and appendices. One obvious example is that the typeface that is used is not the same throughout the textbook. In addition, the sections in the Lial, Steffensen, Johnson textbook are designated as "1.2"; whereas, the sections in the Washington textbook are designated as "2-3".

This custom textbook is divided into "Parts" instead of "Chapters" since, in several cases, material for the "Part" was taken from different chapters or different source textbooks.

The original <u>section number, section title, and page number</u> of the source textbooks are included on each page in the custom textbook. In addition, for the ease of use, the <u>*custom part number, section number, section title, and page number*</u> are included on each page. This **custom information** is also included in the table of contents and, therefore, is the key to successfully navigating throughout the custom textbook.

Another major difference that is included in this custom textbook is that the answers to section and chapter exercises and problems are included at the end of each part of the textbook instead of all together at the end of the textbook.

Supplementary Material For Students

- *Student Solutions Manual for Essentials of Geometry for College Students* by Lial, Steffensen and Johnson, Harper Collins, 1990. This contains the step-by-step solutions for the odd-numbered text exercises and for all of the chapter review and practice test problems.

- *Student's Solutions Manual for Basic Technical Mathematics* by Allyn J. Washington, 7th Edition, Addison, Wesley, Longman, 2000. This contains the detailed solutions for every other odd-numbered section exercise.

- <u>Web Site</u> at http://www.technicalmath.com/btm/btm_1/index_1.htm. This contains activities, chapter openers, chapter quizzes, and lists of supplements.

Supplementary Material For Instructors

- <u>The Instructor's Test Manual</u> for *Essentials of Geometry for College Students* by Lial, Steffensen and Johnson, Harper Collins, 1990. This contains two ready-to-duplicate tests for each chapter and two final exams. Additional problems are included for use as in-class examples or on quizzes and tests. Answers are provided to all of these problems.

- <u>The Instructor's Answer and Solutions Manual</u> for *Essentials of Geometry for College Students* by Lial, Steffensen and Johnson, Harper Collins, 1990. This contains answers and step-by-step solutions to the even-numbered text exercises.

- <u>Five-color Overhead Transparency Overlays</u> for *Essentials of Geometry for College Students* by Lial, Steffensen and Johnson, Harper Collins, 1990. This contains 25 step-by-step constructions and 22 two-color transparencies for classroom use.

- <u>Instructor's Solutions Manual</u> for *Basic Technical Mathematics* by Allyn J. Washington, 7th Edition, Addison, Wesley, Longman, 2000. This contains detailed solutions to every section exercise.

- <u>Answer Book</u> for *Basic Technical Mathematics* by Allyn J. Washington, 7th Edition, Addison, Wesley, Longman, 2000. This contains answers to all exercises, including review exercises.

- <u>Printed Test Bank, TestGen-EQ and QuizMaster-EQ</u> for *Basic Technical Mathematics* by Allyn J. Washington, 7th Edition, Addison, Wesley, Longman, 2000. For more information about these supplements, contact Addison Wesley Longman.

- <u>Web Site</u> at http://www.technicalmath.com/btm/btm_1/index_1.htm. This contains activities, chapter openers, chapter quizzes, and lists of supplements.

<u>Acknowledgements</u>

This custom textbook project began with initial discussions of several Ivy Tech State College mathematics faculty members during spring 2000. Additional groundwork was done during summer and fall 2000, with the result of the "MAT 121 (Geometry-Trigonometry) Custom Textbook Committee" being formed late fall 2001. The committee held its first meeting in January 2001.

Special thanks go to Loren Hall, Director of Curriculum Planning, Central Office, Ivy Tech State College, for his support of this project.

Additional thanks go to all of the people who helped in this project. This includes Ivy Tech State College faculty and staff members and Nola Akala and Dave Chwalick of Addison Wesley Longman and Kurt Jaenicke of Pearson Custom Publishing.

<u>The MAT 121 (Geometry-Trigonometry) Custom Textbook Committee</u>

Dale Downs................ Ivy Tech State College – East Chicago, IN
Melinda Fox.............. Ivy Tech State College – Indianapolis, IN
Ed Gallo................... Ivy Tech State College – Fort Wayne, IN
Bill Graesser.............. Ivy Tech State College – Richmond, IN
Paul Hessert............... Ivy Tech State College – Bloomington, IN
Dan Ledsome.............. Ivy Tech State College – South Bend, IN
Susan Newman-Bourne... Ivy Tech State College – Sellersburg, IN
Kathie Potter.............. Ivy Tech State College – Evansville, IN

GEOMETRY

PART 1 – BASIC GEOMETRICAL CONCEPTS

Part 1
Section 1.1

1.2 Points, Lines, and Planes

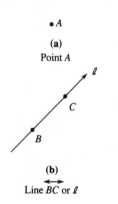

(a)
Point A

(b)
Line $\overleftrightarrow{BC}$ or ℓ

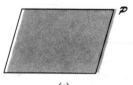

(c)
Plane $\mathcal{P}$

Figure 1.1

In Section 1.1 we discussed axiomatic systems and discovered that such systems consist of undefined terms, definitions, postulates (or axioms), and theorems. The undefined terms provide a starting point for developing an axiomatic system. In geometry, we begin with the following undefined terms:

set, point, line, plane.

Any attempt to define these terms would require more words that are undefined. Intuitively, we have some idea of their meaning. A **set** is a collection or group of objects. A **point** can be thought of as an object that determines a position but that has no dimension (length, width, or height). We can symbolize a point with a dot and label it with a capital letter, such as the point A shown in Figure 1.1(a).

A **line** can be thought of as a set of points in a one-dimensional straight figure that extends in opposite directions without ending. Figure 1.1(b) shows a representation of a line passing through the two points B and C. The arrowheads indicate that the line continues in that direction without ending. We symbolize a line such as this using $\overleftrightarrow{BC}$ or $\overleftrightarrow{CB}$, or when appropriate, by using a lowercase letter such as ℓ.

Finally, a **plane** is a set of points in a flat surface, such as the face of a blackboard, having two dimensions and extending without boundary. We often represent a plane as shown in Figure 1.1(c) and symbolize planes using a script letter such as $\mathcal{P}$.

Have you ever looked closely at the screen on a television set? The surface is composed of thousands of small dots that glow when hit by an electron beam. When viewed from a distance, the individual dots blend together forming the picture. Each minute dot serves as a model for a point, one of the simplest geometric figures that we study.

DEFINITION: SPACE AND GEOMETRIC FIGURES

The set of all points is called **space.** Any set of points, lines, or planes in space is called a **geometric figure.**

We can think of geometry as the study of properties of geometric figures. Some of these properties must be assumed in the form of postulates.

POSTULATE 1.1

Given any two distinct points in space, there is exactly one line that passes through them.

Intuitively, Postulate 1.1 tells us that we can draw one and only one straight line through two different points.

POSTULATE 1.2

Given any three distinct points in space not on the same line, there is exactly one plane that passes through them.

Figure 1.2(a) shows the plane containing the three points *A*, *B*, and *C*. Notice that *A*, *B*, and *C* are not on the same line. If three points such as *D*, *E*, and *F* are on the same line as in Figure 1.2(b), we can see that more than one plane can contain them.

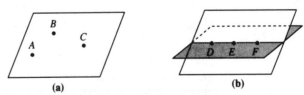

(a)   (b)

Figure 1.2   Points in Planes

POSTULATE 1.3

The line determined by any two distinct points in a plane is also contained in the plane.

From Postulate 1.3 we see that when we draw lines between points in a given plane, we always remain in the plane. The next postulate guarantees that there are more points in space than those found in any given plane.

POSTULATE 1.4

No plane contains all points in space.

The next postulate has numerous applications in algebra.

POSTULATE 1.5 RULER POSTULATE

There is a one-to-one correspondence between the set of all points on a line and the set of all real numbers.

If we draw a line, select a point on it (called the **origin**), mark off equal units in both directions, and label these points with integers, the result is called a **number line.** See Figure 1.3. The number corresponding to a given point on the line is called the **coordinate** of the point, and when we identify a point with a given real number, we are **plotting** the point associated with the number.

Origin
$$\longleftarrow \quad -3 \;\; -2 \;\; -1 \quad 0 \quad 1 \quad 2 \quad 3 \quad \longrightarrow$$

Figure 1.3 Number Line

EXAMPLE 1 Plot the points associated with the real numbers $\frac{1}{2}$, $-\frac{3}{4}$, $\sqrt{2}$, and 2.5 on a number line.

Start with a number line like the one in Figure 1.3. Because $\frac{1}{2}$ is halfway between 0 and 1, we locate the point midway between them. The points corresponding to $-\frac{3}{4}$ and 2.5 are determined similarly. We can find the approximate location of the point corresponding to $\sqrt{2}$ by recognizing that $\sqrt{2}$ is approximately 1.4. The four points are plotted in Figure 1.4. ◼

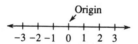

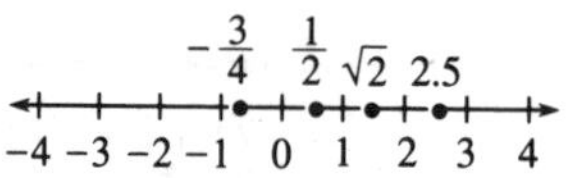

$$-4 \;\; -3 \;\; -2 \;\; -1 \quad 0 \quad 1 \quad 2 \quad 3 \quad 4$$

Figure 1.4 Points on a Number Line

PRACTICE EXERCISE 1

Approximate the coordinates of points *A*, *B*, *C*, and *D* on the number line.

$$C \quad D$$

$$-3 \quad B \; -1 \quad 0 \quad 1 \quad 2 \quad A \quad 4$$

Because there are infinitely many real numbers, there are infinitely many points on any given line. This conclusion is actually a theorem, a statement that can be proved. When proving certain theorems in geometry, we will use some of the following postulates from algebra.

POSTULATE 1.6   THE REFLEXIVE LAW

Any quantity is equal to itself. ($x = x$)

POSTULATE 1.7   THE SYMMETRIC LAW

If x and y are any two quantities and $x = y$, then $y = x$.

POSTULATE 1.8   THE TRANSITIVE LAW

If x, y, and z are any three quantities with $x = y$ and $y = z$, then $x = z$.

POSTULATE 1.9   THE ADDITION-SUBTRACTION LAW

If w, x, y, and z are any four quantities with $w = x$ and $y = z$, then $w + y = x + z$ and $w - y = x - z$.

The addition-subtraction law states that if equal quantities are added to or subtracted from equal quantities, the results are also equal.

POSTULATE 1.10   THE MULTIPLICATION-DIVISION LAW

If w, x, y, and z are any four quantities with $w = x$ and $y = z$, then

$$wy = xz \text{ and } \frac{w}{y} = \frac{x}{z} \text{ (provided } y \neq 0 \text{ and } z \neq 0\text{).}$$

The multiplication-division law states that if equal quantities are multiplied or divided by equal quantities (division by zero excluded), the results are also equal.

POSTULATE 1.11 THE SUBSTITUTION LAW

If x and y are any two quantities with $x = y$, then x can be substituted for y in any expression containing y.

POSTULATE 1.12 THE DISTRIBUTIVE LAW

If x, y, and z are any three quantities, then $x(y + z) = xy + xz$.

Postulates 1.6–1.12 are used extensively when solving algebraic equations. We illustrate this in the following exercises.

ANSWER TO PRACTICE EXERCISE: **1.** A: 3; B: -2; C: $-\dfrac{1}{2}$; D: $\dfrac{7}{4}$

1.2 EXERCISES

1. How many lines can be drawn between two distinct points?

2. How many planes are determined by three distinct points that are not on the same line?

3. If distinct points A and B are in plane $\mathcal{P}$, and point C is on the line determined by A and B, what can be said about C relative to $\mathcal{P}$?

4. If $\mathcal{P}$ is a plane and A is a point in space, must A be on $\mathcal{P}$?

In Exercises 5–8, A, B, and C are distinct points, ℓ and m are lines, and $\mathcal{P}$ is a plane. Name the postulate illustrated by each statement.

5. If A and B are on ℓ, and A and B are on m, then $m = \ell$.

6. If A and B are on ℓ, ℓ is in $\mathcal{P}$, and C is on ℓ, then C is in $\mathcal{P}$.

7. There is a point A such that A is not in $\mathcal{P}$.

8. If A and B are on ℓ, A is on m, and $\ell \neq m$, then B is not on m.

9. Construct a number line and plot the points associated with the real numbers $3, \dfrac{7}{8}, -\dfrac{1}{3}, -1.5$, and $\sqrt{3}$.

10. Construct a number line and plot the points associated with the real numbers $-3, \dfrac{1}{4}, -\dfrac{4}{3}, 3.2$, and $-\sqrt{5}$.

In Exercises 11–12, approximate the coordinates of points A, B, C, and D on the given number lines.

11.

D   C
⟷+•+—+•+—+—+•+—+•+⟶
  -4 B -2 -1 0 1 A 3 4

12.

D   C
⟷+•+—+•+—+—+•+—+•+⟶
 -4 -3 A -1 B 1 2 3 4

In Exercises 13–18, complete each statement using the specified postulate.

13. Reflexive law: $5 = \underline{\quad?\quad}$.

14. Transitive law: If $a = b$ and $b = 3$, then $a = \underline{\quad?\quad}$.

15. Addition-subtraction law: If $a = b$, then $a + 7 = b + \underline{\quad?\quad}$.

16. Multiplication-division law: If $2x = 6$, then $x = \underline{\quad?\quad}$.

17. Symmetric law: If $a = -3$, then $-3 = \underline{\quad?\quad}$.

Answer *true* or *false* in Exercises 18–22.

18. By the reflexive law, $-2 = -2$.

19. If $w = 7$ and $7 = x$, then $w = x$ by the symmetric law.

20. If $x + 1 = 8$, then $x = 7$ by the addition-subtraction law.

21. If $\frac{1}{3}y = 2$, then $y = 6$ by the addition-subtraction law.

22. If $8 = x$ then $x = 8$ by the reflexive law.

In Exercises 23–24, give the postulate that supports each indicated step in the solution of the equation.

23. Solve $3x + 2 = 4 + 5x$.

STATEMENTS	REASONS
1. $3x + 2 = 4 + 5x$	1. Given
2. $3x + 2 - 4 = 4 - 4 + 5x$	2. _____
3. $3x - 2 = 5x$	3. Simplify
4. $3x - 3x - 2 = 5x - 3x$	4. _____
5. $-2 = 2x$	5. Simplify
6. $\frac{1}{2}(-2x) = \frac{1}{2}(2x)$	6. _____
7. $-1 = x$	7. Simplify
8. $x = -1$	8. _____

Check: -1 in $3x + 2 = 4 + 5x$

9. $3(-1) + 2 = 4 + 5(-1)$	9. _____
10. $-1 = -1$	10. Simplify

24. Solve $\frac{2}{3}x + 1 = x$.

STATEMENTS	REASONS
1. $\frac{2}{3}x + 1 = x$	1. Given
2. $3\left[\frac{2}{3}x + 1\right] = 3x$	2. _____
3. $2x + 3 = 3x$	3. _____
4. $2x - 2x + 3 = 3x - 2x$	4. _____
5. $3 = x$	5. Simplify
6. $x = 3$	6. _____

Check: 3 in $\frac{2}{3}x + 1 = x$

7. $\frac{2}{3}(3) + 1 = 3$	7. _____
8. $3 = 3$	8. Simplify

25. Can a given point exist on two distinct lines? On five distinct lines?

26. Can two distinct points both exist on two distinct lines?

27. Can a given line exist in two distinct planes? In five distinct planes?

28. Can two given lines with no point in common exist in the same plane?

29. Explain why stools are often made with three legs rather than four, to provide greater stability.

Section 1.2

1.3 SEGMENTS, RAYS, AND ANGLES

Figure 1.5   Points Between
A and B

A line can be thought of as a geometric figure consisting of points that extend infinitely far in opposite directions. We now consider two new figures that are parts of a line. Another undefined term, *between,* describes the position of points on a line in relation to two given points on that line. Intuitively, points on the colored portion of the line in Figure 1.5 are said to be *between* points A and B.

DEFINITION: LINE SEGMENT

Let A and B be two distinct points on a line. The geometric figure consisting of all points between A and B, including A and B, is called a **line segment** or **segment,** denoted by $\overline{AB}$ or $\overline{BA}$. The points A and B are called **endpoints** of $\overline{AB}$.

Recall that the line determined by distinct points A and B is denoted by $\overleftrightarrow{AB}$ or $\overleftrightarrow{BA}$, which distinguishes it from the segment $\overline{AB}$ or $\overline{BA}$. The **length** of segment $\overline{AB}$ is the distance between the endpoints A and B and is often denoted by AB.

The next postulate provides a way to find the length of a segment that is made up of other segments. Refer to Figure 1.6.

POSTULATE 1.13   SEGMENT ADDITION POSTULATE

Let A, B, and C be three points on the same line with B between A and C. Then $AC = AB + BC$, $BC = AC - AB$, and $AB = AC - BC$.

The segment addition postulate can be applied to many problems whose solutions also require basic algebra.

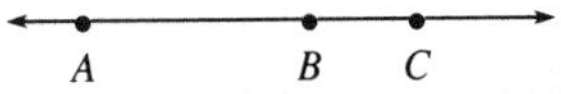

$AC = AB + BC$, $BC = AC - AB$,
and $AB = AC - BC$

Figure 1.6   Segment Addition

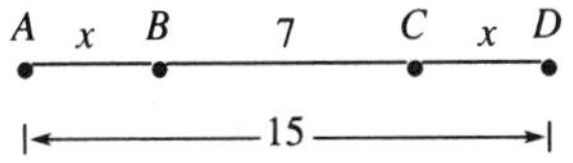

Figure 1.7

EXAMPLE 1   In Figure 1.7, $AD = 15$, $BC = 7$, and $AB = CD$. Find AB.

Let $AB = x$. Then because $AB = CD$, $CD = x$. By extending the segment addition postulate we have

$$AD = AB + BC + CD.$$

Substitute 15 for AD, 7 for BC, and x for both AB and CD to obtain

$$15 = x + 7 + x.$$

$15 = 2x + 7$	Collect like terms
$8 = 2x$	Subtract 7 from both sides
$4 = x$	Divide both sides by 2

Thus, $AB = 4$. ∎

PRACTICE EXERCISE 1

Use the figure below to find the value of x.

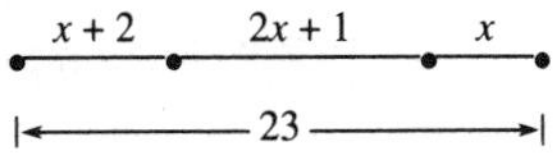

$x + 2$ $2x + 1$ x

$\longmapsto$ ———— 23 ———— $\longmapsto$

DEFINITION: RAY

Let A and B be two distinct points on a line. The geometric figure consisting of the point A together with all points on $\overleftrightarrow{AB}$ on the same side of A as B is called a **ray,** denoted by $\overrightarrow{AB}$. The point A is called the **endpoint** of $\overrightarrow{AB}$.

In Figure 1.8, the ray $\overrightarrow{AB}$ is shown in color. Unlike the notations for segments and lines, the rays $\overrightarrow{AB}$ and $\overrightarrow{BA}$ are different. A ray has only one endpoint and it is always written first. Taken together, rays $\overrightarrow{AB}$ and $\overrightarrow{BA}$ make up the line $\overleftrightarrow{AB}$.

Figure 1.8   Ray $\overrightarrow{AB}$ **Figure 1.9**

E X A M P L E 2   Use Figure 1.9 to answer each question.

(a) Is Q on $\overline{PR}$?   No   (b) Is Q on $\overleftrightarrow{PR}$?   Yes
(c) Is Q on $\overrightarrow{PR}$?   Yes   (d) Is Q on $\overrightarrow{RP}$?   No
(e) What are the endpoints of $\overline{PR}$?   *P* and *R*
(f) What are the endpoints of $\overrightarrow{PR}$?   Only *P*
(g) What are the endpoints of $\overleftrightarrow{PR}$?   There are no endpoints.
(h) Are $\overline{PQ}$ and $\overline{QP}$ the same?   Yes
(i) Are $\overrightarrow{PQ}$ and $\overrightarrow{QP}$ the same?   No
(j) If $PQ = 5$ cm and $RQ = 2$ cm, what is the length of $\overline{PR}$?   3 cm   ◪

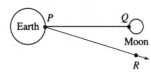

Scientists have measured the distance between the earth and the moon to within a few centimeters. A laser beam is directed from point *P* and reflected back to the earth from a mirror that was left by the Apollo astronauts at point *Q*. The time it takes for the beam to return to earth can be measured and used to calculate the distance from the earth to the moon. The two points *P* and *Q* along with the laser beam provide a model of a segment. A laser beam directed into space from *P* through *R* serves as a model for a ray.

PRACTICE EXERCISE 2

Draw two points X and Y and place point Z on $\overleftrightarrow{XY}$ but not on $\overrightarrow{XY}$. Use your figure to answer the following questions.

(a) Is Z on $\overrightarrow{YX}$?
(b) Is Z on $\overline{YX}$?
(c) Is Y on $\overrightarrow{ZX}$?
(d) What are the endpoints of $\overrightarrow{XY}$?
(e) What are the endpoints of $\overline{XY}$?
(f) Are $\overrightarrow{XY}$ and $\overrightarrow{YX}$ the same?
(g) If $ZX = 3$ cm and $XY = 5$ cm, what is the length of $\overline{ZY}$?

The degree as a unit of angular measure originated with the ancient Sumerians. The Sumerians thought that it took the earth 360 days to revolve around the sun. They assumed the earth's orbit was a circle and that the earth traveled at a constant speed. Thus, to traverse completely around a circle required 360 units of time (days) so that in 1 day, the earth would travel $\frac{1}{360}$ of a circle. The Sumerians defined the measure of the angle formed by $\frac{1}{360}$ of a circle as a degree.

The *angle* is one of the most important figures studied in geometry.

DEFINITION: ANGLE

An **angle** is a geometric figure consisting of two rays that share a common endpoint, called the **vertex** of the angle. The rays are called **sides** of the angle.

Angles are named in three ways. Consider the angle formed by rays $\overrightarrow{AC}$ and $\overrightarrow{AB}$ in Figure 1.10. We use the three points on the angle, A, B, and C, and call the angle $\angle CAB$ or $\angle BAC$ (the symbol $\angle$ is read "angle"). Notice in both cases the vertex is written between the other two points. When no confusion can arise, we simply name the angle $\angle A$, using only the vertex point. The third possibility is to write a small letter or number such as 1 in the position shown in Figure 1.10 and call the angle $\angle 1$.

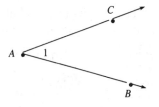

Figure 1.10 $\angle$CAB

We are familiar with measuring the length of a segment using a suitable unit of measure such as inch, centimeter, foot, or meter. In order to measure an angle, we need a measuring unit. The most common unit is the **degree** (°). An angle with measure 0° is formed by two coinciding rays such as $\overrightarrow{AB}$ and $\overrightarrow{AC}$ in Figure 1.11.

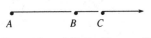

Figure 1.11 $\angle$BAC Has Measure 0°

If we rotate ray $\overrightarrow{AB}$ in a counterclockwise direction from ray $\overrightarrow{AC}$ in Figure 1.11, the two rays form larger and larger angles as shown in Figure 1.12.

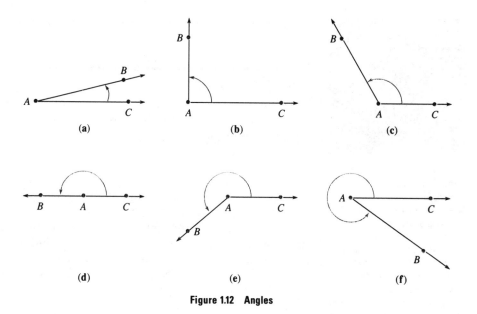

Figure 1.12   Angles

If $\overrightarrow{AB}$ in Figure 1.11 is allowed to rotate completely around until it coincides with ray $\overrightarrow{AC}$ again, the resulting angle is said to measure 360°. Thus, an angle of measure 1° is formed by making $\dfrac{1}{360}$ of a complete rotation. An angle of measure 1° is shown in Figure 1.13.

Figure 1.13   Angle Measuring 1°

The approximate measure of an angle in degrees can be found by using a protractor shown in Figure 1.14.

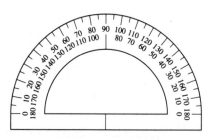

Figure 1.14   Protractor

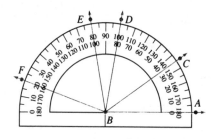

Figure 1.15   Measuring Angles

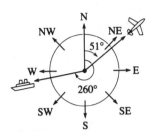

The navigator on an airplane or a ship uses angles measured in degrees to give the direction of travel of the craft. The angle between due north and the direction of travel, measured in degrees in a clockwise direction, is called the navigational direction or course of the craft. The airplane in the figure is flying on a course of 51° while the ship is sailing a course of 260°.

Figure 1.15 shows how a protractor is used to measure various angles. $\angle ABC$ has measure 35°, $\angle ABD$ has measure 80°, $\angle ABE$ has measure 100°, and $\angle ABF$ has measure 160°. Rather than say "$\angle ABC$ has measure 35°," we simply write $\angle ABC = 35°$. Also, when two angles have the same measure, we simply say that the angles are **equal.**

In some practical applications, angles must be measured with greater precision. One degree is divided into 60 equal parts called **minutes** ('), and one minute is divided into 60 equal parts called **seconds** ("). Thus, the measure of an angle might be given as 55°28'48".

Certain angles are given special names.

DEFINITION: SPECIAL ANGLES

An angle whose sides form a line is called a **straight angle** and has measure 180°. An angle with measure 90° is called a **right angle.**
An angle with measure between 0° and 90° is called an **acute angle.**
An angle with measure between 90° and 180° is called an **obtuse angle.**

EXAMPLE 3 Use Figure 1.16 to answer each question.

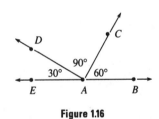

Figure 1.16

(a) Is $\angle BAE$ a straight angle?   Yes

(b) Is $\angle EAD$ an acute angle?   Yes

(c) Is $\angle CAE$ a right angle?   No

(d) Is $\angle DAB$ an obtuse angle?   Yes   ∎

Two acute angles or two obtuse angles need not be equal. However, right angles are equal.

POSTULATE 1.14   RIGHT-ANGLE POSTULATE
All right angles are equal.

Some pairs of angles have properties that are useful in many applications.

DEFINITION: COMPLEMENTARY AND SUPPLEMENTARY ANGLES

Two angles whose measures total 90° are called **complementary angles** and each is called the **complement** of the other. Two angles whose measures total 180° are called **supplementary angles,** and each is called the **supplement** of the other.

EXAMPLE 4

(a) If $\angle A = 35°$ and $\angle B = 55°$, then $\angle A$ and $\angle B$ are complementary because $35° + 55° = 90°$.

(b) If $\angle C = 120°15'45''$ and $\angle D = 59°44'15''$, then because
$120°15'45'' + 59°44'15''$

$$
\begin{aligned}
&= 120°15' + 59°44' + 60'' &\quad 45'' + 15'' = 60'' \\
&= 120°15' + 59°44' + 1' &\quad 60'' = 1' \\
&= 120°15' + 59°45' &\quad 44' + 1' = 45' \\
&= 120° + 59° + 15' + 45' \\
&= 120° + 59° + 60' &\quad 15' + 45' = 60' \\
&= 120° + 59° + 1° &\quad 60' = 1° \\
&= 180°,
\end{aligned}
$$

$\angle C$ and $\angle D$ are supplementary angles.

(c) If $\angle P = 20°$, $\angle Q = 30°$, and $\angle R = 40°$, although $20° + 30° + 40° = 90°$, we do not call the angles complementary. The definition of complementary angles involves only two angles (not three or more) that sum to 90°. ◼

PRACTICE EXERCISE 3

(a) If $\angle A = 27°$ and $\angle A$ and $\angle B$ are complementary, find the measure of $\angle B$.

(b) If $\angle P = 74°26'52''$ and $\angle P$ and $\angle Q$ are supplementary, find the measure of $\angle Q$.

EXAMPLE 5   If $\angle A = (2x)°$, $\angle B = (x - 6)°$, and $\angle A$ and $\angle B$ are complementary, find x.

Because $\angle A$ and $\angle B$ are complementary, $\angle A + \angle B = 90°$. Substituting, we have

$$
\begin{aligned}
2x + (x - 6) &= 90. \\
2x + x - 6 &= 90 \\
3x - 6 &= 90 \\
3x &= 96 \\
x &= 32 \quad ◼
\end{aligned}
$$

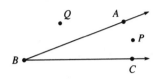

Figure 1.17 Points Interior and Exterior to ∠ABC

Two undefined terms that are useful when working with angles are *interior* and *exterior*. Consider $\angle ABC$ and points P and Q as shown in Figure 1.17. We say that P is in the **interior** of $\angle ABC$ and Q is **exterior** to $\angle ABC$.

DEFINITION: ADJACENT ANGLES

Two angles are called **adjacent angles** if they have a common vertex and share a common side.

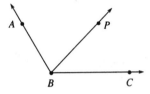

Figure 1.18 Adjacent Angles

For example, in Figure 1.18, $\angle ABP$ and $\angle PBC$ are adjacent, but $\angle ABC$ and $\angle ABP$ and $\angle ABC$ and $\angle PBC$ are not. Notice that intuitively, $\angle ABP$ and $\angle CBP$ are adjacent angles if P is in the interior of $\angle ABC$.

Figure 1.18 can also be used to clarify the next postulate.

POSTULATE 1.15 ANGLE ADDITION POSTULATE

Let A, B, and C be points that determine $\angle ABC$ with P a point in the interior of the angle. Then $\angle ABC = \angle ABP + \angle PBC$, $\angle PBC = \angle ABC - \angle ABP$, and $\angle ABP = \angle ABC - \angle PBC$.

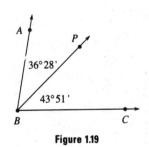

Figure 1.19

E X A M P L E 6 Suppose that $\angle ABP$ and $\angle PBC$ are adjacent angles and that $\angle ABP = 36°28'$ and $\angle PBC = 43°51'$. Find the measure of $\angle ABC$. Figure 1.19 shows a sketch of the given angles from which we can see that because P is in the interior of $\angle ABC$, by Postulate 1.15,

$$\angle ABC = \angle ABP + \angle PBC$$
$$= 36°28' + 43°51'$$
$$= 79°79'$$
$$= 80°19' \qquad 79' = 60' + 19' = 1°19' \qquad ◨$$

ANSWERS TO PRACTICE EXERCISES: **1.** $x = 5$ **2. (a)** yes **(b)** no **(c)** yes **(d)** only X **(e)** X and Y **(f)** no **(g)** 8 cm **3. (a)** $63°$ **(b)** $105°33'8''$ **4.** $y = 21$

1.3 EXERCISES

Consider the line $\overleftrightarrow{AB}$ with point C between A and B and ray $\overrightarrow{CD}$ as shown below. Use this figure and answer *true* or *false* in Exercises 1–20.

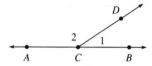

1. Point B is on $\overrightarrow{AC}$.

2. Point A is on $\overrightarrow{CB}$.

3. Point C is on $\overrightarrow{AB}$.

4. Point B is on $\overleftrightarrow{AC}$.

5. If $AC = 10$ cm and $CB = 13$ cm, then $AB = 23$ cm.

6. If $AB = 30$ cm and $AC = 12$ cm then $CB = 18$ cm.

7. $\overrightarrow{CA}$ and $\overrightarrow{AC}$ are the same.

8. $\angle 1$ is another name for $\angle DCB$.

9. $\angle ACD$ is another name for $\angle 2$.

10. C is the endpoint of $\overrightarrow{BC}$.

11. A and B are endpoints of $\overrightarrow{AB}$.

12. A and C are endpoints of $\overline{AC}$.

13. The vertex of $\angle 1$ is C.

14. The vertex of $\angle DCA$ is A.

15. $\angle ACB$ is a right angle.

16. $\angle BCA$ is a straight angle.

17. $\angle 1$ and $\angle 2$ are adjacent angles.

18. $\angle 1$ and $\angle 2$ are complementary angles.

19. $\angle DCB$ is an acute angle.

20. $\angle 1$ is the supplement of $\angle DCA$.

Exercises 21–26 refer to the figure below. Give the measure of each angle.

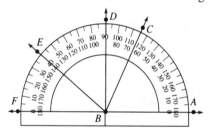

21. $\angle ABC$

22. $\angle EBF$

23. $\angle ABD$

24. $\angle ABE$

25. $\angle FBC$

26. $\angle CBE$

Find the complement of each angle in Exercises 27–30.

27. $18°$

28. $64°$

29. $36°40'$

30. $71°45'20''$

Find the supplement of each angle in Exercises 31–34.

31. $74°$

32. $136°$

33. $57°35'$

34. $110°35'40''$

35. What angle has the same measure as its complement?

36. What angle has the same measure as its supplement?

37. What is the complement of the supplement of an angle measuring $130°$?

38. What is the supplement of the complement of an angle measuring $50°$?

39. What is the complement of the complement of an angle measuring $25°$?

40. What is the supplement of the supplement of an angle measuring $160°$?

41. What is the measure of an angle whose supplement is four times its complement?

42. What is the measure of an angle whose supplement is three times its complement?

State whether each angle given in Exercises 43–51 is straight, right, acute, or obtuse.

43. 65° **44.** 115° **45.** 180° **46.** 90°

47. The complement of an angle measuring 42°.

48. The supplement of an angle measuring 42°.

49. The complement of any acute angle.

50. The supplement of any obtuse angle.

51. The supplement of a right angle.

In Exercises 52–55, $\angle ABP$ and $\angle PBC$ are adjacent angles. Find the measure of $\angle ABC$.

52. $\angle ABP = 62°20'$ and $\angle PBC = 31°50'$

53. $\angle ABP = 49°55'$ and $\angle PBC = 57°15'$

54. $\angle ABP = 27°25'41''$ and $\angle PBC = 52°51'35''$

55. $\angle ABP = 120°38'22''$ and $\angle PBC = 18°41'54''$

56. On $\overleftrightarrow{AB}$, how many points are located 5 cm from point A?

57. On $\overleftrightarrow{AB}$, how many points are located 5 cm from point B?

58. On $\overrightarrow{AB}$, how many points are located 5 cm from point A?

59. On $\overrightarrow{AB}$, how many points are located 5 cm from point B if $AB = 10$ cm?

60. On $\overline{AB}$, how many points are located 5 cm from point A if $AB = 10$ cm?

61. On $\overrightarrow{AB}$, how many points are located 5 cm from point B?

62. Give the number of acute or obtuse angles formed by each of the following. Assume that no two rays are on the same line. Make a sketch in each case.
   (a) Two distinct rays with the same endpoint.
   (b) Three distinct rays with the same endpoint.
   (c) Four distinct rays with the same endpoint.
   (d) Five distinct rays with the same endpoint.

63. After solving Exercise 62, can you determine a formula (in terms of n) that gives the number of acute or obtuse angles formed by n distinct rays with the same endpoint, no two of which are on the same line?

In Exercises 64–65, find the value of x in each figure.

64.

65.

66. If $\angle A = (5y)°$, $\angle B = (y + 6)°$, and $\angle A$ and $\angle B$ are complementary, find y.

67. If $\angle R = (30 - y)°$, $\angle S = (9y - 10)°$, and $\angle R$ and $\angle S$ are supplementary, find y.

Section 1.3

2.3 CONSTRUCTIONS INVOLVING LINES AND ANGLES

Part of geometry involves making accurate drawings of geometric figures. Such drawings are called **geometric constructions.** Two instruments are used to make constructions, a **straightedge** and a **compass.** A straightedge, a ruler with no marks of scale, is used to draw a line between two points. (We often use a standard ruler but do not use it to measure lengths.) A compass is used to draw circles, or portions of circles, called **arcs.** (Circles and arcs will be studied in more detail in Chapter 7.)

The first construction we consider involves duplicating a given line segment.

The bronze sculpture, Geometria, by Renaissance sculptor Antonio del Pollaiolo (1433–98) depicts the study of geometry. It shows the construction of a geometric figure using a compass and a straightedge. The sculpture appears on the base of the tomb of Pope Sixtus IV and is located in St. Peter's Cathedral in Rome.

CONSTRUCTION 2.1
Construct a line segment with the same length as a given line segment.

Given: Line segment $\overline{AB}$ (See Figure 2.8.)

To Construct: Line segment $\overline{CD}$ with $CD = AB$.

Construction:

1. Draw a line $\overleftrightarrow{CE}$ containing point C.
2. Place the point of a compass at point A and the pencil point at point B.
3. Without changing the distance between these points on the compass, place the point of the compass at point C and with the pencil point draw an arc that intersects $\overleftrightarrow{CE}$. The point of intersection of the arc and $\overleftrightarrow{CE}$ determines the point D. $\overline{CD}$ is the desired line segment.

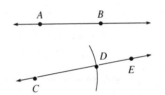

Figure 2.8   Reconstructing Segment Length

The next construction involves duplicating a given angle.

CONSTRUCTION 2.2
Construct an angle with the same measure as a given angle.

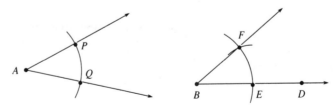

Figure 2.9   Reconstructing Angle Measure

Given: $\angle A$ (See Figure 2.9.)

To Construct: $\angle B$ such that $\angle A = \angle B$

Construction:

1. Draw ray $\overrightarrow{BD}$.

2. Choose a convenient setting of the compass, place the point at A and draw an arc that intersects the sides of $\angle A$ at two points, for instance P and Q.

3. Without changing the compass setting, place the point at B and draw a suitable arc that intersects $\overrightarrow{BD}$ at a point, for instance E.

4. Place the points of the compass so that one is at Q and the other is at P.

5. Without changing the compass setting, place the point at E and draw an arc that intercepts the arc drawn in Step 3. Label this point F.

6. Draw ray $\overrightarrow{BF}$ to form the second side of the desired angle, $\angle B$.

Next we divide a line segment into two equal parts.

DEFINITION: LINE SEGMENT BISECTION

Let $\overline{AB}$ be a line segment. To **bisect** $\overline{AB}$ is to identify a point C between A and B such that $AC = CB$. The point C is called the **midpoint** of $\overline{AB}$. Any line or line segment that contains the midpoint C but no other point of $\overline{AB}$ is called a **bisector** of $\overline{AB}$.

CONSTRUCTION 2.3

Construct a bisector of a given line segment.

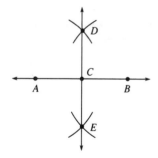

Figure 2.10   Segment Bisector

Given: Line segment $\overline{AB}$ (See Figure 2.10.)

To Construct: A bisector $\overleftrightarrow{CD}$ of $\overline{AB}$

Construction:

1. Set the compass so that the distance between the point and the pencil is greater than $\dfrac{AB}{2}$.

2. Set the point at A and draw two arcs, one above $\overline{AB}$ and the other below $\overline{AB}$. Repeat this procedure using the same compass setting with the point at B.

3. The arcs drawn in Step 2 should intersect at two points we label D and E.

4. Draw the line $\overleftrightarrow{DE}$. Then $\overleftrightarrow{DE}$ is a bisector of $\overline{AB}$ and determines midpoint C.

Construction 2.3 shows that a given line segment has a midpoint. The next postulate guarantees that this midpoint is unique.

POSTULATE 2.1   MIDPOINT POSTULATE
Each line segment has exactly one midpoint.

When two lines intersect and form right angles, we call the lines *perpendicular*.

DEFINITION: PERPENDICULAR LINES
Two lines are **perpendicular** if they intersect and form equal adjacent angles. If $\overleftrightarrow{AB}$ is perpendicular to $\overleftrightarrow{CD}$, we write $\overleftrightarrow{AB} \perp \overleftrightarrow{CD}$. Two line segments are perpendicular if they intersect and are contained in perpendicular lines.

In Figure 2.11, lines ℓ and m are perpendicular if and only if $\angle 1 = \angle 2$. When $\ell \perp m$, we represent this fact in figures using the symbol ∟ as shown. Also, in Figure 2.12, $\overline{AB} \perp \overline{CD}$ provided $\overleftrightarrow{AB} \perp \overleftrightarrow{CD}$.

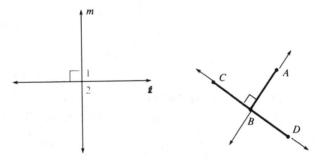

Figure 2.11   Perpendicular Lines   Figure 2.12   Perpendicular Segments

Although a line segment can have many bisectors, the most important one is the *perpendicular bisector*. Construction 2.3 shows this bisector.

DEFINITION: PERPENDICULAR BISECTOR OF A SEGMENT
A line that both bisects and is perpendicular to a given line segment is called a **perpendicular bisector** of the segment.

We assume that the perpendicular bisector of a segment is unique.

POSTULATE 2.2   PERPENDICULAR BISECTOR POSTULATE
Each given line segment has exactly one perpendicular bisector.

In the next construction we find a line perpendicular to a given line passing through a given point on the line.

CONSTRUCTION 2.4

Construct a line perpendicular to a given line passing through a given point on the line.

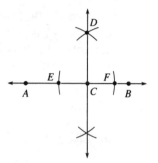

Figure 2.13

Given: Line $\overleftrightarrow{AB}$ with point C on $\overleftrightarrow{AB}$ (See Figure 2.13.)

To Construct: A line $\overleftrightarrow{DC}$ such that $\overleftrightarrow{DC} \perp \overleftrightarrow{AB}$

Construction:

1. Choose a convenient setting for the compass, place the point at C, and make two arcs that intersect line $\overleftrightarrow{AB}$. Label these points E and F.

2. Use Construction 2.3 to draw the perpendicular bisector of the segment $\overline{EF}$. The result, $\overleftrightarrow{DC}$ in Figure 2.13, is the desired line perpendicular to $\overleftrightarrow{AB}$ at the point C.

POSTULATE 2.3

There is exactly one line perpendicular to a given line passing through a given point on the line.

Next we consider finding a line perpendicular to a given line passing through a given point *not* on the line.

CONSTRUCTION 2.5

Construct a line perpendicular to a given line passing through a given point not on that line.

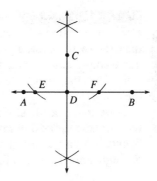

Figure 2.14

Given: Line $\overleftrightarrow{AB}$ with point C not on $\overleftrightarrow{AB}$ (See Figure 2.14.)

To Construct: A line $\overleftrightarrow{CD}$ such that $\overleftrightarrow{CD} \perp \overleftrightarrow{AB}$

Construction:

1. Choose a convenient setting for the compass, place the point at $C,$ and make two arcs that intersect line $\overleftrightarrow{AB}$. Label these points E and F.

2. Use Construction 2.3 to draw the perpendicular bisector of the segment $\overline{EF}$. The result, $\overleftrightarrow{CD}$ in Figure 2.14, is the desired line perpendicular to $\overleftrightarrow{AB}$ and passing through C.

POSTULATE 2.4

There is exactly one line perpendicular to a given line passing through a given point not on that line.

We said that the **distance** between two points A and B is the length of the segment $\overline{AB}$, denoted by AB. Construction 2.5 and Postulate 2.4 give us a way to find the *distance* from a point to a line. Use Figure 2.14 as a reference for the following definition.

DEFINITION: DISTANCE FROM A POINT TO A LINE

Let $\overleftrightarrow{AB}$ be a line with C a point not on $\overleftrightarrow{AB}$. If D is the point on $\overleftrightarrow{AB}$ such that $\overleftrightarrow{CD} \perp \overleftrightarrow{AB}$, the **distance** from C to $\overleftrightarrow{AB}$ is CD, the length of $\overline{CD}$.

We now have a way to solve the applied problem given in the chapter introduction.

<u>E X A M P L E 1</u>   A family is building a recreational cabin at the edge of a wide mountain valley containing a stream that flows north to south. To supply the cabin with water, a pipe must be laid from the cabin to the stream. To minimize construction costs, the family plans to use the least amount of pipe possible. How can they determine the point on the stream bank that is closest to the cabin?

If we think of the stream as a straight line, and the cabin as a point not on the line, the desired point on the bank of the stream, labeled P in Figure 2.15 below, is found by constructing the line ℓ perpendicular to the stream passing through a point, the cabin, not on that line.   ◾

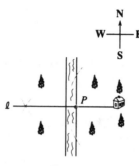

Figure 2.15

We have considered the problem of bisecting a line segment, and now we'll try to bisect an angle.

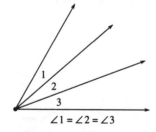

$\angle 1 = \angle 2 = \angle 3$

For years mathematicians tried to find a way to trisect (divide into three equal angles) an angle using only a straightedge and compass. Some special angles (such as a straight angle) can be trisected, but the methods used do not carry over to more general angles. In fact, it has now been proved that it is impossible to trisect an arbitrary angle by construction.

DEFINITION: ANGLE BISECTION

Let $\angle ABC$ be an angle. To **bisect** $\angle ABC$ is to identify a ray $\overrightarrow{BD}$, where D is in the interior of $\angle ABC$ and $\angle ABD = \angle DBC$. The ray $\overrightarrow{BD}$ is called the **bisector** of $\angle ABC$.

CONSTRUCTION 2.6

Construct a bisector of a given angle.

Given: $\angle ABC$ (See Figure 2.16 on the next page.)

To Construct: Ray $\overrightarrow{BD}$ that bisects $\angle ABC$

Construction:

1. Choose a convenient setting for the compass, place the point at B, the vertex of $\angle ABC$, and make two arcs that intersect $\overrightarrow{BA}$ and $\overrightarrow{BC}$. Label these points E and F.

2. Choose a convenient setting for the compass so the distance between the pencil and the point is greater than $\dfrac{EF}{2}$. Set the point at E and draw an arc interior to $\angle ABC$. Then set the point at F and draw a second arc with the same compass setting that intercepts the first arc at a point we label D.

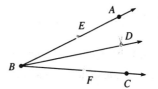

Figure 2.16   Angle Bisector

3. Draw the ray $\overrightarrow{BD}$. $\overrightarrow{BD}$ is the desired bisector of $\angle ABC$. We shall assume that the bisector of an angle is unique.

POSTULATE 2.5   ANGLE BISECTOR POSTULATE

Each angle has exactly one bisector.

2.3 EXERCISES

1. Draw a line segment $\overline{AB}$ approximately 3 inches in length, and a line ℓ. Construct $\overline{CD}$ on ℓ such that $AB = CD$.

2. Draw a line segment $\overline{AB}$ approximately 2 inches in length, and a line ℓ. Construct $\overline{CD}$ on ℓ such that CD is twice AB.

3. Draw an acute angle and then construct another acute angle with the same measure.

4. Draw an obtuse angle and then construct another obtuse angle with the same measure.

5. Draw an acute angle and then construct another angle whose measure is twice that of the first.

6. Draw an obtuse angle and then construct another angle whose measure is twice that of the first.

7. Draw a line segment $\overline{AB}$ approximately 2 inches in length and locate the midpoint of the segment by bisecting it.

8. Draw a line segment $\overline{AB}$ approximately 4 inches in length and divide the segment into four equal parts by first bisecting $\overline{AB}$ and then bisecting each resulting part.

9. Draw a line segment $\overline{AB}$ approximately 3 inches in length and construct the perpendicular bisector of $\overline{AB}$.

10. Draw a line ℓ and select two points P and Q on ℓ. Construct the perpendicular bisector of $\overline{PQ}$ and locate the midpoint of $\overline{PQ}$.

11. Draw a line ℓ and select a point P on ℓ. Construct the line through P and perpendicular to ℓ.

12. Draw a line ℓ and select a point P not on ℓ. Construct the line through P and perpendicular to ℓ.

13. Draw an acute angle and construct its bisector.

14. Draw an obtuse angle and construct its bisector.

15. Draw an acute angle and use construction techniques to divide the angle into four equal angles.

16. Draw an obtuse angle and use construction techniques to divide the angle into four equal angles.

17. What is the distinction between a ruler and a straightedge?

18. How many midpoints does a line segment have?

19. How many perpendicular bisectors does a line segment have?

20. How many bisectors does a line segment have?

21. Draw a line ℓ with a point P not on ℓ. Construct the line m through P and perpendicular to ℓ and label the point of intersection of ℓ and m as Q. The length of $\overline{PQ}$ is the distance from P to ℓ. Use a ruler to measure $\overline{PQ}$ and approximate this distance.

Assume that every point on the perpendicular bisector of a line segment with endpoints A and B is equidistant from A and B. Also, assume that every point on the bisector of an angle is equidistant from the sides of the angle. Use this information and the figure on the right in Exercises 22–24.

22. A ranger wishes to drill a well at the edge of the forest equidistant from the cabin and the ranger station. Explain how she should locate this point at the forest's edge.

23. A ranger wishes to drill a well at the edge of the forest equidistant from the stream and the road. Explain how he should locate this point at the forest's edge.

24. A meteorologist wishes to place a weather station in the meadow equidistant from the ranger station, the bridge, and the cabin. Explain how she should locate this point.

Section 1.4

4.2 TRANSVERSALS AND ANGLES

One of the best ways to study two parallel lines is to consider the various angles that are formed when a third line intersects them.

> **DEFINITION: TRANSVERSAL**
>
> A **transversal** is a line that intersects two distinct lines in two distinct points.

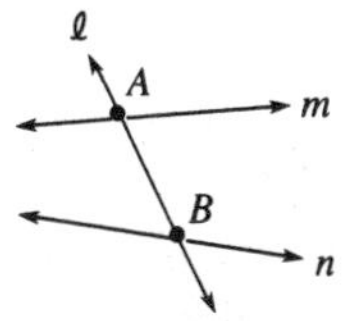

In Figure 4.4(a) ℓ is a transversal that **cuts** (intersects) lines m and n in the two points A and B, respectively. However, in Figure 4.4(b), s is not a transversal because it intersects t and u in only one point P.

When a transversal cuts two lines, several pairs of angles are formed.

Transversal
(a)

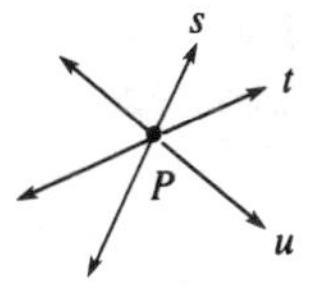

Not a Transversal
(b)

Figure 4.4

> **DEFINITION: ANGLES FORMED BY A TRANSVERSAL**
>
> Suppose two lines are cut by a transversal.
> 1. The nonadjacent angles on opposite sides of the transversal but on the interior of the two lines are called **alternate interior angles.**
> 2. The nonadjacent angles on the same side of the transversal and in the same corresponding positions with respect to the two lines are called **corresponding angles.**
> 3. The nonadjacent angles on opposite sides of the transversal and on the exterior of the two lines are called **alternate exterior angles.**

In Figure 4.5, ℓ is a transversal that cuts m and n. There are two pairs of alternate interior angles: $\angle 4$ and $\angle 6$; and $\angle 3$ and $\angle 5$. There are four pairs of cor-

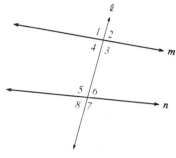

Figure 4.5

responding angles: $\angle 1$ and $\angle 5$; $\angle 2$ and $\angle 6$; $\angle 3$ and $\angle 7$; and $\angle 4$ and $\angle 8$. There are two pairs of alternate exterior angles: $\angle 1$ and $\angle 7$; and $\angle 2$ and $\angle 8$.

A pair of alternate interior angles can be used to show that two lines are parallel.

THEOREM 4.2

If two lines are cut by a transversal and a pair of alternate interior angles are equal, then the lines are parallel.

Given: Lines m and n cut by
  transversal ℓ
  $\angle 1 = \angle 2$ (See Figure 4.6.)

Prove: $m \parallel n$

Construction: Construct the midpoint
  of $\overline{AB}$, C.
  Construct $\overleftrightarrow{CD} \perp m$ through C.

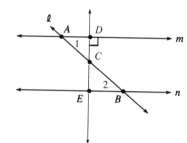

Figure 4.6

Proof:

STATEMENTS	REASONS
1. m and n are lines with transversal ℓ	1. Given
2. C is the midpoint of $\overline{AB}$	2. Construction 2.3
3. $AC = CB$	3. Def. of midpoint
4. $\overleftrightarrow{CD} \perp m$	4. Construction 2.5
5. $\angle ADC$ is a right angle	5. $\perp$ lines form rt. $\angle$'s
6. $\angle DCA$ and $\angle BCE$ are vertical angles	6. Def. vert. $\angle$'s
7. $\angle DCA = \angle BCE$	7. Vert. $\angle$'s are $=$
8. $\angle 1 = \angle 2$	8. Given
9. $\triangle ACD \cong \triangle BEC$	9. ASA = ASA
10. $\angle ADC = \angle CEB$	10. cpoctae
11. $\angle CEB$ is a right angle	11. Substitution law
12. $\overleftrightarrow{CD} \perp n$	12. Lines forming rt $\angle$'s are $\perp$
13. $m \parallel n$	13. Two lines $\perp$ to third line are $\parallel$

Corresponding angles can also be used to show that lines are parallel.

THEOREM 4.3

If two lines are cut by a transversal and a pair of corresponding angles are equal, then the lines are parallel.

Given: Lines *m* and *n* cut by
transversal ℓ
$\angle 1 = \angle 2$ (See Figure 4.7.)

Prove: $m \parallel n$

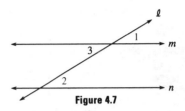

Figure 4.7

Proof:

STATEMENTS	REASONS
1. $\angle 1 = \angle 2$	1. Given
2. $\angle 1$ and $\angle 3$ are vertical angles	2. Def. vert. $\angle$'s
3. $\angle 3 = \angle 1$	3. Vert. $\angle$'s are =
4. $\angle 3 = \angle 2$	4. Trans. law
5. $m \parallel n$	5. If alt. int. $\angle$'s are = lines are $\parallel$

THEOREM 4.4

If two lines are cut by a transversal and a pair of alternate exterior angles are equal, then the lines are parallel.

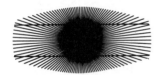

Sometimes our eyes play tricks on us. The two horizontal lines in the figure above, cut by many transversals, are actually parallel. Do they appear this way to you?

The proof of this theorem is similar to that for Theorem 4.3 and is left for you to do as an exercise.

THEOREM 4.5

If two lines are cut by a transversal and two interior angles on the same side of the transversal are supplementary, then the lines are parallel.

PRACTICE EXERCISE 1

Complete the proof of Theorem 4.5.

Given: Lines *m* and *n* cut by
transversal ℓ
$\angle 1$ and $\angle 2$ are supplementary

Prove: $m \parallel n$

Proof:

STATEMENTS	REASONS
1. $\angle 1$ and $\angle 2$ are supplementary	1. _____
2. $\angle 3$ and $\angle 2$ are supplementary	2. _____
3. _____	3. Supp. of same $\angle$ are =
4. $m \parallel n$.	4. _____

The walls and corners in the rooms of a house are usually not perfectly vertical. A paper hanger uses a plumb line, a string with a weight attached to it, to form a vertical line that is then used to align the first piece of wallpaper. Properties of parallel lines guarantee that the remaining strips of paper will be vertical when seams are aligned.

We now have five ways to prove that two lines m and n are parallel.

1. m and n are both $\perp$ to ℓ. (Theorem 4.1)
2. Alternate interior angles are equal. (Theorem 4.2)
3. Corresponding angles are equal. (Theorem 4.3)
4. Alternate exterior angles are equal. (Theorem 4.4)
5. Interior angles on the same side of a transversal are supplementary. (Theorem 4.5)

The converse of each of these theorems is also true.

THEOREM 4.6   (CONVERSE OF THEOREM 4.1)

If two lines are parallel and a third line is perpendicular to one of them, then it is also perpendicular to the other.

Given: $m \parallel n$
      $\ell \perp m$ (See Figure 4.8.)

Prove: $\ell \perp n$

Construction: Construct line s through P so that $s \perp \ell$. We must show that s and n are the same line.

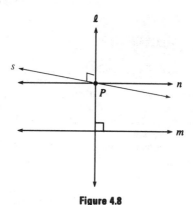

Figure 4.8

Proof:

STATEMENTS	REASONS
1. Construct s through P with $s \perp \ell$	1. Construction 2.4
2. $\ell \perp m$	2. Given
3. $m \parallel s$	3. Lines $\perp$ third line are $\parallel$
4. $m \parallel n$	4. Given
5. s and n are the same line	5. Parallel post.
6. $\ell \perp n$	6. Because $s \perp \ell$ and n and s are the same

---

THEOREM 4.7   (CONVERSE OF THEOREM 4.2)

If two parallel lines are cut by a transversal, then all pairs of alternate interior angles are equal.

Given: $m \parallel n$ with ℓ a transversal
(See Figure 4.9.)

Prove: $\angle 1 = \angle 2$

We give an indirect proof by showing
that the assumption $\angle 1 \neq \angle 2$ leads
to a contradiction.

Proof:

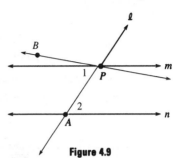

Figure 4.9

STATEMENTS	REASONS
1. Assume $\angle 1 \neq \angle 2$	1. Assumption
2. Construct $\angle APB$ such that $\angle APB = \angle 2$	2. Construction 2.2
3. $\overline{BP} \parallel n$	3. Alt. int. $\angle$'s are $=$
4. $m \parallel n$	4. Given

Because $\angle APB = \angle 2$ and $\angle 2 \neq \angle 1$, $\angle APB \neq \angle 1$, so $\overline{BP}$ and m are two distinct lines through P parallel to n, a contradiction of the parallel postulate. Thus, $\angle 1 \neq \angle 2$ leads to a contradiction forcing us to conclude that $\angle 1 = \angle 2$. We could show that the other pair of alternate interior angles are also equal using a similar proof.

THEOREM 4.8 (CONVERSE OF THEOREM 4.3)

If two parallel lines are cut by a transversal, then all pairs of corresponding angles are equal.

When the pieces in a quilt are sewn together, much care must be taken to maintain equal angles so that the appropriate sides of each quilt block remain parallel. Which theorems involving lines cut by a transversal are suggested by the quilt shown?

PRACTICE EXERCISE 2

Complete the proof of Theorem 4.8.

Given: $m \parallel n$ and m and n are cut by transversal ℓ

Prove: $\angle 1 = \angle 2$

Proof:

STATEMENTS	REASONS
1. $m \parallel n$	1. _____
2. $\angle 2 = \angle 3$	2. _____
3. _____	3. Def. of vert. $\angle$'s
4. $\angle 3 = \angle 1$	4. _____
5. _____	5. Trans. and sym. laws

The remaining corresponding angles are proved equal in a similar way.

The proof of the next theorem is similar to that of Theorem 4.8 and is left for you to do as an exercise.

THEOREM 4.9   (CONVERSE OF THEOREM 4.4)

If two parallel lines are cut by a transversal, then all pairs of alternate exterior angles are equal.

THEOREM 4.10   (CONVERSE OF THEOREM 4.5)

If two parallel lines are cut by a transversal, then all pairs of interior angles on the same side of the transversal are supplementary.

The proof of Theorem 4.10 is left for you to do as an exercise.

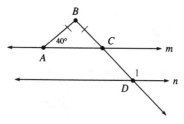

Figure 4.10

E X A M P L E 1   In Figure 4.10, $m \parallel n$ and $AB = BC$. What is the measure of $\angle 1$?

Because $AB = BC$, $\angle BCA = 40°$. Because $\angle BCA$ and $\angle ACD$ are supplementary, $\angle ACD = 140°$. Because $\angle 1$ and $\angle ACD$ are alternate interior angles formed by transversal $\overleftrightarrow{BD}$ cutting parallel lines m and n, $\angle 1 = 140°$.   ∎

ANSWERS TO PRACTICE EXERCISES: **1.** 1. Given 2. Adj. ∠'s whose non-common sides are in a line are supp. 3. $\angle 1 = \angle 3$ 4. If alt. int. ∠'s are = the lines are ∥. **2.** 1. Given 2. If ∥ lines are cut by a transv. the alt. int. ∠'s are = 3. $\angle 3$ and $\angle 1$ are vert. ∠'s 4. Vert. ∠'s are = 5. $\angle 1 = \angle 2$

4.2 EXERCISES

Exercises 1–12 refer to the figure below in which $m \parallel n$ and ℓ is a transversal.

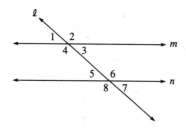

1. List two pairs of alternate interior angles.

2. List two pairs of alternate exterior angles.

3. List four pairs of corresponding angles.

4. List four angles that are supplementary to $\angle 1$.

5. List four angles that are supplementary to $\angle 2$.

6. List three angles that are equal to $\angle 1$.

7. List three angles that are equal to $\angle 2$.

8. If $\angle 1 = 48°$, find the measure of every other angle.

9. If $\angle 6 = 135°$, find the measure of every other angle.

10. Find the measure of each angle if $\angle 4$ is 30° more than twice $\angle 5$.

11. Find the measure of each angle if $\angle 6$ is 15° more than twice $\angle 1$.

12. Find the measure of each angle if $\angle 2$ is 10° more than $\angle 8$.

Exercises 13–20 refer to the figure below.

13. If $\angle 2 = \angle 4$, can $\overleftrightarrow{BC}$ and $\overleftrightarrow{DE}$ intersect?

14. If $\angle 1 = \angle 4$, can $\overleftrightarrow{BC}$ and $\overleftrightarrow{DE}$ intersect?

15. If $\angle 2 = \angle 5$, can $\overleftrightarrow{BC}$ and $\overleftrightarrow{DE}$ intersect?

16. If $\angle 3$ and $\angle 5$ are supplementary, can $\overleftrightarrow{BC}$ and $\overleftrightarrow{DE}$ intersect?

17. If $AB = AC$ and $\angle 5 = \angle 6$, can $\overleftrightarrow{BC}$ and $\overleftrightarrow{DE}$ intersect?

18. If $AB = AC$ and $\angle 4 = \angle 6$, can $\overleftrightarrow{BC}$ and $\overleftrightarrow{DE}$ intersect?

19. If $AD = AE$ and $\angle 5$ and $\angle 3$ are supplementary, are $\overleftrightarrow{BC}$ and $\overleftrightarrow{DE}$ parallel?

20. If $AD = AE$ and $\angle 4 = \angle 6$, are $\overleftrightarrow{BC}$ and $\overleftrightarrow{DE}$ parallel?

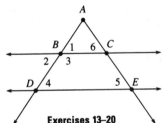

Exercises 13–20

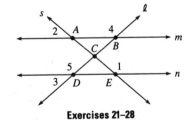

Exercises 21–28

Use the figure above in Exercises 21–28.

21. *Given:* $\angle 1$ is supplementary to $\angle 2$
    Prove: $m \parallel n$

22. *Given:* $\angle 3$ is supplementary to $\angle 4$
    Prove: $m \parallel n$

23. *Given:* $m \parallel n$
         $AB = DE$
    Prove: $\triangle ABC \cong \triangle CDE$

24. *Given:* $m \parallel n$
         $\angle 1 = \angle 5$
    Prove: $\triangle ABC$ is isosceles

25. *Given:* C is the midpoint of $\overline{AE}$ and $\overline{BD}$
    Prove: $m \parallel n$

26. *Given:* $m \parallel n$
         $CD = CE$
    Prove: $AC = BC$

27. *Given:* $AC = CE$
         $m \parallel n$
    Prove: $DC = CB$

28. *Given:* $AB = DE$
         $AD = BE$ (Draw auxiliary lines.)
    Prove: $m \parallel n$

29. Prove Theorem 4.4.

30. Prove Theorem 4.9.

31. Prove Theorem 4.10.

32. Use the figure below to find the values of x and y that make $\overline{AB} \parallel \overline{CD}$ and $\overline{AD} \parallel \overline{BC}$.

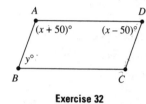

Exercise 32

33. Use the figure below to find the values of x and y that make $\overline{AB} \parallel \overline{CD}$ and $\overline{BC} \parallel \overline{DE}$.

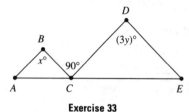

Exercise 33

34. Use the figure below to find the values of x and y that make $m \parallel n$.

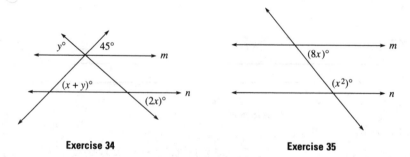

Exercise 34   **Exercise 35**

35. Use the figure above to find the value of x that makes $m \parallel n$.

36. Prove that if a line is drawn through the vertex of an isosceles triangle parallel to the base, then it bisects the exterior angle at the vertex.

Section 1.5

4.3 POLYGONS AND ANGLES

A triangle is a special case of a general class of geometric figures called *polygons*. Recall that a triangle is composed of three distinct segments no two of which are on the same line.

DEFINITION: POLYGON

A **polygon** is composed of n distinct segments in a plane and possesses the following properties: the segments intersect *only* at their endpoints; exactly two segments contain each endpoint; and no two consecutive segments are on the same line. Each segment is called a **side** of the polygon, and each endpoint is called a **vertex** of the polygon.

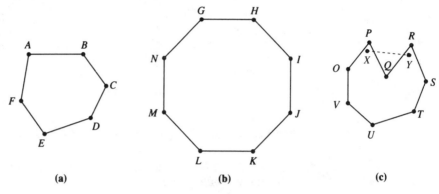

Figure 4.11   Polygons

Figure 4.11 shows several polygons. The polygon in Figure 4.11(c) possesses a property that we wish to avoid in our work. The polygons that we consider will be assumed to be *convex*.

DEFINITION: CONVEX POLYGON

A polygon is **convex** if, for all pairs of points X and Y in the interior of the polygon, the segment $\overline{XY}$ is completely in the interior of the polygon.

What could be more geometrically impressive than the honeycomb of a bee? Note that each opening is in the shape of a convex polygon with six sides.

Notice that the polygon in Figure 4.11(c) is not convex because there are points on $\overline{XY}$ that are not interior to the polygon. The remaining two polygons in Figure 4.11 are convex. When we use the term *polygon* from now on, we will mean *convex polygon*.

DEFINITION: REGULAR POLYGON

A polygon is a **regular polygon** if all its sides are equal and all its angles are equal.

Perhaps the most famous polygonal building in the world is the Pentagon in Washington, D.C.

The polygon in Figure 4.11(b) is a regular polygon because $GH = HI = IJ = JK = KL = LM = MN = NG$ and $\angle GHI = \angle HIJ = \angle IJK = \angle JKL = \angle KLM = \angle LMN = \angle MNG = \angle NGH$. Another example of a regular polygon is an equilateral (equiangular) triangle.

Polygons are given special names according to their number of sides as shown in the following table.

Number of Sides	Polygon
3	triangle
4	quadrilateral
5	pentagon
6	hexagon
7	heptagon
8	octagon
9	nonagon
10	decagon
n	n-gon

The polygon in Figure 4.11(a) is a hexagon and the polygon in Figure 4.11(b) is a regular octagon.

The next postulate gives the relationship between the number of sides and the number of angles of a polygon.

POSTULATE 4.2

A polygon has the same number of angles as sides.

DEFINITION: DIAGONAL OF A POLYGON

A **diagonal** of a polygon is a segment that joins two nonadjacent vertices.

In Figure 4.11(a) for example, if we were to construct segment $\overline{AD}$, then $\overline{AD}$ would be a diagonal of the hexagon. Notice in the definition of a diagonal that the term *nonadjacent* is important. Segments joining adjacent vertices are sides, not diagonals.

We have previously defined the perimeter of a triangle. This definition can be extended to all polygons.

DEFINITION: PERIMETER OF A POLYGON

The **perimeter** of a polygon is the sum of the lengths of its sides.

EXAMPLE 1   Consider the polygon in Figure 4.12.

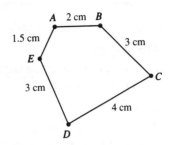

Figure 4.12   Perimeter of a Polygon

(a) What kind of polygon is this? Because it has 5 sides, it is a pentagon.

(b) How many diagonals does it have? Because the diagonals are $\overline{AC}, \overline{AD},$ $\overline{BD}, \overline{BE},$ and $\overline{CE}$, there are 5 diagonals.

(c) What is the perimeter of the polygon? The perimeter is

$$P = AB + BC + CD + DE + EA.$$
$$= 2 + 3 + 4 + 3 + 1.5 = 13.5 \text{ cm} \quad ∎$$

To determine properties of the angles of any polygon, we will first prove several theorems about the angles of a triangle and use the results in more general cases. To do this we need to be able to construct the line parallel to a given line and passing through a point not on the given line.

CONSTRUCTION 4.1
Construct the line parallel to a given line that passes through a point not on the given line.

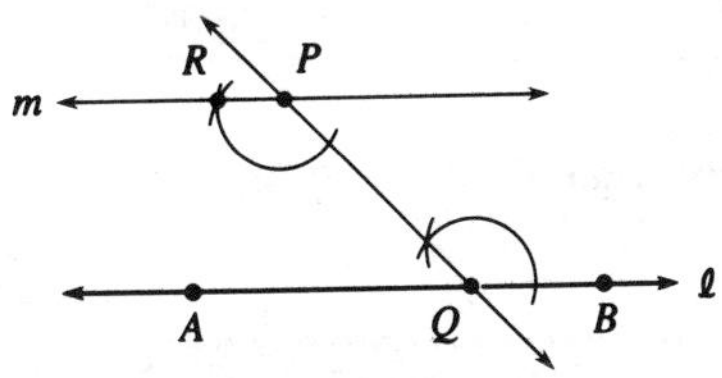

Figure 4.13

Given: Line ℓ and point P (See Figure 4.13.)

To Construct: Line m through P such that $m \parallel \ell$

Construction:

1. Draw any line through P that intersects ℓ at a point we label Q.

2. At P, use Construction 2.2 to construct $\angle RPQ$ such that $\angle RPQ = \angle PQB$.

3. Line $\overleftrightarrow{RP}$, which is equal to m, is the desired line because $m \parallel \ell$ since $\angle RPQ$ and $\angle PQB$ are equal alternate interior angles. By the parallel postulate, m is *the* line satisfying the given conditions.

The followers of Pythagoras (about 584–495 B.C.) are thought to have been the first to prove the next important theorem.

> ### THEOREM 4.11
> The sum of the measures of the angles of a triangle is 180°.

Given: $\triangle ABC$

Prove: $\angle A + \angle 1 + \angle B = 180°$

Construction: Construct line $\overleftrightarrow{ED}$ through C parallel to $\overline{AB}$.

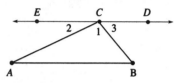

Figure 4.14

Proof:

STATEMENTS	REASONS
1. $\overline{ED} \parallel \overline{AB}$ and C is on $\overline{ED}$	1. Construction 4.1
2. $\angle ECD$ is a straight angle and $\angle ECD = 180°$	2. Def. of st. $\angle$
3. $\angle 2 + \angle 1 + \angle 3 = 180°$	3. Angle add. post.
4. $\angle A = \angle 2$ and $\angle B = \angle 3$	4. Alt. int. $\angle$'s are $=$
5. $\angle A + \angle 1 + \angle B = 180°$	5. Substitution law

Theorem 4.11 gives rise to a series of corollaries, the proofs of which are requested in the exercises.

> ### COROLLARY 4.12
> Any triangle can have at most one right angle or at most one obtuse angle.

> ### COROLLARY 4.13
> If two angles of one triangle are equal, respectively, to two angles of another triangle, then the third angles are also equal.

The next corollary gives us another way to prove that two triangles are congruent.

> ### COROLLARY 4.14   AAS = AAS
> If two angles and any side of one triangle are equal, respectively, to two angles and the corresponding side of another triangle, then the triangles are congruent.

Many floor coverings are made by joining together various polygons without leaving gaps or overlapping the edges. Such coverings are called *tessellations*. The tessellation shown above is made up of squares and regular octagons. Can you find other examples of tessellations?

PRACTICE EXERCISE 1

Complete the proof of Corollary 4.14.

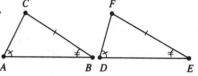

Given: △ABC and △DEF

∠A = ∠D and ∠B = ∠E

CB = FE

Prove: △ABC ≅ △DEF

Proof:

STATEMENTS	REASONS
1. ∠A = ∠D and ∠B = ∠E	1. _____
2. _____	2. If 2 ∠'s of one △ = 2 ∠'s of 2nd △, the 3rd ∠'s are =
3. _____	3. Given
4. △ABC ≅ △DEF	4. _____

The proof of the next corollary is requested in the exercises.

COROLLARY 4.15

The measure of an exterior angle of a triangle is equal to the sum of the measures of the nonadjacent interior angles.

We now turn our attention to the angles of polygons in general.

THEOREM 4.16

The sum of the measures of the angles of a polygon with n sides is given by the formula $S = (n - 2)180°$.

It is difficult to write a formal two-column proof of this theorem. Instead, we will present a paragraph-style proof using the polygon in Figure 4.15.

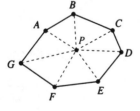

Figure 4.15

PROOF: Select a point P in the interior of the polygon and construct segments joining P to each vertex of the polygon. Because the polygon has n sides, we will obtain n triangles. Because the sum of the angle measures of a triangle is 180°, the sum of the angle measures of these n triangles is $n(180°)$. However, the angles of the triangles with their vertex at P are not parts of the angles of the polygon. Because the sum of these angle measures is 360°, we must subtract this amount from $n(180°)$. Then,

$$n(180°) - 360° = n(180°) - 2(180°)$$
$$= (n - 2)180°.$$

Although the polygon in Figure 4.16 has seven sides, we can see that this polygon was used for illustrative purposes only and that the formula

$$S = (n - 2)180°$$

works for any number of sides n. Notice that when $n = 3$ (a triangle), we obtain $S = (3 - 2)180° = (1)180° = 180°$, the same result we obtained earlier. ■

COROLLARY 4.17

The measure of each angle of a regular polygon with n sides is given by the formula $a = \dfrac{(n - 2)180°}{n}$.

PROOF: Because there are n equal angles in a regular polygon with n sides, if a is the measure of one of these angles, na is the sum of all these measures. By Theorem 4.16,

$$na = (n - 2)180°$$

from which the desired formula results by dividing both sides by n. ■

EXAMPLE 2   Find the sum of the angle measures of a hexagon. Because a hexagon has 6 sides, $n = 6$ in the formula $S = (n - 2)180°$. Thus,

$$S = (6 - 2)180° = (4)180° = 720°. \quad◪$$

PRACTICE EXERCISE 2

What is the measure of each angle of a regular hexagon?

Sometimes the angles of a polygon are called **interior angles** of the polygon to distinguish them from *exterior angles*. In the polygon in Figure 4.16, $\angle ABF$ is called an **exterior angle** of the polygon.

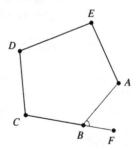

Figure 4.16   Exterior Angle of a Polygon

THEOREM 4.18

The sum of the measures of the exterior angles of a polygon, one at each vertex, is 360°.

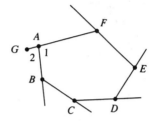

Figure 4.17

PROOF: Consider the polygon in Figure 4.17. Through each vertex we have a straight angle each of which is formed by one interior angle and one exterior angle. For example, straight angle $\angle FAG$ at vertex A is formed by interior angle $\angle 1$ and exterior angle $\angle 2$ because $\angle FAG = \angle 1 + \angle 2$. The total measure of these n straight angles is $(n)180°$, and the sum of the n interior angles of the polygon is $(n - 2)180°$. If we let T be the sum of the n exterior angles, then

$$T + (n - 2)180° = (n)180°.$$

$T + (n)(180°) - (2)(180°) = (n)180°$	Distributive law
$T - (2)(180°) = 0$	Subtract $(n)180°$ from both sides
$T - 360° = 0$	$(2)(180°) = 360°$
$T = 360°$	Add $360°$ to both sides

Thus, the sum of the exterior angles is 360°. ■

COROLLARY 4.19

The measure of each exterior angle of a regular polygon with n sides is determined with the formula $e = \dfrac{360°}{n}$.

The proof of Corollary 4.19 is left for you to do as an exercise.

EXAMPLE 3 What is the measure of each exterior angle of a regular hexagon? Because a hexagon has 6 sides, substitute 6 for n in $e = \dfrac{360°}{n}$.

$$e = \frac{360°}{6} = 60° \quad \blacksquare$$

ANSWERS TO PRACTICE EXERCISES: **1.** 1. Given 2. $\angle C = \angle F$ 3. $CB = FE$ 4. ASA = ASA **2.** 120°

4.3 EXERCISES

In Exercises 1–8, answer each of the following questions for a regular polygon with the given number of sides. (a) What is the name of the polygon? (b) What is the sum of the angles of the polygon? (c) What is the measure of each angle of the polygon? (d) What is the sum of the measures of the exterior angles of the polygon? (e) What is the measure of each exterior angle of the polygon? (f) If each side is 5 cm long, what is the perimeter of the polygon?

1. 3	**2.** 4	**3.** 5	**4.** 6
5. 7	**6.** 8	**7.** 9	**8.** 10

In Exercises 9–12, solve the equation $S = (n - 2)180°$ for n when S is a given value. Find the number of sides of each polygon (if possible) if the given value corresponds to the number of degrees in the sum of the interior angles of a polygon. Remember that n must be a whole number greater than 2, or no such polygon can exist.

9. 1620°	**10.** 2700°	**11.** 2000°	**12.** 3200°

In Exercises 13–16, solve the equation $a = \dfrac{(n - 2)180°}{n}$ for n when a is a given value. Find the number of sides of each polygon (if possible) if the given value is the measure of one interior angle of a regular polygon.

13. 157.5°	**14.** 162°	**15.** 145°	**16.** 105°

17. Two exterior angles of a triangle sum to 200°. What is the measure of the third exterior angle?

18. Three exterior angles of a quadrilateral sum to 300°. What is the measure of the fourth exterior angle?

19. As the number of sides of a regular polygon increases, does each exterior angle increase or decrease?

20. As the number of sides of a regular polygon increases, does an interior angle increase or decrease?

21. What is the smallest angle that any regular polygon can have?

22. What is the largest exterior angle that any regular polygon can have?

23. Find the number of sides of a polygon if the sum of its angles is twice the sum of its exterior angles.

24. If the number of sides of a polygon were doubled, the sum of the angles of the polygon would be increased by 900°. How many sides does the original polygon have?

25. If the sum of the angles of a polygon is equal to the sum of the exterior angles of the polygon, how many sides does the polygon have?

26. By how many degrees is the sum of the angles of a polygon increased when the number of sides is increased by 4?

27. Prove Corollary 4.12.

28. Prove Corollary 4.13.

29. Prove Corollary 4.15.

30. Prove that the exterior angles of a regular polygon are equal.

31. Prove Corollary 4.19.

32. Prove that every point on the bisector of an angle is equidistant from the sides of the angle.

Use the figure below in Exercises 33–34.

33. A city planner wishes to locate the point in Central Park that is equidistant from Elm Street, Washington Avenue, and Park Way. Explain how she can determine this point. [Hint: Use Exercise 32.]

34. Explain how a city planner can find the point in Central Park that is equidistant from a library at point *A*, a monument at point *B*, and a fountain at point *C*.

Section 1.6

4.5 RECTANGLES, SQUARES, AND TRAPEZOIDS

A *rectangle* is a special type of parallelogram that has many useful applications.

> **DEFINITION: RECTANGLE**
>
> A **rectangle** is a parallelogram with one right angle.

The symbol □ represents the word *rectangle*. Because a rectangle is also a parallelogram, all of the properties of parallelograms are also properties of rectangles. For example, the opposite sides and opposite angles of a rectangle are equal. The next theorem follows from Theorems 4.23 and 4.24 and is left for you to do as an exercise.

> **THEOREM 4.32**
>
> All angles of a rectangle are right angles.

> **THEOREM 4.33**
>
> The diagonals of a rectangle are equal.

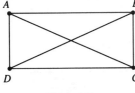

Figure 4.25

Given: □*ABCD* (See Figure 4.25.)

Prove: $AC = BD$

Proof:

STATEMENTS	REASONS
1. □*ABCD*	1. Given
2. $AD = BC$	2. Opp. sides of a □ are =
3. $DC = DC$	3. Reflexive law
4. ∠*ADC* and ∠*BCD* are right angles	4. All ∠'s of □ are rt. ∠'s
5. ∠*ADC* = ∠*BCD*	5. All rt. ∠'s are =
6. △*ADC* ≅ △*BCD*	6. SAS = SAS
7. $AC = BD$	7. cpoctae

The converse of Theorem 4.33 is also true and provides us with another method for proving that a parallelogram is a rectangle.

THEOREM 4.34
If the diagonals of a parallelogram are equal, then the parallelogram is a rectangle.

Theorem 4.34 has many practical applications. To show that a quadrilateral is a rectangle, you must do more than show that the opposite sides are equal (the figure might simply be a parallelogram). Also, it might not be possible to show that the figure has a right angle, but it might be possible to measure the diagonals. For example, a construction worker might measure the diagonals of a foundation for a house to be sure he is laying a rectangular foundation and not simply a foundation with equal opposite sides.

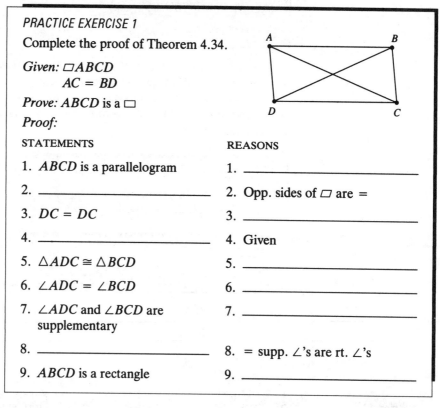

PRACTICE EXERCISE 1

Complete the proof of Theorem 4.34.

Given: □*ABCD*
     AC = BD

Prove: ABCD is a ▭

Proof:

STATEMENTS	REASONS
1. *ABCD* is a parallelogram	1. _____
2. _____	2. Opp. sides of □ are =
3. *DC = DC*	3. _____
4. _____	4. Given
5. △*ADC* ≅ △*BCD*	5. _____
6. ∠*ADC* = ∠*BCD*	6. _____
7. ∠*ADC* and ∠*BCD* are supplementary	7. _____
8. _____	8. = supp. ∠'s are rt. ∠'s
9. *ABCD* is a rectangle	9. _____

DEFINITION: SQUARE
A square is a rhombus with a right angle.

The symbol ▭ represents the word *square*. Because a rhombus is a parallelogram, a square is a parallelogram with a right angle, making it a rectangle. Because all sides of a rhombus are equal, a square is a rectangle with all sides equal. Thus, a square has all the properties of both a rhombus and a rectangle.

For example, the diagonals of a square are perpendicular, they bisect each other, and they bisect the angles of the square. Notice that every square is a rhombus, but not every rhombus is a square. Similarly, every square is a rectangle, but not every rectangle is a square.

Because rectangles and squares are perhaps the most important quadrilaterals, we should be able to construct them.

CONSTRUCTION 4.2
Construct a rectangle when two adjacent sides are given.

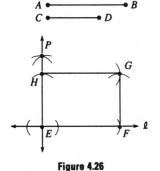

Figure 4.26

Given: Segments $\overline{AB}$ and $\overline{CD}$ (See Figure 4.26.)

To Construct: $\square EFGH$ with $EF = AB$ and $EH = CD$

Construction:

1. Draw line ℓ, identify point E on ℓ, use Construction 2.4 to construct $\overleftrightarrow{EP} \perp \ell$.

2. Use Construction 2.1 to copy $\overline{AB}$ onto line ℓ obtaining $\overline{EF}$, and to copy $\overline{CD}$ onto $\overleftrightarrow{EP}$ obtaining $\overline{EH}$.

3. Set the compass for length AB, place the tip at H, and make an arc. Now set the compass for length CD, place the tip at F, and make an arc that intersects the first arc in point G.

4. Use a straightedge to draw segments $\overline{HG}$ and $\overline{FG}$. Then $EFGH$ is the desired rectangle because it is a parallelogram ($EH = FG$ and $EF = HG$) with right angle $\angle HEF$.

Constructing a square with a given side consists of the same steps as in Construction 4.2 except that $AB = CD$. The remaining construction is left for you to do as an exercise.

CONSTRUCTION 4.3
Construct a square when a side is given.

The following two theorems will be needed for working with the next quadrilateral we will discuss, a *trapezoid.* Recall from Section 2.3 that the distance from a point to a line is the length of a perpendicular segment drawn from the point to the line. We use this fact to prove the following theorem.

THEOREM 4.35
Two parallel lines are always the same distance apart.

Given: $\ell \parallel m$ with A and B arbitrary
  points on ℓ, and C and D on m
  $\overline{AC} \perp m$ and $\overline{BD} \perp m$
  AC is the distance from A to m
  BD is the distance from B to m
  (See Figure 4.27.)

Prove: ℓ and m are always the same
  distance apart

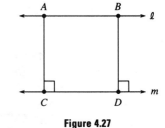

Figure 4.27

Proof:

STATEMENTS	REASONS
1. $\ell \parallel m$, $\overline{AC} \perp m$, and $\overline{BD} \perp m$	1. Given
2. $\overline{AC} \parallel \overline{BD}$	2. Lines $\perp$ to third line are $\parallel$
3. $ABCD$ is a parallelogram	3. Opp. sides are $\parallel$
4. $AC = BD$	4. Opp. sides of $\square$ are $=$
5. Because A and B were arbitrary points on ℓ, ℓ and m are always the same distance apart	5. All points on ℓ are the same distance from m

---

THEOREM 4.36

The segment joining the midpoints of two sides of a triangle is parallel
to the third side and equal to one-half of it.

Given: $\triangle ABC$ with D the midpoint
  of $\overline{AB}$ and E the midpoint of $\overline{AC}$
  (See Figure 4.28.)

Prove: $\overline{DE} \parallel \overline{BC}$ and $DE = \frac{1}{2}BC$

Auxiliary lines: Extend $\overline{DE}$ to point
  F so that $DE = EF$ by
  Construction 2.1
  Draw segment $\overline{FC}$

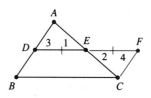

Figure 4.28

Proof:

STATEMENTS	REASONS
1. D is the midpoint of $\overline{AB}$, and E is the midpoint of $\overline{AC}$ in $\triangle ABC$	1. Given
2. $AE = EC$ and $AD = DB$	2. Def. of midpt.
3. $\angle 1 = \angle 2$	3. Vert. $\angle$'s are $=$
4. $DE = EF$	4. By construction
5. $\triangle ADE \cong \triangle EFC$	5. SAS $=$ SAS
6. $FC = AD$	6. cpoctae
7. $FC = DB$	7. Transitive law

8. $\angle 3 = \angle 4$	8. cpoctae
9. $\overline{FC} \parallel \overline{DB}$	9. Alt. int. $\angle$'s are $=$
10. $BCFD$ is a parallelogram	10. Opp. sides are $=$ and $\parallel$
11. $\overline{DE} \parallel \overline{BC}$	11. Opp. sides of $\square$ are $\parallel$
12. $DF = BC$	12. Opp. sides of $\square$ are $=$
13. $DF = DE + EF$	13. Seg. add. post.
14. $DF = DE + DE$	14. Substitution law
15. $DF = 2DE$	15. Distributive law
16. $2DE = BC$	16. Substitution law
17. $DE = \dfrac{1}{2}BC$	17. Mult.-div. law

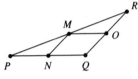

Figure 4.29

EXAMPLE 1   Refer to $\triangle PQR$ in Figure 4.29. If M is the midpoint of $\overline{PR}$, N is the midpoint of $\overline{PQ}$, and $MN = 5$ cm, find the length of $\overline{QR}$. By Theorem 4.36, $MN = \dfrac{1}{2}QR$, so $QR = 10$ cm. ◼

PRACTICE EXERCISE 2

Refer to $\triangle PQR$ in Figure 4.29. Assume $\triangle PQR$ is isosceles with base $\overline{PR}$ and $RQ = 30$ inches, and M and O are the midpoints of $\overline{PR}$ and $\overline{QR}$, respectively. Find the length of $\overline{MO}$.

DEFINITION: TRAPEZOID

A **trapezoid** is a quadrilateral with exactly one pair of parallel sides. The parallel sides are called **bases** and the nonparallel sides are called **legs**. If the legs of a trapezoid are equal, the trapezoid is an **isosceles trapezoid**. A pair of angles of a trapezoid are called **base angles** if they include the same base.

A trapezoid is a figure with properties similar to those of a triangle and a parallelogram. Figure 4.30 shows a trapezoid with bases $\overline{AB}$ and $\overline{CD}$ and sides $\overline{AD}$ and $\overline{BC}$. One pair of base angles is $\angle D$ and $\angle C$, and the other pair is $\angle A$ and $\angle B$. If AD and BC were equal, the trapezoid would be isosceles.

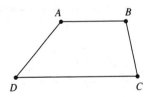

Figure 4.30   Trapezoid

THEOREM 4.37

The base angles of an isosceles trapezoid are equal.

Given: Isosceles trapezoid $ABCD$ with $\overline{AB} \parallel \overline{DC}$ (See Figure 4.31.)

Prove: $\angle D = \angle C$

Auxiliary lines: Construct $\overline{AE}$ through A parallel to $\overline{BC}$ using Construction 4.1

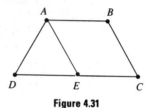

Figure 4.31

Proof:

STATEMENTS	REASONS
1. Isosceles trapezoid $ABCD$ with $\overline{AB} \parallel \overline{DC}$.	1. Given
2. $\overline{AE} \parallel \overline{BC}$	2. By construction
3. $AECB$ is a parallelogram	3. Opp. sides are $\parallel$
4. $BC = AE$	4. Opp. sides of $\square$ are $=$
5. $AD = BC$	5. Def. isos. trapezoid
6. $AD = AE$	6. Transitive law
7. $\angle D = \angle AED$	7. $\angle$'s opp $=$ sides are $=$
8. $\angle AED = \angle C$	8. Corr. $\angle$'s are $=$
9. $\angle D = \angle C$	9. Transitive law

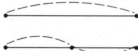

THEOREM 4.38

The diagonals of an isosceles trapezoid are equal.

When the string on a guitar is plucked, the vibration creates the sound we hear. Pythagoras knew that the length of the string is related to the pitch of the note. The string in the top figure produces a certain note. If you press the center of the string and pluck it, the note heard is one octave above the first. In general, the most pleasing notes to our ear are formed by dividing the string into an equal number of congruent segments.

The proof of Theorem 4.38 is left for you to do as an exercise.

DEFINITION: MEDIAN OF A TRAPEZOID

The segment joining the midpoints of the legs of a trapezoid is the **median of the trapezoid.**

THEOREM 4.39

The median of a trapezoid is parallel to the bases and equal to one-half their sum.

The proof of Theorem 4.39 is requested in the exercises.

The next theorem provides a way to divide a given line segment into any number of equal parts.

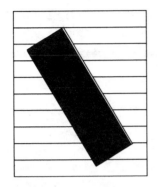

A student wants to cut a rectangular piece of plastic into seven congruent rectangles all with length equal to the width of the plastic rectangle. Assume that a measuring device is not available. Explain how the student can discover where to make the cuts by placing the plastic rectangle on a piece of ruled paper. What theorem are you using?

THEOREM 4.40

If three or more parallel lines intercept equal segments on one transversal, then they intercept equal segments on all transversals.

The proof of Theorem 4.40 is requested in the exercises.

CONSTRUCTION 4.4

Divide a given segment into a given number of equal segments.

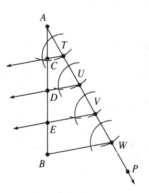

Figure 4.32

Given: Segment $\overline{AB}$ (See Figure 4.32.)

To Construct: Divide $\overline{AB}$ into n equal parts. For purposes of illustration, let $n = 4$. The technique we will use works for any n.

Construction:

1. Choose point P not on $\overleftrightarrow{AB}$ and draw ray $\overrightarrow{AP}$.

2. Set the compass at any length and mark off equal segments $\overline{AT}$, $\overline{TU}$, $\overline{UV}$, and $\overline{VW}$, and draw segment $\overline{BW}$.

3. Use Construction 2.2 to construct $\angle ATC$, $\angle TUD$, $\angle UVE$ all of which are equal to $\angle VWB$. The points C, D, and E divide $\overline{AB}$ into equal segments $\overline{AC}$, $\overline{CD}$, $\overline{DE}$, and $\overline{EB}$ by Theorem 4.40 because $\overline{AB}$ and $\overline{AP}$ are transversals intercepting parallel lines $\overline{TC}$, $\overline{UD}$ $\overline{VE}$, and $\overline{WB}$.

ANSWERS TO PRACTICE EXERCISES: **1.** 1. Given   2. *AD* = *BC*
3. Reflexive law   4. *AC* = *BD*   5. SSS = SSS   6. cpoctae   7. Consec. ∠'s of
▱ are supp.   8. ∠*ADC* and ∠*BCD* are right angles   9. Def. of ▱   **2.** 15
inches

4.5 EXERCISES

Exercises 1–20 refer to the figure below in which *ABCD* is a trapezoid with
bases $\overline{AB}$ and $\overline{CD}$, $\overline{EG} \perp \overline{DC}$ and $\overline{FH} \perp \overline{DC}$, *E* the midpoint of $\overline{AD}$, and *F*
the midpoint of $\overline{BC}$. Answer true or false.

1. $\overline{AB} \parallel \overline{DC}$.

2. $\overline{AD} \parallel \overline{BC}$.

3. $\overline{EF} \parallel \overline{AB}$.

4. $\overline{EF} \parallel \overline{DC}$.

5. *EG* = *FH*.

6. *AC* = *BD*.

7. *EFHG* is a parallelogram.

8. *EFHG* is a rhombus.

9. *EFHG* is a rectangle.

10. *EFHG* is a square.

11. *EFHG* is a trapezoid.

12. *EH* = *FG*.

13. $\overline{EH}$ and $\overline{FG}$ bisect each other.

14. $\overline{EH} \perp \overline{FG}$.

15. If *AB* = 4 cm and *DC* = 6 cm, then *EF* = 5 cm.

16. If *EF* = 10 inches, then *AB* + *CD* = 30 inches.

17. If ∠*ADC* = 75°, then ∠*BAD* = 105°.

18. If ∠*ADC* = 75° and *AD* = *BC*, then ∠*BCD* = 75°.

19. If ∠*BAD* = 110° and *AD* = *BC*, then ∠*ADC* = 110°.

20. If *AD* = *BC*, then *AC* = *DB*.

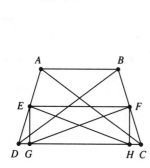

Exercises 1–20

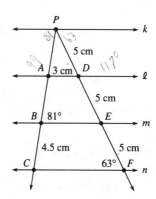

Exercises 21–28

Exercises 21–28 refer to the figure above in which *k* ∥ ℓ, ℓ ∥ *m,* and *m* ∥ *n.* Find
the value of each of the following.

21. *PA*

22. *AB*

23. ∠*PAD*

24. ∠*BCF*

25. *BE*

26. *CF*

27. ∠*DAB*

28. ∠*APD*

29. Complete the proof of Theorem 4.39.

Given: Trapezoid $ABCD$ with $\overline{AB} \parallel \overline{CD}$ and median $\overline{EF}$

Prove: $\overline{EF} \parallel \overline{AB}$, $\overline{EF} \parallel \overline{CD}$, and

$$EF = \frac{1}{2}(AB + CD)$$

Auxiliary lines: Construct $\overleftrightarrow{AF}$. By the parallel postulate $\overleftrightarrow{AF}$ must intersect $\overleftrightarrow{DC}$ at a point, call it G.

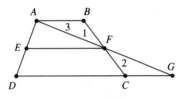

Exercise 29

Proof:

STATEMENTS	REASONS
1. $\overleftrightarrow{AF}$ intersects $\overleftrightarrow{DC}$ at G	1. _____
2. _____	2. Given
3. E is the midpoint of $\overline{AD}$ and F is the midpoint of $\overline{BC}$	3. _____
4. _____	4. Def. of midpoint
5. $\angle 1 = \angle 2$	5. _____
6. _____	6. Given
7. $\angle 3 = \angle G$	7. _____
8. $\triangle ABF \cong \triangle FCG$	8. _____
9. $AF = FG$ and $AB = CG$	9. _____
10. $EF = \frac{1}{2}DG$	10. Theorem 4.36
11. $\overline{DG} = \overline{CG} + \overline{DC}$	11. _____
12. $\overline{DG} = \overline{AB} + \overline{DC}$	12. _____
13. $EF = \frac{1}{2}(AB + DC)$	13. Substitution law
14. $\overline{EF} \parallel \overline{DC}$	14. Theorem 4.36
15. $\overline{EF} \parallel \overline{AB}$	15. _____

30. Complete the proof of Theorem 4.40.

Given: $\ell \parallel m$ and $m \parallel n$
    $AB = BC$

Prove: $DE = EF$

Auxiliary lines: Construct $\overline{AG} \parallel \overline{DE}$ and $\overline{BH} \parallel \overline{EF}$ using Construction 4.1.

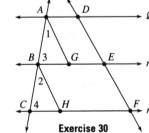

Exercise 30

Proof:

STATEMENTS	REASONS
1. $\overline{AG} \parallel \overline{DE}$ and $\overline{BH} \parallel \overline{EF}$	1. _____

2. $\overline{AG} \parallel \overline{BH}$ 2. _____

3. $\angle 1 = \angle 2$ 3. _____

4. _____   4. Given

5. $\angle 3 = \angle 4$ 5. _____

6. _____   6. ASA = ASA

7. _____   7. cpoctae

8. *ADEG* and *BEFH* are   8. _____
   parallelograms

9. *DE = AG* and *EF = BH*   9. _____

10. _____   10. Sym. and Trans. laws

31. Prove Theorem 4.32.   **32.** Prove Theorem 4.38.

33. Prove that the segments joining the midpoints of the consecutive sides of any quadrilateral form a parallelogram.

34. Prove that the bisectors of two consecutive angles of a parallelogram are perpendicular.

35. Prove that the segments joining the midpoints of the sides of an equilateral triangle form another equilateral triangle.

36. Prove that the segment joining the midpoints of the adjacent sides of a rectangle form a rhombus.

37. Construct a rectangle with sides measuring 3 inches and 2 inches.

38. Construct a square with each side measuring 2 inches.

39. Jeanne wants to enclose a garden with a fence in the shape of a rectangle 15 ft by 20 ft. To be certain she has formed a rectangle, she measures the diagonals and finds they are equal. Does this make the garden rectangular in shape?

40. Galen wishes to find the distance between two points *A* and *B* on opposite sides of a lake. He places a stake at point *C* and determines the midpoints of $\overline{AC}$ and $\overline{BC}$ to be *D* and *E*, respectively (see the figure below). He measures the length of $\overline{DE}$ and finds it to be 56 ft. What is the length of $\overline{AB}$?

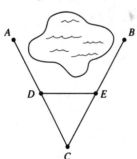

Exercise 40

Section 1.1

1.2

PRACTICE EXERCISE

1. Since A is in the position of 3 on the
   number line, the coordinate of A is 3.
   Since B is in the position of -2 on the
   number line, the coordinate of B is -2.
   Since C is half way between -1 and 0, the
   coordinate of C is $-\frac{1}{2}$.   Since D is about
   $\frac{3}{4}$ of the way from 1 to 2, the coordinate of
   D is $1 + \frac{3}{4} = \frac{7}{4}$.

SECTION EXERCISES

1. exactly one

3. C is in plane $\mathcal{P}$

5. Postulate 1.1

7. Postulate 1.4

9. The graph is in the text.

11. A:2 ; B:-3 ; C:3.5 ; D: $-\frac{1}{2}$

13. 5

15. 7

17. a

19. false; transitive law

21. false; multiplication-division law

23. 2. Postulate 1.9   4. Postulate 1.9
    6. Postulate 1.10   8. Postulate 1.7
    9. Postulate 1.11

25. yes ; yes

27. yes ; yes

29. By Postulate 1.2, three distinct points
    (the ends of the legs) all lie in the
    same plane (the floor on which the stool
    stands). However, four points (the ends of
    a 4-legged stool) need not all lie in the
    same plane (the floor on which that stool
    stands).

Section 1.2

1.3

PRACTICE EXERCISES

1. By the extension of the segment addition
   postulate, the three segments of length
   x + 2, 2x + 1, and x must add to equal 23.
   Thus, we must solve:

   (x + 2) + (2x + 1) + x = 23

   $\qquad$ x + 2 + 2x + 1 + x = 23   Clear parentheses

   $\qquad\qquad$ 4x + 3 = 23   Combine terms

   $\qquad\qquad$ 4x = 20   Subtract 3 from
   $\qquad\qquad\qquad\qquad$ both sides

   $\qquad\qquad$ $x = \frac{20}{4}$ Divide both
   $\qquad\qquad\qquad\qquad$ sides by 4

   $\qquad\qquad$ x = 5   Simplify

2. First sketch a figure showing Z on $\overrightarrow{XY}$ but
   not on $\overrightarrow{XY}$.

(a) Then Z is on $\overrightarrow{YX}$ but not on $\overrightarrow{XY}$.

(b) Z is not on the segment $\overline{YX}$ which includes
    only points between X and Y along with
    X and Y.

(c) Then Y is on $\overrightarrow{ZX}$ but not on $\overrightarrow{XZ}$.

(d) $\overrightarrow{XY}$ only has one endpoint (like every
    ray) which is X.

(e) The endpoints of the segment $\overline{XY}$ are X and
    Y (which is true for any segment, a
    segment has two endpoints).

(f) $\overrightarrow{XY}$ and $\overrightarrow{YX}$ are different rays. Notice
    that Z is on $\overrightarrow{YX}$ but not on $\overrightarrow{XY}$.

(g) Since ZY = ZX + XY by the segment
    addition postulate, substituting we
    have:

    ZY = 3 + 5 = 8 cm

3. (a) If ∠A = 27° and ∠A and ∠B are complementary, then

$$∠A + ∠B = 90°.$$

Substitute 27° for ∠A and solve for ∠B.

$$27° + ∠B = 90°$$
$$∠B = 90° - 27°$$
$$∠B = 63°$$

(b) If ∠P = 74°26'52" and ∠P and ∠Q are supplementary, then

$$∠P + ∠Q = 180°.$$

Substitute 74°26'52" for ∠P and solve for ∠Q.

$$74°26'52" + ∠Q = 180°$$
$$∠Q = 180° - 74°26'52"$$

To find ∠Q we must "borrow" minutes and seconds from degrees as follows.

$$180° = 179°60' = 179°59'60"$$

Then

$$180° - 74°26'52" = 179°59'60" - 74°26'52"$$
$$= (179° - 74°) + (59' - 26')$$
$$+ (60" - 52")$$
$$= 105° + 33' + 8"$$
$$= 105°33'8"$$

4. If ∠P and ∠Q are supplementary then

$$∠P + ∠Q = 180°$$

Substitute (2y - 9)° for ∠P and (7y)° for ∠Q and solve for y.

$$(2y - 9)° + (7y)° = 180°$$
$$(2y - 9) + (7y) = 180$$
$$2y - 9 + 7y = 180$$
$$9y - 9 = 180$$
$$9y = 189$$
$$y = 21$$

SECTION EXERCISES

1. true

3. true

5. true

7. false (the rays are opposite in direction)

9. true

11. false (a line has no end points)

13. true

15. false (∠ACB is a straight angle)

17. true

19. true

21. 65°

23. 90°

25. 115°

27. 72° (subtract 18° from 90°)

29. 53°20' (subtract 36°40' from 90°)

31. 106° (subtract 74° from 180°)

33. 122°25' (subtract 57°35' from 180°)

35. 45°

37. 40°

39. 25°

41. 60° (solve 180 - x = 4(90 - x))

43. acute

45. straight

47. acute

49. acute

51. right

6   Section 1.3

53. 107°10' (add the angles)

55. 139°20'16" (add the angles)

57. two

59. two

61. It depends on the length of $\overline{AB}$. If AB < 5 there is only one. If AB $\geq$ 5 there are two.

63. $\dfrac{n(n-1)}{2}$

65. x = 9 (solve (25 - x) + x + 3x = 52)

67. y = 20 (solve (30 - y) + (9y - 10) = 180)

Section 1.3

2.3

SECTION EXERCISES

1. Use Construction 2.1.

3. Use Construction 2.2.

5. Use Construction 2.2 twice.

7. Use Construction 2.3.

9. Use Construction 2.3.

11. Use Construction 2.4.

13. Use Construction 2.6.

15. Use Construction 2.6 three times.

17. A ruler is used to measure lengths, but a straightedge is used only to draw a straight line between two points.

19. exactly one

21. Use Construction 2.5.

23. Construct the bisector of the angle with vertex at the bridge and sides containing the ranger station and the cabin. Locate the point of intersection of this bisector (ray) and the edge of the forest.

Section 1.4

4.2

PRACTICE EXERCISES

1. The reason for Statement 1 is: Given

   The reason for Statement 2 is: Adj. ∠'s whose noncommon sides are in a line are supp.
     Note that ∠3 and ∠2 are adjacent angles and their noncommon sides are both in line n.

   Statement 3 is: ∠1 = ∠3
     Note that ∠1 and ∠3 are both supplementary to the same angle, ∠2, thus are equal.

   The reason for Statement 4 is: If alt. int. ∠'s are = the lines are ∥.

2. The reason for Statement 1 is: Given

   The reason for Statement 2 is: If ∥ lines are cut by transv. the alt. int. ∠'s are =.
     Note that ∠2 and ∠3 are alternate interior angles formed by transversal l cutting parallel lines m and n.

   Statement 3 is: ∠3 and ∠1 are vertical angles
     By definition, ∠3 and ∠1 are vertical angles.

Note that ∠1 and ∠3 are equal alternate interior angles formed by the transversal l that cuts lines m and n.

The reason for Statement 4 is: Vertical ∠'s are =

Statement 5 is: ∠1 = ∠2
   Since ∠2 = ∠3 and ∠3 = ∠1, ∠2 = ∠1 by the transitive law, and so ∠1 = ∠2 by the symmetric law. We might also have used the Substitution law for the reason.

SECTION EXERCISES

1. ∠3 and ∠5 ; ∠4 and ∠6

3. ∠1 and ∠5 ; ∠2 and ∠6 ; ∠3 and ∠7 ; ∠4 and ∠8

5. ∠1, ∠3, ∠5, ∠7

7. ∠4, ∠6, ∠8

9. ∠2 = ∠4 = ∠8 = 135°, ∠1 = ∠3 = ∠5 = ∠7 = 45°

11. ∠1 = ∠3 = ∠5 = ∠7 = 55°, ∠2 = ∠4 = ∠6 = ∠8 = 125°

13. no

15. yes

17. no

19. yes

21. Proof:

STATEMENTS	REASONS
1. ∠1 is supplementary to ∠2	1. Given
2. ∠1 is supplementary to ∠CED	2. Adj. ∠'s whose noncommon sides are in line are supp.
3. ∠2 = ∠CED	3. Supp. of = ∠'s are =
4. m ∥ n	4. Corr. ∠'s are =

23. Proof:

STATEMENTS	REASONS
1. m ∥ n	1. Given
2. ∠BAC = ∠CED and ∠ABC = ∠CDE	2. Alt. int. ∠'s are =
3. AB = DE	3. Given
4. △ABC ≅ △CDE	4. ASA = ASA

25. Proof:

STATEMENTS	REASONS
1. C is midpoint of $\overline{AE}$ and $\overline{BD}$	1. Given
2. AC = CE and BC = CD	2. Def. of midpt.
3. ∠ACB = ∠DCE	3. Vert. ∠'s are =
4. △ACB ≅ △DCE	4. SAS = SAS
5. ∠ABC = ∠CDE	5. cpoctae
6. m ∥ n	6. Alt. int. ∠'s are =

27. Proof:

STATEMENTS	REASONS
1. AC = CE	1. Given
2. m ‖ n	2. Given
3. ∠BAC = ∠CED	3. Alt. int. ∠'s are =
4. ∠ACB = ∠DCE	4. Vert. ∠'s are =
5. △ABC ≅ △CDE	5. ASA = ASA
6. DC = CB	6. cpoctae

29. Given: Lines m and n cut by transversal
ℓ, ∠1 = ∠2

Prove: m ‖ n

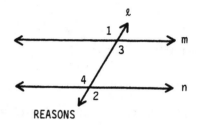

Proof:

STATEMENTS	REASONS
1. m and n are cut by transversal ℓ and ∠1 = ∠2	1. Given
2. ∠1 and ∠3 are vertical angles as are ∠2 and ∠4	2. Def. vert. ∠'s
3. ∠1 = ∠3 and ∠2 = ∠4	3. Vert. ∠'s are =
4. ∠3 = ∠4	4. Sym. & trans. laws using 1 and 3
5. m ‖ n	5. If alt. int. ∠'s are = the lines are ‖

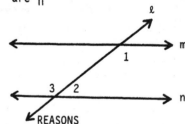

31. Given: m ‖ n and m and n are cut by
transversal ℓ

Prove: ∠1 and ∠2 are supplementary

Proof:

STATEMENTS	REASONS
1. m ‖ n	1. Given
2. ∠1 = ∠3	2. Alt. int. ∠'s are =
3. ∠3 and ∠2 are adjacent angles	3. Def. of adj. ∠'s
4. ∠3 is supplementary to ∠2	4. Adj. ∠'s whose noncommon sides are in line are supp.
5. ∠1 is supplementary to ∠2	5. Substitution law

33. For $\overline{AB}$ to be parallel to $\overline{CD}$, transversal $\overline{BC}$ must form equal alternate interior angles ∠ABC and ∠BCD. Since ∠ABC = x° and ∠BCD = 90°, x = 90. For $\overline{BC}$ to be parallel to $\overline{DE}$, transversal $\overline{DC}$ must form equal alternate interior angles ∠EDC and ∠BCD. Since ∠EDC = (3y)° and ∠BCD = 90°, 3y = 90 so that y = 30.

35. For m to be parallel to n, the interior angles on the same side of the transversal must be supplementary. Thus, we must solve

$$8x + x^2 = 180$$
$$x^2 + 8x - 180 = 0$$
$$(x - 10)(x + 18) = 0 \quad \text{Factor}$$
$$x - 10 = 0 \ \text{ or } \ x + 18 = 0 \quad \text{Zero-product rule}$$
$$x = 10 \quad \text{ or } \quad x = -18$$

Since x cannot be negative in this case, we discard -18 as a solution. Thus, x = 10.

Section 1.5

4.3

PRACTICE EXERCISES

1. The reason for Statement 1 is: Given

   Statement 2 is: $\angle C = \angle F$
   Since $\angle A = \angle D$ and $\angle B = \angle E$, the third angles of each triangle, $\angle C$ and $\angle F$, must also be equal.

   Statement 3 is: $CB = FE$
   Note this is the only remaining piece of given information.

   The reason for Statement 4 is: ASA = ASA
   Since $\angle B = \angle E$, $\angle C = \angle F$, and the included sides $\overline{CB}$ and $\overline{FE}$ are also equal, the triangles are congruent.

2. In Example 1 we found that the sum of the measures of the angles of a hexagon is 720°. If the hexagon is regular, by Corollary 4.17, the measure of each equal angle is

   $$a = \frac{(n - 2)180°}{n} = \frac{720°}{6} = 120°.$$

SECTION EXERCISES

1. (a) triangle (b) 180° (c) 60° (d) 360°
   (e) 120° (f) 15 cm

3. (a) pentagon (b) 540° (c) 108° (d) 360°
   (e) 72° (f) 25 cm

5. (a) heptagon (b) 900° (c) about 128.6°
   (d) 360° (e) about 51.4° (f) 35 cm

7. (a) nonagon (b) 1260° (c) 140° (d) 360°
   (e) 40° (f) 45 cm

9. Solve $1620 = (n - 2)180$ for n.

   $\dfrac{1620}{180} = n - 2$ Divide both sides by 180

   $9 = n - 2$

   $11 = n$ Add 2 to both sides

   Thus the polygon has 11 sides.

11. Solve $2000 = (n - 2)(180)$ for n.

   $\dfrac{2000}{180} = n - 2$

   $11.\overline{1} = n - 2$

   $13.\overline{1} = n$

   But n must be a whole number. Thus, there is no polygon satisfying these conditions.

13. Solve $157.5 = \dfrac{(n - 2)180}{n}$ for n.

   $157.5n = (n - 2)180$ Multiply both sides by n

   $157.5n = 180n - 360$ Distributive law

   $157.5n - 180n = -360$ Subtract 180n from both sides

   $-22.5n = -360$

   $n = \dfrac{-360}{-22.5} = 16$

   Thus, the polygon has 16 sides.

15. Solve $145 = \dfrac{(n - 2)180}{n}$ for n.

   $145n = (n - 2)(180)$ Multiply both sides by n

   $145n = 180n - 360$ Distributive law

   $-35n = -360$ Subtract 180n from both sides

   $n = \dfrac{-360}{-35} \approx 10.29$

   Since n must be a whole number, there is no polygon satisfying these conditions.

17. Since the sum of the measures of the exterior angles of a triangle is 360°, if x is the measure of the third angle, we must solve:

   $x + 200 = 360$

   $x = 160°$

19. decrease

21. 60° (a triangle)

23. The sum of the angles of a polygon is
S = (n - 2)180°. If this sum is twice the
sum of the exterior angles, 2(360°), we
must solve:

$$(n - 2)180 = 2(360)$$

$$180n - 360 = 720$$

$$180n = 1080$$

$$n = 6$$

Thus, the polygon has 6 sides.

25. The sum of the angles of a polygon is
S = (n - 2)180. The sum of the exterior
angles of a polygon is 360°. If these
are equal we must solve:

$$(n - 2)180 = 360$$

$$180n - 360 = 360$$

$$180n = 720$$

$$n = 4$$

Thus, the polygon has 4 sides.

27. Give an indirect proof by assuming that
a triangle has two right angles or two
obtuse angles. In either case the sum of
the angles of the triangle is greater than
180°, a contradiction.

29. <u>Given</u>:   △ABC with exterior ∠1

<u>Prove</u>:   ∠1 = ∠A + ∠B

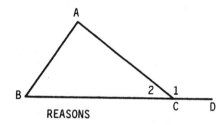

<u>Proof</u>:   STATEMENTS

1. ∠1 is an exterior angle of △ABC
2. ∠A + ∠B + ∠2 = 180°
3. ∠BCD is a straight angle and
∠BCD = 180°
4. ∠1 + ∠2 = ∠BCD
5. ∠1 + ∠2 = 180°
6. ∠1 + ∠2 = ∠A + ∠B + ∠2
7. ∠1 = ∠A + ∠B

REASONS

1. Given
2. Sum of ∠'s of △ = 180°
3. Def. of st. ∠

4. Angle add. post.
5. Sym. and trans. laws
6. Sym. and trans. laws
7. Add.-subt. law

31. This follows directly from Exercise 30
and Theorem 4.18.

33. The desired point is the point of
intersection of the bisectors of ∠DAB and
∠ABC.

Section 1.6

4.5

PRACTICE EXERCISES

1. The reason for Statement 1 is: Given

   Statement 2 is: AD = BC
   $\overline{AD}$ and $\overline{BC}$ are opposite sides of a $\diagup\!\!\!\!\diagdown$
   so are equal

   The reason for Statement 3 is: Reflexive law

   Statement 4 is: AC = BD
      This is the other piece of given information.

   The reason for Statement 5 is: SSS = SSS
      This follows since AC = BD, AD = BC, and
      DC = DC making three sides of one triangle
      equal respectively to three sides of the
      other.

   The reason for Statement 6 is: cpoctae

   The reason for Statement 7 is: Consec. $\angle$'s
   of $\diagup\!\!\!\!\diagdown$ are supp.
      Since $\angle$ADC and $\angle$BCD are consecutive $\angle$'s in

2. Since $\overline{PR}$ is the base of isosceles $\triangle PQR$, the
   legs are $\overline{RQ}$ and $\overline{PQ}$. With RQ = 30 inches,
   PQ = 30 inches also (the legs are equal).
   Since M and O are midpoints of $\overline{PR}$ and $\overline{QR}$,
   respectively, $\overline{MO}$ is parallel to $\overline{PQ}$ and
   equal to one-half of PQ by Theorem 4.36.
   Thus,

   $$MO = \tfrac{1}{2}PQ = \tfrac{1}{2}(30) = 15 \text{ inches.}$$

▱ ABCD   they are supplementary by Theorem 4.24.

Statement 8 is: ∠ADC and ∠BCD are right angles.
  Supplementary angles that are equal must both be 90° making them right angles.

The reason for Statement 9 is: Def. of

▭

A rectangle is a parallelogram with (at least) one right angle.

SECTION EXERCISES

1. true

3. true

5. true

7. true

9. true

11. false

13. true

15. true

17. true

19. false

21. 4.5 cm

23. 81°

25. 6 cm

27. 99°

29. 1. By construction   2. ABCD is a trapezoid with median $\overline{EF}$ 3. Def. of median of trapezoid   4. $\overline{AE} = \overline{ED}$ and BF = FC   5. Vert. ∠'s are =   6. $\overline{AB} \parallel \overline{CD}$ 7. Alt. int. ∠'s are =   8. AAS = AAS   9. cpoctae   11. Seg. Add. post.   12. Substitution law   15. Line ∥ to one of two ∥ lines is ∥ to other.

31. <u>Given</u>:   ABCD is a rectangle with right
           angle ∠A

<u>Prove</u>:   ∠B, ∠C, and ∠D are also right angles.

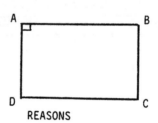

<u>Proof</u>:   STATEMENTS

   1. ABCD is a rectangle with right angle
     ∠A

   2. ∠C = ∠A

   3. ∠C is a right angle

   4. ∠A and ∠B are supplementary

   5. ∠A + ∠B = 180°

   6. 90° + ∠B = 180°

   7. ∠B = 180° - 90° = 90°

   8. ∠B is a right angle

   9. ∠B = ∠D

  10. ∠D is a right angle

REASONS

1. Given

2. Opp. angles of ▱ are =

3. All rt. ∠'s are =

4. Consec. ∠'s of ▱ are supp.

5. Def. of supp. ∠'s

6. Subst. law

7. Add.-subtr. law

8. Def. of rt. ∠

9. Opp. ∠'s of ▱ are =

10. All rt. ∠'s are =

33. <u>Given</u>: Quadrilateral ABCD with midpoints of consecutive sides P, Q, R, and S

<u>Prove</u>: PQRS is a parallelogram

<u>Auxiliary line</u>: Draw diagonal BD of ABCD.

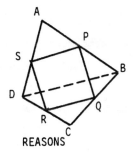

REASONS

<u>Proof</u>:   STATEMENTS

1. Quadrilateral ABCD with midpoints of consecutive sides P, Q, R, and S
2. $\overline{SP} \parallel \overline{DB}$ and $\overline{RQ} \parallel \overline{DB}$

3. $\overline{SP} \parallel \overline{RQ}$
4. $SP = \frac{1}{2}DB$ and $RQ = \frac{1}{2}DB$

5. $SP = RQ$
6. PQRS is a parallelogram

1. Given

2. Seg. joining midpts of sides of Δ are ∥ to 3rd side.
3. Lines ∥ to same line are ∥
4. Seg. joining midpts of sides of Δ = $\frac{1}{2}$ third side
5. Sym. and trans. laws
6. A pair of opp. sides are = and ∥

35. <u>Given</u>: ΔABC is equilateral with midpoints of sides P, Q, and R

<u>Prove</u>: ΔPQR is equilateral

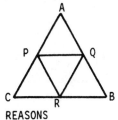

REASONS

<u>Proof</u>:   STATEMENTS

1. ΔABC is equilateral with midpoints of sides P, Q, and R
2. AB = BC = AC
3. $PQ = \frac{1}{2}BC$, $QR = \frac{1}{2}AC$, $PR = \frac{1}{2}AB$

4. $\frac{1}{2}AB = \frac{1}{2}BC = \frac{1}{2}AC$

5. PQ = QR = PR
6. ΔPQR is equilateral

1. Given

2. Def. of equil. Δ
3. Seg. joining midpts of Δ = $\frac{1}{2}$ third side
4. Mult.-div. law

5. Substitution law
6. Def. of equil. Δ

37. Use construction 4.2

39. Yes; by Theorem 4.34.

PART 2 – POLYGONS, CIRCLES, AND SOLIDS

Part 2
Section 2.1

2-2 TRIANGLES

When part of a plane is bounded and closed by straight-line segments, it is called a **polygon.** In general, polygons are named according to the number of sides they have. *A* **triangle** *has three sides, a* **quadrilateral** *has four sides, a* **pentagon** *has five sides, a* **hexagon** *has six sides, and so on.* The polygons of greatest importance are the triangle and the quadrilateral. Therefore, in this section we review the properties of triangles, and in the following section we will consider the quadrilateral. Many of the properties of triangles are important in the study of trigonometry, which we will start in Chapter 4.

Types and Properties of Triangles

There are several important types of triangles. In a **scalene triangle,** no two sides are equal in length. In an **isosceles triangle,** two of the sides are equal in length, and the two *base angles* (the angles opposite the equal sides) are equal. In an **equilateral triangle,** the three sides are equal in length, and each of the three angles is 60°.

One of the most important triangles in scientific and technical applications is the **right triangle.** *In a right triangle, one of the angles is a right angle. The side opposite the right angle is called the* **hypotenuse,** *and the other two sides are called* **legs.** Each of these triangles is illustrated in the following example.

■**EXAMPLE 1**   Figure 2-20(a) shows a scalene triangle. We see that each side is of a different length. Figure 2-20(b) shows an isosceles triangle with two equal sides of 2 in. and equal base angles of 40°. Figure 2-20(c) shows an equilateral triangle, each side of which is 5 cm and each interior angle of which is 60°. Figure 2-20(d) shows a right triangle. The hypotenuse is side *AB*.

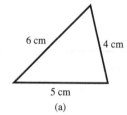
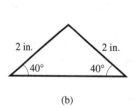
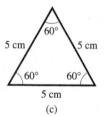
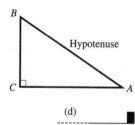

Fig. 2-20   (a)   (b)   (c)   (d)

One very important property of a triangle is that

the sum of the measures of the three angles of a triangle is 180°.

In the next example, we show this property by using material from Section 2-1.

■**EXAMPLE 2**   In Fig. 2-21, since ∠1, ∠2, and ∠3 constitute a straight angle,

$$\angle 1 + \angle 2 + \angle 3 = 180°$$

Also, by noting alternate interior angles, we see that ∠1 = ∠4 and ∠3 = ∠5. Therefore, by substitution we have

$$\angle 4 + \angle 2 + \angle 5 = 180°$$

Therefore, if two of the angles of a triangle are known, the third may be found by subtracting the sum of the first two from 180°.

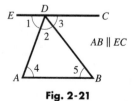

Fig. 2-21

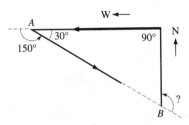

Fig. 2-22

■EXAMPLE 3 An airplane is flying north and then makes a 90° turn to the west. Later it makes another left turn of 150°. What is the angle of a third left turn that will cause the plane to again fly north? See Fig. 2-22.

From Fig. 2-22, we see that the interior angle of the triangle at *A* is the supplement of 150°, or 30°. Since the sum of the measures of the interior angles of the triangle is 180°, the interior angle at *B* is

$$\angle B = 180° - (90° + 30°) = 60°$$

The required angle is the supplement of 60°, which is 120°. ------------■

A line segment drawn from a vertex of a triangle to the *midpoint* of the opposite side is called a **median** of the triangle. A basic property of a triangle is that *the three medians meet at a single point, called the* **centroid** *of the triangle.* See Fig. 2-23. Also, *the three* **angle bisectors** (lines from the vertices that divide the angles in half) *meet at a common point.* See Fig. 2-24.

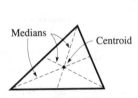

Fig. 2-23

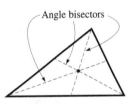

Fig. 2-24

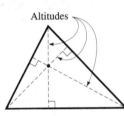

Fig. 2-25

An **altitude** *(or* **height***) of a triangle is the line segment drawn from a vertex perpendicular to the opposite side (or its extension), which is called the* **base** *of the triangle. The three altitudes of a triangle meet at a common point.* See Fig. 2-25. The three common points of the medians, angle bisectors, and altitudes are generally not the same point for a given triangle.

Perimeter and Area of a Triangle

We now consider two of the most basic measures of a plane geometric figure. The first of these is its **perimeter,** *which is the total distance around it.* In the following example we find the perimeter of a triangle.

■EXAMPLE 4 Find the perimeter *p* of a triangle with sides 2.56 m, 3.22 m, and 4.89 m. See Fig. 2-26.

Using the definition of perimeter, for this triangle we have

$$p = 2.56 + 3.22 + 4.89 = 10.67 \text{ m}$$

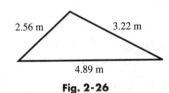

Fig. 2-26

Therefore, the distance around the triangle is 10.67 m. We express the results to hundredths since each side is given to hundredths. ------------■

The second important measure of a geometric figure is its **area.** Although the concept of area is primarily intuitive, it is easily defined and calculated for the basic geometric figures. *Area gives a measure of the surface of the figure,* just as perimeter gives the measure of the distance around it. The formula for the area of a triangle is given on the next page.

The area A of a triangle of base b and altitude h is

$$A = \tfrac{1}{2}bh \qquad\qquad \textbf{(2-2)}$$

The following example illustrates the use of Eq. (2-2).

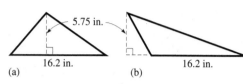

(a)   16.2 in.   (b)   16.2 in.

Fig. 2-27

■EXAMPLE 5   Find the areas of the triangles in Fig. 2-27(a) and Fig. 2-27(b).

Even though the triangles are of different shapes, we see that the base *b* of each triangle is 16.2 in. and that the altitude *h* of each is 5.75 in. Therefore, the area of each triangle is

$$A = \tfrac{1}{2}bh = \tfrac{1}{2}(16.2)(5.75) = 46.6 \text{ in.}^2 \qquad ■$$

Named for Hero (or Heron), a first-century A.D. Greek mathematician.

Another formula for the area of a triangle that is particularly useful when we have *a triangle with three known sides and no right angle* is **Hero's formula,** which is given in Eq. (2-3).

$$A = \sqrt{s(s - a)(s - b)(s - c)},$$
$$\text{where } s = \tfrac{1}{2}(a + b + c) \qquad\qquad \textbf{(2-3)}$$

In Eq. (2-3), *a*, *b*, and *c* are the lengths of the sides and *s* is one-half of the perimeter.

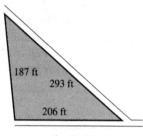

187 ft
293 ft
206 ft

Fig. 2-28

■EXAMPLE 6   A surveyor measures the three sides of a triangular parcel of land between two intersecting straight roads to be 206 ft, 293 ft, and 187 ft, as shown in Fig. 2-28. Find the area of this parcel.

In order to use Eq. (2-3), we first find *s*.

$$s = \tfrac{1}{2}(206 + 293 + 187) = \tfrac{1}{2}(686) = 343 \text{ ft}$$

Now, substituting in Eq. (2-3), we have

$$A = \sqrt{343(343 - 206)(343 - 293)(343 - 187)} = 19{,}100 \text{ ft}^2$$

The result has been rounded off to three significant digits. In using a calculator, the value of *s* is stored in memory and then used to find *A*. It is not necessary to write down anything except the final result.   ■

The Pythagorean Theorem

As we have noted, one of the most important geometric figures in technical applications is the right triangle. A very important property of a right triangle is given by the **Pythagorean theorem,** which states that

*in a **right triangle**, the square of the length of the hypotenuse equals the sum of the squares of the lengths of the other two sides.*

If *c* is the length of the hypotenuse and *a* and *b* are the lengths of the other two sides, the Pythagorean theorem is

Named for the Greek mathematician Pythagoras (sixth-century B.C.).

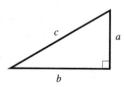

Fig. 2-29

$$c^2 = a^2 + b^2 \qquad\qquad \textbf{(2-4)}$$

See Fig. 2-29.

SOLVING A WORD PROBLEM

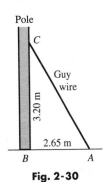

Fig. 2-30

Calculators can be programmed to perform specific calculations. See Appendix C for a graphing calculator program PYTHAGTH. It can be used to find a side of a right triangle, given the other two sides.

■**EXAMPLE 7** A pole is perpendicular to the level ground around it. A guy wire is attached 3.20 m up the pole and at a point on the ground, 2.65 m from the pole. How long is the guy wire?

From the given information, we sketch the pole and guy wire as shown in Fig. 2-30. Using the Pythagorean theorem and then substituting, we have

$$AC^2 = AB^2 + BC^2$$
$$= 2.65^2 + 3.20^2$$
$$AC = \sqrt{2.65^2 + 3.20^2} = 4.15 \text{ m}$$

The guy wire is 4.15 m long. In using the calculator, parentheses are used to group $2.65^2 + 3.20^2$.

Similar Triangles

The perimeter and area of a triangle are measures of its *size*. We now consider the shape of triangles.

Two triangles are **similar** *if they have the same shape (but not necessarily the same size).* There are two very important properties of similar triangles.

> **Properties of Similar Triangles**
> 1. *The corresponding angles of similar triangles are equal.*
> 2. *The corresponding sides of similar triangles are proportional.*

NOTE ▶

If it can be shown that either of these properties is true for two triangles, we may then conclude that the triangles are similar. This means that *if one property is true, then the other is also true.* In two triangles that are similar, *the* **corresponding sides** *are the sides, one in each triangle, which are between the same pair of equal corresponding angles.* These properties are illustrated in the following example.

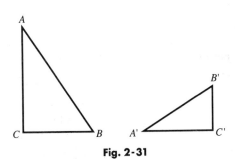

Fig. 2-31

■**EXAMPLE 8** In Fig. 2-31, a pair of similar triangles are shown. They are similar even though the corresponding parts are not in the same position relative to the page. Using standard symbols, we can write $\triangle ABC \sim \triangle A'B'C'$, where $\triangle$ means "triangle" and $\sim$ means "is similar to."

The pairs of corresponding angles are A and A', B and B', and C and C'. This means $A = A'$, $B = B'$, and $C = C'$.

The pairs of corresponding sides are AB and $A'B'$, BC and $B'C'$, and AC and $A'C'$. In order to show that these corresponding sides are proportional, we write

$$\frac{AB}{A'B'} = \frac{BC}{B'C'} = \frac{AC}{A'C'} \longleftarrow \text{ sides of } \triangle ABC \atop \longleftarrow \text{ sides of } \triangle A'B'C'$$

If we know that two triangles are similar, we can use the two basic properties of similar triangles to find the unknown parts of one triangle from the known parts of the other triangle. The following example illustrates how this is done in a practical application.

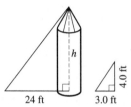

Fig. 2-32

■**EXAMPLE 9**   On level ground a silo casts a shadow 24 ft long. At the same time, a pole 4.0 ft high casts a shadow 3.0 ft long. How tall is the silo? See Fig. 2-32.

The rays of the sun are essentially parallel. The two triangles in Fig. 2-32 are similar since *each has a right angle and the angles at the tops are equal.* The other angles must be equal since the sum of the angles is 180°. The lengths of the hypotenuses are of no importance in this problem, so we use only the other sides in stating the ratios of corresponding sides. Denoting the height of the silo as h, we have

$$\frac{h}{4.0} = \frac{24}{3.0}, \quad h = 32 \text{ ft}$$

We conclude that the silo is 32 ft high. ────────■

One of the most practical uses of similar geometric figures is that of **scale drawings.** Maps, charts, blueprints, and most drawings that appear in books are familiar examples of scale drawings. Actually, there have been many scale drawings used in this book already.

In any scale drawing, all distances are drawn a certain ratio of the distances they represent, and all angles equal the angles they represent. Consider the following example.

■**EXAMPLE 10**   In drawing a map of the area shown in Fig. 2-33, a scale of 1 cm = 200 km is used. In measuring the distance between Chicago and Toronto on the map, we find it to be 3.5 cm. The actual distance x between Chicago and Toronto is found from the proportion

scale
↓

actual distance ⟶ $\dfrac{x}{3.5 \text{ cm}} = \dfrac{200 \text{ km}}{1 \text{ cm}}$ or $x = 700 \text{ km}$
distance on map ⟶

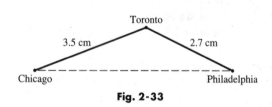

Fig. 2-33

If we did not have the scale but knew that the distance between Chicago and Toronto is 700 km, then by measuring distances on the map between Chicago and Toronto (3.5 cm) and between Toronto and Philadelphia (2.7 cm), we could find the distance between Toronto and Philadelphia. It is found from the following proportion, determined by use of similar triangles:

$$\frac{700 \text{ km}}{3.5 \text{ cm}} = \frac{y}{2.7 \text{ cm}}$$

$$y = \frac{2.7(700)}{3.5} = 540 \text{ km}$$ ────────■

Similarity requires *equal* angles and *proportional* sides. *If the corresponding angles and the corresponding sides of two triangles are equal, the two triangles are* **congruent.** As a result of this definition, the areas and perimeters of congruent triangles are also equal. Informally, we can say that similar triangles have the same shape, whereas congruent triangles have the same shape and same size.

■EXAMPLE 11 A right triangle with legs of 2 in. and 4 in. is congruent to any other right triangle with legs of 2 in. and 4 in. However, it is similar to any right triangle with legs of 5 in. and 10 in., since the corresponding sides are proportional. See Fig. 2-34.

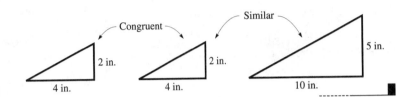

Fig. 2-34

EXERCISES *2-2*

In Exercises 1–4, determine ∠A in the indicated figures.

1. Fig. 2-35(a)
2. Fig. 2-35(b)
3. Fig. 2-35(c)
4. Fig. 2-35(d)

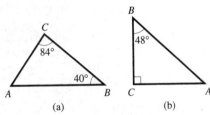

Fig. 2-35

In Exercises 5–8, find the perimeter of each triangle.

5. Fig. 2-36
6. Fig. 2-37

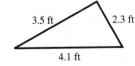

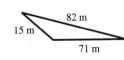

7. An equilateral triangle of side 21.5 cm
8. An isosceles triangle with equal sides of 2.45 in., and third side of 3.22 in.

In Exercises 9–16, find the area of each triangle.

9. Fig. 2-38
10. Fig. 2-39

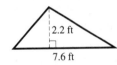

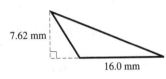

11. Fig. 2-40
12. Fig. 2-41

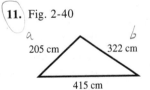

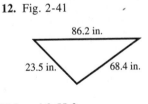

13. Right triangle with legs 3.46 ft and 2.55 ft
14. Right triangle with legs 234 mm and 342 mm
15. An isosceles triangle with equal sides of 0.986 m and third side of 0.884 m
16. An equilateral triangle of side 3.20 yd

In Exercises 17–20, find the third side of the right triangle shown in Fig. 2-42 for the given values.

17. $a = 13.8$ ft, $b = 22.7$ ft
18. $a = 2.48$ m, $b = 1.45$ m
19. $a = 17.5$ cm, $c = 55.1$ cm
20. $b = 0.474$ in., $c = 0.836$ in.

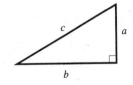

Fig. 2-42

In Exercises 21–24, use the right triangle in Fig. 2-43.

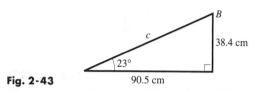

Fig. 2-43

21. Find $\angle B$.   **22.** Find side c.

23. Find the perimeter   **24.** Find the area.

In Exercises 25–40, solve the given problems.

25. In Fig. 2-44, show that $\triangle MKL \sim \triangle MNO$.

26. In Fig. 2-45, show that $\triangle ACB \sim \triangle ADC$.

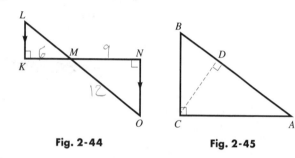

Fig. 2-44   **Fig. 2-45**

27. In Fig. 2-44, if $KN = 15$, $MN = 9$, and $MO = 12$, find LM.

28. In Fig. 2-45, if $AD = 9$ and $AC = 12$, find AB.

29. A tooth on a saw is in the shape of an isosceles triangle. If the angle at the point is 38°, find the two base angles.

30. A transmitting tower is supported by a wire that makes an angle of 52° with the level ground. What is the angle between the tower and the wire?

31. Find the area of a triangular patio with sides of 17.5 ft, 18.7 ft, and 19.5 ft.

32. The Bermuda Triangle is sometimes defined as an equilateral triangle 1600 km on a side, with vertices in Bermuda, Puerto Rico, and the Florida coast. Assuming it is flat, what is its approximate area?

33. The sail of a sailboat is in the shape of a right triangle with sides of 8.0 ft, 15 ft, and 17 ft. What is the area of the sail?

34. Three straight city streets enclose a right-triangular city block. If the shorter sides are 260 m and 320 m, find (a) the area of the block and (b) the distance around the block.

35. An observer is 550 m from the launch pad of a rocket. After the rocket has ascended 750 m, how far is it from the observer?

36. The base of a 20.0-ft ladder is 8.0 ft from a wall. How far up on the wall does the ladder reach?

37. A rectangular room is 18 ft long, 12 ft wide, and 8.0 ft high. What is the length of the longest diagonal from one corner to another corner of the room?

38. On a blueprint, a hallway is 45.6 cm long. The scale is 1.2 cm = 1.0 m. How long is the hallway?

39. Two parallel guy wires are attached to a vertical pole 4.5 m and 5.4 m above the ground. They are secured on the level ground at points 1.2 m apart. How long are the guy wires?

40. To find the width ED of a river, a surveyor places markers at A, B, C, and D, as shown in Fig. 2-46. The markers are placed such that $AB \parallel ED$, $BC = 50.0$ ft, $DC = 312$ ft, and $AB = 80.0$ ft. How wide is the river?

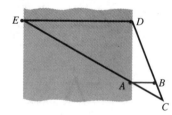

Fig. 2-46

$$12^2 = 9^2$$
$$144 = 81$$
$$\sqrt{63}$$

Section 2.2

3.2 CONGRUENT TRIANGLES

In this section, we compare triangles that are the same size and shape. The term **congruent,** from the Latin words *con* (with) and *gruere* (to agree), is applied to such figures and literally means "in agreement with." Intuitively, congruent triangles can be made to coincide by placing one on top of the other either directly or by *flipping* over one of them.

Because every triangle has six **parts,** three angles and three sides, two congruent triangles have equal parts that can be made to coincide when one is placed on top of the other. In Figure 3.9, $\triangle ABC$ and $\triangle DEF$ are congruent because $\triangle ABC$ can be placed on top of $\triangle DEF$. Also, $\triangle ABC$ and $\triangle GHI$ are congruent because if $\triangle GHI$ were flipped over, it could be made to coincide with $\triangle ABC$. On the other hand, $\triangle ABC$ and $\triangle JKL$ are not congruent because they cannot be made to coincide either directly or by flipping over one of them.

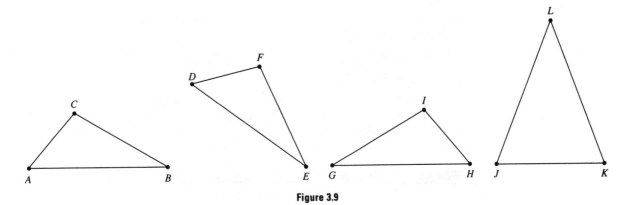

Figure 3.9

The parts of congruent triangles that coincide when one is placed on top of the other are called **corresponding parts.** For example, congruent triangles $\triangle ABC$ and $\triangle DEF$ in Figure 3.9 have six pairs of corresponding parts:

$\angle A$ corresponds to $\angle D$ $\overline{AB}$ corresponds to $\overline{DE}$
$\angle B$ corresponds to $\angle E$ $\overline{BC}$ corresponds to $\overline{EF}$
$\angle C$ corresponds to $\angle F$ $\overline{AC}$ corresponds to $\overline{DF}$

Notice that corresponding angles are opposite corresponding sides, and corresponding sides are opposite corresponding angles. We see that two triangles are congruent when their corresponding parts are equal.

DEFINITION: CONGRUENT TRIANGLES

Two triangles, $\triangle ABC$ and $\triangle DEF$ are **congruent**, written $\triangle ABC \cong \triangle DEF$, whenever $\angle A = \angle D$, $\angle B = \angle E$, $\angle C = \angle F$, $AB = DE$, $BC = EF$, and $AC = DF$.

To avoid giving specific lengths and angle measures, we often mark the parts in working with figures of congruent triangles to indicate those that are equal. Figure 3.10 illustrates this and shows that $\angle A = \angle D$, $\angle B = \angle E$, $\angle C = \angle F$, $AB = DE$, $BC = EF$, and $AC = DF$ in congruent triangles $\triangle ABC$ and $\triangle DEF$.

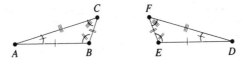

Figure 3.10   Labeling Congruent Triangles

According to our definition, in order to prove that two triangles are congruent, we would need to show that *all* six parts of one are equal to *all* six parts of the other. Fortunately, it is necessary to show congruence using only *three* pairs of corresponding parts as shown in the next three postulates.

> **POSTULATE 3.1   SAS = SAS**
>
> **If two sides and the included angle of one triangle are equal, respectively, to two sides and the included angle of a second triangle, then the triangles are congruent.**

E X A M P L E 1   Verify that $\triangle ABC \cong \triangle DEF$ in Figure 3.11. Because AC and DE are both 12 cm, $\angle C$ and $\angle E$ both measure 24°, and BC and EF are both 13 cm, $\triangle ABC \cong \triangle DEF$ by Postulate 3.1, SAS = SAS.   ■

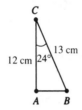

Figure 3.11

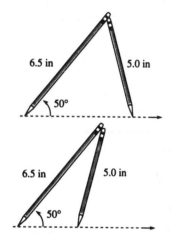

6.5 in   5.0 in

50°

6.5 in   5.0 in

50°

The figure above shows why we *do not* have a SSA postulate for proving triangles congruent. Two noncongruent triangles can be formed with sides measuring 6.5 inches, 5.0 inches, and a nonincluded angle of 50°.

> **POSTULATE 3.2   ASA = ASA**
>
> **If two angles and the included side of one triangle are equal, respectively, to two angles and the included side of a second triangle, then the triangles are congruent.**

E X A M P L E 2   Use the information given in Figure 3.12 to verify that $\triangle PQR \cong \triangle MNO$.

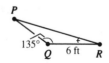
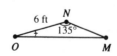

Figure 3.12

Because $QR = 6$ ft and $ON = 6$ ft, $QR = ON$. Also, $\angle Q = \angle N$ because both measure 135°, and we are given that $\angle R = \angle O$. Thus, $\triangle PQR \cong \triangle MNO$ by Postulate 3.2, ASA = ASA.   ■

> *POSTULATE 3.3   SSS = SSS*
> If three sides of one triangle are equal, respectively, to three sides of a
> second triangle, then the triangles are congruent.

PRACTICE EXERCISE 1
Use the information given to verify that $\triangle ABC \cong \triangle STU$.

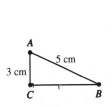 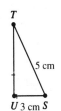

To prove two triangles congruent, we sometimes need to derive information
about equal parts using our knowledge about vertical angles or the fact that two
triangles share a common side. The following two examples illustrate.

E X A M P L E 3   Refer to Figure 3.13.

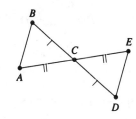

Figure 3.13

Given: $BC = CD$
$\quad\quad\quad AC = CE$

Prove: $\triangle ABC \cong \triangle CDE$

Proof:

STATEMENTS	REASONS
1. $BC = CD$	1. Given
2. $AC = CE$	2. Given
3. $\angle BCA = \angle ECD$	3. Vert. $\angle$'s are =
4. $\triangle ABC \cong \triangle CDE$	4. SAS = SAS ▰

EXAMPLE 4 Refer to Figure 3.14.

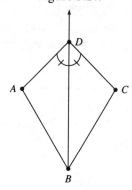

Figure 3.14

Given: $\overrightarrow{BD}$ bisects $\angle ABC$

$\angle ADB = \angle CDB$

Prove: $\triangle ABD \cong \triangle BCD$

Proof:

STATEMENTS	REASONS
1. $\overrightarrow{BD}$ bisects $\angle ABC$	1. Given
2. $\angle ABD = \angle DBC$	2. Def. of $\angle$ bisector
3. $\angle ADB = \angle CDB$	3. Given
4. $BD = BD$	4. Reflexive law
5. $\triangle ABD \cong \triangle BCD$	5. ASA = ASA ▰

NOTE: Although two segments or two angles may appear to be equal, never make this assumption simply because they look the same. When writing proofs, use only given information together with known facts from previously proved theorems, postulates, or definitions. □

The proof of the next theorem is requested in the exercises.

> **THEOREM 3.1 TRANSITIVE LAW FOR CONGRUENT TRIANGLES**
> If $\triangle ABC \cong \triangle DEF$ and $\triangle DEF \cong \triangle GHI$, then $\triangle ABC \cong \triangle GHI$.

Simply stated, Theorem 3.1 says that two triangles congruence to the same triangle are congruent to each other.

ANSWER TO PRACTICE EXERCISE: **1.** The desired congruence can be shown in two ways. Because $AC = 3$ cm and $US = 3$ cm, $AC = US$. Also, we are given that $CB = UT$ and $\angle C = \angle U$ (both are right angles). Thus, $\triangle ABC \cong \triangle STU$ by SAS = SAS. Alternatively, because $AC = US$, $AB = ST$, and $BC = UT$, $\triangle ABC \cong \triangle STU$ by SSS = SSS.

Thales (640–546 B.C.)

Thales of Miletus was a wealthy merchant who became interested in the practical aspects of geometry. In Greece, he taught geometry to many of his friends. His most noteworthy pupil was Pythagoras. Thales has been called the "father of Greek mathematics."

3.2 EXERCISES

Decide whether the triangles given in Exercises 1–6 are congruent. If so, state why.

1.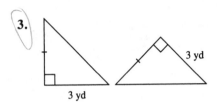

2.

3.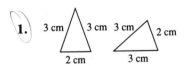

4.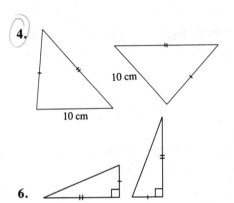

5.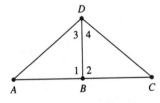

6.

Complete each proof in Exercises 7–10.

7. *Given:* ∠1 = ∠2
   ∠3 = ∠4

   Prove: △*ABD* ≅ △*BCD*

Exercise 7

Proof:

STATEMENTS	REASONS
1. ∠1 = ∠2	1. _____
2. _____	2. Given
3. _____	3. Reflexive law
4. △*ABD* ≅ △*BCD*	4. _____

8. *Given:* C is the midpoint of $\overline{AE}$
$\angle E = \angle A$

Prove: $\triangle ABC \cong \triangle CED$

Proof:

STATEMENTS	REASONS
1. C is the midpoint of $\overline{AE}$	1. _____
2. $AC = CE$	2. _____
3. _____	3. Given
4. $\angle ACB = \angle DCE$	4. _____
5. $\triangle ABC \cong \triangle CED$	5. _____

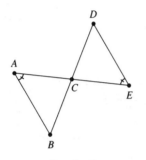

Exercise 8

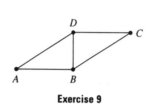

Exercise 9

9. *Given:* $\overline{DB} \perp \overline{AB}$
$\overline{DB} \perp \overline{DC}$
$AB = DC$

Prove: $\triangle ABD \cong \triangle BCD$

Proof:

STATEMENTS	REASONS
1. $\overline{DB} \perp \overline{AB}$ and $\overline{DB} \perp \overline{DC}$	1. _____
2. $\angle ABD$ and $\angle BDC$ are right angles	2. _____
3. _____	3. Rt $\angle$'s are equal
4. _____	4. Reflexive law
5. $AB = DC$	5. _____
6. $\triangle ABD \cong \triangle BCD$	6. _____

10. *Given: AB = CD*
       AC = BD

   Prove: △*ABC* ≅ △*BCD*

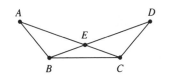

Exercise 10

Proof:

STATEMENTS	REASONS
1. *AB = CD*	1. _____
2. _____	2. Given
3. _____	3. Reflexive law
4. △*ABC* ≅ △*BCD*	4. _____

Write a two-column proof in Exercises 11–18.

11.   *Given:* $\overline{AD}$ bisects $\overline{BE}$
         $\overline{BE}$ bisects $\overline{AD}$

   Prove: △*ABC* ≅ △*CDE*

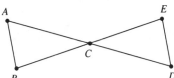

Exercise 11

12.   *Given:* ∠*B* and ∠*E* are right angles
         $\overline{AD}$ bisects $\overline{BE}$

   Prove: △*ABC* ≅ △*CDE*

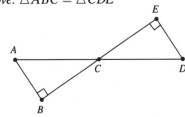

Exercise 12

13.   *Given: AD = BD*
         AE = BC

   Prove: △*ACD* ≅ △*BDE*

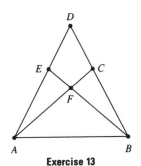

Exercise 13

14.   *Given:* $\overline{DB}$ ⊥ $\overline{AC}$
         $\overline{DB}$ bisects $\overline{AC}$

   Prove: △*ABD* ≅ △*BCD*

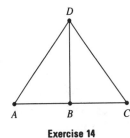

Exercise 14

15. *Given:* $AB = BC$
  $\angle 1 = \angle 2$
Prove: $\triangle ABE \cong \triangle BCD$

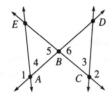

Exercise 15

16. *Given:* $\triangle ABC$ is equilateral
  $\triangle BDC$ is equilateral
Prove: $\triangle ABC \cong \triangle BDC$

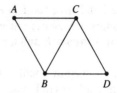

Exercise 16

17. *Given:* $\triangle ACD$ is equilateral
  $\angle 1 = \angle 2$
  $BC = DE$
Prove: $\triangle ABC \cong \triangle ADE$

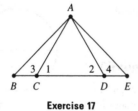

Exercise 17

18. *Given:* $\triangle ACD$ is isosceles with base $\overline{CD}$
  $\angle 1 = \angle 2$
  $BD = CE$
Prove: $\triangle ABC \cong \triangle ADE$

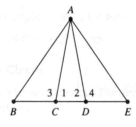

Exercise 18

Use the figure below in Exercises 19–30. You will need to recall what you learned in beginning algebra to solve several equations. Assume that $\triangle ABC \cong \triangle PQR$, $AC = x + 1$, $PR = 3x - 5$, $\angle B = (100 + y)°$, and $\angle Q = (5y + 20)°$.

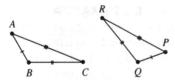

19. Find the value of x.

20. Find the value of y.

21. Find AC.

22. Find PR.

23. Find the measure of $\angle B$.

24. Find the measure of $\angle Q$.

25. $\overline{AC}$ corresponds to which side in $\triangle PQR$?

26. $\overline{QP}$ corresponds to which side in $\triangle ABC$?

27. $\overline{BC}$ corresponds to which side in $\triangle PQR$?

28. $\angle Q$ corresponds to which angle in $\triangle ABC$?

29. $\angle A$ corresponds to which angle in $\triangle PQR$?

30. $\angle R$ corresponds to which angle in $\triangle ABC$?

31. Prove Theorem 3.1.

Section 2.3

6.3 The Pythagorean Theorem

The Pythagorean Theorem is perhaps the most famous and most useful of all theorems in geometry. It has numerous applications in algebra, trigonometry, and calculus as well as many practical applications in everyday life. There is evidence that a special case of the theorem was known to the Egyptians as long ago as 2000 B.C. And it is believed that Pythagoras, in about 525 B.C., gave the first deductive proof of the theorem, probably the one presented by Euclid in his book *Elements*. More than 250 different proofs have since been given, including one by President James A. Garfield in 1876, most of which involve finding areas of various figures. The proof we present now uses Corollary 6.10 and is perhaps the simplest of all the proofs of this theorem.

THEOREM 6.11 THE PYTHAGOREAN THEOREM

In a right triangle, the square of the length of the hypotenuse is equal to the sum of the squares of the lengths of the legs.

Given: Right triangle $\triangle ABC$ with $c = AB$, $b = AC$, and $a = BC$ (See Figure 6.8.)

Prove: $a^2 + b^2 = c^2$

Auxiliary line: Construct altitude $\overline{CD}$ from vertex C to hypotenuse $\overline{AB}$

Proof:

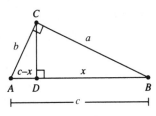

Figure 6.8

STATEMENTS	REASONS
1. $\triangle ABC$ is a right triangle	1. Given
2. $\overline{CD}$ is the altitude from vertex C to hypotenuse $\overline{AB}$	2. By construction
3. $\dfrac{c}{a} = \dfrac{a}{x}$ and $\dfrac{c}{b} = \dfrac{b}{c-x}$	3. Corollary 6.10
4. $a^2 = cx$ and $b^2 = c(c-x)$	4. Means-extremes prop.
5. $a^2 + b^2 = cx + c(c-x)$	5. Add.-subtr. prop.
6. $a^2 + b^2 = c^2$	6. Distributive law and simplify result

NOTE: Often we abbreviate the statement of the Pythagorean Theorem to say "In a right triangle, the sum of the squares of the legs equals the square of the hypotenuse." Also, for convenience, we usually designate the right angle in the right triangle C so we can use $a^2 + b^2 = c^2$ for the Pythagorean Theorem, with a the length of the side opposite $\angle A$, b the length of the side opposite $\angle B$, and c the length of the hypotenuse opposite $\angle C$. □

EXAMPLE 1 In right triangle $\triangle ABC$ (C is the right angle), $a = 12$ cm and $b = 7$ cm. Find the length of the hypotenuse, c.

Substituting into the Pythagorean Theorem we have

$$a^2 + b^2 = c^2$$
$$12^2 + 7^2 = c^2$$
$$144 + 49 = c^2$$
$$193 = c^2$$
$$\sqrt{193} = c$$

The Pooles own a compact station wagon that has a rectangle-shaped rear door opening 28 inches high and 44 inches wide. If they purchase a square piece of wood paneling that is 48 inches on a side, will they be able to transport the paneling in their wagon?

We use only the principal square root in this case because the length of a hypotenuse must be positive. We can also approximate $\sqrt{193}$ using a calculator to find $c = 13.9$ cm, correct to the nearest tenth of a centimeter. ∎

PRACTICE EXERCISE 1
In right triangle $\triangle ABC$, $c = 32$ ft and $a = 18$ ft, find b.

Many applied problems can be solved using the Pythagorean Theorem.

E X A M P L E 2   A 100-foot tower is to be supported by four guy wires attached to the top of the tower and to points on the ground that are 35 ft from the base of the tower. Assume that each wire will require an extra 2 ft for attaching to the tower and to the points on the ground. How much wire will be needed for this project?

We can make a sketch showing one of these wires and the tower as shown in Figure 6.9. The wire forms the hypotenuse of a right triangle with legs measuring 35 ft and 100 ft. Let x be the length of the wire as shown. Then by the Pythagorean Theorem,

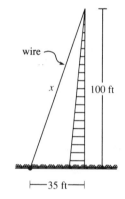

wire

x 100 ft

$\longmapsto$35 ft$\longmapsto$

Figure 6.9

$$x^2 = 35^2 + 100^2$$
$$= 1225 + 10,000$$
$$= 11,255.$$
$$x = \sqrt{11,225} \approx 105.95 \text{ ft}$$

Add the 2 feet for attachment.

$$105.95 + 2 = 107.95 \text{ ft}$$

With four such wires, we would have

$$4(107.95) = 431.8 \text{ ft.}$$

Thus, about 432 ft of wire are required to secure the tower.   ◪

NOTE: In Example 2 we used the symbol $\approx$ which stands for the phrase "is approximately equal to." This is often used in applied problems to indicate approximate or rounded values.   ☐

The converse of the Pythagorean Theorem is also true and can be used to prove that a given triangle is a right triangle when its sides are given.

THEOREM 6.12   CONVERSE OF THE PYTHAGOREAN THEOREM
If the sides of a triangle have lengths a, b, and c, and $a^2 + b^2 = c^2$, then the triangle is a right triangle.

Given: $\triangle ABC$ with $a^2 + b^2 = c^2$
(See Figure 6.10.)

Prove: $\triangle ABC$ is a right triangle

Construction: Construct a right
   triangle $\triangle EFG$ with $e = a$, $f = b$,
   and $\angle G$ a right angle. (If we show
   $\triangle ABC \cong \triangle EFG$, then $\angle C$ is also
   a right angle making $\triangle ABC$ a
   right triangle.)

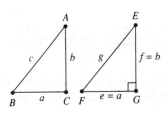

Figure 6.10

Proof:

STATEMENTS	REASONS
1. $\triangle ABC$ with $a^2 + b^2 = c^2$	1. Given
2. $\triangle EFG$ with $e = a$, $f = b$, and $\angle G$ a right angle	2. By construction
3. $e^2 + f^2 = g^2$	3. Pythagorean Theorem
4. $a^2 + b^2 = g^2$	4. Substitution Law
5. $g^2 = c^2$	5. Trans. and Sym. Laws
6. $g = c$	6. The principal square roots of equal numbers are equal
7. $\triangle ABC \cong \triangle EFG$	7. SSS = SSS
8. $\angle C = \angle G$	8. cpoctae
9. $\angle C$ is a right angle	9. From Statement 2 because $\angle G$ is a right angle
10. $\triangle ABC$ is a right triangle	10. Def. of rt. $\triangle$

Pythagoras (About 584–495 B.C.)

Pythagoras was one of the most remarkable mathematicians of all time, giving us many geometry proofs, including one of the theorem bearing his name. He formed a society of mathematicians and philosophers, called the Pythagoreans, that was made up of two groups—listeners and mathematicians. To become a member of the group of mathematicians one had to first prove to be a good listener. The Pythagoreans are credited with discovering the relationship between musical harmony and the length of the strings of a musical instrument, and with developing the concept of irrational numbers.

EXAMPLE 3   A triangle has sides of 10 cm, 24 cm, and 26 cm. Determine if the triangle is a right triangle.

We know by the preceding theorem that a triangle is a right triangle if the sum of the squares of two sides is equal to the square of the other side. Because

$$10^2 = 100, \quad 24^2 = 576, \quad \text{and} \quad 26^2 = 676$$

and

$$10^2 + 24^2 = 100 + 576 = 676 = 26^2,$$

the triangle is a right triangle.   ■

PRACTICE EXERCISE 2

Is a triangle with sides measuring 4 ft, 8 ft, and 9 ft a right triangle?

Certain right triangles with acute angles of 45° and 45° (an isosceles right triangle), and of 30° and 60°, play an important role in the study of trigonometry.

A baseball diamond is a square with sides 90 ft in length. Explain how you would use properties of a 45°-45°-right triangle to find the distance from third base to first base.

These triangles are often referred to as a 45°-45°-right triangle and a 30°-60°-right triangle, respectively. The next two theorems present properties of the sides of these special triangles.

> **THEOREM 6.13   45°-45°-RIGHT TRIANGLE THEOREM**
> In a 45°-45°-right triangle, the hypotenuse is $\sqrt{2}$ times as long as each (equal) leg.

The proof of Theorem 6.13 is left for you to do as an exercise.

> **THEOREM 6.14   30°-60°-RIGHT TRIANGLE THEOREM**
> In a 30°-60°-right triangle, the leg opposite the 30°-angle is one-half as long as the hypotenuse, and the leg opposite the 60°-angle is $\sqrt{3}$ times as long as the leg opposite the 30°-angle and $\dfrac{\sqrt{3}}{2}$ times as long as the hypotenuse.

Given: Right triangle $\triangle ABC$ with $\angle A = 60°$, $\angle B = 30°$ and $\angle C = 90°$
(See Figure 6.11.)

Prove: $b = \dfrac{1}{2}c$, $a = \sqrt{3}b$, and $a = \dfrac{\sqrt{3}}{2}c$.

Construction: Construct the extension of $\overline{AC}$ and $\angle CBD = 30°$ (copy $\angle ABC$) with side intersecting $\overleftrightarrow{AC}$ at D forming $\angle BCD = 90°$

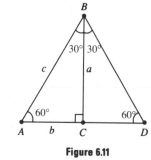

Figure 6.11

Proof:

STATEMENTS	REASONS
1. Right triangle $\triangle ABC$ with $\angle A = 60°$, $\angle B = 30°$, and $\angle C = 90°$	1. Given
2. $\triangle BCD$ with $\angle CBD = 30°$ and $\angle BCD = 90°$	2. By construction
3. $\angle D = 60°$	3. Sum of $\angle$'s of $\triangle = 180°$
4. $AB = BD$	4. Sides opp. $= \angle$'s are $=$
5. $\triangle ABC \cong \triangle BCD$	5. HA = HA
6. $AC = CD$	6. cpoctae
7. $AD = AC + CD$	7. Seg. Add. post.

8. $AD = AC + AC = 2AC$	8. Substitution and distributive laws
9. $\angle ABC = 30° + 30° = 60°$	9. Angle Add. Post.
10. $AD = AB$	10. Sides opp = $\angle$'s are =
11. $2AC = AB$	11. Sym. and trans. laws
12. $AC = \frac{1}{2}AB$	12. Mult.-div. law
13. $b = \frac{1}{2}c$	13. Substitution law
14. $c^2 = a^2 + b^2$	14. Pythagorean Theorem
15. $c^2 = a^2 + \left(\frac{1}{2}c\right)^2$	15. Substitution law
16. $c^2 = a^2 + \frac{1}{4}c^2$	16. Simplify
17. $a^2 = \frac{3}{4}c^2$	17. Simplify
18. $a = \frac{\sqrt{3}}{2}c$	18. Take principal square root of both sides
19. $a = \frac{\sqrt{3}}{2}(2b)$	19. Substitute $2b$ for c because $b = \frac{1}{2}c$
20. $a = \sqrt{3}b$	20. Simplify

We can use Theorem 6.14 to solve the applied problem from the chapter introduction.

EXAMPLE 4   A tightrope performer in a circus begins his act by walking up a wire to a platform that is 120 ft high. If the wire makes an angle of 30° with the horizontal, how far does he walk along the wire to reach the platform?

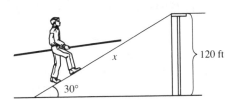

Figure 6.12

Figure 6.12 shows a sketch of the information given. We must find x. By Theorem 6.14, the side opposite the 30°-angle, with length 120 ft, is one-half the hypotenuse, with length x. Thus, we have

$$120 = \frac{1}{2}x$$
$$240 = x.$$

Thus, the tightrope walker walks a distance of 240 ft to reach the platform.   ◼

PRACTICE EXERCISE 3

Two airplanes leave the same airport at the same time, one flying due north and the other flying due east. If each is flying at a rate of 450 mph, use Theorem 6.13 to find the distance between the two after 2 hours, correct to the nearest tenth of a mile.

ANSWERS TO PRACTICE EXERCISES: 1. $b = 10\sqrt{7}$ ft, which is approximately 26.5 ft   **2.** No, because $4^2 + 8^2 \neq 9^2$.   **3.** 1272.8 mi

---

6.3 EXERCISES

In Exercises 1–8, use the Pythagorean Theorem to find the length of the missing side in right triangle $\triangle ABC$ with right angle C.

1. If $a = 3$ cm and $b = 4$ cm, find c.

2. If $a = 12$ yd and $b = 5$ yd, find c.

3. If $b = 25$ ft and $c = 65$ ft, find a.

4. If $a = 12$ cm and $c = 20$ cm, find b.

5. If $a = 6$ yd and $c = 11$ yd, find b.

6. If $b = 14$ ft and $c = 23$ ft, find a.

7. If $c = 2\sqrt{97}$ cm and $a = 8$ cm, find b.

8. If $c = 2\sqrt{130}$ cm and $b = 22$ cm, find a.

In Exercises 9–14, is the triangle with sides of the given lengths a right triangle?

9. 15 cm, 20 cm, 25 cm

10. 15 ft, 36 ft, 39 ft

11. 3 yd, 7 yd, $\sqrt{58}$ yd

12. $3\sqrt{3}$ cm, 6 cm, 3 cm

13. $\sqrt{7}$ ft, $\sqrt{2}$ ft, 9 ft

14. $\sqrt{11}$ yd, $\sqrt{5}$ yd, 16 yd

Exercises 15–26 refer to the 45°-45°-right triangle shown below.

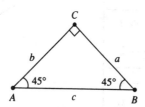

15. If $a = 10$ ft, find c.

16. If $b = 15$ cm, find c.

17. If $a = 3\sqrt{2}$ yd, find b.

18. If $b = 7\sqrt{2}$ ft, find a.

19. If $a = 3\sqrt{2}$ cm, find c.

20. If $b = 7\sqrt{2}$ yd, find c.

21. If $b = 3\sqrt{3}$ ft, find c.

22. If $a = 4\sqrt{5}$ cm, find c.

23. If $c = 6$ yd, find a.

24. If $c = 10$ ft, find b.   **25.** If $c = \dfrac{\sqrt{2}}{2}$ cm, find b.   **26.** If $c = \dfrac{\sqrt{3}}{3}$ yd, find a.

Exercises 27–38 refer to the 30°-60°-right triangle shown below.

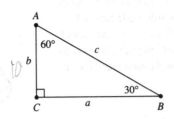

27. If $b = 10$ ft, find c.   **28.** If $b = 60$ cm, find c.   **29.** If $c = 16$ yd, find b.

30. If $c = 34$ ft, find b.   **31.** If $b = 7$ cm, find a.   **32.** If $b = 13$ yd, find a.

33. If $a = 2\sqrt{3}$ ft, find b.   **34.** If $a = 7\sqrt{3}$ cm, find b.   **35.** If $c = \sqrt{3}$ yd, find a.

36. If $c = 8\sqrt{3}$ ft, find a.   **37.** If $a = \sqrt{3}$ cm, find c.   **38.** If $a = 2\sqrt{6}$ yd, find c.

39. If the sides of a square are 4 inches long, what is the length of a diagonal?

40. If a rectangle has sides of 14 ft and 5 ft, what is the length of a diagonal?

41. A ladder 18 ft long is placed against the side of a building with the base of the ladder 6 ft from the building. To the nearest tenth of a foot, how far up the building will the ladder reach?

42. A telephone pole 35 ft tall has a guy wire attached to it 5 ft from the top and tied to a ring on the ground 15 ft from the base of the pole. Assume that an extra 2 feet of wire are needed to attach the wire to the ring and the pole. What length of wire is needed for the job? Give an answer to the nearest tenth of a foot.

43. A 400-foot tower has a guy wire attached to it that makes a 60°-angle with level ground. How far from the base of the tower is the wire anchored? Give an answer correct to the nearest tenth of a foot.

44. Two hikers leave their camp at the same time. When Dick is 6.5 mi due east of the camp, Vickie is due north of Dick and northeast of the camp. How far from the camp is Vickie? Give an answer correct to the nearest tenth of a mile.

45. Find the length of an altitude of an equilateral triangle with sides measuring 10 ft.

46. Find the area of an equilateral triangle with sides measuring 10 ft.

47. Prove Theorem 6.13.

48. Prove that the area of an isosceles right triangle is one-fourth the square of the length of the hypotenuse.

49. Find the length d of a diagonal of a cube with sides of length x. See the figure below.

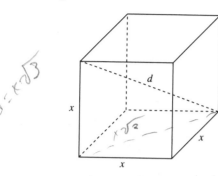

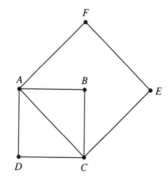

Exercise 49   Exercise 50

50. Prove that the area of square $ABCD$ is half the area of square $ACEF$ in the figure above.

51. Draw a line segment about 1 inch in length. Construct an isosceles right triangle with legs equal in length to this segment. Then the hypotenuse is $\sqrt{2}$ times as long as the given segment. Using this hypotenuse as one leg, construct another right triangle with the second leg equal in length to the original segment. What is the length of the new hypotenuse? Can you continue this process to find a segment with length $\sqrt{4}$ times the length of the original segment? with $\sqrt{5}$ times the length of the original segment?

52. One proof of the Pythagorean Theorem involves expressing algebraically the areas of the two squares given below and equating the results. Notice that each contains copies of a right triangle with legs measuring a and b and hypotenuse measuring c. Note that both squares have sides of length $a + b$ making both areas $(a + b)^2$. Using this information, show that $a^2 + b^2 = c^2$.

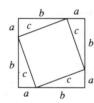

Exercise 52

53. In the left figure for Exercise 52, you probably assumed that the "inside" quadrilateral with sides of length c was a square. Prove that this is indeed the case.

54. Use the figure below to explain why the original statement of the Pythagorean Theorem was: "In a right triangle, the square *on* the hypotenuse is equal to the sum of the squares *on* the legs."

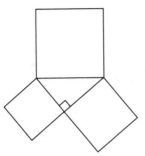

Exercise 54

55. Another proof of the Pythagorean Theorem, the one written by President Garfield, uses the figure given below. Refer to the figure to answer the following:

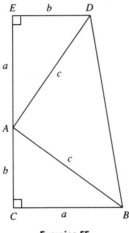

Exercise 55

  (a) Show that $\triangle ABD$ is a right triangle. [Hint: Show $\angle DAB$ is a right angle.]
  (b) Write three expressions for the areas of the three triangles.
  (c) Show that quadrilateral $BCED$ is a trapezoid.
  (d) Write an expression for the area of trapezoid $BCED$.
  (e) Equate an expression for the area of the trapezoid with an expression formed by adding the areas of the three triangles and simplify the result to obtain $a^2 + b^2 = c^2$.

Section 2.4

2-3 QUADRILATERALS

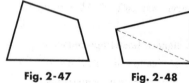

Fig. 2-47   **Fig. 2-48**

In this section we consider another important type of polygon. *A* **quadrilateral** *is a closed plane figure that has four sides,* and these four sides form four interior angles. A general quadrilateral is shown in Fig. 2-47.

A **diagonal** *of a polygon is a straight line segment joining any two nonadjacent vertices.* The dashed line is one of two possible diagonals of the quadrilateral shown in Fig. 2-48.

Types of Quadrilaterals

A **parallelogram** *is a quadrilateral in which opposite sides are parallel.* In a parallelogram, opposite sides are equal and opposite angles are equal. *A* **rhombus** *is a parallelogram with four equal sides.*

A **rectangle** *is a parallelogram in which intersecting sides are perpendicular,* which means that all four interior angles are right angles. In a rectangle, the longer side is usually called the **length** and the shorter side is called the **width.** *A* **square** *is a rectangle with four equal sides.*

A **trapezoid** *is a quadrilateral in which two sides are parallel.* The parallel sides are called the **bases** of the trapezoid.

■EXAMPLE 1　A parallelogram is shown in Fig. 2-49(a). Opposite sides *a* are equal in length, as are opposite sides *b*. A rhombus with equal sides *s* is shown in Fig. 2-49(b). A rectangle is shown in Fig. 2-49(c). The length is labeled *l,* and the width is labeled *w*. A square with equal sides *s* is shown in Fig. 2-49(d). A trapezoid with bases b_1 and b_2 is shown in Fig. 2-49(e).

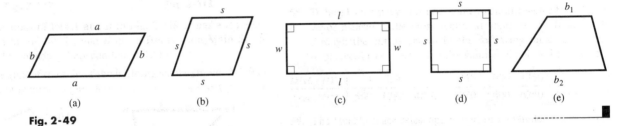

| (a) | (b) | (c) | (d) | (e) |

Fig. 2-49

Perimeter and Area of a Quadrilateral

Since the perimeter of a polygon is the distance around it, *the perimeter of a quadrilateral is the sum of the lengths of its four sides.* Consider the next example.

SOLVING A WORD PROBLEM

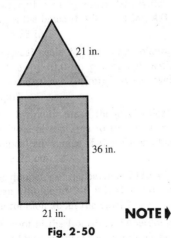

21 in.

36 in.

21 in.

Fig. 2-50

■EXAMPLE 2　An architect designs a room with a rectangular window 36 in. high and 21 in. wide, with another window above in the shape of an equilateral triangle, 21 in. on a side. See Fig. 2-50. How much molding is needed for these windows?

The length of molding is the sum of the perimeters of the windows. For the rectangular window, the opposite sides are equal, which means the perimeter is twice the length *l* plus twice the width *w*. For the equilateral triangle, the perimeter is three times the side *s*. Therefore, the length *L* of molding is

$$L = 2l + 2w + 3s$$
$$= 2(36) + 2(21) + 3(21)$$
$$= 177 \text{ in.}$$

NOTE ▶　We could write down formulas for the perimeters of the different kinds of triangles and quadrilaterals. However, if we *remember the meaning of perimeter as being the total distance around a geometric figure,* such formulas are not necessary.

For the areas of the square, rectangle, parallelogram, and trapezoid, we have the following formulas.

$A = s^2$	Square of side s (Fig. 2-51)	**(2-5)**
$A = lw$	Rectangle of length l and width w (Fig. 2-52)	**(2-6)**
$A = bh$	Parallelogram of base b and height h (Fig. 2-53)	**(2-7)**
$A = \frac{1}{2}h(b_1 + b_2)$	Trapezoid of bases b_1 and b_2, and height h (Fig. 2-54)	**(2-8)**

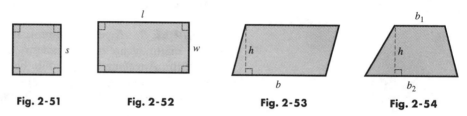

Fig. 2-51   **Fig. 2-52**   **Fig. 2-53**   **Fig. 2-54**

Since a rectangle, a square, and a rhombus are special types of parallelograms, the area of these figures can be found from Eq. (2-7). The area of a trapezoid is of importance when we find areas of irregular geometric figures in Section 2-5.

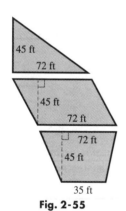

Fig. 2-55

EXAMPLE 3 A city park is designed with lawn areas in the shape of a right triangle, a parallelogram, and a trapezoid, as shown in Fig. 2-55, with walkways between them. Find the area of each section of lawn and the total lawn area.

$$A_1 = \tfrac{1}{2}bh = \tfrac{1}{2}(72)(45) = 1600 \text{ ft}^2 \qquad A_2 = bh = (72)(45) = 3200 \text{ ft}^2$$
$$A_3 = \tfrac{1}{2}h(b_1 + b_2) = \tfrac{1}{2}(45)(72 + 35) = 2400 \text{ ft}^2$$

The total lawn area is about 7200 ft². ────■

Following is an example of another word problem involving a quadrilateral. In this example it is necessary to follow the procedure on page 41 in order to first set up the equation which leads to the solution.

SOLVING A WORD PROBLEM

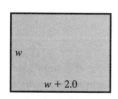

The computer microprocessor chip was first commercially available in 1971.

EXAMPLE 4 The length of a rectangular computer chip is 2.0 mm longer than its width. Find the dimensions of the chip if its perimeter is 26.4 mm.

Since the dimensions, the length and the width, are required, we let $w =$ the width of the chip. Since the length is 2.0 mm more than the width, we know that $w + 2.0 =$ the length of the chip. See Fig. 2-56.

Since the perimeter of a rectangle is twice the length plus twice the width, we have the equation

$$2(w + 2.0) + 2w = 26.4$$

since the perimeter is given as 26.4 mm. This is the equation we need.

Solving this equation, we have

$$2w + 4.0 + 2w = 26.4$$
$$4w = 22.4$$
$$w = 5.6 \text{ mm} \quad \text{and} \quad w + 2.0 = 7.6 \text{ mm}$$

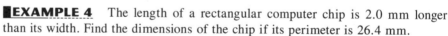

Fig. 2-56

Therefore, the length is 7.6 mm and the width is 5.6 mm. These values check with the statements of the original problem. ────■

EXERCISES *2-3*

In Exercises 1–8, find the perimeter of each figure.

1. Square: side of 0.65 m
2. Rhombus: side of 2.46 ft
3. Rectangle: $l = 46.5$ in., $w = 37.4$ in.
4. Rectangle: $l = 14.2$ cm, $w = 12.6$ cm
5. The parallelogram in Fig. 2-57
6. The parallelogram in Fig. 2-58
7. The trapezoid in Fig. 2-59
8. The trapezoid in Fig. 2-60

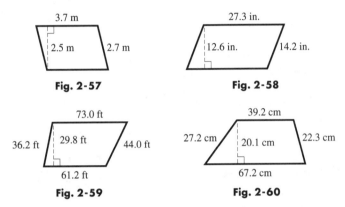

Fig. 2-57   **Fig. 2-58**

Fig. 2-59   **Fig. 2-60**

In Exercises 9–16, find the area of each figure.

9. Square: $s = 2.7$ mm   10. Square: $s = 15.6$ ft
11. Rectangle: $l = 46.5$ in., $w = 37.4$ in.
12. Rectangle: $l = 14.2$ cm, $w = 12.6$ cm
13. The parallelogram in Fig. 2-57
14. The parallelogram in Fig. 2-58
15. The trapezoid in Fig. 2-59
16. The trapezoid in Fig. 2-60

In Exercises 17–20, set up a formula for the indicated perimeter or area. (Do not include dashed lines.)

17. The perimeter of the figure in Fig. 2-61 (a parallelogram and a square attached)
18. The perimeter of the figure in Fig. 2-62 (two trapezoids attached)
19. The area of the figure in Fig. 2-61
20. The area of the figure in Fig. 2-62

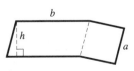

Fig. 2-61

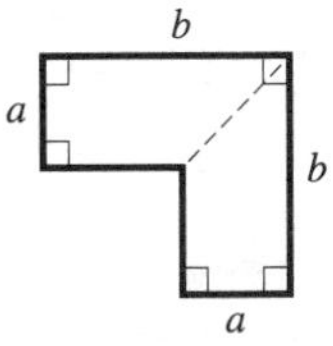

Fig. 2-62

In Exercises 21–28, solve the given problems.

21. A machine part is in the shape of a square with equilateral triangles attached to two sides (see Fig. 2-63). Find the perimeter of the machine part.

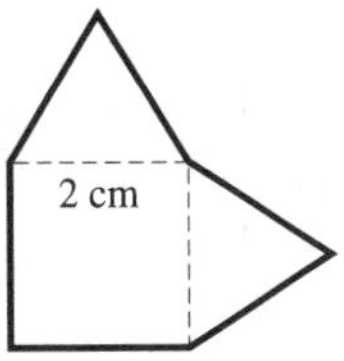

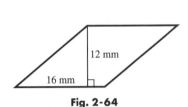

Fig. 2-63   **Fig. 2-64**

22. Part of an electric circuit is wired in the configuration of a rhombus and one of its altitudes as shown in Fig. 2-64. What is the length of wire in this part of the circuit?

23. A beam support in a building is in the shape of a parallelogram, as shown in Fig. 2-65. Find the area of the side of the beam shown.

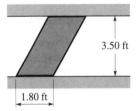

Fig. 2-65 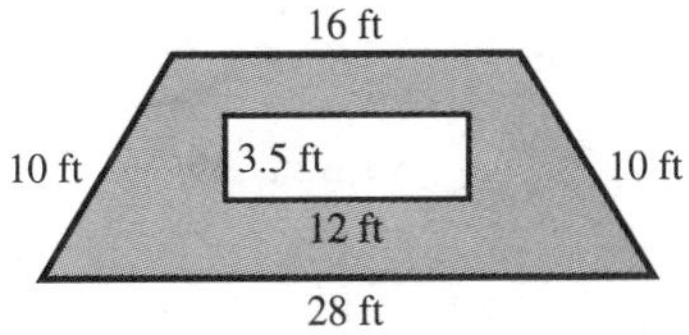   **Fig. 2-66**

24. Each of two walls (with rectangular windows) of an A-frame house has the shape of a trapezoid as shown in Fig. 2-66. If a gallon of paint covers 320 ft², how much paint is required to paint these walls? (All data are accurate to two significant digits.)

25. A walkway 3.0 m wide is constructed along the outside edge of a square courtyard. If the perimeter of the courtyard is 320 m, what is the perimeter of the square formed by the outer edge of the walkway?

26. An architect designs a rectangular window such that the width of the window is 18 in. less than the height. If the perimeter of the window is 180 in., what are its dimensions?

27. A designer plans the top of a rectangular workbench to be four times as long as it is wide, and then determines that if the width is 2.5 ft greater and the length is 4.7 ft less, it would be a square. What are its dimensions?

28. A rectangular security area is enclosed on one side by a wall, and the other sides are fenced. The length of the wall is twice the width of the area. The total cost of building the wall and fence is $13,200. If the wall costs $50.00/m and the fence costs $5.00/m, find the dimensions of the area.

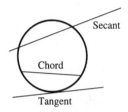

Fig. 2-67

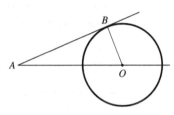

Fig. 2-68

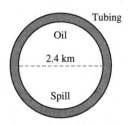

Fig. 2-69

The symbol π (a Greek letter), which we use as a number, was first used in this way as a number in the 1700s.

Section 2.5
2-4 CIRCLES

The next geometric figure we consider is the circle. *All points on a* **circle** *are at the same distance from a fixed point, the* **center** *of the circle. The distance from the center to a point on the circle is the* **radius** *of the circle. The distance between two points on the circle on a line through the center is the* **diameter.** Therefore, the diameter d is twice the radius r, or $d = 2r$. See Fig. 2-67.

There are also certain special types of lines associated with a circle. *A* **chord** *is a line segment having its endpoints on the circle. A* **tangent** *is a line that touches (does not pass through) the circle at one point. A* **secant** *is a line that passes through two points of the circle.* See Fig. 2-68.

An important property of a tangent is that *a tangent to a circle is perpendicular to the radius drawn to the point of contact.* This is illustrated in the next example.

■**EXAMPLE 1**   In Fig. 2-69, O is the center of the circle, and AB is tangent at B. If $\angle OAB = 25°$, find $\angle AOB$.

Since the center is O, OB is a radius of the circle. A tangent is perpendicular to a radius at the point of tangency, which means $\angle ABO = 90°$ so that

$$\angle OAB + \angle OBA = 25° + 90° = 115°$$

Since the sum of the angles of a triangle is 180°, we have

$$\angle AOB = 180° - 115° = 65°$$

Circumference and Area of a Circle

The perimeter of a circle is called the **circumference.** The formulas for the circumference and area of a circle are as follows:

$c = 2\pi r$	Circumference of a circle of radius r	**(2-9)**
$A = \pi r^2$	Area of a circle of radius r	**(2-10)**

Here, π equals approximately 3.1416. In using a calculator, π can be entered by using the $\boxed{\pi}$ key.

■**EXAMPLE 2**   A circular oil spill has a diameter of 2.4 km. This oil spill is to be enclosed within a length of special flexible tubing. What is the area of the spill, and how long must the tubing be? See Fig. 2-70.

We find the area by using Eq. (2-10). Since $d = 2r$, $r = d/2 = 1.2$ km. Therefore, the area is

$$A = \pi r^2 = \pi(1.2)^2$$
$$= 4.5 \text{ km}^2$$

The length of the tubing needed to enclose the oil spill is the circumference of the circle. Therefore,

$$c = 2\pi r = 2\pi(1.2) \qquad \text{note that } c = \pi d$$
$$= 7.5 \text{ km}$$

Results have been rounded off to two significant digits, the accuracy of d.

Many applied problems involve a combination of geometric figures. The following example illustrates one such combination.

SOLVING A WORD PROBLEM

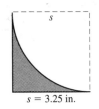

$s = 3.25$ in.

Fig. 2-71

▌EXAMPLE 3   A machine part is a square of side 3.25 in. with a quarter circle removed (see Fig. 2-71). Find the perimeter and the area of one side of the part.

Setting up a formula for the perimeter, we add the two sides of length *s* to *one-fourth of the circumference of a circle with radius s*. For the area, we *subtract the area of one-fourth of a circle from the area of the square*. This gives

$$p = \underset{\substack{\text{bottom}\\\text{and left}}}{2s} + \underset{\substack{\text{circular}\\\text{section}}}{\frac{2\pi s}{4}} = 2s + \frac{\pi s}{2} \qquad A = \underset{\text{square}}{s^2} - \underset{\substack{\text{quarter}\\\text{circle}}}{\frac{\pi s^2}{4}}$$

where *s* is the side of the square and the radius of the circle. Evaluating, we have

$$p = 2(3.25) + \frac{\pi(3.25)}{2} = 11.6 \text{ in.}$$

$$A = 3.25^2 - \frac{\pi(3.25)^2}{4} = 2.27 \text{ in.}^2$$

Circular Arcs and Angles

An **arc** *is part of a circle, and an angle formed at the center by two radii is a* **central angle.** The measure of an arc is the same as the central angle between the ends of the radii that define the arc. *A* **sector** *of a circle is the region bounded by two radii and the arc they intercept. A* **segment** *of a circle is the region bounded by a chord and its arc.* (There are two possible segments for a given chord. The smaller region is a *minor segment,* and the larger region is a *major segment.*). These are illustrated in the following example.

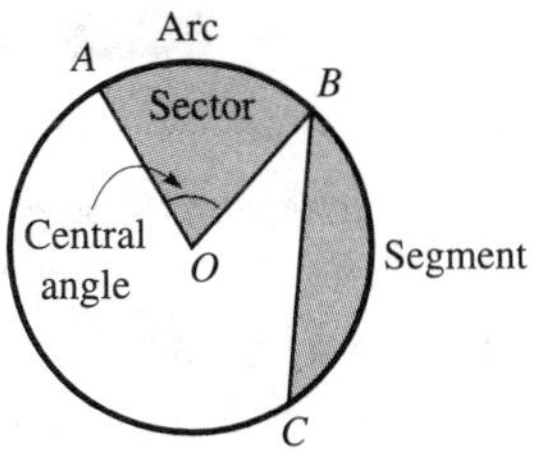

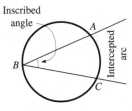

Fig. 2-72

▌EXAMPLE 4   In Fig. 2-72, a sector of the circle is between radii *OA* and *OB* and arc *AB* (which is denoted by $\overset{\frown}{AB}$). If the measure of the central angle at *O* between the radii is 70°, the measure of $\overset{\frown}{AB}$ is also 70°.

In Fig. 2-72, a segment of the circle is between chord *BC* and arc *BC* ($\overset{\frown}{BC}$).   ▌

An **inscribed angle** *of an arc is one for which the endpoints of the arc are points on the sides of the angle and for which the vertex is a point (not an endpoint) of the arc.* An important property of a circle is that *the measure of an inscribed angle is one-half of its intercepted arc.*

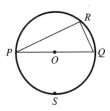

Fig. 2-73   **Fig. 2-74**

▌EXAMPLE 5   **(a)** In the circle shown in Fig. 2-73, $\angle ABC$ is inscribed in $\overset{\frown}{ABC}$, and it intercepts $\overset{\frown}{AC}$. If $\overset{\frown}{AC} = 60°$, then $\angle ABC = 30°$.

(b) In the circle shown in Fig. 2-74, *PQ* is a diameter, and $\angle PRQ$ is inscribed in the semicircular $\overset{\frown}{PRQ}$. Since $\overset{\frown}{PSQ} = 180°$, $\angle PRQ = 90°$. From this we conclude that *an angle inscribed in a semicircle is a right angle.*   ▌

Radian Measure of an Angle

To this point we have measured all angles in degrees. There is another measure of an angle, the *radian*, which is defined in terms of an arc of a circle. We will find it of importance when we study trigonometry.

If a central angle of a circle intercepts an arc equal in length to the radius of the circle, the measure of the central angle is defined as one **radian.** See Fig. 2-75. Since the radius can be marked off along the circumference 2π times (about 6.283 times), we see that 2π rad = 360° (where rad is the symbol for radian). Therefore,

$$\pi \text{ rad} = 180° \tag{2-11}$$

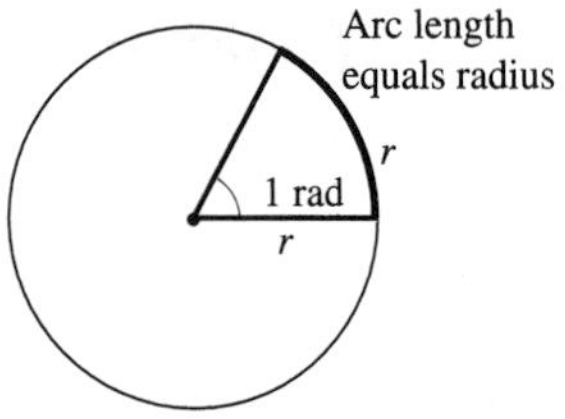

Arc length equals radius

1 rad

Fig. 2-75

is a basic relationship between radians and degrees.

■ **EXAMPLE 6**   (a) If we divide each side of Eq. (2-11) by π, we get

$$1 \text{ rad} = 57.3°$$

where the result has been rounded off.

(b) To change an angle of 118.2° to radian measure, we have

$$118.2° = 118.2°\left(\frac{\pi \text{ rad}}{180°}\right) = 2.06 \text{ rad}$$

By multiplying 118.2° by π rad/180°, the unit of measurement that remains is rad, since the degrees "cancel." We will review radian measure again when we study trigonometry.

EXERCISES *2-4*

In Exercises 1–4, refer to the circle with center at O in Fig. 2-76. Identify the following.

1. (a) A secant line
   (b) A tangent line
2. (a) Two chords
   (b) An inscribed angle
3. (a) Two perpendicular lines
   (b) An isosceles triangle
4. (a) A segment
   (b) A sector with an acute central angle

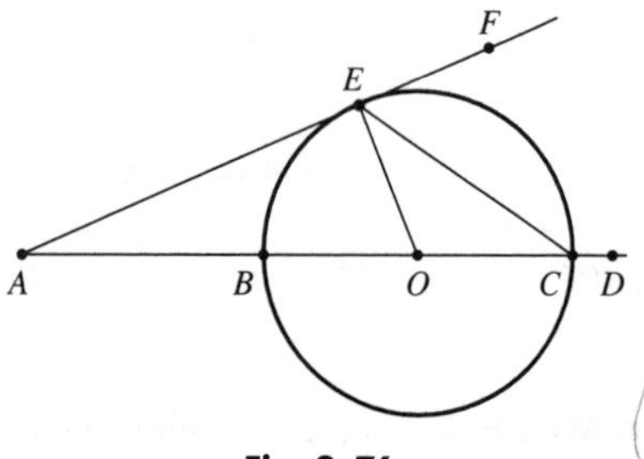

Fig. 2-76

In Exercises 5–8, find the circumference of the circle with the given radius or diameter.

5. $r = 2.75$ ft
6. $r = 0.563$ m
7. $d = 23.1$ mm
8. $d = 8.2$ in.

In Exercises 9–12, find the area of the circle with the given radius or diameter.

9. $r = 0.0952$ yd
10. $r = 45.8$ cm
11. $d = 2.33$ m
12. $d = 12.56$ ft

In Exercises 13–16, refer to Fig. 2-77, where AB is a diameter, TB is a tangent line at B, and $\angle ABC = 65°$. Determine the indicated angles.

13. $\angle CBT$
14. $\angle BCT$
15. $\angle CAB$
16. $\angle BTC$

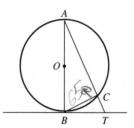

Fig. 2-77

In Exercises 17–20, refer to Fig. 2-78. Determine the indicated arcs and angles.

17. $\overset{\frown}{BC}$

18. $\overset{\frown}{AB}$

19. $\angle ABC$

20. $\angle ACB$

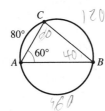

Fig. 2-78

In Exercises 21–24, change the given angles to radian measure.

21. $22.5°$ **22.** $60.0°$ **23.** $125.2°$ **24.** $323.0°$

In Exercises 25–28, find a formula for the indicated perimeter or area.

Fig. 2-79

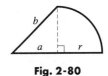

Fig. 2-80

25. The perimeter of the quarter-circle in Fig. 2-79

26. The perimeter of the figure in Fig. 2-80. A quarter-circle is attached to a triangle

27. The area of the segment of the quarter-circle in Fig. 2-79

28. The area of the figure in Fig. 2-80

In Exercises 29–36, solve the given problems.

29. The radius of the earth's equator is 3960 mi. What is the circumference?

30. As a ball bearing rolls along a straight track, it makes 11.0 revolutions while traveling a distance of 109 mm. Find its radius.

31. Using a tape measure, the circumference of a tree is found to be 112 in. What is the diameter of the tree (assuming a circular cross section)?

32. What is the area of the largest circle that can be cut from a rectangular plate 21.2 cm by 15.8 cm?

33. A patio is designed with semicircular areas attached to a square, as shown in Fig. 2-81. Find the area of the patio.

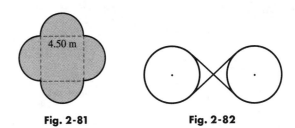

Fig. 2-81   **Fig. 2-82**

34. Find the length of the pulley belt shown in Fig. 2-82, if the belt crosses at right angles. The radius of each pulley wheel is 5.50 in.

(W) 35. The velocity of an object moving in a circular path is directed tangent to the circle in which it is moving. A stone on a string moves in a vertical circle, and the string breaks after 5.5 revolutions. If the string was initially in a vertical position, in what direction does it move after the string breaks? Explain.

36. Part of a circular gear with 24 teeth is shown in Fig. 2-83. Find the indicated angle.

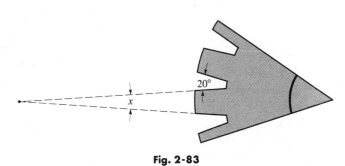

Fig. 2-83

Section 2.6

2-5 MEASUREMENT OF IRREGULAR AREAS

To this point the figures for which we have found areas are well defined, and the areas can be found by direct use of a specific formula. In practice, however, it may be necessary to find the area of a figure with an irregular perimeter or one for which there is no specific formula. In this section we show two methods of finding a very good *approximation* of such an area. These methods are particularly useful in technical areas such as surveying, architecture, and mechanical design.

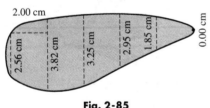

Fig. 2-84

The Trapezoidal Rule

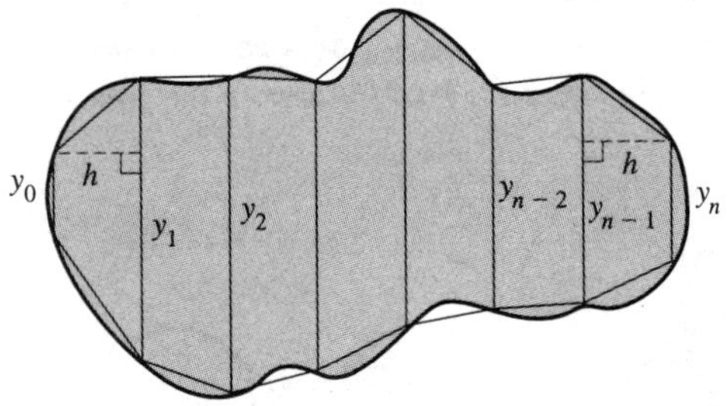

The first method is based on dividing the required area into trapezoids with equal heights. Considering the area shown in Fig. 2-84, we draw parallel lines at n equal intervals between the edges of the area. We then join the ends of these parallel line segments to form adjacent trapezoids. The sum of the areas of the trapezoids gives a good approximation to the required area.

Calling the lengths of the parallel lines $y_0, y_1, y_2, \ldots, y_n$ and the height of each trapezoid h (the distance between the parallel lines), the total area A is the sum of areas of all the trapezoids. This gives us

$$
A = \underbrace{\frac{h}{2}(y_0 + y_1)}_{\substack{\text{first} \\ \text{trapezoid}}} + \underbrace{\frac{h}{2}(y_1 + y_2)}_{\substack{\text{second} \\ \text{trapezoid}}} + \underbrace{\frac{h}{2}(y_2 + y_3)}_{\substack{\text{third} \\ \text{trapezoid}}} + \cdots + \underbrace{\frac{h}{2}(y_{n-2} + y_{n-1})}_{\substack{\text{next-to-last} \\ \text{trapezoid}}} + \underbrace{\frac{h}{2}(y_{n-1} + y_n)}_{\substack{\text{last} \\ \text{trapezoid}}}
$$

$$
= \frac{h}{2}(y_0 + y_1 + y_1 + y_2 + y_2 + y_3 + \cdots + y_{n-2} + y_{n-1} + y_{n-1} + y_n)
$$

Therefore, the approximate area is

$$
A = \frac{h}{2}(y_0 + 2y_1 + 2y_2 + \cdots + 2y_{n-1} + y_n) \tag{2-12}
$$

Equation (2-12) is known as the **trapezoidal rule.** The following examples illustrate its use.

■**EXAMPLE 1**   A plate cam for opening and closing a valve is shown in Fig. 2-85. Widths of the face of the cam are shown at 2.00-cm intervals. Find the area of the face of the cam.

From the figure we see that

$$y_0 = 2.56 \text{ cm}, \quad y_1 = 3.82 \text{ cm}, \quad y_2 = 3.25 \text{ cm}, \quad y_3 = 2.95 \text{ cm},$$
$$y_4 = 1.85 \text{ cm}, \quad y_5 = 0.00 \text{ cm}$$

(In making such measurements, often a y-value at one end (or both ends) is zero. In such a case, the end "trapezoid" is actually a triangle.) From the given information in this example, $h = 2.00$ cm. Therefore, using the trapezoidal rule, Eq. (2-12), we have

$$
A = \frac{2.00}{2}[2.56 + 2(3.82) + 2(3.25) + 2(2.95) + 2(1.85) + 0.00]
$$
$$
= 26.3 \text{ cm}^2
$$

The area of the face of the cam is approximately 26.3 cm². ─────────■

Fig. 2-85

2.00 cm

2.56 cm 3.82 cm 3.25 cm 2.95 cm 1.85 cm 0.00 cm

When approximating the area with trapezoids, we omit small parts of the area for some trapezoids and include small extra areas for other trapezoids. The omitted areas often approximate the extra areas, which makes the approximation better. Also, the use of smaller intervals improves the approximation since the total omitted area or total extra area is smaller.

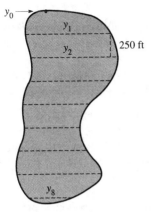

Fig. 2-86

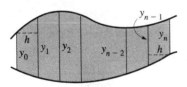

Parabola

Fig. 2-87

Fig. 2-88

Named for the English mathematician
Thomas Simpson (1710–1761).

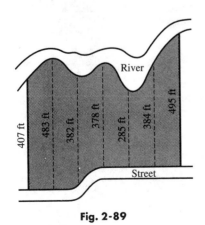

Fig. 2-89

EXAMPLE 2 A surveyor measures the width of a small lake at 250-ft intervals from one end of the lake, as shown in Fig. 2-86. The widths found are as follows:

Distance from one end (ft)	0	250	500	750	1000	1250	1500	1750	2000
Width (ft)	0	940	920	890	740	550	770	960	220

From the table we see that $y_0 = 0$ ft, $y_1 = 940$ ft,..., $y_8 = 220$ ft, and $h = 250$ ft. Therefore, using the trapezoidal rule, the approximate area of the lake is found as follows:

$$A = \frac{250}{2}[0 + 2(940) + 2(920) + 2(890) + 2(740) + 2(550) + 2(770) + 2(960) + 220]$$

$$= 1,500,000 \text{ ft}^2$$

Simpson's Rule

For the second method of measuring an irregular area, we also draw parallel lines at equal intervals between the edges of the area. We then join the ends of these parallel lines with curved *arcs*. This takes into account the fact that the perimeters of most figures are curved. The arcs used in this method are not arcs of a circle, but arcs of a *parabola*. A parabola is shown in Fig. 2-87 and is discussed in detail in Chapter 21. (Examples of parabolas are (1) the path of a ball that has been thrown and (2) the cross section of a microwave "dish.")

The development of this method requires advanced mathematics. Therefore, we will simply state the formula to be used. It might be noted that the form of the equation is similar to that of the trapezoidal rule.

The approximate area of the geometric figure shown in Fig. 2-88 is given by

$$A = \frac{h}{3}(y_0 + 4y_1 + 2y_2 + 4y_3 + \cdots + 2y_{n-2} + 4y_{n-1} + y_n) \qquad \textbf{(2-13)}$$

Equation (2-13) is known as **Simpson's rule.** *In using Eq. (2-13),* *the number n of intervals of width h must be even.*

EXAMPLE 3 A parking lot is proposed for a riverfront area in a town. The town engineer measured the widths of the area at 100 ft (three sig. digits) intervals, as shown in Fig. 2-89. Find the area available for parking.

First we see that there are six intervals, which means Eq. (2-13) may be used. With $y_0 = 407$ ft, $y_1 = 483$ ft,..., $y_6 = 495$ ft, and $h = 100$ ft, we have

$$A = \frac{100}{3}[407 + 4(483) + 2(382) + 4(378) + 2(285) + 4(384) + 495]$$

$$= 241,000 \text{ ft}^2$$

For most areas, Simpson's rule gives a somewhat better approximation than the trapezoidal rule. The accuracy of Simpson's rule is also usually improved by using smaller intervals.

See the chapter introduction.

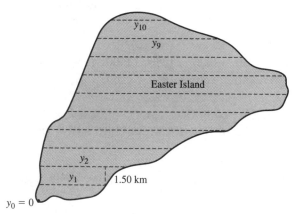

Fig. 2-90

EXAMPLE 4   From an aerial photograph, a cartographer determines the width of Easter Island at 1.50-km intervals as shown in Fig. 2-90. The widths found are as follows:

Distance from south end (km)	0	1.50	3.00	4.50	6.00	7.50	9.00	10.5	12.0	13.5	15.0
Width (km)	0	4.8	5.7	10.5	15.2	18.5	18.8	17.9	11.3	8.8	3.1

Since there are ten intervals, Simpson's rule may be used. From the table we have the following values: $y_0 = 0$, $y_1 = 4.5$, $y_2 = 5.4, \ldots, y_9 = 8.3$, $y_{10} = 2.6$, and $h = 1.5$. Using Simpson's rule, the cartographer would approximate the area of Easter Island as follows:

$$A = \frac{1.50}{3}(0 + 4(4.8) + 2(5.7) + 4(10.5) + 2(15.2) + 4(18.5)$$
$$+ 2(18.8) + 4(17.9) + 2(11.3) + 4(8.8) + 3.1) = 174 \text{ km}^2$$

EXERCISES 2-5

In Exercises 1–12, calculate the indicated areas. All data are accurate to at least two significant digits.

1. The widths of a kidney-shaped swimming pool were measured at 2.0-m intervals as shown in Fig. 2-91. Calculate the surface area of the pool, using the trapezoidal rule.

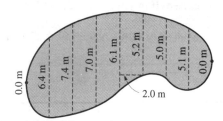

Fig. 2-91

2. Calculate the surface area of the swimming pool in Fig. 2-91, using Simpson's rule.

3. The widths of a cross section of an airplane wing are measured at 1.00-ft intervals as shown in Fig. 2-92. Calculate the area of the cross section, using Simpson's rule.

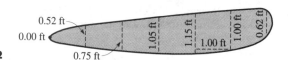

Fig. 2-92

4. Calculate the area of the cross section of the airplane wing in Fig. 2-92, using the trapezoidal rule.

5. Using aerial photography, the widths of an area burned by a forest fire were measured at 0.5-mi intervals as shown in the following table.

Distance (mi)	0.0	0.5	1.0	1.5	2.0	2.5	3.0	3.5	4.0
Width (mi)	0.6	2.2	4.7	3.1	3.6	1.6	2.2	1.5	0.8

Determine the area burned by the fire by using the trapezoidal rule.

6. Find the area burned by the forest fire of Exercise 5, using Simpson's rule.

7. A cartographer measured the width of Kruger National Park (and game reserve) in South Africa at 6.0-mm intervals on a map, as shown in Fig. 2-93. The widths are shown in the list that follows. Find the area of the park if the scale of the map is 1.0 mm = 6.0 km.

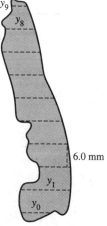

$y_0 = 7$ mm, $y_1 = 15$ mm
$y_2 = 7$ mm, $y_3 = 11$ mm
$y_4 = 13$ mm, $y_5 = 10$ mm
$y_6 = 9$ mm, $y_7 = 12$ mm
$y_8 = 8$ mm, $y_9 = 3$ mm

Fig. 2-93

8. The widths of an oval-shaped floor were measured at 1.5-m intervals, as shown in the following table.

Distance (m)	0.0	1.5	3.0	4.5	6.0	7.5	9.0	10.5	12.0
Width (m)	0.0	5.0	7.2	8.3	8.6	8.3	7.2	5.0	0.0

Find the area of the floor by using Simpson's rule.

9. The widths of the baseball playing area in Boston's Fenway Park at 45-ft intervals are shown in Fig. 2-94. Find the playing area using the trapezoidal rule.

10. Find the playing area of Fenway Park (see Exercise 9) by Simpson's rule.

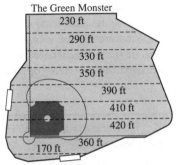

The Green Monster
230 ft
290 ft
330 ft
350 ft
390 ft
410 ft
420 ft
170 ft 360 ft

Fig. 2-94

11. Soundings taken across a river channel give the following values of distance from one shore with the corresponding depth of the channel.

Distance (ft)	0	50	100	150	200	250	300	350	400	450	500
Depth (ft)	5	12	17	21	22	25	26	16	10	8	0

Find the area of the channel using Simpson's rule.

12. The widths of a bell crank are measured at 2.0-in. intervals, as shown in Fig. 2-95. Find the area of the bell crank if the two connector holes are each 2.50 in. in diameter.

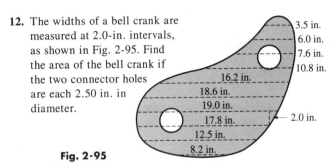

3.5 in.
6.0 in.
7.6 in.
10.8 in.
16.2 in.
18.6 in.
19.0 in.
17.8 in.   2.0 in.
12.5 in.
8.2 in.

Fig. 2-95

In Exercises 13–16, calculate the area of the circle by the indicated method.

The lengths of parallel chords of a circle that are 0.250 in. apart are given in the following table. The diameter of the circle is 2.000 in. The distance shown is the distance from one end of a diameter.

Distance (in.)	0.000	0.250	0.500	0.750	1.000	1.250	1.500	1.750	2.000
Length (in.)	0.000	1.323	1.732	1.936	2.000	1.936	1.732	1.323	0.000

Using the formula $A = \pi r^2$, the area of the circle is 3.14 in.^{2}.

W 13. Find the area of the circle using the trapezoidal rule and only the values of distance of 0.000 in., 0.500 in., 1.000 in., 1.500 in., and 2.000 in. with the corresponding values of the chord lengths. Explain why the value found is less than 3.14 in.^{2}.

W 14. Find the area of the circle using the trapezoidal rule and all values in the table. Explain why the value found is closer to 3.14 in.^{2} than the value found in Exercise 13.

W 15. Find the area of the circle using Simpson's rule and the same table values as in Exercise 13. Explain why the value found is closer to 3.14 in.^{2} than the value found in Exercise 13.

W 16. Find the area of the circle using Simpson's rule and all values in the table. Explain why the value found is closer to 3.14 in.^{2} than the value found in Exercise 15.

Section 2.7

2-6 SOLID GEOMETRIC FIGURES

We now review the formulas for the *volume* and *surface area* of some basic solid geometric figures. Just as area is a measure of the surface of a plane geometric figure, **volume** is a measure of the space occupied by a solid geometric figure.

One of the most common solid figures is the **rectangular solid.** This figure has six sides **(faces),** and opposite sides are rectangles. All intersecting sides are perpendicular to each other. The **bases** of the rectangular solid are the top and bottom faces. A **cube** is a rectangular solid with all six faces being equal squares.

A **right circular cylinder** is *generated* by rotating a rectangle about one of its sides. Each **base** is a circle, and the *cylindrical surface* is perpendicular to each of the bases. The **height** is one side of the rectangle, and the **radius** of the base is the other side.

A **right circular cone** is generated by rotating a right triangle about one of its legs. The **base** is a circle, and the **slant height** is the hypotenuse of the right triangle. The **height** is one leg of the right triangle, and the **radius** of the base is the other leg.

The bases of a **right prism** are equal and parallel polygons, and the sides are rectangles. The **height** of a prism is the perpendicular distance between bases. The base of a **pyramid** is a polygon, and the other faces, the **lateral faces**, are triangles that meet at a common point, the **vertex.** A **regular pyramid** has congruent triangles for its lateral faces.

A **sphere** is generated by rotating a circle about a diameter. The **radius** is a line segment joining the center and a point on the sphere. The **diameter** is a line segment through the center and having its endpoints on the sphere.

In the following formulas, V represents the *volume*, A represents the *total surface area*, S represents the *lateral surface area* (bases not included), B represents the *area of the base*, and p represents the *perimeter of the base.*

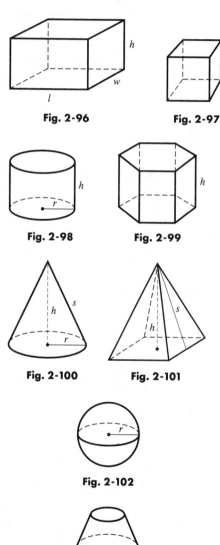

Fig. 2-96   **Fig. 2-97**

Fig. 2-98   **Fig. 2-99**

Fig. 2-100   **Fig. 2-101**

Fig. 2-102

Fig. 2-103

$V = lwh$ $A = 2lw + 2lh + 2wh$	Rectangular solid (Fig. 2-96)	(2-14) (2-15)
$V = e^3$ $A = 6e^2$	Cube (Fig. 2-97)	(2-16) (2-17)
$V = \pi r^2 h$ $A = 2\pi r^2 + 2\pi rh$ $S = 2\pi rh$	Right circular cylinder (Fig. 2-98)	(2-18) (2-19) (2-20)
$V = Bh$ $S = ph$	Right prism (Fig. 2-99)	(2-21) (2-22)
$V = \frac{1}{3}\pi r^2 h$ $A = \pi r^2 + \pi rs$ $S = \pi rs$	Right circular cone (Fig. 2-100)	(2-23) (2-24) (2-25)
$V = \frac{1}{3}Bh$ $S = \frac{1}{2}ps$	Regular pyramid (Fig. 2-101)	(2-26) (2-27)
$V = \frac{4}{3}\pi r^3$ $A = 4\pi r^2$	Sphere (Fig. 2-102)	(2-28) (2-29)

Equation (2-21) is valid for any prism, and Eq. (2-26) is valid for any pyramid. There are other types of cylinders and cones, but we shall restrict our attention to right circular cylinders and right circular cones, and we will often use "cylinder" or "cone" when referring to them.

The **frustum** of a cone or pyramid is the solid figure that remains after the top is cut off by a plane parallel to the base. Figure 2-103 shows the frustum of a cone.

EXAMPLE 1 What volume of concrete is needed for a driveway 25.0 m long, 2.75 m wide, and 0.100 m thick?

The driveway is a rectangular solid for which $l = 25.0$ m, $w = 2.75$ m, and $h = 0.100$ m. Using Eq. (2-14), we have

$$V = (25.0)(2.75)(0.100) = 6.88 \text{ m}^3$$

SOLVING A WORD PROBLEM

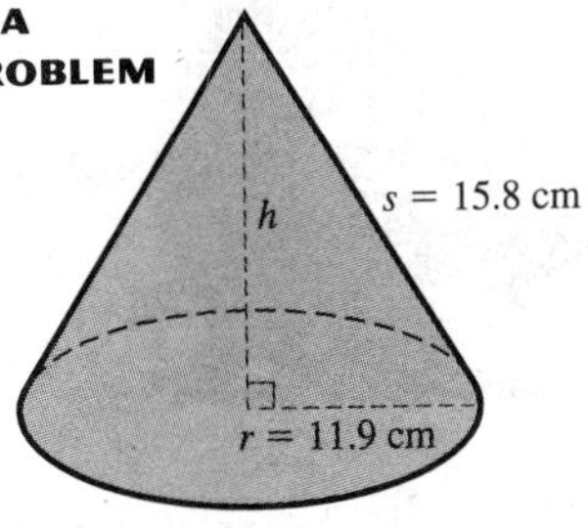

Fig. 2-104

EXAMPLE 2 Calculate the volume of a right circular cone for which the radius $r = 11.9$ cm and the *slant height s = 15.8 cm*. See Fig. 2-104.

To find the volume using Eq. (2-23), we need the radius and height of the cone. Therefore, we must first find the height. As noted, the radius and height are the legs of a right triangle. and the slant height is the hypotenuse. To find the height we *use the Pythagorean theorem.*

$$s^2 = r^2 + h^2 \qquad \text{Pythagorean theorem}$$
$$h^2 = s^2 - r^2 \qquad \text{solve for } h$$
$$h = \sqrt{s^2 - r^2}$$
$$= \sqrt{15.8^2 - 11.9^2} = 10.4 \text{ cm}$$

Now, calculating the volume (in using a calculator it is not necessary to record the value of h), we have

$$V = \tfrac{1}{3}\pi r^2 h \qquad \text{Eq. (2-23)}$$
$$= \tfrac{1}{3}\pi(11.9^2)(10.4) \qquad \text{substituting}$$
$$= 1540 \text{ cm}^3$$

SOLVING A WORD PROBLEM

$h = 122$ ft

$r = 40.0$ ft

Fig. 2-105

EXAMPLE 3 A grain storage building is in the shape of a cylinder surmounted by a hemisphere *(half a sphere)*. See Fig. 2-105. Find the volume of grain that can be stored if the height of the cylinder is 122 ft and its radius is 40.0 ft.

The total volume of the structure is the volume of the cylinder plus the volume of the hemisphere. By the construction we see that the radius of the hemisphere is the same as the radius of the cylinder. Therefore,

$$
\overset{\text{cylinder}}{} \quad \overset{\text{hemisphere}}{}
$$
$$V = \pi r^2 h + \tfrac{1}{2}(\tfrac{4}{3}\pi r^3) = \pi r^2 h + \tfrac{2}{3}\pi r^3$$
$$= \pi(40.0)^2(122) + \tfrac{2}{3}\pi(40.0)^3$$
$$= 747{,}000 \text{ ft}^3$$

━━━━━━━━━━ EXERCISES *2-6* ━━━━━━━━━━

In Exercises 1–16, find the volume or area of each solid figure for the given values. See Figs. 2-96 to 2-102.

1. Volume of cube: $e = 7.15$ ft

2. Volume of right circular cylinder: $r = 23.5$ cm, $h = 48.4$ cm

3. Total surface area of right circular cylinder: $r = 6.89$ m, $h = 2.33$ m

4. Area of sphere: $r = 67$ in.

5. Volume of sphere: $r = 0.877$ yd

6. Volume of right circular cone: $r = 25.1$ mm, $h = 5.66$ mm

7. Lateral area of right circular cone: $r = 78.0$ cm, $s = 83.8$ cm

8. Lateral area of regular pyramid: $p = 3.45$ ft, $s = 2.72$ ft

9. Volume of regular pyramid: square base of side 16 in., $h = 13$ in.

10. Volume of right prism: square base of side 29.0 cm, $h = 11.2$ cm

11. Lateral area of regular prism: equilateral triangle base of side 1.092 m, $h = 1.025$ m

12. Lateral area of right circular cylinder: diameter $= 25.0$ ft, $h = 34.7$ ft

13. Volume of hemisphere: diameter $= 0.83$ yd

14. Volume of regular pyramid: square base of side 22.4 m, $s = 14.2$ m

15. Total surface area of right circular cone: $r = 0.339$ cm, $h = 0.274$ cm

16. Total surface area of pyramid: all faces and base are equilateral triangles of side 3.67 in.

In Exercises 17–28, find the indicated areas and volumes.

17. A rectangular box is to be used to store radioactive materials. The inside of the box is 12.0 in. long, 9.50 in. wide, and 8.75 in. deep. What is the area of sheet lead that must be used to line the inside of the box?

18. A swimming pool is 50.0 ft wide, 78.0 ft long, 3.50 ft deep at one end, and 8.50 ft deep at the other end. How many cubic feet of water can it hold? (The slope on the bottom is constant.)

19. The Alaskan oil pipeline is 750 mi long and has a diameter of 4.0 ft. What is the maximum volume of the pipeline?

20. A glass prism used in the study of optics has a right triangular base. The legs of the triangle are 3.00 cm and 4.00 cm. The prism is 8.50 cm high. What is the total surface area of the prism? See Fig. 2-106.

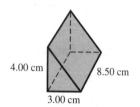

4.00 cm   8.50 cm

3.00 cm

Fig. 2-106

21. The Great Pyramid of Egypt has a square base approximately 250 yd on a side. The height of the pyramid is about 160 yd. What is its volume? See Fig. 2-107.

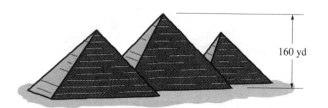

160 yd

Fig. 2-107

22. A paper cup is in the shape of a cone with radius 1.80 in. and height 3.50 in. What is the surface area of the cup?

23. *Spaceship Earth* (shown in Fig. 2-108) at Epcot Center in Florida is a sphere of 165 ft in diameter. What is the volume of *Spaceship Earth?*

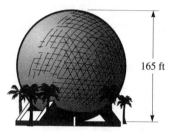

165 ft

Fig. 2-108

24. The diameter of a spherical balloon is 12 cm. It is then further inflated until its diameter is 24 cm. By how much was the surface area increased?

25. A special wedge in the shape of a regular pyramid has a square base 16.0 mm on a side. The height of the wedge is 40.0 mm. What is the total surface area of the wedge?

26. What is the area of a paper label that is to cover the lateral surface of a cylindrical can 3.00 in. in diameter and 4.25 in. high? The ends of the label will overlap 0.25 in. when the label is placed on the can.

27. A dipstick is made to measure the volume remaining in the conical container shown in Fig. 2-109. How far below the full mark (at the top of the container) on the stick should the mark for half-full be placed?

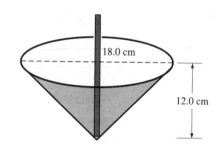

18.0 cm

12.0 cm

Fig. 2-109

28. The side view of a rivet is shown in Fig. 2-110. It is a conical part on a cylindrical part. Find the volume of the rivet.

0.625 in.   2.75 in.

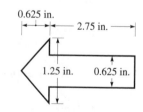

1.25 in.   0.625 in.

Fig. 2-110

Section 2.8

CHAPTER EQUATIONS

Line segments	Fig. 2-8	$\dfrac{a}{b} = \dfrac{c}{d}$	(2-1)
Triangle		$A = \frac{1}{2}bh$	(2-2)
Hero's formula		$A = \sqrt{s(s-a)(s-b)(s-c)}$, where $s = \frac{1}{2}(a+b+c)$	(2-3)
Pythagorean theorem	Fig. 2-29	$c^2 = a^2 + b^2$	(2-4)
Square	Fig. 2-51	$A = s^2$	(2-5)
Rectangle	Fig. 2-52	$A = lw$	(2-6)
Parallelogram	Fig. 2-53	$A = bh$	(2-7)
Trapezoid	Fig. 2-54	$A = \frac{1}{2}h(b_1 + b_2)$	(2-8)
Circle		$c = 2\pi r$	(2-9)
		$A = \pi r^2$	(2-10)
Radians	Fig. 2-75	$\pi \text{ rad} = 180°$	(2-11)
Trapezoidal rule	Fig. 2-84	$A = \dfrac{h}{2}(y_0 + 2y_1 + 2y_2 + \cdots + 2y_{n-1} + y_n)$	(2-12)
Simpson's rule	Fig. 2-88	$A = \dfrac{h}{3}(y_0 + 4y_1 + 2y_2 + 4y_3 + \cdots + 2y_{n-2} + 4y_{n-1} + y_n)$	(2-13)
Rectangular solid	Fig. 2-96	$V = lwh$	(2-14)
		$A = 2lw + 2lh + 2wh$	(2-15)
Cube	Fig. 2-97	$V = e^3$	(2-16)
		$A = 6e^2$	(2-17)
Right circular cylinder	Fig. 2-98	$V = \pi r^2 h$	(2-18)
		$A = 2\pi r^2 + 2\pi rh$	(2-19)
		$S = 2\pi rh$	(2-20)
Right prism	Fig. 2-99	$V = Bh$	(2-21)
		$S = ph$	(2-22)
Right circular cone	Fig. 2-100	$V = \frac{1}{3}\pi r^2 h$	(2-23)
		$A = \pi r^2 + \pi rs$	(2-24)
		$S = \pi rs$	(2-25)
Regular pyramid	Fig. 2-101	$V = \frac{1}{3}Bh$	(2-26)
		$S = \frac{1}{2}ps$	(2-27)
Sphere	Fig. 2-102	$V = \frac{4}{3}\pi r^3$	(2-28)
		$A = 4\pi r^2$	(2-29)

REVIEW EXERCISES

In Exercises 1–4, use Fig. 2-111. Determine the indicated angles.

1. ∠CGE   **2.** ∠EGF   **3.** ∠DGH   **4.** ∠EGI

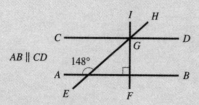

$AB \parallel CD$

Fig. 2-111

In Exercises 5–12, find the indicated sides of the right triangle shown in Fig. 2-112.

5. $a = 9$, $b = 40$, $c = ?$

6. $a = 14$, $b = 48$, $c = ?$

7. $a = 40$, $c = 58$, $b = ?$

8. $b = 56$, $c = 65$, $a = ?$

9. $a = 6.30$, $b = 3.80$, $c = ?$

10. $a = 126$, $b = 251$, $c = ?$

11. $b = 29.3$, $c = 36.1$, $a = ?$

12. $a = 0.782$, $c = 0.885$, $b = ?$

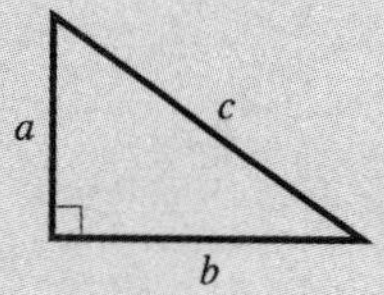

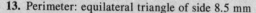

Fig. 2-112

In Exercises 13–20, find the perimeter or area of the indicated figure.

13. Perimeter: equilateral triangle of side 8.5 mm

14. Perimeter: rhombus of side 15.2 in.

15. Area: triangle, $b = 3.25$ ft, $h = 1.88$ ft

16. Area: triangle of sides 17.5 cm, 13.8 cm, 11.9 cm

17. Circumference of circle: $d = 98.4$ mm

18. Perimeter: rectangle, $l = 2.98$ yd, $w = 1.86$ yd

19. Area: trapezoid, $b_1 = 67.2$ in., $b_2 = 83.8$ in., $h = 34.2$ in.

20. Area: circle, $d = 32.8$ m

In Exercises 21–24, find the volume of the indicated solid geometric figure.

21. Prism: base is right triangle with legs 26.0 cm and 34.0 cm, height is 14.0 cm

22. Cylinder: base radius 36.0 in., height 24.0 in.

23. Pyramid: base area 3850 ft², height 125 ft

24. Sphere: diameter 22.1 mm

In Exercises 25–28, find the surface area of the indicated solid geometric figure.

25. Total area of cube of edge 5.20 m

26. Total area of cylinder: base diameter 1.20 ft, height 5.80 ft

27. Lateral area of cone: base radius 18.2 in., height 11.5 in.

28. Total area of sphere: diameter 0.884 m

In Exercises 29–32, use Fig. 2-113. Line CT is tangent to the circle with center at O. Find the indicated angles.

29. ∠BTA

30. ∠TAB

31. ∠BTC

32. ∠ABT

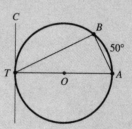

Fig. 2-113

In Exercises 33–36, use Fig. 2-114. Given that AB = 4, BC = 4, CD = 6, and ∠ADC = 53°, find the indicated angle and lengths.

33. ∠ABE

34. AD

35. BE

36. AE

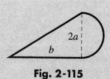

Fig. 2-114

In Exercises 37–40, find the formulas for the indicated perimeters and areas.

37. Perimeter of Fig. 2-115 (a right triangle and semicircle attached)

38. Perimeter of Fig. 2-116 (a square with a quarter circle at each end)

39. Area of Fig. 2-115   **40.** Area of Fig. 2-116

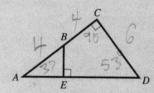

Fig. 2-115 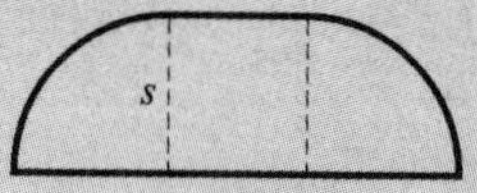   **Fig. 2-116**

In Exercises 41–44, answer the given questions and explain your reasoning.

41. Is a square also a rectangle, a parallelogram, and a rhombus?

42. If the measures of two angles of one triangle equal the measures of the measures of two angles of a second triangle, are the two triangles similar?

Ⓦ **43.** If the dimensions of a plane geometric figure are each multiplied by *n*, by how much is the area multiplied? Explain, using a circle to illustrate.

Ⓦ **44.** If the dimensions of a solid geometric figure are each multiplied by *n*, by how much is the volume multiplied? Explain, using a cube to illustrate.

In Exercises 45–64, solve the given problems.

45. A ramp for the disabled is designed so that it rises 1.2 m over a horizontal distance of 7.8 m. How long is the ramp?

46. An airplane is 2100 ft directly above one end of a 9500-ft runway. How far is the plane from the glide-slope indicator on the ground at the other end of the runway?

47. A radio transmitting tower is supported by guy wires. The tower and three parallel guy wires are shown in Fig. 2-117. Find the distance *AB* along the tower.

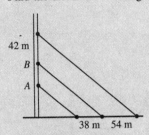

Fig. 2-117

48. Find the areas of lots *A* and *B* in Fig. 2-118. *A* has a frontage on Main St. of 140 ft, and *B* has a frontage on Main St. of 84 ft. The boundary between lots is 120 ft.

49. Find the area of the side of the building shown in Fig. 2-119 (a triangle over a rectangle).

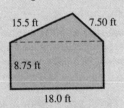

Fig. 2-119

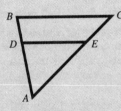

Fig. 2-120

50. The metal support in the form of △*ABC* shown in Fig. 2-120 is strengthened by brace *DE*, which is parallel to *BC*. How long is the brace if *AB* = 24 in., *AD* = 16 in., and *BC* = 33 in.?

51. A typical scale for an aerial photograph is 1/18450. In an 8.00-in.-by-10.0-in. photograph with this scale, what is the longest distance (in mi) between two locations in the photograph?

52. For a hydraulic press, the mechanical advantage is the ratio of the large piston area to the small piston area. Find the mechanical advantage if the pistons have diameters of 3.10 cm and 2.25 cm.

53. The diameter of the earth is 7920 mi, and a satellite is in orbit at an altitude of 210 mi. How far does the satellite travel in one rotation about the earth?

54. The roof of the Louisiana Superdome in New Orleans is supported by a circular steel tension ring 651 m in circumference. Find the area covered by the roof.

55. A rectangular piece of wallboard is 8.0 ft long and 4.0 ft wide. Two 1.0-ft diameter holes are cut out for heating ducts. What is the area of the remaining piece?

56. The diameter of the sun is 1.38×10^6 km, the diameter of the earth is 1.27×10^4 km, and the distance from the earth to the sun (center to center) is 1.50×10^8 km. What is the distance from the center of the earth to the end of the shadow due to the rays from the sun?

57. Using aerial photography, the width of an oil spill is measured at 250-m intervals, as shown in Fig. 2-121. Using Simpson's rule, find the area of the oil spill.

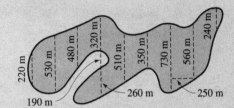

Fig. 2-121

58. To build a highway, it is necessary to cut through a hill. A surveyor measured the cross-sectional areas at 250-ft intervals through the cut as shown in the following table. Using the trapezoidal rule, determine the volume of soil to be removed.

Dist. (ft)	0	250	500	750	1000	1250	1500	1750
Area (ft²)	560	1780	4650	6730	5600	6280	2260	230

59. The Hubble space telescope is within a cylinder 4.3 m in diameter and 13 m long. What is the volume within this cylinder?

60. A horizontal cross section of a concrete bridge pier is a regular hexagon (six sides, all equal in length, and all internal angles are equal), each side of which is 2.50 m long. If the height of the pier is 6.75 m, what is the volume of concrete in the pier?

61. Two persons are talking to each other on cellular phones. One is 2.4 mi from the relay tower, and the other is 3.7 mi from the tower. If the angle between their signals at the tower is 90.0°, how far apart are the two persons?

62. A railroad track 1000.00 ft long expands 0.20 ft (2.4 in.) during the afternoon (due to an increase in temperature of about 30°F). Assuming that the track cannot move at either end and that the increase in length causes a bend straight up in the middle of the track, how high is the top of the bend?

63. A hot-water tank is in the shape of a right circular cylinder surmounted by a hemisphere. The total height of the tank is 6.75 ft, and the diameter of the base is 2.50 ft. How many gallons does the tank hold? (7.48 gal = 1.00 ft³)

64. A tent is in the shape of a regular pyramid surmounted on a cube. If the edge of the cube is 2.50 m and the total height of the tent is 3.25 m, find the area of the material used in making the tent (not including any floor area).

Writing Exercise

65. The Pentagon, headquarters of the U.S. Department of Defense, is one of the world's largest office buildings. It is a regular pentagon (five sides, all equal in length, and all internal angles are equal) 921 ft on a side, with a diagonal of length 1490 ft. Using these data, draw a sketch and write one or two paragraphs to explain how to find the area covered within the outside perimeter of the Pentagon. (What is the area?)

PRACTICE TEST

1. In Fig. 2-122, determine $\angle 1$.

2. In Fig. 2-122, determine $\angle 2$.

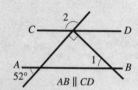

Fig. 2-122 $AB \parallel CD$

3. A tree is 8.0 ft high and casts a shadow 10.0 ft long. At the same time, a telephone pole casts a shadow 25.0 ft long. How tall is the pole?

4. Find the area of a triangle with sides of 2.46 cm, 3.65 cm, and 4.07 cm.

5. What is the diagonal distance along the floor between corners of a rectangular room 12.5 ft wide and 17.0 ft long?

6. Find the surface area of a tennis ball whose circumference is 21.0 cm.

7. Find the volume of a right circular cone of radius 2.08 m and height 1.78 m.

8. In Fig. 2-123, find $\angle 1$.

9. In Fig. 2-123, find $\angle 2$.

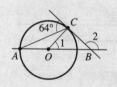

Fig. 2-123   **Fig. 2-124**

10. In Fig. 2-124, find the perimeter of the figure shown. It is a square with a semicircle removed.

11. In Fig. 2-124, find the area of the figure shown.

12. The width of a marshy area is measured at 50-ft intervals, with the results shown in the following table. Using the trapezoidal rule, find the area of the marsh. (All data accurate to two or more significant digits.)

Distance (ft)	0	50	100	150	200	250	300
Width (ft)	0	90	145	260	205	110	20

Section 2.2

3.2

PRACTICE EXERCISES

1. We can show the desired congruence in two
   ways:

   First, since AC = 3 cm and US = 3 cm,
   AC = US. Also we are given that CB = UT,
   and that ∠C and ∠U are right angles making
   ∠C = ∠U. Then △ABC ≅ △STU by SAS = SAS.

   Second, since AB = 5 cm and TS = 5 cm,
   AB = TS. Also, since AC = 3 cm and
   US = 3 cm, AC = US. And since we are also
   given that CB = UT, △ABC ≅ △STU by SSS = SSS.

SECTION EXERCISES

1. congruent by SSS = SSS

3. Since right angles are equal, the triangles
   are congruent by SAS = SAS.

5. congruent by ASA = ASA

7. 1. Given   2. ∠3 = ∠4   3. BD = BD
   4. ASA = ASA

9. 1. Given   2. ⊥ lines form rt. ∠'s
   3. ∠ABD = ∠BDC   4. $\overline{DB} = \overline{DB}$ 5. Given
   6. SAS = SAS

11. <u>Proof:</u>

STATEMENTS	REASONS
1. $\overline{AD}$ bisects $\overline{BE}$	1. Given
2. C is the midpoint of $\overline{BE}$	2. Def. of bisector
3. BC = CE	3. Def. of midpoint
4. $\overline{BE}$ bisects $\overline{AD}$	4. Given
5. C is the midpoint of $\overline{AD}$	5. Def. of bisector
6. AC = CD	6. Def. of midpoint
7. ∠ACB = ∠DCE	7. Vert. ∠'s are =
8. △ABC ≅ △CDE	8. SAS = SAS

13. <u>Proof:</u>

STATEMENTS	REASONS
1. AD = BD	1. Given
2. AE = BC	2. Given
3. ED = AD - AE and CD = BD - BC	3. Segment add. post.
4. ED = CD	4. Add.-Subtr. Law
5. ∠D = ∠D	5. Reflexive Law
6. △ACD ≅ △BDE	6. SAS = SAS

15. <u>Proof</u>:   STATEMENTS   REASONS

     1. AB = BC   1. Given

     2. ∠1 = ∠2   2. Given

     3. ∠4 is supplementary to ∠1 and   3. Adj. ∠'s whose noncommon sides are
        ∠3 is supplementary to ∠2   in line are supp.

     4. ∠4 = ∠3   4. Supp. of = ∠'s are =

     5. ∠5 = ∠6   5. Vert. ∠'s are =

     6. ∆ABE ≅ ∆BCD   6. ASA = ASA

17. <u>Proof</u>:   STATEMENTS   REASONS

     1. ∆ACD is equilateral   1. Given

     2. AC = AD   2. Def. of equilateral ∆

     3. ∠1 = ∠2   3. Given

     4. ∠3 and ∠1 are supplementary and   4. Adj. ∠'s whose noncommon sides are
        ∠4 and ∠2 are supplementary   in line are supp.

     5. ∠3 = ∠4   5. Supp. of = ∠'s are =

     6. BC = DE   6. Given

     7. ∆ABC ≅ ∆ADE   7. SAS = SAS

19. Since AC = PR, we must solve   21. Since AC = x + 1 and x = 3 (by Exercise
                                                19), substituting 3 for x we obtain
     x + 1 = 3x - 5.
                                                    AC = 3 + 1 = 4.
       1 = 2x - 5   Subtract x from both sides

       6 = 2x   Add 5 to both sides

       3 = x   Divide both sides by 2

23. Since ∠B = (100 + y)° and y = 20 (by   25. $\overline{RP}$
    Exercise 20), substituting 20 for y we obtain

       ∠B = (100 + 20)° = 120°.

27. $\overline{RQ}$ 29. ∠P

31. Refer to the figure below in which corresponding sides of congruent
    triangles are identified.

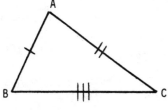
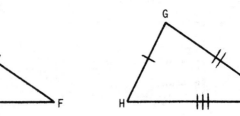

    <u>Given</u>: ∆ABC ≅ ∆DEF and ∆DEF ≅ ∆GHI

    <u>Prove</u>: ∆ABC ≅ ∆GHI

Proof: STATEMENTS   REASONS

1. $\triangle ABC \cong \triangle DEF$ 1. Given
2. AB = DE, AC = DF, BC = EF   2. cpoctae
3. $\triangle DEF \cong \triangle GHI$ 3. Given
4. DE = GH, DF = GI, EF = HI   4. cpoctae
5. AB = GH, AC = GI, BC = HI   5. Using 2 and 4 and the trans. law
6. $\triangle ABC \cong \triangle GHI$ 6. SSS = SSS

Section 2.3
6.3

PRACTICE EXERCISES

1. Use the Pythagorean Theorem $a^2 + b^2 = c^2$
   with c = 32 and a = 18 and solve for b.

$$a^2 + b^2 = c^2$$
$$(18)^2 + b^2 = (32)^2$$
$$b^2 = (32)^2 - (18)^2$$
$$b^2 = 1024 - 324$$
$$b^2 = 700$$
$$b = \sqrt{700} = \sqrt{(100)(7)} = 10\sqrt{7}$$

Thus, $b = 10\sqrt{7}$ ft (Note we only use the
positive value for length). Rounded to the
nearest tenth, this is about 26.5 ft.

3. We make a sketch of the problem as shown
   to the right. After two hours, each has
   traveled

$$2(450) = 900 \text{ miles.}$$

By the Pythagorean Theorem,

$$x^2 = (900)^2 + (900)^2$$
$$x^2 = 2(900)^2$$
$$x = \sqrt{2(900)^2}$$
$$x = 900\sqrt{2} \approx 1272.8 \text{ mi}$$

2. The triangle cannot be a right triangle
   since the longest side, 9 ft, would have
   to be the hypotenuse and

$$9^2 \neq 8^2 + 4^2$$

since

$$81 \neq 64 + 16 = 80$$

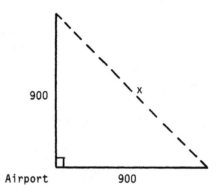

900

x

Airport   900

SECTION EXERCISES

1. Substitute into the Pythagorean theorem
$$a^2 + b^2 = c^2$$
$$3^2 + 4^2 = c^2$$
$$9 + 16 = c^2$$
$$25 = c^2$$
$$\pm\sqrt{25} = c$$
$$\pm 5 = c$$
Discard -5. Thus, c = 5 cm.

3. Substitute into the Pythagorean theorem.
$$a^2 + b^2 = c^2$$
$$a^2 + 25^2 = 65^2$$
$$a^2 + 625 = 4225$$
$$a^2 = 3600$$
$$a = \pm\sqrt{3600} = \pm 60$$
Discard -60. Thus, a = 60 ft.

5. Substitute into the Pythagorean theorem.
$$a^2 + b^2 = c^2$$
$$6^2 + b^2 = 11^2$$
$$36 + b^2 = 121$$
$$b^2 = 85$$
$$b = \pm\sqrt{85}$$
Discard $-\sqrt{85}$. Thus, $b = \sqrt{85}$ yd.

7. Substitute into the Pythagorean theorem.
$$a^2 + b^2 = c^2$$
$$8^2 + b^2 = (2\sqrt{97})^2$$
$$64 + b^2 = 4(97) = 388$$
$$b^2 = 324$$
$$b = \pm\sqrt{324} = \pm 18$$
Discard -18. Thus, b = 18 cm.

9. Yes; by the converse of the Pythagorean theorem, $15^2 + 20^2 = 225 + 400 = 625 = 25^2$.

11. Yes; by the converse of the Pythagorean theorem, $3^2 + 7^2 = 9 + 49 = 58 = (\sqrt{58})^2$.

13. No; since $(\sqrt{7})^2 + (\sqrt{2})^2 = 7 + 2 = 9 \neq 81 = 9^2$.

15. By Theorem 6.13, $c = \sqrt{2}a = (\sqrt{2})(10)$
$= 10\sqrt{2}$ ft.

17. Since $b = a$ and $a = 3\sqrt{2}$ yd, $b = 3\sqrt{2}$ yd.

19. By Theorem 6.13, $c = \sqrt{2}a = \sqrt{2}(3\sqrt{2})$
$= 3(\sqrt{2})(\sqrt{2}) = 3(2) = 6$ cm.

21. By Theorem 6.13, $c = \sqrt{2}b = \sqrt{2}(3\sqrt{3})$
$= 3\sqrt{2}\,\sqrt{3} = 3\sqrt{6}$ ft.

23. By Theorem 6.13, $c = \sqrt{2}a$. Substitute 6 for c and solve for a: $6 = \sqrt{2}a$ so that $a = \dfrac{6}{\sqrt{2}} = \dfrac{6\sqrt{2}}{\sqrt{2}\,\sqrt{2}} = \dfrac{6\sqrt{2}}{2} = 3\sqrt{2}$ yd.

25. By Theorem 6.13, $c = \sqrt{2}b$. Substitute $\dfrac{\sqrt{2}}{2}$ for c and solve for b: $\dfrac{\sqrt{2}}{2} = \sqrt{2}b$ so that $b = \dfrac{\sqrt{2}}{2} \cdot \dfrac{1}{\sqrt{2}} = \dfrac{1}{2}$ cm.

27. By Theorem 6.14, $b = \dfrac{1}{2}c$ so $10 = \dfrac{1}{2}c$ making $c = 20$ ft.

29. By Theorem 6.14, $b = \dfrac{1}{2}c$ so $b = \dfrac{1}{2}(16) = $
$= 8$ yd.

31. By Theorem 6.14, $a = \sqrt{3}b = \sqrt{3}(7) = 7\sqrt{3}$ cm.

33. By Theorem 6.14, $a = \sqrt{3}b$ so that $2\sqrt{3} = \sqrt{3}b$. Dividing both sides by $\sqrt{3}$ gives $b = 2$ ft.

35. By Theorem 6.14, $a = \dfrac{\sqrt{3}}{2}c = \dfrac{\sqrt{3}}{2}(\sqrt{3}) = \dfrac{\sqrt{3}\,\sqrt{3}}{2}$
$= \dfrac{3}{2}$ yd.

37. By Theorem 6.14, $a = \dfrac{\sqrt{3}}{2}c$. Thus, $\sqrt{3} = \dfrac{\sqrt{3}}{2}c$.
Multiply both sides by $\dfrac{2}{\sqrt{3}}$: $\dfrac{2}{\sqrt{3}}(\sqrt{3}) = c$.

Thus, $c = 2$ cm.

39. The diagonal, d, of a square with sides 4 inches long is the hypotenuse of a right triangle with legs 4 inches. By the Pythagorean theorem,
$$d^2 = 4^2 + 4^2 = 16 + 16 = 32$$
$$d = \pm\sqrt{32} = \pm\sqrt{16\cdot2} = \pm4\sqrt{2}$$

Discard the negative value $-4\sqrt{2}$. Thus, the diagonal is $4\sqrt{2}$ inches, approximately 5.66 inches, correct to the nearest hundredth.

41. Consider the figure to the right. Use the Pythagorean Theorem to find x.
$$x^2 + 6^2 = 18^2$$
$$x^2 + 36 = 324$$
$$x^2 = 288$$
$$x = \pm\sqrt{288} = \pm\sqrt{144\cdot2} = \pm12\sqrt{2}$$

Discard the negative value $-12\sqrt{2}$. Thus, the ladder will reach $12\sqrt{2}$ ft, approximately 17.0 ft, up the side of the building.

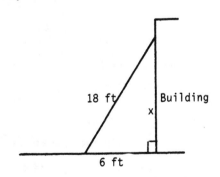

18 ft   Building

x

6 ft

43. Consider the figure to the right.

Since the triangle formed is a 30°-60°-right triangle, the side opposite the 30°-angle, x, is given in terms of the side opposite the 60°-angle by

$$400 = \sqrt{3}x.$$

Divide both sides by $\sqrt{3}$.

$$x = \frac{400}{\sqrt{3}} = \frac{400\sqrt{3}}{\sqrt{3}\,\sqrt{3}} = \frac{400\sqrt{3}}{3} \approx 230.94011$$

Thus, to the nearest tenth of a foot, the wire is 230.9 ft from the base of the tower.

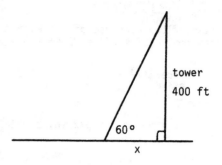

45. Consider the equilateral triangle with sides 10 ft shown to the right. Each angle measures 60°. Draw an altitude from A to $\overline{BC}$. Then $\triangle ABD$ is a 30°-60°-right triangle. By Theorem 6.14, $AD = \sqrt{3}BD = \sqrt{3}(5) = 5\sqrt{3}$. Thus, the altitude of the triangle is $5\sqrt{3}$ ft (approximately 8.66 ft).

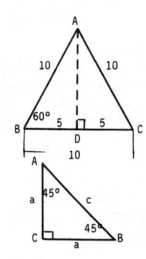

47. Given: $\triangle ABC$ is a 45°-45°-right triangle with legs of length a and hypotenuse of length c

Prove: $c = \sqrt{2}a$

Proof: STATEMENTS   REASONS

1. ABC is a 45°-45°-right triangle   1. Given
   with legs a and hypotenuse c

2. $a^2 + a^2 = c^2$ 2. Pythagorean theorem

3. $2a^2 = c^2$ 3. Distributive law

4. $\pm\sqrt{2a^2} = c$ 4. Take square root both sides

5. $\pm\sqrt{2}a = c$ 5. $\sqrt{a^2} = a$

6. $c = \sqrt{2}a$ 6. The length c cannot be negative

49. Find the length of diagonal d in the cube with sides x shown to the right. First draw diagonal of the base y. Then y can be found by the Pythagorean theorem.

$$x^2 + x^2 = y^2$$
$$2x^2 = y^2$$
$$\sqrt{2}x = y$$

Now find d using the Pythagorean theorem again.

$$x^2 + y^2 = d^2$$
$$x^2 + (\sqrt{2}x)^2 = d^2$$
$$x^2 + 2x^2 = d^2$$
$$3x^2 = d^2$$
$$\sqrt{3x^2} = d$$
$$\sqrt{3}x = d$$

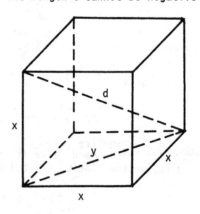

Note we only use the positive root in each case. Thus, diagonal d has length $\sqrt{3}x$ where x is the length of each side of the cube.

51. $\sqrt{3}$ times the length of the original segment. The process can be continued to find a segment $\sqrt{n}$ times the length of the original segment for n = 2, 3, 4, 5, ...

53. The quadrilateral is clearly a rhombus, and show it contains a right angle by showing the angle is the supplement of the angle formed by adding the two acute angles of the right triangle.

55. (a) Show ∠DAB is a right angle by an argument similar to that in Exercise 53.

(b) Use the formula for the area of a triangle three times.

(c) Show that $\overline{ED} \parallel \overline{CB}$ since each is $\perp$ to same line.

(d) Use the formula for the area of a trapezoid.

(e) When the two expressions are equated, the result simplifies to $a^2 + b^2 = c^2$.

Section 2.1
Exercises 2-2, page 57

1. 56°   **3.** 48°   **5.** 9.9 ft   **7.** 64.5 cm   **9.** 8.4 ft^2

11. 32,300 cm^2 **13.** 4.41 ft^2 **15.** 0.390 m^2

17. 26.6 ft   **19.** 52.2 cm   **21.** 67°   **23.** 227.2 cm

25. $\angle K = \angle N = 90°$; $\angle LMK = \angle OMN$;
$\angle KLM = \angle NOM$; $\triangle MKL \sim \triangle MNO$

27. 8   **29.** 71°   **31.** 148 ft^2 **33.** 60 ft^2 **35.** 930 m

37. 23 ft   **39.** 7.5 m, 9.0 m

Section 2.4
Exercises 2-3, page 61

1. 2.6 m   **3.** 167.8 in.   **5.** 12.8 m   **7.** 214.4 ft

9. 7.3 mm^2 **11.** 1740 in.^{2} **13.** 9.3 m^2 **15.** 2000 ft^2

17. $p = 4a + 2b$ **19.** $A = bh + a^2$ **21.** 12 cm

23. 6.30 ft^2 **25.** 344 m   **27.** 2.4 ft, 9.6 ft

Section 2.5
Exercises 2-4, page 64

1. (a) AD (b) AF **3.** (a) $AF \perp OE$ (b) $\triangle OEC$ **5.** 17.3 ft

7. 72.6 mm   **9.** 0.0285 yd^2 **11.** 4.26 m^2 **13.** 25°

15. 25°   **17.** 120°   **19.** 40°   **21.** 0.393 rad

23. 2.185 rad   **25.** $p = \frac{1}{2}\pi r + 2r$ **27.** $A = \frac{1}{4}\pi r^2 - \frac{1}{2}r^2$

29. 24,900 mi   **31.** 35.7 in.   **33.** 52.1 m^2

35. horizontally and opposite to original direction

Section 2.6
Exercises 2-5, page 68

1. 84 m^2 **3.** 4.9 ft^2 **5.** 9.8 mi^2 **7.** 19,000 km^2

9. 120,000 ft^2 **11.** 8100 ft^2

13. 2.73 in.^{2} The trapezoids are inside the boundary and do not
include some of the area.

15. 2.98 in.^{2} The ends of the areas are curved so that they can get
closer to the boundary.

Section 2.7
Exercises 2-6, page 71

1. 366 ft^3 **3.** 399 m^2 **5.** 2.83 yd^3 **7.** 20,500 cm^2

9. 1100 in.^{3} **11.** 3.358 m^2 **13.** 0.15 yd^3

15. 0.825 cm^2 **17.** 604 in.^{2}

19. 0.00034 mi$^3 = 5.0 \times 10^7$ ft^3 **21.** 3.3×10^6 yd^3

23. 2,350,000 ft^3 **25.** 1560 mm^2 **27.** 2.5 cm

Section 2.8
Review Exercises for Chapter 2, page 74

1. 32°   **3.** 32°   **5.** 41   **7.** 42   **9.** 7.36   **11.** 21.1

13. 25.5 mm   **15.** 3.06 ft^2 **17.** 309 mm   **19.** 2580 in.^{2}

21. 6190 cm^3 **23.** 160,000 ft^3 **25.** 162 m^2

27. 1230 in.^{2} **29.** 25°   **31.** 65°   **33.** 53°   **35.** 2.4

37. $p = \pi a + b + \sqrt{4a^2 + b^2}$ **39.** $A = ab + \frac{1}{2}\pi a^2$

41. yes   **43.** n^2; $A = \pi(nr)^2 = n^2(\pi r^2)$ **45.** 7.9 m

47. 30 m   **49.** 215 ft^2 **51.** 3.73 mi   **53.** 26,200 mi

55. 30 ft^2 **57.** 1.0×10^6 m^2 **59.** 190 m^3 **61.** 4.4 mi

63. 233 gal

Part 2

GEOMETRY

Section 2.1

2.2 Triangles

1. $\angle A = 180° - 84° - 40° = 56°$

5. $p = 3.5 + 2.3 + 4.1 = 9.9$ ft

9. $A = \frac{1}{2}bh = \frac{1}{2}(7.6)(2.2) = 8.4$ ft^2

13. $A = \frac{1}{2}bh = \frac{1}{2}(3.46)(2.55) = 4.41$ ft^2

17. $c = \sqrt{13.8^2 + 22.7^2} = 26.6$ ft

21. $\angle B = 90° - 23° = 67°$

25. $\angle LMK$ and $\angle OMN$ are vertical angles and thus equal $\Rightarrow \angle KLM = \angle MON$. The corresponding angles are equal and the triangles are similar.

29. Each base angle is $\dfrac{180° - 38°}{2} = 71°$

33. $A = \frac{1}{2}bh = \frac{1}{2}(8.0)(15) = 60$ ft^2

37. $d = \sqrt{18^2 + 12^2 + (8.0)^2} = 23$ ft

Section 2.4

2.3 Quadrilaterals

1. $p = 4s = 4(0.65) = 2.6$ m

5. $p = 2\ell + 2w = 2(3.7) + 2(2.7) = 12.8 = 13$ m to two significant digits

9. $A = s^2 = 2.7^2 = 7.3$ mm^2

13. $A = bh = 3.7(2.5) = 9.3$ m^2

17. $p = 2b + 4a$

21. $p = 6(2) = 12$ cm

25. For the courtyard: $s = \dfrac{p}{4} = \dfrac{320}{4} = 80$. For the outer edge of the walkway:

$p = 4s = 4(80 + 6) = 344$ m.

Section 2.5

2.4 Circles

1. (a) AD is a secant line.   **(b)** AEF is a tangent line.

5. $c = 2\pi r = 2\pi(2.75) = 17.3$ ft   **9.** $A = \pi r^2 = \pi(0.0952^2) = 0.0285$ yd^2

13. $\angle CBT = 90° - \angle ABC = 90° - 65° = 25°$

17. ARC BC $= 2(60°) = 120°$ **21.** $22.5° \left(\dfrac{\pi}{180°}\right) = 0.393$ rad

25. $P = \dfrac{1}{4}(2\pi r) + 2r = \dfrac{\pi r}{2} + 2r$ **29.** $C = 2\pi r = 2\pi \cdot 3960 = 24{,}900$ mi

33. $A = 2\left(\dfrac{\pi D^2}{4}\right) + s^2 = \dfrac{\pi(4.50^2)}{2} + 4.50^2 = 52.1$ m^2

Section 2.6

2.5 Measurement of Irregular Areas

1. $A_{\text{trap}} = \dfrac{2.0}{2}[0.0 + 2(6.4) + 2(7.4) + 2(7.0) + 2(6.1) + 2(5.2) + 2(5.0) + 2(5.1) + 0.0]$

$A_{\text{trap}} = 84.4 = 84$ m^2 to two significant digits

5. $A_{\text{trap}} = \dfrac{0.5}{2}[0.6 + 2(2.2) + 2(4.7) + 2(3.1) + 2(3.6) + 2(1.6) + 2(2.2) + 2(1.5) + 0.8]$

$A_{\text{trap}} = 9.8$ mi^2

9. $A_{\text{trap}} = \dfrac{45}{2}[170 + 2(360) + 2(420) + 2(410) + 2(390) + 2(350) + 2(330) + 2(290) + 230]$

$A_{\text{trap}} = 120{,}000$ ft^2

13. $A_{\text{trap}} = \dfrac{0.500}{2}[0.0 + 2(1.732) + 2(2.000) + 2(1.732) + 0.0] = 2.73$ in^2

This value is less than 3.14 in^2 because all of the trapezoids are inscribed.

Section 2.7

2.6 Solid Geometric Figures

1. $V = e^3 = 7.15^3 = 366$ ft^3 **5.** $V = \dfrac{4}{3}\pi r^3 = \dfrac{4}{3}\pi(0.877^3) = 2.83$ yd^3

9. $V = \dfrac{1}{3}Bh = \dfrac{1}{3}(16^2)(13) = 1100$ in^3 **13.** $V = \dfrac{1}{2}\left(\dfrac{4}{3}\pi r^3\right) = \dfrac{2}{3}\pi\left(\dfrac{0.83}{2}\right)^3 = 0.15$ yd^3

17. $A = 2\ell h + 2\ell w + 2wh = 2(12.0)(8.75) + 2(12.0)(9.50) + 2(9.50)(8.75)$
$A = 604$ in^2

21. $V = \frac{1}{3}BH = \frac{1}{3}(250^2)(160) = 3,300,000 \text{ yd}^3$

25. $A = l^2 + \frac{1}{2}ps = 16.0^2 + \frac{1}{2}(4)(16)\sqrt{8.0^2 + 40.0^2} = 1560 \text{ mm}^2$

Section 2.8

Chapter 2 Review Exercises

1. $\angle CGE = 180° - 148° = 32°$

5. $c = \sqrt{9^2 + 40^2} = 41$

9. $c = \sqrt{6.30^2 + 3.80^2} = 7.36$

13. $P = 3s = 3(8.5) = 25.5 \text{ mm}$

17. $C = \pi d = \pi(98.4) = 309 \text{ mm}$

21. $V = Bh = \frac{1}{2}(26.0)(34.0)(14.0) = 6190 \text{ cm}^3$

25. $A = 6e^2 = 6(5.20^2) = 162 \text{ m}^2$

29. $\angle BTA = \frac{50°}{2} = 25°$

33. $\angle ABE = 90° - 37° = 53°$

37. $P = b + \sqrt{b^2 + (2a)^2} + \frac{1}{2}\pi(2a) = b + \sqrt{b^2 + 4a^2} + \pi a$

41. A square is a rectangle with four equal sides and a rectangle is a parallelogram with perpendicular intersecting sides so a square is a parallelogram. A rhombus is a parallelogram with four equal sides and since a square is a parallelogram, a square is a rhombus.

45. $L = \sqrt{1.2^2 + 7.8^2} = 7.9 \text{ m}$

49. $s = \dfrac{18.0 + 15.5 + 7.50}{2} = 20.5, \quad A = \ell w + \sqrt{s(s-a)(s-b)(s-c)}$

$A = 18.0(8.75) + \sqrt{20.5(20.5 - 18.0)(20.5 - 15.5)(20.5 - 7.50)} = 215 \text{ ft}^2$

53. $c = \pi D = \pi(7920 + 2(210)) = 26{,}200 \text{ mi}$

57. $A = \dfrac{250}{3}[220 + 4(530) + 2(480) + 4(320 + 190 + 260) + 2(510) + 4(350) + 2(730) + 4(560) + 240]$

$A = 1{,}000{,}000 \text{ m}^2$

61. $d = \sqrt{2.4^2 + 3.7^2} = 4.4 \text{ mi}$

65. Label the vertices of the pentagon ABCDE. The area is the sum of the areas of three triangles, one with sides 921, 1490, and 1490 and two with sides 921, 921, and 1490. The semi-perimeters are given by

$$s_1 = \frac{921 + 921 + 1490}{2} = 1666 \text{ and } s_2 = \frac{921 + 1490 + 1490}{2} = 1950.5.$$

$A = 2\sqrt{1666(1666 - 921)(1666 - 921)(1666 - 1490)} + \sqrt{1950.5(1950.5 - 1490)(1950.5 - 1490)(1950.5 - 921)}$
$\quad = 1{,}460{,}000 \text{ ft}^2$

Part 2
Chapter 2

1. $\angle 1 + \angle 3 + 90° = 180°$ (sum of angles of a triangle)
$\angle 3 = 52°$ (vertical angles)
$\angle 1 = 180° - 90° - 52° = 38°$

2. $\angle 2 + \angle 4 = 180°$ (straight angle)
$\angle 4 = 52°$ (corresponding angles)
$\angle 2 + 52° = 180°$
$\angle 2 = 128°$

C-1

3.

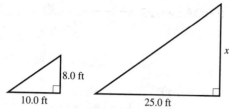

$$\frac{x}{8.0} = \frac{25.0}{10.0} \qquad x = \frac{8.0(25.0)}{10.0} = 20.0 \text{ ft}$$

4. Use Hero's formula:

$s = \frac{1}{2}(2.46 + 3.65 + 4.07) = 5.09$ cm

$A = \sqrt{5.09(5.09 - 2.46)(5.09 - 3.65)(5.09 - 4.07)}$

$\quad = 4.43$ cm^2

5. $d^2 = 12.5^2 + 17.0^2$

$\quad d = \sqrt{12.5^2 + 17.0^2}$

$\quad\quad = 21.1$ ft

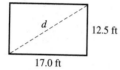

6. $\quad c = 2\pi r \qquad A = 4\pi r^2$

$\quad 21.0 = 2\pi r$

$\quad\quad r = \dfrac{10.5}{\pi} \qquad = 4\pi\left(\dfrac{10.5}{\pi}\right)^2 = \dfrac{4(10.5^2)}{\pi}$

$\quad\quad\quad\quad\quad\quad = 140$ cm^2

7. $V = \frac{1}{3}\pi r^2 h = \frac{1}{3}\pi(2.08^2)(1.78)$

$\quad\quad = 8.06$ m^3

8. $\angle ACO + 64° = 90°$ (tangent perpendicular to radius)

$\quad\quad \angle ACO = 26°$

$\quad\quad\quad \angle A = \angle ACO = 26°$ (isosceles triangle)

$\quad\quad\quad \frac{1}{2}\overset{\frown}{CD} = 26°$ (intercepted arc)

$\quad\quad\quad \overset{\frown}{CD} = 52°$

$\quad\quad\quad \angle 1 = 52°$ (central angle)

9. $\angle CBO + \angle 1 + 90° = 180°$ (sum of angles of triangle)

$\quad \angle CBO + 52° + 90° = 180°$

$\quad\quad\quad\quad \angle CBO = 180° - 52° - 90° = 38°$

$\quad\quad \angle 2 + \angle CBO = 180°$ (straight angle)

$\quad\quad \angle 2 + 38° = 180°$

$\quad\quad\quad\quad \angle 2 = 142°$

10. $r = \frac{1}{2}(2.25)$ cm

$\quad p = 3(2.25) + \frac{1}{2}(2\pi)\left[\frac{1}{2}(2.25)\right]$

$\quad\quad = 10.3$ cm

2.25 cm

11. $A = 2.25^2 - \frac{1}{2}\pi[\frac{1}{2}(2.25)]^2 = 3.07$ cm^2

12. $A = \frac{1}{2}(50)[0 + 2(90) + 2(145) + 2(260)$

$\quad\quad + 2(205) + 2(110) + 20]$

$\quad\quad = 41,000$ ft^2

PART 3 – CIRCLES

7

CIRCLES

In this chapter we study properties of a circle and the arcs, lines, and angles associated with a circle. We'll also consider regular polygons as they are inscribed in and circumscribed around circles.

The circle is frequently used in architecture and design because of its symmetric properties. Other applications of circles are found in science and engineering, including the one given below which is solved in Section 7.3, Example 1.

Assume that a cross section of the earth is a circle with radius 4000 mi. If a communications satellite is in orbit 110 mi above the surface of the earth, what is the approximate distance from the satellite to the horizon, the farthest point that can be seen on the surface of the earth?

230

Section 3.1

7.1 CIRCLES AND ARCS

One of the most familiar of all geometric figures is the *circle*. We'll begin by reviewing a few familiar terms and introducing some new ones.

DEFINITION: CIRCLE

A **circle** is the set of all points in a plane that are located a fixed distance from a fixed point called its **center.** A line segment joining the center of a circle to one of its points is called the **radius** of the circle.

Figure 7.1 shows a circle with center O and radius $\overline{OP}$. Although the radius of a circle is a segment, it is common practice to call the radius the length of the segment and denote the radius by r. For example, if $OP = 5$ cm in Figure 7.1, we might say that the radius of the circle is $r = 5$ cm. The segment $\overline{QR}$ in Figure 7.1 passing through center O is called a **diameter** of the circle. We often use d to represent the diameter of a circle. In this case $d = QR$, and it follows that $QR = QO + OR = r + r = 2r$, which proves the following theorem.

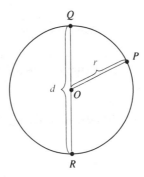

Figure 7.1

THEOREM 7.1

The diameter d of a circle is twice the radius r of the circle. That is, $d = 2r$.

The **circumference** of a circle is the distance around the circle (similar to the perimeter of a polygon). The ratio of the circumference C of any circle to its diameter d is the constant irrational number **pi,** denoted by π. Thus,

$$\pi = \frac{C}{d}.$$

We often approximate π using 3.14, but the actual value is the unending non-repeating decimal 3.14159265358. . . .

POSTULATE 7.1   CIRCUMFERENCE OF A CIRCLE

The circumference C of any circle with radius r and diameter d is determined with the formula $C = 2\pi r = \pi d$.

EXAMPLE 1   Find the circumference of a circle with radius 3.50 cm. Give an approximate value of the circumference, correct to the nearest hundredth of a centimeter, using $\pi \approx 3.14$.

Because $C = 2\pi r$, substituting 3.5 for r, we have $C = 2\pi(3.50) = 7\pi$ cm as the exact value of the circumference. Substituting 3.14 for π we find $C = 7\pi \approx 7(3.14) = 21.98$ cm.   ◨

NOTE: If you have a scientific calculator and use the $\boxed{\pi}$ key in your calculations, the answers shown on the display will not always be exactly the same as those for which you use 3.14 for π.   □

PRACTICE EXERCISE 1

What is the radius of a circle, correct to the nearest tenth of a foot, if the circumference is 23.0 ft?

The next postulate gives the formula for the area of a circle. Figure 7.2 helps to show why the formula is true.

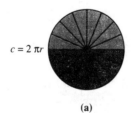
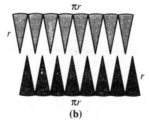
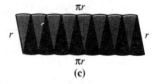

(a)   (b)   (c)

Figure 7.2

Suppose we cut the circle in Figure 7.2(a) along all the radii (plural of radius). When we place the top half of the circle above the bottom half as in Figure 7.2(b) and then slide them together as in Figure 7.2(c), the figure formed is approximately a parallelogram with height r. The length of the base of the "parallelogram" is πr because $2\pi r$ is the circumference, and half the circle is on the

top and half is on the bottom. Because the area of a parallelogram is determined with the formula $A = bh$, the area of the circle is

$$A = bh = (\pi r)(r) = \pi r^2.$$

POSTULATE 7.2   AREA OF A CIRCLE

The area of a circle with radius r is determined with the formula
$A = \pi r^2$.

EXAMPLE 2   In the machine part shown in Figure 7.3, each circular
hole has radius 3 cm. Using 3.14 for π, find the area of the remaining metal.

First find the area of the trapezoid.

$$\begin{aligned}
A &= \frac{1}{2}(b + b')h \\
&= \frac{1}{2}(16 + 24)(14) \\
&= \frac{1}{2}(40)(14) \\
&= (20)(14) = 280 \text{ cm}^2
\end{aligned}$$

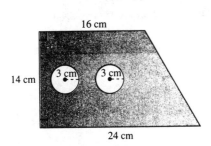

16 cm

14 cm   3 cm   3 cm

24 cm

Figure 7.3

Now find the area of each circular hole.

$$A = \pi r^2 \approx 3.14(3)^2 = (3.14)(9) = 28.3 \text{ cm}^2$$

Thus, the two circles have a combined area of

$$2(28.3) = 56.6 \text{ cm}^2.$$

The area of the remaining metal is the area of the trapezoid minus the area of
the circles, $280 - 56.6 = 223.4$. Thus, the remaining area is 223.4 cm². ◧

PRACTICE EXERCISE 2

A triangle with base 10 inches and height 5 inches has three holes drilled
through it, each with diameter 2 inches. What is the remaining area of
the triangle after the holes are drilled? Use 3.14 for π.

Recall that two geometric figures are congruent if they can be made to
coincide.

POSTULATE 7.3   CONGRUENT CIRCLES

If two circles are congruent, then their radii and diameters are equal.
Conversely, if the radii or diameters are equal, then two circles are
congruent.

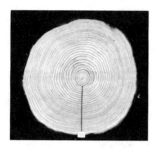

All circles are similar in shape, and thus there is no need for a formal definition of similarity. Circles that lie in the same plane and have a common center are called *concentric circles*. The concentric circles of tree rings are used by foresters to study the climate and the ecology of the region in which the tree grew.

NOTE: As we've seen in postulates and definitions, many times both the direct statement and its converse are true. By stating "if and only if," both statements can be made at the same time. For example, Postulate 7.3 could be written as follows: Two circles are congruent if and only if their radii or their diameters are equal.   □

The study of a circle's continuous parts reveals its many properties.

> ### DEFINITION: ARCS AND SEMICIRCLES
> An **arc** of a circle forms a continuous part of the circle. An arc of a circle whose endpoints are the endpoints of a diameter of the circle is called a **semicircle.** An arc that is longer than a semicircle is called a **major arc** of the circle, and an arc that is shorter than a semicircle is called a **minor arc** of the circle.

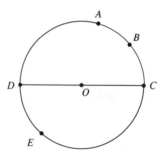

Figure 7.4   Arcs and Semicircles

Arcs of a circle can be named using three points on the arc. In Figure 7.4, minor arc ABC (shown in color), denoted by $\overset{\frown}{ABC}$ has endpoints A and C. Major arc $\overset{\frown}{ADC}$ has the same endpoints as minor arc $\overset{\frown}{ABC}$ (shown in black). If $\overline{DC}$ is a diameter of the circle, then $\overset{\frown}{DAC}$ and $\overset{\frown}{DEC}$ are both semicircles. If we use two letters to name an arc, such as $\overset{\frown}{AC}$, we always mean the minor arc with endpoints A and C. That is, $\overset{\frown}{AC} = \overset{\frown}{ABC}$ in Figure 7.4.

The next postulate is similar to Postulate 1.13 for segments.

> ### POSTULATE 7.4   ARC ADDITION POSTULATE
> Let A, B, and C be three points on the same circle with B between A and C. Then $\overset{\frown}{AC} = \overset{\frown}{AB} + \overset{\frown}{BC}$, $\overset{\frown}{BC} = \overset{\frown}{AC} - \overset{\frown}{AB}$, and $\overset{\frown}{AB} = \overset{\frown}{AC} - \overset{\frown}{BC}$.

Contrary to what we might expect, arcs are *not* measured using their length. Instead, the measure of an arc is given using an angle in a circle.

> **DEFINITION: CENTRAL ANGLE**
>
> An angle with sides that are radii of a circle and vertex the center of the circle is called a **central angle.**

Figure 7.5 shows central angle $\angle AOB$ that **intercepts** minor arc $\overarc{AB}$.

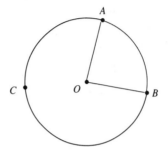

Figure 7.5   Central Angle $\angle AOB$

> **DEFINITION: MEASURE OF AN ARC**
>
> The **measure of an arc** is the number of degrees in the central angle that intercepts the arc.

If $\angle AOB = 84°$ in Figure 7.5, then the measure of $\overarc{AB}$ is $84°$. We often abbreviate this statement and simply say that $\overarc{AB} = 84°$. Because $360° - 84° = 276°$, the measure of $\overarc{ACB}$ is $276°$. Notice that every minor arc has a measure less than $180°$, every major arc has a measure greater than $180°$, and every semicircle has a measure equal to $180°$. Also, equal central angles intercept equal arcs.

> **DEFINITION: INSCRIBED ANGLE**
>
> An angle whose vertex is on a circle and whose sides intersect the circle in two other points is called an **inscribed angle.**

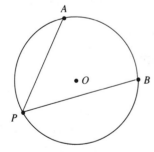

Figure 7.6   Inscribed Angle $\angle APB$

In Figure 7.6, $\angle APB$ is an inscribed angle in the circle with center O. We say that $\angle APB$ **intercepts** $\overarc{AB}$ and is **inscribed** in $\overarc{APB}$. The next theorem presents a property involving the measure of an inscribed angle.

THEOREM 7.2

The measure of an inscribed angle is one-half the measure of its intercepted arc.

The complete proof of Theorem 7.2 can be accomplished by considering three cases.

Case 1: The center of the circle is on one of the sides of the inscribed angle.

Case 2: The center of the circle is in the interior of the inscribed angle.

Case 3: The center of the circle is in the exterior of the inscribed angle.

We will prove the theorem for Case 1. Proofs of Cases 2 and 3 can be accomplished by constructing a line segment through the center of the circle and following the proof of Case 1. Proof of Case 1:

Given: Inscribed angle $\angle APB$ with O on $\overline{PB}$ (See Figure 7.7.)

Prove: $\angle APB = \frac{1}{2}\overarc{AB}$

Auxiliary line: Construct Segment $\overline{AO}$

Proof:

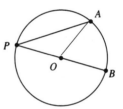

Figure 7.7

STATEMENTS	REASONS
1. O is on side $\overline{PB}$ of inscribed angle $\angle APB$	1. Given
2. $\angle AOB = \overarc{AB}$	2. Def. of measure of arc
3. $PO = AO$	3. Radii are equal
4. $\angle APB = \angle A$	4. $\angle$'s opp. = sides are =
5. $\angle APB + \angle A = \angle AOB$	5. Ext. $\angle$ = sum of nonadj. int. $\angle$'s
6. $\angle APB + \angle APB = \angle AOB$	6. Substitution law
7. $2\angle APB = \angle AOB$	7. Distributive law
8. $\angle APB = \frac{1}{2}\angle AOB$	8. Mult.-div. law
9. $\angle APB = \frac{1}{2}\overarc{AB}$	9. Substitution law

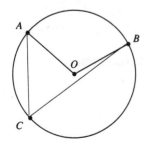

Figure 7.8

EXAMPLE 3   In Figure 7.8, assume that $\angle AOB = 116°$. What is the measure of $\angle ACB$?

Because central angle $\angle AOB = 116°$, $\overarc{AB} = 116°$. With inscribed angle $\angle ACB$ intercepting $\overarc{AB}$, its measure is one-half the measure of $\overarc{AB}$. Thus,

$$\angle ACB = \frac{1}{2}\overarc{AB} = \frac{1}{2}(116°) = 58°. \quad \blacksquare$$

To find the center of a given circle, a student places a sheet of paper with one corner on the circle at point *P*, locates points *Q* and *R*, and draws chord *QR*.

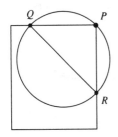

She then places the paper so that the corner is on another point *S* on the circle, locates points *T* and *V*, and draws chord *TV*.

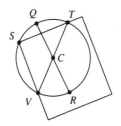

The point of intersection of $\overline{QR}$ and *TV*, *C*, is the center of the circle. Can you explain why this procedure works?

PRACTICE EXERCISE 3

Assume that $\angle ACB = 60°$ in Figure 7.8. What is the measure of $\overset{\frown}{AB}$? What is the measure of $\overset{\frown}{ACB}$?

Theorem 7.2 has two useful corollaries.

COROLLARY 7.3

Inscribed angles that intercept the same or equal arcs are equal.

COROLLARY 7.4

Every angle inscribed in a semicircle is a right angle.

EXAMPLE 4   Use Figure 7.9 to answer the following.

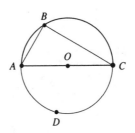

Figure 7.9

(a) What is the measure of $\overset{\frown}{ADC}$?
Because $\overset{\frown}{ADC}$ is a semicircle, $\overset{\frown}{ADC} = 180°$

(b) What is the measure of $\angle ABC$?
Because $\angle ABC$ is inscribed in semicircle $\overset{\frown}{ABC}$, $\angle ABC$ is a right angle so, $\angle ABC = 90°$. ◪

ANSWERS TO PRACTICE EXERCISES: **1.** 3.7 ft   **2.** 15.6 in²   **3.** $\overset{\frown}{AB} = 120°$; $\overset{\frown}{ACB} = 240°$

7.1 EXERCISES

In Exercises 1–4, find the diameter of each circle with the given radius.

1. $r = 11$ in   **2.** $r = 5.8$ cm   **3.** $r = \dfrac{3}{4}$ ft   **4.** $r = 13.25$ yd

In Exercises 5–8, find the radius of each circle with the given diameter.

5. $d = 16$ in   **6.** $d = 4.8$ cm   **7.** $d = \dfrac{2}{3}$ ft   **8.** $d = 22.42$ yd

In Exercises 9–12, find the circumference and area of each circle with the given radius or diameter. Leave the answer in terms of π.

9. $r = 7$ yd   **10.** $r = 6.2$ mi   **11.** $d = \dfrac{4}{3}$ cm   **12.** $d = 12.78$ ft

In Exercises 13–16, find the approximate circumference and area of each circle with the given radius or diameter by using 3.14 for π.

13. $r = 4.10$ ft   **14.** $r = \dfrac{3}{4}$ cm   **15.** $d = 12.00$ mi   **16.** $d = 18.36$ yd

17. How much more cross-sectional area is there for water to pass through in a $\dfrac{3}{4}$-inch diameter water hose than there is in a $\dfrac{1}{2}$-inch diameter water hose? Use 3.14 for π.

18. A circular garden has radius 9 m. If a 1-meter-wide circular walk surrounds it, what is the area of the walk? Use 3.14 for π. [Hint: Find the area of a circle with 10-meter radius and subtract the area of the garden.]

19. A 12-inch diameter pizza costs $4.50. A 16-inch diameter pizza costs $7.50. Which pizza costs less per square inch? Use 3.14 for π.

20. A patio is in the shape of a trapezoid with bases 8.1 yd and 6.7 yd and height 5.8 yd. A circular dining area in the center of the patio has diameter 3.2 yd and is covered with Mexican tile. Assuming no waste, how much will it cost to the nearest dollar, to cover the remainder of the patio with outdoor carpeting that costs $18.50 per square yard? Use 3.14 for π.

In Exercises 21–24, find the area of metal remaining on each machine part with circular holes drilled in it. Use 3.14 for π.

21.

22 mm

22.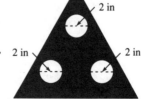

2 in

2 in   2 in

9 in

23.

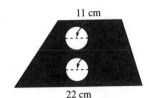

11 cm

22 cm

24.

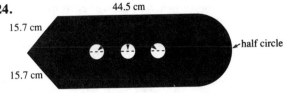

44.5 cm

15.7 cm

15.7 cm

half circle

25. Use the figure below to answer each question.
  (a) What is ∠*AOC* called with respect to the circle?
  (b) What is ∠*ABC* called with respect to the circle?
  (c) What is the measure of $\overset{\frown}{AC}$?
  (d) What is the measure of $\overset{\frown}{ABC}$?
  (e) What is the measure of ∠*ABC*?
  (f) What is the measure of the arc intercepted by ∠*ABC*?

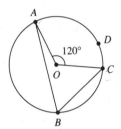

Exercise 25

26. Use the figure below to answer each question.
  (a) What is ∠*AOC* called with respect to the circle?
  (b) What is ∠*ABC* called with respect to the circle?
  (c) What is the measure of ∠*AOC*?
  (d) What is the measure of $\overset{\frown}{AC}$?
  (e) What is the measure of $\overset{\frown}{ABC}$?
  (f) What is the measure of the arc intercepted by ∠*ABC*?

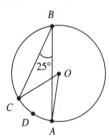

Exercise 26

27. Use the figure below to answer each question.
    (a) What is the measure of $\overset{\frown}{ADC}$?
    (b) What is the measure of $\overset{\frown}{ABC}$?
    (c) What is the measure of $\angle AOC$?
    (d) What is the measure of $\angle AEC$?

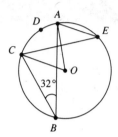

Exercise 27

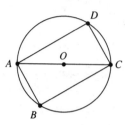

Exercise 28

28. Use the figure above to answer each question.
    (a) What is the measure of $\angle AOC$?
    (b) What is the measure of $\overset{\frown}{ABC}$?
    (c) What is the measure of $\angle ABC$?
    (d) What is the measure of $\angle ADC$?

29. *Given:* $\overline{AB} \perp \overline{BC}$
    Prove: $\overset{\frown}{ADC} = 180°$

30. *Given:* $\overline{AB} \parallel \overline{CD}$
    Prove: $\overset{\frown}{AC} = \overset{\frown}{BD}$
    [Hint: Draw auxiliary segment $\overline{AD}$.]

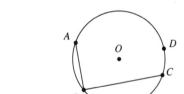

Exercise 29

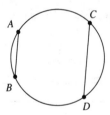

Exercise 30

31. *Given:* $\overline{AB}$ is a diameter
    $\overline{AC} \parallel \overline{OD}$
    Prove: $\overset{\frown}{BD} = \overset{\frown}{DC}$

32. *Given:* $\overline{AB}$ is a diameter
    $\overline{CD} \perp \overline{AB}$
    Prove: $(CD)^2 = (AD)(DB)$

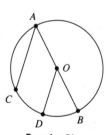

Exercise 31

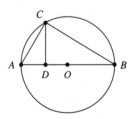

Exercise 32

In Exercises 33–34, assume that the earth is 93,000,000 miles from the sun and that the orbit of the earth is a circle. Use 3.14 for π.

33. What distance does the earth travel during one year?

34. What distance does the earth travel during one day? [*Note:* Use 365 days in a year.]

35. What distance does the earth travel during one minute?

Section 3.2

7.2 CHORDS AND SECANTS

In Section 7.1 we studied some of the properties of radii and diameters of a circle. Now we'll examine several properties of other segments and lines relative to a circle.

DEFINITION: CHORD

A line segment joining two distinct points on a circle is called a **chord** of the circle.

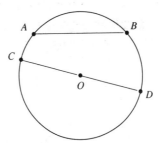

Figure 7.10   Chords of a Circle

In Figure 7.10, $\overline{AB}$ is a chord of the circle centered at point O. Notice that diameter $\overline{CD}$ is a special chord that passes through the center O. We say that minor arc $\overset{\frown}{AB}$ is the arc formed by chord $\overline{AB}$.

THEOREM 7.5

When two chords of a circle intersect, each angle formed is equal to one-half the sum of its intercepted arc and the arc intercepted by its vertical angle.

The Greek astronomer Eratosthenes (about 276–192 B.C.) was first to calculate the circumference of the earth. In the third century B.C., he accomplished this amazing feat by assuming that the earth was a sphere and that the sun's rays were parallel lines. His approximation for the earth's circumference was extremely close to the accepted value determined by sophisticated modern technology.

Given: Chords $\overline{AB}$ and $\overline{CD}$ that intersect at point P (See Figure 7.11.)

Prove: $\angle 1 = \frac{1}{2}(\widehat{BC} + \widehat{AD})$

Auxiliary line: Construct segment $\overline{AC}$

Proof:

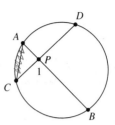

Figure 7.11

STATEMENTS	REASONS
1. Chords $\overline{AB}$ and $\overline{CD}$ intersect at point P	1. Given
2. $\angle CAB = \frac{1}{2}\widehat{BC}$ and $\angle ACD = \frac{1}{2}\widehat{AD}$	2. Inscribed $\angle$'s have meas. = to $\frac{1}{2}$ intercepted arc
3. $\angle 1 = \angle CAB + \angle ACD$	3. Ext. $\angle$ of $\triangle$ = sum nonadj. int. $\angle$'s
4. $\angle 1 = \frac{1}{2}\widehat{BC} + \frac{1}{2}\widehat{AD}$	4. Substitution law
5. $\angle 1 = \frac{1}{2}(\widehat{BC} + \widehat{AD})$	5. Distributive law

EXAMPLE 1 In Figure 7.12, assume that $\widehat{AC} = 30°$ and $\widehat{DB} = 52°$. Find the measure of $\angle 1$.

By Theorem 7.5,

$$\angle 1 = \frac{1}{2}(\widehat{AC} + \widehat{BD})$$
$$= \frac{1}{2}(30° + 52°)$$
$$= \frac{1}{2}(82°) = 41°. \quad \blacksquare$$

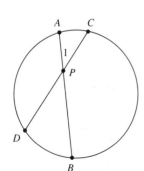

Figure 7.12

PRACTICE EXERCISE 1

In Figure 7.12, assume that $\widehat{AD} = 112°$ and $\widehat{BC} = 176°$. Find the measure of $\angle 1$.

THEOREM 7.6
In the same circle, the arcs formed by equal chords are equal.

Given: $\overline{AB}$ and $\overline{CD}$ are chords with
   $AB = CD$ (See Figure 7.13.)

Prove: $\overset{\frown}{AB} = \overset{\frown}{CD}$

Auxiliary lines: Construct radii $\overline{AO}$,
   $\overline{BO}$, $\overline{CO}$ and $\overline{DO}$

Proof:

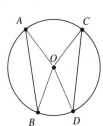

Figure 7.13

STATEMENTS	REASONS
1. $\overline{AB}$ and $\overline{CD}$ are chords with $AB = CD$	1. Given
2. $\overline{AO}$, $\overline{BO}$, $\overline{CO}$, and $\overline{DO}$ are radii	2. By construction
3. $AO = BO = CO = DO$	3. Radii are =
4. $\triangle AOB \cong \triangle COD$	4. SSS = SSS
5. $\angle AOB = \angle COD$	5. cpoctae
6. $\overset{\frown}{AB} = \overset{\frown}{CD}$	6. Def. of measure of an arc

The converse of Theorem 7.6 is also true, and its proof is requested in the exercises.

THEOREM 7.7

In the same circle, the chords formed by equal arcs are equal.

DEFINITION: BISECTOR OF AN ARC

A line that divides an arc into two arcs with the same measure is called a **bisector** of the arc.

THEOREM 7.8

A line drawn from the center of a circle perpendicular to a chord bisects the chord and the arc formed by the chord.

Given: Chord $\overline{AB}$ with $\overline{OD} \perp \overline{AB}$
   (See Figure 7.14.)

Prove: $AD = DB$ and $\overset{\frown}{AC} = \overset{\frown}{CB}$

Auxiliary lines: Construct radii $\overline{OA}$
   and $\overline{OB}$

Proof:

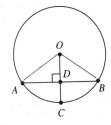

Figure 7.14

STATEMENTS	REASONS
1. $\overline{AB}$ is a chord with $\overline{OD} \perp \overline{AB}$	1. Given
2. $OA = OB$	2. Radii are =

3. $OD = OD$	3. Reflexive law
4. $\triangle ADO \cong \triangle BDO$	4. HL = HL
5. $AD = DB$	5. cpoctae
6. $\angle AOC = \angle BOC$	6. cpoctae
7. $\overarc{AC} = \overarc{CB}$	7. Def. of measure of an arc

The converse of Theorem 7.8 is also true.

THEOREM 7.9

A line drawn from the center of a circle to the midpoint of a chord (not a diameter) or to the midpoint of the arc formed by the chord is perpendicular to the chord.

The proof of Theorem 7.9 is requested in the exercises.

EXAMPLE 2 In Figure 7.15, $AB = 14$ cm, $ED = 7$ cm, and $\overarc{AB} = 84°$. Find CE and $\overarc{FD}$.

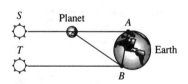

When an object is seen from two different positions, it seems to change location. The change is called *parallax*. Astronomers calculate the distance to a planet or star by using information resulting from the parallax. When a planet is viewed from two points on earth, from *A* it appears in line with star *S*, but from *B* it is not. By measuring various angles in this figure, an astronomer can approximate the distance to the planet.

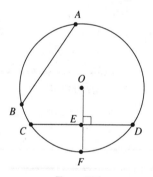

Figure 7.15

Because $\overline{OE} \perp \overline{CD}$, $\overline{OE}$ bisects chord $\overline{CD}$ and arc $\overarc{CD}$ by Theorem 7.8. Then $CE = ED$, so $CE = 7$ cm. Because chords $\overline{AB}$ and $\overline{CD}$ are both 14 cm in length, by Theorem 7.6 $\overarc{AB} = \overarc{CD} = 84°$. Then $\overarc{FD}$ is one-half of $\overarc{CD}$, so $\overarc{FD} = 42°$. ∎

THEOREM 7.10

In the same circle, equal chords are equidistant from the center of the circle.

Given: Chords $\overline{AB}$ and $\overline{CD}$ with
$AB = CD$ (See Figure 7.16.)

Auxiliary lines: Construct $\overline{OE} \perp \overline{AB}$,
$\overline{OF} \perp \overline{CD}$, and radii $\overline{AO}$ and $\overline{CO}$

Prove: $OE = OF$

Proof:

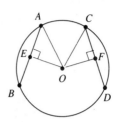

Figure 7.16

STATEMENTS	REASONS
1. $\overline{AB}$ and $\overline{CD}$ are chords with $AB = CD$	1. Given
2. $\overline{OE} \perp \overline{AB}$, $\overline{OF} \perp \overline{CD}$, and $\overline{AO}$ and $\overline{CO}$ are radii	2. By construction
3. $AO = CO$	3. Radii are equal
4. $AE = EB$ and $CF = FD$	4. Line from center $\perp$ chord bisects the chord
5. $AB = AE + EB$ and $CD = CF + FD$	5. Seg. add. post.
6. $AB = 2AE$ and $CD = 2CF$	6. Substitution and distributive laws
7. $AE = CF$	7. Substitution and mult.-div. law
8. $\triangle AEO \cong \triangle CFO$	8. HL = HL
9. $OE = OF$	9. cpoctae

The converse of Theorem 7.10 is also true, and its proof is requested in the exercises.

THEOREM 7.11

In the same circle, chords equidistant from the center of the circle are equal.

EXAMPLE 3 In Figure 7.17, $CF = 5$ ft, $OE = 7$ ft, and $AB = 10$ ft. Find OF.

Because $\overline{OF} \perp \overline{CD}$, F is the midpoint of $\overline{CD}$. Thus $CF = FD = 5$ ft making $CD = 10$ ft. Because $AB = 10$ ft, $CD = AB$, and by Theorem 7.10, $OE = OF$. Thus, $OF = 7$ ft. ▰

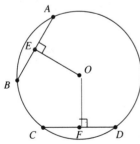

Figure 7.17

THEOREM 7.12

The perpendicular bisector of a chord passes through the center of the circle.

PRACTICE EXERCISE 2

Complete the proof of Theorem 7.12.

Given: $\overline{CE}$ is the perpendicular bisector of chord $\overline{AB}$

Prove: $\overline{CE}$ passes through O

Auxiliary line: Construct radii $\overline{AO}$ and $\overline{BO}$

Proof:

STATEMENTS	REASONS
1. $\overline{CE} \perp \overline{AB}$ and $AE = EB$	1. _____
2. _____	2. Radii are $=$
3. $\triangle AOB$ is isosceles	3. _____
4. _____	4. Def. of base of isos. $\triangle$
5. _____	5. $\perp$ bisector of base of isos. $\triangle$ passes through vertex

The next example shows how Theorem 7.12 can be used to determine the center of a given arc or circle.

EXAMPLE 4 A curve in a highway has the shape of an arc of a circle as shown in Figure 7.18. Explain how to find the center of this arc (the center of the circle that contains the arc).

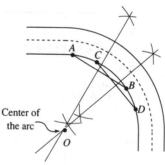

Figure 7.18

Select two points A and B on the arc and construct the perpendicular bisector of $\overline{AB}$. Now select two other points C and D on the arc and construct the perpendicular bisector of $\overline{CD}$. Because both of these bisectors pass through the center of the circle by Theorem 7.12, the point at which they intersect must be the center of the circle, hence the center of the arc. ∎

NOTE: All theorems considered thus far in this section are true for congruent circles as well as for the same circle. □

We can use similar triangles to prove a property of chords that intersect inside a circle.

THEOREM 7.13

If two chords intersect inside a circle, the product of the lengths of the segments of one chord is equal to the product of the lengths of the segments of the other.

Given: Chords $\overline{AB}$ and $\overline{CD}$ that intersect at point P
(See Figure 7.19.)

Prove: $(AP)(PB) = (CP)(PD)$

Auxiliary lines: Construct $\overline{AC}$ and $\overline{BD}$

Proof:

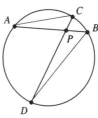

Figure 7.19

STATEMENTS	REASONS
1. Chords $\overline{AB}$ and $\overline{CD}$ intersect at P	1. Given
2. $\overline{AC}$ and $\overline{BD}$ are chords	2. By construction
3. $\angle A = \angle D$ and $\angle C = \angle B$	3. Inscribed angles intercepting $=$ arcs are $=$
4. $\triangle APC \sim \triangle BPD$	4. AA $\sim$ AA
5. $\dfrac{AP}{PD} = \dfrac{CP}{PB}$	5. Corr. sides of $\sim$ $\triangle$'s are proportional
6. $(AP)(PB) = (CP)(PD)$	6. Means-extremes prop.

PRACTICE EXERCISE 3

Refer to Figure 7.19 in which $AP = 3$ cm, $CP = 4$ cm, and $PD = 6$ cm. Find PB.

A line and a circle in the same plane can intersect in one or two points or none at all. Lines that intersect a circle in two points have several important properties.

DEFINITION: SECANT

If a line intersects a circle in two points, the line is called a **secant.**

Line ℓ in Figure 7.20 is a secant that intersects the circle in points A and B. Notice that this secant determines chord $\overline{AB}$. All secants determine a chord. The next theorem gives a relationship between two secants and arcs on the circle.

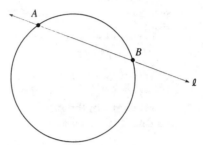

Figure 7.20   Secant

THEOREM 7.14

If two secants intersect forming an angle outside the circle, then the measure of this angle is one-half the difference of the intercepted arcs.

Given: Secants $\overleftrightarrow{PA}$ and $\overleftrightarrow{PB}$ forming exterior angle $\angle APB$ (See Figure 7.21.)

Prove: $\angle APB = \dfrac{1}{2}(\widehat{AB} - \widehat{CD})$

Auxiliary line: Construct $\overline{BC}$

Proof:

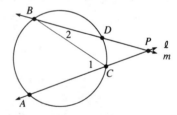

Figure 7.21

STATEMENTS	REASONS
1. Secants $\overleftrightarrow{PA}$ and $\overleftrightarrow{PB}$ forming $\angle APB$	1. Given
2. $\angle 1 = \angle 2 + \angle APB$	2. Ext $\angle$ of $\triangle$ = sum of remote int. $\angle$'s
3. $\angle APB = \angle 1 - \angle 2$	3. Add.-subtr. law
4. $\angle 1 = \dfrac{1}{2}\widehat{AB}$ and $\angle 2 = \dfrac{1}{2}\widehat{CD}$	4. Inscribed $\angle = \dfrac{1}{2}$ meas. of its intercepted arc
5. $\angle APB = \dfrac{1}{2}\widehat{AB} - \dfrac{1}{2}\widehat{CD}$	5. Substitution law
6. $\angle APB = \dfrac{1}{2}(\widehat{AB} - \widehat{CD})$	6. Distributive law

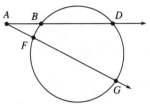

Figure 7.22

EXAMPLE 5 Refer to Figure 7.22. Assume that $\overset{\frown}{DG} = 110°$ and $\overset{\frown}{BF} = 40°$. Find $\angle A$.

By Theorem 7.14,

$$\angle A = \frac{1}{2}(\overset{\frown}{DG} - \overset{\frown}{BF})$$

$$= \frac{1}{2}(110° - 40°)$$

$$= \frac{1}{2}(70°) = 35° \quad \blacksquare$$

The next theorem is similar to Theorem 7.13.

THEOREM 7.15

If two secants are drawn to a circle from an external point, the product of the lengths of one secant segment and its external segment is equal to the product of the lengths of the other secant segment and its external segment.

Given: Secants $\overleftrightarrow{PA}$ and $\overleftrightarrow{PB}$
    PA and *PB* are the lengths of the two secant segments
    (See Figure 7.23.)

Prove: $(PA)(PC) = (PB)(PD)$

Auxiliary lines: Construct segments $\overline{AD}$ and $\overline{BC}$

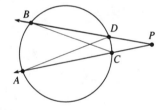

Figure 7.23

Proof:

STATEMENTS	REASONS
1. *PA* and *PB* are the lengths of the secant segments formed by secants $\overleftrightarrow{PA}$ and $\overleftrightarrow{PB}$	1. Given
2. $\angle DBC = \angle DAC$	2. Both inscribed $\angle$'s intercept same arc
3. $\angle P = \angle P$	3. Reflexive law
4. $\triangle APD \sim \triangle BPC$	4. AA $\sim$ AA
5. $\dfrac{PA}{PB} = \dfrac{PD}{PC}$	5. Corr. sides of $\sim \triangle$'s are proportional
6. $(PA)(PC) = (PB)(PD)$	6. Means-extremes prop.

EXAMPLE 6   In Figure 7.23 on page 249, assume that $BD = 8$ cm, $PD = 7$ cm, and $PC = 6$ cm. Find AC.

Let $x = AC$, then $PA = AC + PC = x + 6$. Also, $PB = BD + PD = 8 + 7 = 15$. Use Theorem 7.15 and substitute.

$$(PA)(PC) = (PB)(PD)$$
$$(x + 6)(6) = (15)(7)$$
$$6x + 36 = 105$$
$$6x = 69$$
$$x = 11.5$$

Thus, $AC = 11.5$ cm. ◪

ANSWERS TO PRACTICE EXERCISES: **1.** 36° **2.** 1. Given 2. $AO = BO$
3. Def. of isos. △ 4. $\overline{AB}$ is the base of $\triangle AOB$ 5. $\overline{CE}$ passes through O
3. 8 cm

7.2 EXERCISES

Exercises 1–10 refer to the figure below.

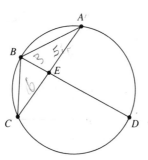

1. If $\overparen{AB} = 58°$ and $\overparen{CD} = 130°$, find $\angle AEB$.   **2.** If $\overparen{BC} = 64°$ and $\overparen{AD} = 120°$, find $\angle AED$.

3. If $AB = BC$ and $\overparen{BC} = 60°$, find $\overparen{AB}$.   **4.** If $\overparen{AB} = \overparen{BC}$ and $AB = 8$ cm, find BC.

5. If $\overline{BD}$ passes through the center of the circle and is perpendicular to $\overline{AC}$, and $AE = 12$ inches, find CE.

6. If $\overline{BD}$ passes through the center of the circle and is perpendicular to $\overline{AC}$, and $\overparen{AB} = 55°$, find $\overparen{BC}$.

7. If $\overline{BD}$ passes through the center of the circle, $AE = 5$ ft, and $CE = 5$ ft, find $\angle AED$.

8. If $\overline{BD}$ passes through the center of the circle, $\overparen{AB} = 63°$, and $\overparen{BC} = 63°$, find $\angle DEC$.

9. If $AE = 5$ cm, $EC = 6$ cm, and $BE = 3$ cm, find ED.

10. If $BE = 4$ ft, $ED = 6$ ft, and $AE = 3$ ft, find CE.

Exercises 11–16 refer to the figure below in which O is the center of the circle.

11. If $AB = 14$ ft, $CD = 14$ ft, and $OF = 11$ ft, find OE.

12. If $OE = 7$ cm, $OF = 7$ cm, and $AB = 9$ cm, find CD.

13. If $AE = 4$ cm, $OE = 5$ cm, and $OF = 5$ cm, find DF.

14. If $OE = 6$ ft, $OF = 6$ ft, and $\overset{\frown}{AGB} = 60°$, find $\overset{\frown}{CHD}$.

15. If $\overset{\frown}{AGB} = \overset{\frown}{DHC}$ and $OE = 15$ cm, find OF.

16. If $\overset{\frown}{AG} = \overset{\frown}{HC}$ and $OF = 9$ inches, find OE.

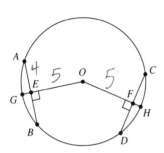

Exercises 11–16

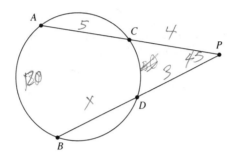

Exercises 17–24

Exercises 17–24 refer to the figure above.

17. If $\overset{\frown}{AB} = 130°$ and $\overset{\frown}{CD} = 50°$, find $\angle P$.

18. If $\overset{\frown}{AB} = 125°$ and $\overset{\frown}{CD} = 47°$, find $\angle P$.

19. If $\overset{\frown}{AB} = 120°$ and $\angle P = 45°$, find $\overset{\frown}{CD}$.

20. If $\overset{\frown}{CD} = 56°$ and $\angle P = 42°$, find $\overset{\frown}{AB}$.

21. If $AP = 12$ ft, $CP = 5$ ft, and $PB = 15$ ft, find PD.

22. If $BP = 25$ yd, $AP = 15$ yd, and $CP = 5$ yd, find PD.

23. If $AC = 5$ cm, $CP = 4$ cm, and $DP = 3$ cm, find BD.

24. If $BD = 3$ ft, $DP = 5$ ft, and $AC = 6$ ft, find CP.

Exercises 25–26 refer to the figure below.

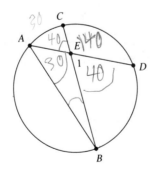

25. If $\angle 1 = 40°$ and $\angle DAB = 30°$, find $\overset{\frown}{AC}$ and $\angle ABC$.

26. If $\angle 1 = 50°$ and $\angle DAB = 35°$, find $\overset{\frown}{AC}$ and $\angle ABC$.

27. *Given:* $\overset{\frown}{BC} + \overset{\frown}{AD} = 180°$
    Prove: $\overline{AC} \perp \overline{BD}$

28. *Given:* $AB = BC$

    Prove: $\angle P = \dfrac{1}{2}(\overset{\frown}{AB} - \overset{\frown}{AD})$

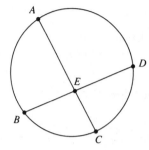

Exercise 27

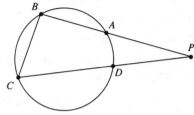

Exercise 28

29. If two equal chords of a circle intersect, prove that the segments of one are equal, respectively, to the segments of the other.

30. If two equal chords $\overline{AB}$ and $\overline{CD}$ meet at point P when extended, prove that the secant segments $\overline{AP}$ and $\overline{CP}$ are equal.

31. Prove Theorem 7.7.

32. Prove Theorem 7.9.

33. Prove Theorem 7.11.

34. How far is a 12-centimeter chord from the center of a circle with diameter 20 cm?

35. What is the radius of a circle in which a chord 10 inches long is 1 inch from the midpoint of the arc it forms?

Section 3.3

7.3 TANGENTS

In Section 7.2 we studied secants, lines that intersect a circle in two distinct points. We'll now consider lines that intersect a circle in exactly one point.

DEFINITION: TANGENT

If a line intersects a circle in one and only one point, the line is called a **tangent** to the circle. The point of intersection is called a **point of tangency.**

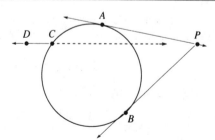

Figure 7.24   Tangent Lines

In Figure 7.24, $\overleftrightarrow{AP}$ is a tangent to the circle with A the point of tangency. We might say that ray $\overrightarrow{PB}$ and segment $\overline{PB}$ are tangent to the circle because they are contained in the tangent line $\overleftrightarrow{BP}$. $\overleftrightarrow{AP}$ and $\overleftrightarrow{BP}$ are said to be tangents to the circle from the same common external point P. Notice that $\overleftrightarrow{DC}$ is not a tangent because when $\overline{DC}$ is extended, it will intersect the circle in two points. Actually, $\overleftrightarrow{DC}$ is a secant.

The next two properties of a tangent can be proved using properties of right triangles that will be presented in Chapter 8; however, here we'll consider them as postulates.

POSTULATE 7.5

If a line is perpendicular to a radius of a circle and passes through the point where the radius intersects the circle, then the line is a tangent.

POSTULATE 7.6

A radius drawn to the point of tangency of a tangent is perpendicular to the tangent.

Postulate 7.5 provides a convenient way to construct a tangent to a circle at a point on the circle.

CONSTRUCTION 7.1

Construct a tangent to a circle at a given point on the circle.

Given: P is a point on a circle with center O (See Figure 7.25.)

To Construct: $\overleftrightarrow{AP}$ tangent to the circle

Construction:

1. Construct radius $\overline{OP}$ and extend it forming $\overrightarrow{OP}$.
2. Use Construction 2.4 to construct $\overleftrightarrow{AP}$ perpendicular to $\overleftrightarrow{OP}$ passing through P. By Postulate 7.5, $\overleftrightarrow{AP}$ is the desired tangent.

Postulate 7.5 together with Corollary 7.4 give us a way to construct a tangent to a circle from a point outside the circle.

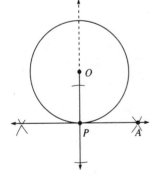

Figure 7.25

CONSTRUCTION 7.2

Construct a tangent to a circle from a point outside the circle.

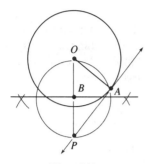

Figure 7.26

Given: P is a point outside a circle with center O (See Figure 7.26.)

To Construct: $\overleftrightarrow{PA}$ tangent to the circle

Construction:

1. Construct $\overline{OP}$ and use Construction 2.3 to locate the midpoint B of $\overline{OP}$.
2. Construct the circle with B as the center and PB as the radius.
3. Let A be a point of intersection of the two circles.
4. Construct $\overleftrightarrow{PA}$ and $\overline{OA}$. Then by Corollary 7.4, $\angle OAP$ is a right angle because it is inscribed in a semicircle. Thus, $\overleftrightarrow{PA} \perp \overline{OA}$, and by Postulate 7.5, $\overleftrightarrow{PA}$ is a desired tangent.

The next example solves the applied problem given in the chapter introduction.

E X A M P L E   1   Assume that a cross-section of the earth is a circle with radius 4000 mi. If a communications satellite is in orbit 110 mi above the surface of the earth, what is the approximate distance from the satellite to the horizon, the farthest point that can be seen on the surface of the earth?

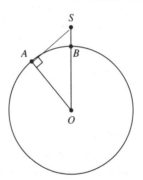

Figure 7.27

In Figure 7.27, S corresponds to the satellite, $\overline{OA}$ the radius of the earth, and SB the height of the satellite above the surface of the earth. The distance from the satellite to the horizon is SA, the length of segment $\overline{SA}$, which is included in tangent $\overleftrightarrow{SA}$ to the earth's surface from S. Because $\triangle AOS$ is a right triangle, we can use the Pythagorean Theorem to obtain

$$(OS)^2 = (SA)^2 + (OA)^2.$$

Thus,

$$\begin{aligned}
(SA)^2 &= (OS)^2 - (OA)^2 \\
&= [OB + SB]^2 - (OA)^2 \\
&= [4000 + 110]^2 - (4000)^2 \\
&= (4110)^2 - (4000)^2 \\
&= 892{,}100.
\end{aligned}$$

Figuring the square root with a calculator we have
$$SA \approx 945.$$

Thus, the distance to the horizon is about 945 mi. ◼

PRACTICE EXERCISE 1

Repeat Example 1 for a space station located 95 mi above the surface of the earth.

We now consider two properties of angles, one formed by a tangent and a chord and the other formed by a tangent and a secant.

THEOREM 7.16

The angle formed by a tangent and a chord has a measure one-half its intercepted arc.

Given: $\angle APB$ formed by tangent $\overleftrightarrow{PB}$ and chord $\overline{PA}$
(See Figure 7.28.)

Prove: $\angle APB = \frac{1}{2}\overparen{AP}$

Auxiliary line: Construct diameter $\overline{CP}$

Proof:

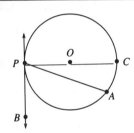

Figure 7.28

STATEMENTS	REASONS
1. $\angle APB$ is formed by tangent $\overleftrightarrow{PB}$ and chord $\overline{PA}$	1. Given
2. $\overline{CP}$ is a diameter forming semicircle $\overparen{CAP}$	2. By construction
3. $\angle APB = \angle CPB - \angle CPA$	3. Angle add. post.
4. $\angle CPB = 90°$	4. Radius drawn to pt. of tangency is $\perp$ to tan.
5. $\angle CPA = \frac{1}{2}\overparen{AC}$	5. Inscribed $\angle = \frac{1}{2}$ intercepted arc
6. $\angle APB = 90° - \frac{1}{2}\overparen{AC}$	6. Substitution law
7. $2\angle APB = 180° - \overparen{AC}$	7. Mult.-div. law
8. $\overparen{CAP} = 180°$	8. Semicircle measures 180°
9. $2\angle APB = \overparen{CAP} - \overparen{AC}$	9. Substitution law
10. $\overparen{CAP} - \overparen{AC} = \overparen{AP}$	10. Arc add. post.
11. $2\angle APB = \overparen{AP}$	11. Transitive law
12. $\angle APB = \frac{1}{2}\overparen{AP}$	12. Mult.-div. law

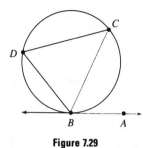

Figure 7.29

E X A M P L E 2 In Figure 7.29, $\overleftrightarrow{AB}$ is a tangent and $\angle CDB = 64°$. Find $\angle CBA$.

Because $\angle CDB$ is an inscribed angle intercepting arc $\overset{\frown}{BC}$, and $\angle CDB = 64°$, $\overset{\frown}{BC} = 128°$. Thus, by Theorem 7.16, $\angle CBA = \frac{1}{2}(128°) = 64°$. ∎

THEOREM 7.17

The angle formed by the intersection of a tangent and a secant has a measure one-half the difference of the intercepted arcs.

Given: Tangent $\overleftrightarrow{AP}$ and secant $\overleftrightarrow{PC}$
(See Figure 7.30.)

Prove: $\angle P = \frac{1}{2}(\overset{\frown}{AC} - \overset{\frown}{AB})$

Auxiliary line: Construct chord $\overline{AC}$

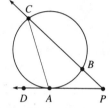

Figure 7.30

Proof:

STATEMENTS	REASONS
1. $\overleftrightarrow{AP}$ is a tangent and $\overleftrightarrow{PC}$ is a secant forming $\angle P$	1. Given
2. $\overline{AC}$ is a chord	2. By construction
3. $\angle CAD = \angle ACB + \angle P$	2. Ext. $\angle$ of $\triangle$ = sum remote int. $\angle$'s
4. $\angle P = \angle CAD - \angle ACB$	4. Add.-subtr. law
5. $\angle CAD = \frac{1}{2}\overset{\frown}{AC}$	5. The $\angle$ formed by tan. and chord $= \frac{1}{2}$ intercepted arc
6. $\angle ACB = \frac{1}{2}\overset{\frown}{AB}$	6. Measure of inscribed $\angle$
7. $\angle P = \frac{1}{2}\overset{\frown}{AC} - \frac{1}{2}\overset{\frown}{AB}$	7. Substitution law
8. $\angle P = \frac{1}{2}(\overset{\frown}{AC} - \overset{\frown}{AB})$	8. Distributive law

The proof of the next theorem is similar to that for Theorem 7.17 and is left for you to do as an exercise.

THEOREM 7.18

The angle formed by the intersection of two tangents has a measure one-half the difference of the intercepted arcs.

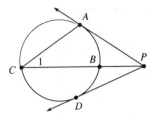

Figure 7.31

EXAMPLE 3   Refer to Figure 7.31. If $\angle 1 = 30°$ and $\angle APB = 34°$, find $\overarc{AC}$.

By Theorem 7.17,

$$\angle APB = \frac{1}{2}(\overarc{AC} - \overarc{AB}).$$

Because $\angle 1 = 30°$, $\overarc{AB} = 60°$. Substituting, we have

$$34° = \frac{1}{2}(\overarc{AC} - 60°)$$
$$68° = \overarc{AC} - 60° \qquad \text{Multiply both sides by 2}$$
$$128° = \overarc{AC}. \qquad \text{Add } 60° \text{ to both sides}$$

Thus, $\overarc{AC} = 128°$. ◨

PRACTICE EXERCISE 2

Refer to Figure 7.31. If $\overarc{ACD} = 236°$, find $\angle APD$.

THEOREM 7.19

Two tangent segments to a circle from the same point have equal lengths.

Given: $\overleftrightarrow{PA}$ and $\overleftrightarrow{PB}$ are tangents to a circle with center O (See Figure 7.32.)

Prove: $PA = PB$

Auxiliary lines: Construct radii $\overline{OA}$ and $\overline{OB}$ and segment $\overline{OP}$

Proof:

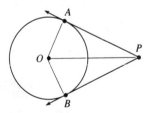

Figure 7.32

STATEMENTS	REASONS
1. $\overleftrightarrow{PA}$ and $\overleftrightarrow{PB}$ are tangents to a circle with center O	1. Given
2. $\overline{OA}$ and $\overline{OB}$ are radii	2. By construction
3. $\overline{OA} \perp \overline{AP}$ and $\overline{OB} \perp \overline{PB}$	3. Radii are $\perp$ to tangents
4. $\triangle AOP$ and $\triangle BOP$ are right triangles	4. Def. rt. $\triangle$
5. $OA = OB$	5. Radii are $=$
6. $OP = OP$	6. Reflexive law
7. $\triangle AOP \cong \triangle BOP$	7. HL $=$ HL
8. $PA = PB$	8. cpoctae

THEOREM 7.20

If a secant and a tangent are drawn to a circle from an external point, the length of the tangent segment is the mean proportional between the length of the secant segment and its external segment.

Given: $\overleftrightarrow{AP}$ is a tangent and $\overleftrightarrow{PC}$ is a secant to circle with center O (See Figure 7.33.)

Prove: $\dfrac{PC}{PA} = \dfrac{PA}{PB}$

Auxiliary lines: Construct segments $\overline{AB}$ and $\overline{AC}$

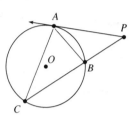

Figure 7.33

Proof:

STATEMENTS	REASONS
1. $\overleftrightarrow{AP}$ is a tangent and $\overleftrightarrow{PC}$ is a secant	1. Given
2. $\angle C = \dfrac{1}{2}\widehat{AB}$	2. Measure of inscribed $\angle$
3. $\angle PAB = \dfrac{1}{2}\widehat{AB}$	3. The $\angle$ formed by tan. and chord $= \dfrac{1}{2}$ intercepted arc
4. $\angle C = \angle PAB$	4. Sym. and Trans. laws
5. $\angle P = \angle P$	5. Reflexive law
6. $\triangle APB \sim \triangle APC$	6. AA ~ AA
7. $\dfrac{PC}{PA} = \dfrac{PA}{PB}$	7. Corr. sides of $\sim \triangle$'s are proportional

EXAMPLE 4 Refer to Figure 7.33. Assume that $PA = 10$ cm and $PB = 6$ cm. Find BC.

Let $x = BC$. Then $PC = BC + PB = x + 6$.
By Theorem 7.20,

$$\frac{PC}{PA} = \frac{PA}{PB}.$$

Substituting, we obtain

$$\frac{x + 6}{10} = \frac{10}{6}.$$

$6(x + 6) = (10)(10)$	Means-extremes property
$6x + 36 = 100$	Distributive law
$6x = 64$	Subtract 36 from both sides
$x = 10.666\ldots$	Divide by 6

The gears in a watch illustrate many properties of tangent circles.

When a decimal has a repeating block of digits such as the digit 6 in 10.666 . . . , we usually write the answer as $10.\overline{6}$, placing a bar over the repeating digit or digits. Thus, $BC = 10.\overline{6}$ cm. ◩

We have seen that a line and a circle can intersect in one or two points or none at all. A similar situation exists for two circles. If two circles intersect in exactly one point, the circles are said to be **tangent** to each other. Two possibilities exist. In Figure 7.34(a), the circles are **tangent internally** with point of tangency P, and in Figure 7.34(b), the circles are **tangent externally** with point of tangency Q.

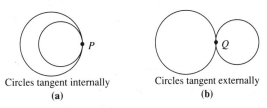

Circles tangent internally
(a)

Circles tangent externally
(b)

Figure 7.34

If two circles do not intersect, the circles can have a **common tangent.** If the circles are located on the same side of a common tangent, as in Figure 7.35(a), the tangent is called a **common external tangent.** If the circles are located on opposite sides of a common tangent, as in Figure 7.35(b), the tangent is called a **common internal tangent.**

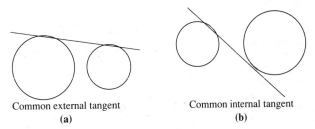

Common external tangent
(a)

Common internal tangent
(b)

Figure 7.35

DEFINITION: LINE OF CENTERS
The line passing through the centers of two circles is called their **line of centers.**

The proof of the following theorem follows from Postulates 7.6 and 2.3 and is left for you to do as an exercise.

> **THEOREM 7.21**
>
> If two circles are tangent internally or externally, the point of tangency is on their line of centers.

The next theorem also involves the line of centers of two circles.

> **THEOREM 7.22**
>
> If two circles intersect in two points, then their line of centers is the perpendicular bisector of their common chord.

Given: Two circles with centers O and P that intersect at points A and B. (See Figure 7.36.)

Prove: $\overline{OP} \perp \overline{AB}$ and $AC = BC$

Auxiliary lines: Construct radii $\overline{OA}$, $\overline{OB}$, $\overline{PA}$, and $\overline{PB}$

Proof:

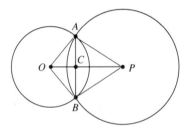

Figure 7.36

STATEMENTS	REASONS
1. Two circles centered at O and P intersect at points A and B.	1. Given
2. $OA = OB$ and $PA = PB$	2. Radii are =
3. $OP = OP$	3. Reflexive law
4. $\triangle AOP \cong \triangle BOP$	4. SSS = SSS
5. $\angle AOP = \angle BOP$	5. cpoctae
6. $OC = OC$	6. Reflexive law
7. $\triangle AOC \cong \triangle BOC$	7. SAS = SAS
8. $AC = BC$	8. cpoctae
9. $\angle ACO = \angle BCO$	9. cpoctae
10. $\angle ACO$ and $\angle BCO$ are adjacent angles	10. Def. adj. $\angle$'s
11. $\overline{OP} \perp \overline{AB}$	11. Def. of $\perp$ lines

We'll conclude this section with two constructions involving common external and internal tangents to a circle.

> **CONSTRUCTION 7.3**
>
> Construct a common external tangent to two given circles that are not congruent.

Region of Total Eclipse

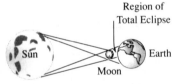

Sun   Moon   Earth

A solar eclipse occurs when the moon passes between the earth and the sun and blocks the sun's rays. Some areas of the earth experience no eclipse at all while others experience a partial eclipse, and a small area will be in total eclipse. The lines drawn tangent to the sun and moon in the figure show the areas affected by the eclipse. A total eclipse occurs in the area between the two external tangents.

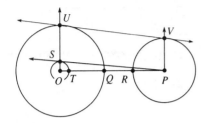

Figure 7.37

Given: Two noncongruent circles with centers O and P (See Figure 7.37.)

To Construct: $\overleftrightarrow{UV}$, an external tangent to both circles

Construction:

1. Construct $\overline{OP}$ obtaining points Q and R, the intersections of the circles and the segment.
2. Construct $\overline{QT}$ on $\overline{QO}$ such that $QT = RP$.
3. Construct a circle centered at O with radius OT.
4. Use Construction 7.2 to construct a tangent to the circle in Step 3 from point P, $\overleftrightarrow{PS}$.
5. Construct $\overrightarrow{OS}$ intersecting the original circle at point U.
6. Construct $\overrightarrow{PV}$ through P parallel to $\overrightarrow{OU}$ using Construction 4.1.
7. Construct $\overleftrightarrow{UV}$. Because $\square USPV$ is a rectangle, $\overleftrightarrow{UV}$ is the desired tangent.

CONSTRUCTION 7.4

Construct a common internal tangent to two given circles.

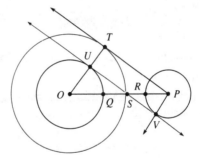

Figure 7.38

Given: Two circles with centers O and P (See Figure 7.38.)

To Construct: $\overleftrightarrow{UV}$, an internal tangent to both circles

Construction:

1. Construct $\overline{OP}$ obtaining points Q and R, the intersections of the circles and the segment.
2. Construct $\overline{QS}$ on $\overline{QP}$ such that $QS = RP$.
3. Construct a circle centered at O with radius OS.
4. Use Construction 7.2 to construct a tangent to this circle from P, $\overleftrightarrow{PT}$.
5. Construct $\overline{OT}$ with point U the intersection of $\overline{OT}$ with the original circle.
6. Use Construction 4.1 to construct line $\overleftrightarrow{PV}$ through P parallel to $\overline{OT}$ intersecting the original circle at V.
7. Construct $\overleftrightarrow{UV}$. Because $\square UTPV$ is a rectangle, $\overleftrightarrow{UV}$ is the desired tangent.

ANSWERS TO PRACTICE EXERCISES: **1.** 877 mi **2.** 56°

7.3 Exercises

Exercises 1–22 refer to the figure below.

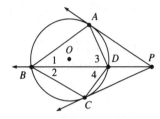

1. If $\overset{\frown}{AD} = 70°$, find $\angle PAD$.   **2.** If $\overset{\frown}{CD} = 60°$, find $\angle PCD$.   **3.** If $\angle 1 = 36°$, find $\angle PAD$.

4. If $\angle 2 = 29°$, find $\angle PCD$.   **5.** If $\angle PAD = 40°$, find $\angle 1$.   **6.** If $\angle PCD = 35°$, find $\angle 2$.

7. If $\overset{\frown}{AB} = 140°$ and $\overset{\frown}{AD} = 70°$, find $\angle APD$.   **8.** If $\overset{\frown}{BC} = 85°$ and $\overset{\frown}{CD} = 61°$, find $\angle CPD$.

9. If $\angle 1 = 36°$ and $\angle 3 = 70°$, find $\angle APD$.   **10.** If $\angle 2 = 30°$ and $\angle 4 = 50°$, find $\angle CPD$.

11. If $\angle APD = 40°$ and $\overset{\frown}{AB} = 138°$, find $\angle 1$.   **12.** If $\angle CPD = 30°$ and $\overset{\frown}{BC} = 80°$, find $\angle 2$.

13. If $\overset{\frown}{ADC} = 130°$, find $\angle APC$.   **14.** If $\overset{\frown}{ABC} = 240°$, find $\angle APC$.

15. If $\angle 1 = 35°$ and $\angle 2 = 30°$, find $\angle APC$.   **16.** If $\angle 3 = 70°$ and $\angle 4 = 50°$, find $\angle APC$.

17. If $AP = 17$ cm, find CP.   **18.** If $PC = 24$ yd, find PA.

19. If $AP = 12$ cm and $BP = 18$ cm, find DP.   **20.** If $PC = 8$ ft and $PB = 12$ ft, find PD.

21. If $AP = 15$ yd and $DP = 10$ yd, find BD.   **22.** If $PC = 24$ cm and $PD = 18$ cm, find BD.

23. If two circles do not intersect and neither is inside the other, how many common internal tangents do the circles have?

24. If two circles do not intersect and neither is inside the other, how many common external tangents do the circles have?

25. *Given:* $\overleftrightarrow{PA}$ and $\overleftrightarrow{PB}$ are tangents to the circle

   Prove: $\angle P + \overset{\frown}{ACB} = 180°$

26. *Given:* $\overleftrightarrow{PA}$ is tangent to the circle with center O

   Prove: $\triangle APB \sim \triangle APC$

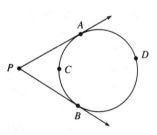

Exercise 25

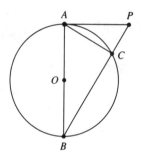

Exercise 26

27. *Given:* $\overleftrightarrow{AB}$ and $\overleftrightarrow{CD}$ are common external tangents to the circles that are not congruent.

   Prove: AB = CD

28. *Given:* $\overleftrightarrow{AB}$ and $\overleftrightarrow{CD}$ are common internal tangents to the circles

   Prove: AB = CD

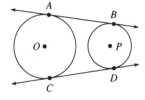

Exercise 27

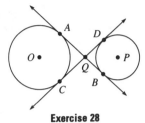

Exercise 28

29. Prove Theorem 7.18.   **30.** Prove Theorem 7.21.

31. Construct a tangent to a circle at a point on the circle.

32. Construct a tangent to a circle from a point outside the circle.

33. Construct a common external tangent to two circles that do not intersect and have unequal radii.

34. Construct a common external tangent to two circles that do not intersect and have equal radii.

35. Construct a common internal tangent to two circles that do not intersect and have unequal radii.

36. Construct a common internal tangent to two circles that do not intersect and have equal radii.

37. From a balloon 1 mi high, how far away, to the nearest tenth of a mile, is the horizon, the farthest point that can be seen on the surface of the earth?

38. An airplane is flying at an altitude of 6 mi. To the nearest tenth of a mile, how far is the airplane from the horizon?

A large screen television is placed on a shelf on a wall in a sports lounge. Where is the best place to sit to view the screen? If you sit too close or too far, the viewing angle will be decreased as shown in the figure below left. The answer to our question involves finding the largest viewing angle. Suppose we draw a sketch describing the problem as shown below right.

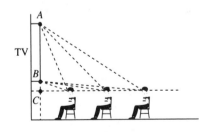

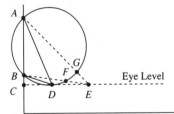

We can show that the best view can be found where the circle through A B is tangent to the eye-level line at point D. Because $\angle ADB = \frac{1}{2}\widehat{AB}$ and at any other point E, $\angle AEB = \frac{1}{2}(\widehat{AB} - \widehat{FG})$, $\angle ADB$ will be greater than $\angle AEB$.

By Theorem 7.20, the length of tangent segment $\overline{CD}$ is the mean proportional between the length of the secant segment $\overline{AC}$ and its external segment $\overline{BC}$. Thus,

$$\frac{AC}{CD} = \frac{CD}{BC} \text{ or } (CD)^2 = (AC)(BC).$$

It then follows that $CD = \sqrt{(AC)(BC)}$. Use this information in Exercises 39–40.

39. The base of a TV screen is 5 ft above eye level and the screen is 4 ft high. How far away should a viewer sit to have the maximum viewing angle?

40. A picture is hanging on a wall in a gallery. If the picture is 3 ft high and the base of the picture is 5 ft above eye level, how far should a viewer stand to have the maximum viewing angle?

Section 3.4

7.4 CIRCLES AND REGULAR POLYGONS

In this section we will study relationships between circles and polygons.

DEFINITION: INSCRIBED AND CIRCUMSCRIBED CIRCLES AND POLYGONS

If a polygon has its vertices on a circle, the polygon is **inscribed in the circle** and the circle is **circumscribed around the polygon.** If each side of a polygon is tangent to a circle, the polygon is **circumscribed around the circle** and the circle is **inscribed in the polygon.**

In Figure 7.39(a), quadrilateral $ABCD$ is inscribed in the circle centered at O and the circle centered at O is circumscribed around the quadrilateral. In Figure 7.39(b), $\triangle QRS$ is circumscribed around the circle centered at P and the circle centered at P is inscribed in the triangle.

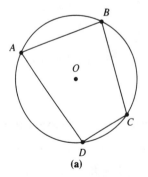
(a)

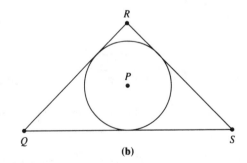
(b)

Figure 7.39

Karl Fredrick Gauss (1777–1855)

Karl Fredrick Gauss was one of the greatest mathematicians of all time. Even during his lifetime, he was called "the prince of mathematicians." He made many major contributions to arithmetic, number theory, algebra, astronomy, biology, physics, and, of course, geometry. At the age of 19, Gauss proved by considering points on a circle that a regular polygon with 17 sides can be constructed using a straightedge and a compass. He considered this to be one of his greatest achievements.

> **THEOREM 7.23**
>
> If a quadrilateral is inscribed in a circle, the opposite angles are supplementary.

Given: ABCD is a quadrilateral inscribed in a circle (See Figure 7.40.)

Prove: $\angle A$ and $\angle C$ are supplementary and $\angle B$ and $\angle D$ are supplementary

Proof:

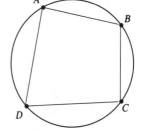

Figure 7.40

STATEMENTS	REASONS
1. Quadrilateral *ABCD* is inscribed in a circle	1. Given
2. $\angle A = \frac{1}{2}\widehat{BCD}$ and $\angle C = \frac{1}{2}\widehat{DAB}$	2. Measure of inscribed $\angle$
3. $\widehat{BCD} + \widehat{DAB} = 360°$	3. Arc add. post.
4. $\angle A + \angle C = \frac{1}{2}\widehat{BCD} + \frac{1}{2}\widehat{DAB}$	4. Add.-subtr. law
5. $\angle A + \angle C = \frac{1}{2}(\widehat{BCD} + \widehat{DAB})$	5. Distributive law
6. $\angle A + \angle C = \frac{1}{2}(360°)$	6. Substitution law
7. $\angle A + \angle C = 180°$	7. Simplify
8. $\angle A$ and $\angle C$ are supplementary	8. Def. of supp. $\angle$'s

We could show that $\angle B$ and $\angle D$ are supplementary in a similar manner.

The proof of the next theorem follows from Theorem 7.23 and the definition of a rectangle. The proof is requested in the exercises.

> **THEOREM 7.24**
>
> If a parallelogram is inscribed in a circle, then it is a rectangle.

Circles with regular polygons have many special properties. The following theorems introduce some of them.

> **THEOREM 7.25**
>
> If a circle is divided into *n* equal arcs, *n* > 2, then the chords formed by these arcs form a regular *n*-gon.

The proof of Theorem 7.25 follows by noting that equal arcs have equal chords, and that each angle of the *n*-gon formed is one-half the sum of four equal arcs.

> **THEOREM 7.26**
>
> If a circle is divided into *n* equal arcs, *n* > 2, and tangents are constructed to the circle at the endpoints of each arc, then the figure formed by these tangents is a regular *n*-gon.

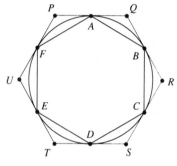

Figure 7.41

The following paragraph-style proof to this theorem shows 6 equal arcs, but note that the same proof can be applied to any number of arcs *n*, *n* > 2. Refer to Figure 7.41.

PROOF: Because $\overset{\frown}{AB} = \overset{\frown}{BC} = \overset{\frown}{CD} = \overset{\frown}{DE} = \overset{\frown}{EF} = \overset{\frown}{FA}$, the corresponding chords are also equal making $AB = BC = CD = DE = EF = FA$. Because the tangent segments to a circle from a point outside the circle are equal, $\triangle AQB$, $\triangle BRC$, $\triangle CSD$, $\triangle DTE$, $\triangle EUF$, and $\triangle FPA$ are all isosceles triangles. Because angles formed by a chord and a tangent each measure one-half the intercepted arc, and because the arcs are all equal, the base angles of the six triangles are all equal. Thus, all six triangles are congruent by ASA = ASA. Hence, $\angle P = \angle Q = \angle R = \angle S = \angle T = \angle U$ because they are corresponding parts of congruent triangles, making all angles of the hexagon equal. Also, because $\overline{PQ}$, $\overline{QR}$, $\overline{RS}$, $\overline{ST}$, $\overline{TU}$, and $\overline{UP}$ are all formed by adding two equal segments, $PQ = QR = RS = ST = TU = UP$. Thus, because all angles and all sides are equal, *PQRSTU* is a regular hexagon.   ∎

If we are given a circle, and we have a way to determine *n* equal arcs on the circle, we can use Theorems 7.25 and 7.26 to inscribe and circumscribe a regular *n*-gon in and around the circle.

EXAMPLE 1   Inscribe a regular octagon in a circle.

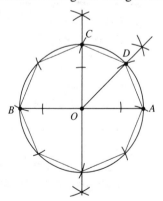

Figure 7.42

Consider the circle in Figure 7.42. Choose a point A on the circle and construct radius $\overline{OA}$, extended to form diameter $\overline{BA}$. Use Construction 2.4 to form the perpendicular bisector of $\overline{BA}$ containing $\overline{OC}$, and use Construction 2.6 to bisect $\angle AOC$ obtaining $\overline{OD}$. Using length AD, mark off eight equal arcs around the circle starting at point A. The chords formed by these arcs give the desired regular octagon. ◼

PRACTICE EXERCISE 1

Circumscribe a regular octagon around the circle given in Example 1.

We now consider the problem of circumscribing a circle around a given regular polygon. You will be asked in the exercises to prove that the construction that follows does indeed result in the required circle.

CONSTRUCTION 7.5

Construct a circle that is circumscribed around a given regular polygon.

The construction uses a regular pentagon, but note that you can use any regular polygon.

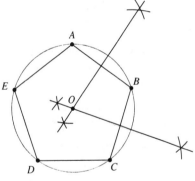

Figure 7.43

Given: Regular pentagon $ABCDE$ (See Figure 7.43.)

To Construct: A circle that is circumscribed around $ABCDE$

Construction:

1. Use Construction 2.4 to form the perpendicular bisectors of two adjacent sides, for instance $\overline{AB}$ and $\overline{BC}$. The bisectors intersect in point O.

2. Use O as the center and AO as the radius and construct a circle. This is the desired circle circumscribed around $ABCDE$.

Next we'll inscribe a circle in a given regular polygon. You will be asked in the exercises to prove that the construction results in the required circle.

CONSTRUCTION 7.6

Construct a circle that is inscribed in a given regular polygon.

The construction uses a regular hexagon, but note that you can use any regular polygon.

Given: Regular hexagon *ABCDEF* (See Figure 7.44.)

To Construct: A circle that is inscribed in *ABCDEF*

Construction:

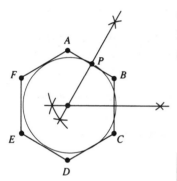

Figure 7.44

1. Use Construction 2.4 to form the perpendicular bisector of two adjacent sides, for instance $\overline{AB}$ and $\overline{BC}$. The bisectors intersect in point *O*.
2. Let *P* be the midpoint of $\overline{AB}$. Use *O* as the center and *OP* as the radius and construct a circle. This is the desired circle inscribed in *ABCDEF*.

DEFINITION: CENTER OF A REGULAR POLYGON

The **center of a regular polygon** is the center of the circle circumscribed around the polygon.

In view of Constructions 7.5 and 7.6, the center of a regular polygon is also the center of the circle that is inscribed in the polygon because the center points coincide.

DEFINITION: RADIUS OF A REGULAR POLYGON

A **radius of a regular polygon** is the segment joining the center of the polygon to one of its vertices.

THEOREM 7.27

All radii of a regular polygon are equal in length.

The proof of Theorem 7.27 is requested in the exercises.

DEFINITION: CENTRAL ANGLE OF A REGULAR POLYGON

A **central angle of a regular polygon** is an angle formed by two radii to two adjacent vertices.

THEOREM 7.28

All central angles of a regular polygon have the same measure.

The proof of Theorem 7.28 is requested in the exercises.

Because there are *n* equal central angles in a regular *n*-gon and these angles sum to 360°, the proof of the formula given in the next theorem should be obvious.

THEOREM 7.29

The measure *a* of each central angle in a regular *n*-gon is determined with the formula

$$a = \frac{360°}{n}.$$

E X A M P L E 2   Find the measure of each central angle in a regular octagon.

Because an octagon has 8 sides, by Theorem 7.29 we substitute 8 for *n* in the formula

$$a = \frac{360°}{n}.$$
$$a = \frac{360°}{8} = 45°$$

Thus, in Figure 7.45, central angle $\angle AOB$ has measure 45°.   ∎

PRACTICE EXERCISE 2

Find the number of sides in a regular polygon if each central angle measures 24°.

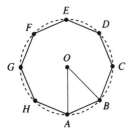

Figure 7.45

ANSWERS TO PRACTICE EXERCISES: **1.** Begin by dividing the circle into 8 equal arcs using the method shown in Example 1. Use Construction 7.1 to construct the tangent to the circle at each of these eight points. The points of intersection of these tangents form the vertices of the circumscribed octagon. **2.** 15 sides

7.4 EXERCISES

Exercises 1–8 refer to the figure below in which quadrilateral *ABCD* is inscribed in the circle centered at *O*.

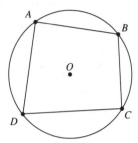

1. If ∠A = 86°, what is the measure of ∠C?   2. If ∠B = 97°, what is the measure of ∠D?
3. Assume that ∠A + ∠B + ∠C = 276°. Find ∠B.   4. Assume that ∠B + ∠C + ∠D = 269°. Find ∠C.
5. If $\overline{AB} \parallel \overline{DC}$ and AB = DC, find ∠A.   6. If AB = DC and AD = BC, find ∠B.
7. If ∠A = ∠C, find ∠C.   8. If AB = BC = CD = DA, find ∠D.

9. Draw a circle and divide it into four equal arcs by constructing the perpendicular bisector of a diameter. Inscribe a square in the circle.

10. Circumscribe a square around a given circle. [Hint: Refer to Exercise 9.]

11. Draw a circle and divide it into six equal arcs. Inscribe a regular hexagon in the circle.

12. Circumscribe a regular hexagon around a given circle.

13. Draw a circle and divide it into three equal arcs. Inscribe an equilateral triangle in the circle. [Hint: You may want to divide the circle into six equal arcs first. The length of a side of a regular inscribed hexagon is equal to the radius.]

14. Circumscribe an equilateral triangle around a given circle. [Hint: Refer to Exercise 13.]

15. Construct a square and inscribe a circle in it.

16. Construct a square and circumscribe a circle around it.

17. Construct an equilateral triangle and circumscribe a circle around it.

18. Construct an equilateral triangle and inscribe a circle in it.

In Exercises 19–24, find the measure of each central angle of the given regular polygon.

19. equilateral triangle   20. square   21. regular pentagon
22. regular hexagon   23. regular nonagon   24. regular decagon

In Exercises 25–28, find the number of sides in a regular polygon if each central angle has the given measure.

25. 45°   26. 30°   27. 20°   28. 15°

29. Prove Theorem 7.24.

30. Prove that Construction 7.5 provides the required circumscribed circle.

31. Prove that Construction 7.6 provides the required inscribed circle.

32. Prove Theorem 7.27.

33. Prove Theorem 7.28.

34. Find the perimeter of a regular hexagon that is circumscribed around a circle with radius 4 cm.

35. Find the length of a side of an equilateral triangle that is inscribed in a circle with radius 4 cm.

36. To inscribe a regular pentagon $ABCDE$ in a circle centered at O (see the figure below), select a point A on the circle, construct radius $\overline{OA}$, and construct radius $\overline{OP} \perp \overline{OA}$. Construct the midpoint Q of $\overline{OP}$, and draw segment $\overline{QA}$. Bisect $\angle OQA$ to obtain R on $\overline{OA}$. Construct $\overline{BR} \perp \overline{OA}$. Then $\overline{AB}$ is one side of the desired pentagon. Use AB to mark off five equal arcs on the circle to complete the pentagon. Draw a circle with radius about 2 inches in length and inscribe a regular pentagon in the circle. Then circumscribe a regular pentagon around the circle by constructing lines perpendicular to radii drawn to each vertex.

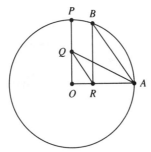

Exercise 36

Section 3.5

7.5 SECTORS, ARC LENGTH, AND AREA

If we cut a piece from a pizza as shown in Figure 7.46, the slice is an example of a *sector* of a circle.

Figure 7.46   Sector of a Circle

> **DEFINITION: SECTOR**
> A **sector** of a circle is a region bounded by two radii of the circle and the arc of the circle determined by the radii.

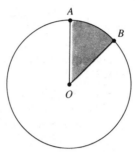

Figure 7.47   Sector

The sector of the circle shown in color in Figure 7.47, denoted by sector AOB, is formed by radii $\overline{OA}$ and $\overline{OB}$ and arc $\overparen{AB}$. Assume that the measure of $\overparen{AB}$ is 45°, that is $\angle AOB = 45°$. Then because 45° is one-eighth of 360°, the area of the sector is one-eighth the area of the circle. In view of this, it is reasonable to accept the next postulate.

> **POSTULATE 7.7   AREA OF A SECTOR**
> The area of a sector of a circle with radius r whose arc has measure $m°$ is determined with the formula
> $$A = \frac{m}{360}\pi r^2.$$

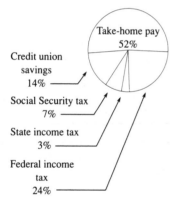

Take-home pay 52%
Credit union savings 14%
Social Security tax 7%
State income tax 3%
Federal income tax 24%

One way to form a mental image of statistical data is to display the data using a *circle graph*. The size of a sector of the circle can visually convey the information presented. The circle graph above shows the distribution of Mr. Whitney's monthly income. You have probably seen graphs like this in newspapers and magazines.

EXAMPLE 1   What is the area of a slice of pizza cut from a pizza with diameter 20 inches if the arc of the slice measures 30°?

Substitute 30 for m and 10 for r in the formula

$$A = \frac{m}{360}\pi r^2.$$
$$= \frac{30}{360}\pi(10)^2$$
$$= \frac{1}{12}\pi(100)$$
$$= \frac{25}{3}\pi$$

The actual area is $\dfrac{25}{3}\pi$ in² which can be approximated by 26.2 in², using 3.14 for π and rounding to the nearest tenth of a square inch.   ◪

We defined the measure of an arc to be the measure of its central angle. We now consider the problem of finding the *length* of an arc. In Figure 7.47, if AB = 45°, because 45° is one-eighth of 360°, it is reasonable to assume that the length of the arc would be one-eighth the circumference of the circle.

POSTULATE 7.8   ARC LENGTH

The **length of an arc** measuring $m°$ in a circle with radius r is determined with the formula

$$L = \frac{m}{360}2\pi r = \frac{m}{180}\pi r.$$

E X A M P L E 2   What is the length of an arc measuring 30° in a circle with radius 15 cm?

Substitute 30 for m and 15 for r in the formula

$$L = \frac{m}{180}\pi r.$$
$$= \frac{30}{180}\pi(15)$$
$$= \frac{5}{2}\pi$$

The actual length is $\dfrac{5}{2}\pi$ cm which can be approximated by 7.9 cm, using 3.14 for π and rounding to the nearest tenth of a centimeter.   ◪

Another important construction in a circle is a *segment.*

DEFINITION: SEGMENT OF A CIRCLE

A **segment** of a circle is a region bounded by a chord of the circle and the arc formed by the chord.

The color region in Figure 7.48 is a segment of the circle. To find the area of this segment, find the area of sector AOB and subtract the area of $\triangle AOB$.

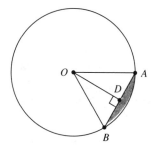

Figure 7.48   Segment of a Circle

EXAMPLE 3   Find the area of the segment of the circle in Figure 7.48 if $\angle AOB = 60°$ and $AO = 20$ cm.

Construct altitude $\overline{OD}$ of $\triangle AOB$. Because $\angle AOB = 60°$, $\angle AOD = 30°$. With $OA = 20$ cm, $DA = 10$ cm and $OD = 10\sqrt{3}$ cm using properties of a 30°-60°-right triangle. Then $AB = 2DA = 20$ cm, so

$$\text{Area } \triangle AOB = \frac{1}{2}(AB)(OD).$$
$$= \frac{1}{2}(20)(10\sqrt{3})$$
$$= 100\sqrt{3} \text{ cm}^2$$

The area of sector AOB is $\frac{60}{360}\pi(20)^2 = \frac{200}{3}\pi$ cm^2.

Thus, the area of the segment is

$$\left(\frac{200}{3}\pi - 100\sqrt{3}\right) \text{ cm}^2$$

which can be approximated by 36.1 cm^2.   ◼

Previously we considered areas of triangles and certain quadrilaterals such as parallelograms, rectangles, and trapezoids. We'll now show how to find the area of any regular polygon using the notion of an *apothem* of a regular polygon.

DEFINITION: APOTHEM OF A REGULAR POLYGON

An **apothem of a regular polygon** is a line segment from the center of the polygon perpendicular to one of its sides.

In Figure 7.49, $\overline{OP}$ is an apothem of hexagon $ABCDEF$ inscribed in the circle with center O.

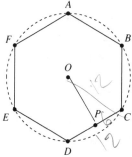

Figure 7.49   Apothem

> **THEOREM 7.30**
>
> Every apothem of a regular polygon has the same length.

The proof of Theorem 7.30 follows from Theorem 7.10 and is left for you to do as an exercise. Because every apothem of a regular polygon has the same length, as stated in Theorem 7.30, we often say that any apothem of a regular polygon is *the* apothem of the regular polygon.

> **THEOREM 7.31**
>
> The apothem of a regular polygon bisects its respective side.

The proof of Theorem 7.31 follows from Theorem 7.8 and is left for you to do as an exercise.

Consider the regular hexagon $ABCDEF$ in Figure 7.50 with apothem $\overline{OP}$. The area of $ABCDEF$ is the sum of the areas of congruent triangles $\triangle ABO$, $\triangle BCO$, $\triangle CDO$, $\triangle DEO$, $\triangle EFO$, and $\triangle FAO$. The area of $\triangle ABO$ is

$$\frac{1}{2}(AB)(OP).$$

Similarly, we can find the area of each of the five remaining triangles. If we add these areas together and simplify, we obtain

$$\frac{1}{2}(OP)(AB + BC + CD + DE + EF + FA).$$

Let p be the perimeter of $ABCDEF$, then

$$p = AB + BC + CD + DE + EF + FA.$$

Let a be the length of the apothem. Then the sum of the areas of the triangles, which is equal to the area of the regular hexagon, simplifies to

$$A = \frac{1}{2}ap.$$

A similar argument can be given for any regular polygon, which would provide the proof of the next theorem.

> **THEOREM 7.32   AREA OF A REGULAR POLYGON**
>
> The area of a regular polygon with apothem of length a and perimeter p is determined with the formula
>
> $$A = \frac{1}{2}ap.$$

E X A M P L E 4   Find the area of a regular hexagon with sides measuring 12 cm.

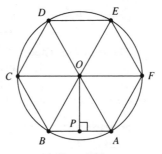

Figure 7.50

Refer to Figure 7.50. The measure of central angle $\angle AOB$ is $\dfrac{360°}{6} = 60°$ by Theorem 7.29. Then $\angle AOP = 30°$ so $\triangle AOP$ is a 30°-60°-right triangle. Because $AB = 12$ cm and $AP = 6$ cm, hypotenuse $AO = 12$ cm. Thus, the side opposite the 60° angle, the apothem, has length $\dfrac{\sqrt{3}}{2}(12) = 6\sqrt{3}$ cm. The perimeter of the hexagon is $6(12) = 72$ cm. Substitute $6\sqrt{3}$ for a and 72 for p in the formula

$$A = \frac{1}{2}ap.$$
$$A = \frac{1}{2}(6\sqrt{3})(72)$$
$$= 216\sqrt{3}$$

Thus, the exact area is $216\sqrt{3}$ cm², which can be approximated by 374.1 cm², correct to the nearest tenth of a square centimeter.   ◪

PRACTICE EXERCISE 1

Use the formula $A = \frac{1}{2}ap$ to find the area of a square. Compare the result with the formula for the area of a square given in Chapter 4.

In Postulate 7.2, we said that the area of a circle is determined with the formula $A = \pi r^2$. The following example shows how the formula for the area of a regular polygon can lead us to the formula for the area of a circle. Suppose we are given a circle. If we inscribe a square in the circle, the area of the square would give an approximation for the area of the circle. It would not be a very good approximation because the area of the four segments of the circle would

Figure 7.51

not be included. If we bisect the four equal arcs and construct the inscribed octagon as shown in Figure 7.51, the area of the octagon would clearly be a better approximation for the area of the circle.

If we repeat this process forming a regular 16-gon, the area of the 16-gon would be an even better approximation for the area of the circle. Continuing in this manner, we would obtain a better and better approximation of the area of the circle. The area of each regular polygon is

$$A = \frac{1}{2}ap,$$

and as the process continues, a is approaching the radius of the circle r, and the perimeter p is approaching the circumference of the circle, $2\pi r$. Thus, the area is approaching

$$A = \frac{1}{2}r(2\pi r) = \pi r^2.$$

NOTE: Because it is not always easy to find the length of the apothem of a regular polygon with many sides, we often approximate the area of such a polygon with the area of its circumscribed circle. If the apothem is known but the perimeter is not, approximate the perimeter using $r = a$ for the inscribed circle.   ☐

ANSWER TO PRACTICE EXERCISE: **1.** Both formulas give $A = s^2$.

7.5 EXERCISES

In Exercises 1–4, find the area of each grey sector and the length of its arc.

1.
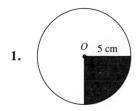

2.

3.
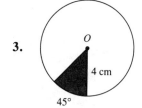

4.
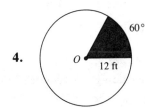

In Exercises 5–10, find the area of each grey region of the circle. Use 3.14 for π and give the answer correct to the nearest tenth.

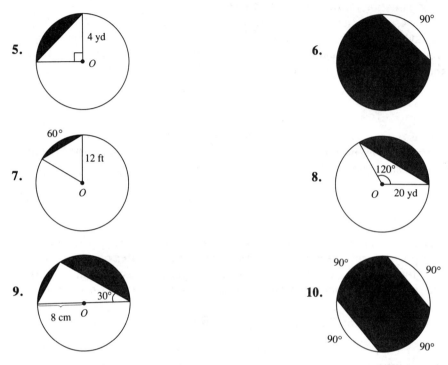

5.

6.

7.

8.

9.

10.

11. Find the area of a sector of a circle if the diameter of the circle is 8.2 cm and the arc of the sector is 30°. Give answer correct to the nearest tenth of a square centimeter.

12. Find the area of a sector of a circle if the diameter of the circle is 21.5 ft and the arc of the sector is 60°. Give answer correct to the nearest tenth of a square foot.

13. The area of a sector of a circle is 24π yd². If the arc of the sector is 60°, find the diameter of the circle.

14. The area of a sector of a circle is 50π cm². If the arc of the sector is 45°, find the diameter of the circle.

15. A regular polygon has perimeter 80 yd and apothem 10 yd. Find its area.

16. A regular polygon has perimeter 144 cm and apothem 18 cm. Find its area.

17. Find the area of a regular hexagon with sides 16 ft.

18. Find the area of a regular hexagon with sides 12 ft.

19. The area of a regular hexagon is $1350\sqrt{3}$ cm². Find the length of a side.

20. The area of a regular hexagon is $864\sqrt{3}$ yd². Find the length of a side.

21. Estimate the area of a regular 16-gon with apothem 12 ft. [Hint: Find the area of the inscribed circle using $A = \pi r^2$.]

22. Estimate the area of a regular 20-gon with apothem 8.5 cm.

In Exercises 23–24, find the area of the grey region. Give answer correct to the nearest tenth.

4 cm	4 yd
Exercise 23	**Exercise 24**

23. The arcs have their centers at the vertices of the equilateral triangle.

24. The arcs have their centers at opposite vertices of the square.

25. Prove Theorem 7.30.

26. Prove Theorem 7.31.

27. In the figure below, the two circles have a common center with radii 60 yd and 70 yd. The grey region corresponds to a jogging track. What is the area of the track, to the nearest tenth of a square yard?

Exercise 27

28. In the figure below, the externally tangent circles with centers O and P have radii 6 ft and 2 ft, respectively. What is the area of the grey region, correct to the nearest tenth of a square foot?

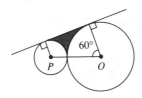

Exercise 28

Section 3.6
CHAPTER 7 REVIEW

KEY TERMS AND SYMBOLS

7.1 circle, p. 231
center, p. 231
radius, p. 231
diameter, p. 231
circumference, p. 231
pi (π), p. 231
semicircle, p. 234
major arc, p. 234
minor arc, p. 234
central angle, p. 235
intercepts, p. 235
measure of an arc, p. 235
inscribed angle, p. 235
7.2 chord, p. 241

bisector of an arc, p. 243
secant, p. 247
7.3 tangent, p. 252
point of tangency, p. 252
tangent internally, p. 259
tangent externally, p. 259
common tangent, p. 259
common external tangent,
  p. 259
common internal tangent,
  p. 259
7.4 inscribed polygon, p. 264
circumscribed polygon,
  p. 264

inscribed circle, p. 264
circumscribed circle, p. 264
center of a regular
  polygon, p. 268
radius of a regular
  polygon, p. 268
central angle of a regular
  polygon, p. 269
7.5 sector, p. 272
length of an arc, p. 273
segment (of a circle),
  p. 273
apothem, p. 274

PROOF TECHNIQUES

To Prove:

Inscribed Angles Equal

1. Show that they intercept the same arc. (Corollary 7.3, p. 237)
2. Show that each is inscribed in a semicircle and is thus a right angle. (Corollary 7.4, p. 237)

Chords are Equal

1. Show that they are formed by equal arcs. (Theorem 7.7, p. 243)
2. Show that they are equidistant from the center of the circle. (Theorem 7.10, p. 244)

Line is a Tangent

1. Show it is perpendicular to a radius at the point of tangency. (Postulate 7.5, p. 253)

Figure Is a Regular *n*-gon

1. Show that it is inscribed in a circle using chords determined by dividing the circle into *n* equal arcs. (Theorem 7.25, p. 265)
2. Show that it is circumscribed around a circle using tangent lines determined by dividing the circle into *n* equal arcs. (Theorem 7.26, p. 266)

REVIEW EXERCISES

Section 7.1

1. Find the diameter of the circle with radius 2.6 cm.

2. Find the radius of the circle with diameter $\frac{4}{5}$ yd.

3. Find the approximate circumference and area of the circle with diameter 9.2 ft. Use 3.14 for π.

4. A machine part is in the shape of an equilateral triangle 10 inches on a side. A hole with diameter 3 inches is drilled in the center of the part. To the nearest tenth, what is the area of remaining metal?

5. Refer to the figure to the right to answer each question.
   (a) What is $\angle AOB$ called with respect to the circle?
   (b) What is $\angle ACB$ called with respect to the circle?
   (c) What is the measure of $\widehat{AB}$?
   (d) What is the measure of $\widehat{ACB}$?
   (e) What is the measure of $\angle ACB$?

6. Prove that vertical angles with vertices at the center of a circle intercept equal arcs on the circle.

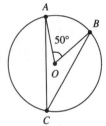

Exercise 5

Section 7.2

Exercises 7–10 refer to the figure below.

7. If $\widehat{BC} = 56°$ and $\widehat{AD} = 132°$, find $\angle BPC$.　　8. If $CD = DA$ and $\widehat{CD} = 135°$, find $\widehat{DA}$.

9. If $\overline{BD} \perp \overline{CA}$ and $\overline{BD}$ passes through the center of the circle, find CP if $AP = 17$ cm.

10. If $AP = 5$ ft, $CP = 6$ ft, and $BP = 3$ ft, find PD.

11. If two chords in a circle are equal, what can be said about their distance from the center of the circle?

Exercises 12–14 refer to the figure below.

12. If $\widehat{BD} = 68°$ and $\widehat{AC} = 28°$, find $\angle P$.　　13. If $\widehat{AC} = 30°$ and $\angle P = 24°$, find $\widehat{BD}$.

14. If $PB = 12$ ft, $PA = 3$ ft, and $PC = 4$ ft, find PD.

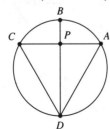

Exercises 7–10

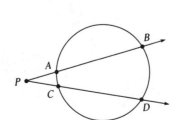

Exercises 12–14

281

15. *Given:* $ABCD$ is a rectangle
   Prove: $\overset{\frown}{AB} = \overset{\frown}{CD}$

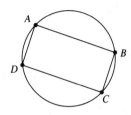

Exercise 15

16. *Given:* $\overline{AD} \perp \overline{BC}$ and $\overline{AD}$ contains the center O
   Prove: $\overset{\frown}{AB} = \overset{\frown}{AC}$

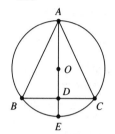

Exercise 16

Section 7.3

Exercises 17–22 refer to the figure below.

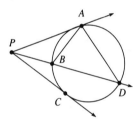

17. If $\overset{\frown}{AB} = 66°$, find $\angle PAB$.

18. If $\angle ADB = 35°$, find $\angle PAB$.

19. If $\overset{\frown}{AD} = 130°$ and $\overset{\frown}{AB} = 64°$, find $\angle APD$.

20. If $\overset{\frown}{ABC} = 130°$, find $\angle APC$.

21. If $AP = 38$ cm, find CP.

22. If $AP = 20$ ft and $DP = 30$ ft, find BP.

23. *Given:* $\overset{\frown}{BD} = 2\overset{\frown}{AC}$
   Prove: $PC = BC$

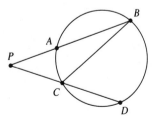

Exercise 23

24. *Given:* $\overline{AD}$ and $\overline{DC}$ are tangent to the circle and $ABCD$ is a parallelogram

   Prove: $ABCD$ is a rhombus

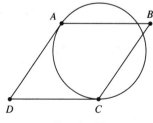

Exercise 24

282

25. *Given:* $\overline{AB}$ is a common internal tangent to the circles centered at O and P, and $\overleftrightarrow{OP}$ is the line of centers

Prove: $\angle O = \angle P$

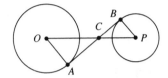

Exercise 25

26. Prove that if two circles are tangent externally, tangents to the circles from a point on their common internal tangent are equal.

27. Construct a tangent to a circle at a point on the circle.

28. If an airplane is flying at an altitude of 5 mi, how far to the nearest tenth of a mile is the airplane from the horizon? Use 4000 mi for the radius of the earth.

Section 7.4

Exercises 29–30 refer to the figure below.

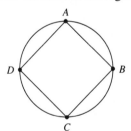

29. If $\angle D = 88°$, find $\angle B$.   **30.** If $\overline{AD} \parallel \overline{BC}$ and $AD = BC$, find $\angle D$.

31. Inscribe a square in a circle. Bisect a side of the square and use the result to inscribe a regular octagon in the circle.

32. Construct a regular hexagon and inscribe a circle in it.

33. What is the measure of each central angle in a regular 18-gon?

34. How many sides does a regular polygon have if each central angle has measure 10°?

35. Find the length of a side of a regular hexagon that is inscribed in a circle with radius 14 cm.

36. Prove that a radius of a regular polygon bisects an interior angle of the polygon.

283

37. Find the area of a sector of a circle, correct to the nearest tenth of a square inch if the radius of the circle is 11.4 inches and the arc of the sector is 18°. Use 3.14 for π.

38. Find the area of a segment of a circle formed by two radii measuring 10 cm that form a central angle of 60°. Give the area correct to the nearest tenth of a square centimeter. Use 3.14 for π.

39. Find the area of a regular hexagon with sides 30 yd. Give the area correct to the nearest tenth of a square yard.

40. Estimate the area of a regular 30-gon with apothem 15.5 ft. Use 3.14 for π.

41. Find the area of the grey region in the figure below. The arcs are semicircles with centers at the midpoints of the sides of the square. Leave your answer in terms of π.

4 yd

Exercise 41

42. To the nearest tenth, what is the length of an arc in a circle of radius 5.2 ft formed by a central angle measuring 40°?

PRACTICE TEST

1. Find the circumference and area of a circle with diameter 12.6 cm. Use 3.14 for π and give answers correct to the nearest tenth.

Problems 2–5 refer to the figure below in which O is the center of the circle, $\angle BOD = 130°$, $\angle ADC = 30°$, $BE = 6$ cm, $EC = 2$ cm, $AE = 4$ cm.

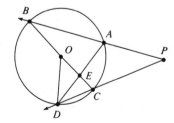

2. Find $\angle BAD$.   **3.** Find $\angle P$.   **4.** Find DE.   **5.** Find $\angle AEC$.

284

Problems 6–7 refer to the figure below in which O is the center of the circle.

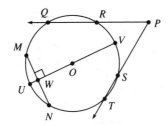

6. If $\overline{MN} \perp \overline{UV}$ and $MW = 4$ cm, find NW.

7. If $PQ = 12$ cm, $PR = 6$ cm, and $PT = 9$ cm find PS.

8. If $\overline{PA}$ and $\overline{PB}$ are two tangents to a circle at points A and B from common point P outside the circle, and $PA = 15$ ft, find PB.

9. Construct a tangent to a circle from a point outside the circle.

10. Quadrilateral $ABCD$ is inscribed in a circle with $\angle A$ opposite $\angle C$. If $\angle B = 100°$, find $\angle D$.

11. Construct an equilateral triangle and inscribe a circle in it.

12. What is the measure of each central angle in a regular octagon?

13. Find the area of a regular polygon with perimeter 56 yd and apothem 7 yd.

14. Find the area of a segment of a circle formed by the chord joining the endpoints of two radii each measuring 8 cm and forming a central angle of 60°.

15. Prove that the tangents to a circle at the ends of a diameter are parallel.

285

Part 3

CHAPTER 7

7.1 **Section 3.1**

PRACTICE EXERCISES

1. Since the circumference of a circle is given by

$$C = 2\pi r,$$

substitute 23.0 for C and 3.14 for π and solve for r.

$$23.0 = 2(3.14)r$$

$$\frac{23.0}{2(3.14)} = r$$

$$3.6624204 \approx r$$

Thus, to the nearest tenth of a foot, r = 3.7 ft.

3. Since $\angle ACB = 60°$ and $\angle ACB$ is an inscribed angle,

$$\angle ACB = \frac{1}{2}\overparen{AB},$$

thus,

$$60° = \frac{1}{2}\overparen{AB}$$

$$120° = \overparen{AB}$$

Also,

$$\overparen{ACB} = 360° - \overparen{AB} = 360° - 120° = 240°.$$

2. First find the area of the triangle.

$$A_{Triangle} = \frac{1}{2}bh = \frac{1}{2}(10)(5) = 25 \text{ in}^2$$

The area of each circular hole is

$$A_{circle} = \pi r^2 = \pi(1)^2 = \pi \approx 3.14 \text{ in}^2.$$

The desired area is the area of the triangle minus three times the area of one circular hole.

$$A = 25 - 3(3.14) = 15.58 \approx 15.6 \text{ in}^2.$$

SECTION EXERCISES

1. d = 2r = 2(11) = 22 in

5. Since d = 2r, $r = \frac{d}{2} = \frac{16}{2} = 8$ in.

9. $C = 2\pi r = 2\pi(7) = 14\pi$ yd;
   $A = \pi r^2 = \pi(7)^2 = 49\pi$ yd^2

13. $C = 2\pi r = 2(3.14)(4.10) = 25.75$ ft;
    $A = \pi r^2 = (3.14)(4.10)^2 = 52.78$ ft^2

17. The cross-sectional area of a $\frac{3}{4}$-inch diameter pipe is $A = \pi r^2 = (3.14)\left(\frac{3}{8}\right)^2$. The cross-sectional area of a $\frac{1}{2}$-inch diameter pipe is $A = \pi r^2 = (3.14)\left(\frac{1}{4}\right)^2$.

3. d = 2r = $2\left(\frac{3}{4}\right)$ = 6 ft

7. Since d = 2r, $r = \frac{d}{2} = \frac{\frac{2}{3}}{2} = \frac{2}{3} \cdot \frac{1}{2} = \frac{1}{3}$ ft.

11. Since d = 2r, $r = \frac{d}{2} = \frac{\frac{4}{3}}{2} = \frac{4}{3} \cdot \frac{1}{2} = \frac{2}{3}$ cm.

    $C = 2\pi r = 2\pi\left(\frac{2}{3}\right) = \frac{4}{3}\pi$ cm ;
    $A = \pi r^2 = \pi\left(\frac{2}{3}\right)^2 = \pi\left(\frac{4}{9}\right) = \frac{4}{9}\pi$ cm^2

15. Since d = 2r, $r = \frac{d}{2} = \frac{12.00}{2} = 6.00$.

    $C = 2\pi r = 2(3.14)(6.00) = 37.68$ mi;
    $A = \pi r^2 = (3.14)(6.00)^2 = 113.04$ mi^2

19. The area of a 12-inch diameter pizza is
    $A = \pi r^2 = (3.14)(6)^2 = 113.04$ in^2.

    The cost per square inch is given by

    $$\frac{4.50}{113.04} = \$0.0398.$$

Thus, the amount of additional area is

$(3.14)(\frac{3}{8})^2 - (3.14)(\frac{1}{4})^2 = 0.2453125,$

which is approximately 0.25 in².

The area of a 16-inch diameter pizza is

$A = \pi r^2 = (3.14)(8)^2 = 200.96.$

The cost per square inch is given by

$\frac{7.50}{200.96} = \$0.0373.$

Thus, the 16-inch pizza costs less per square inch.

21. Area of Parallelogram = bh = (22)(12)

$= 264$ mm²

Area of Circle = $\pi r^2 = 3.14(3)^2 = 28.26$ mm²

Area of Shaded Part = 264 - 28.26

$= 235.74$ mm²

23. Area of Trapezoid = $\frac{1}{2}(b + b')h$

$= \frac{1}{2}(11 + 22)(11)$

$= 181.5$ cm²

Area of one circle = $\pi r^2 = (3.14)(2.5)^2$

$= 19.625$ cm²

Area of Shaded Part = 181.5 - 2(19.625)

$= 142.25$ cm²

25. (a) central angle   (b) inscribed angle
(c) Since central angle $\angle AOC = 120°$,
$\overarc{AC} = 120°$.   (d) $\overarc{ABC} = 360° - \overarc{AC} =$
$= 360° - 120° = 240°$ (e) $\angle ABC = \frac{1}{2}\overarc{AC}$
$= \frac{1}{2}(120°) = 60°$ (f) The arc intercepted by
$\angle ABC$ is twice the measure of $\angle ABC$, which
is $2(60°) = 120°$.

27. (a) Since inscribed angle $\angle CBA = 32°$,
central angle $\angle COA = 64°$. Thus,
$\overarc{ADC} = 64°$ also.   (b) $\overarc{ABC} = 360° - 64°$
$= 296°$.   (c) $\angle AOC = 64°$ (twice inscribed
angle $\angle ABC$ which is 32°).   (d) $\angle AEC$
$= \angle ABC = 32°$.

29. <u>Proof:</u>

STATEMENTS	REASONS
1. $\overline{AB} \perp \overline{BC}$	1. Given
2. $\angle ABC$ is a right angle	2. $\perp$ lines form rt $\angle$'s
3. $\angle ABC = 90°$	3. Def. of rt. $\angle$
4. $\frac{1}{2}\overarc{ADC} = \angle ABC$	4. Theorem 7.2
5. $\overarc{ADC} = 2\angle ABC$	5. Mult.-div. law
6. $\overarc{ADC} = 2(90°) = 180°$	6. Substitution law

31. <u>Construction:</u> Draw radius $\overline{OC}$

<u>Proof:</u>

STATEMENTS	REASONS
1. $\overline{AB}$ is a diameter	1. Given
2. $\overline{AC} \parallel \overline{OD}$	2. Given
3. $\overline{OC}$ is a radius	3. By construction
4. $\angle CAO = \angle DOB$	4. Corr. $\angle$'s are =
5. $\overline{AO} = \overline{OC}$	5. Radii are =
6. $\angle CAO = \angle ACO$	6. $\angle$'s opp = sides of $\triangle$ are =
7. $\angle ACO = \angle COD$	7. Alt. int. $\angle$'s are =
8. $\angle CAO = \angle COD$	8. Transitive law
9. $\angle DOB = \angle COD$	9. Substitution law
10. $\overarc{BD} = \angle DOB$ and $\overarc{DC} = \angle COD$	10. Def. of measure of arc
11. $\overarc{BD} = \overarc{DC}$	11. Sym. and trans. laws

33. The distance the earth travels in one year is equal to the circumference of a circle with radius 93,000,000.

$$C = 2\pi r = 2(3.14)(93,000,000)$$
$$= 5.8404 \times 10^8 \text{ miles}$$

The answer is given in scientific notation as shown on a calculator.

35. To find the distance traveled in one minute, divide the distance traveled in one year (Exercise 33) by

$$(365)(24)(60)$$

to obtain 1111.19 miles.

Section 3.2

7.2

PRACTICE EXERCISES

1. Since $\overset{\frown}{AD} = 112°$ and $\overset{\frown}{BC} = 176°$, by Theorem 7.5,

$$\angle APD = \frac{1}{2}(\overset{\frown}{AD} + \overset{\frown}{BC})$$
$$= \frac{1}{2}(112° + 176°)$$
$$= \frac{1}{2}(288°)$$
$$= 144°$$

Since $\angle 1$ and $\angle APD$ are supplementary,

$$\angle 1 + \angle APD = 180°$$
$$\angle 1 + 144° = 180°$$
$$\angle 1 = 180° - 144°$$
$$\angle 1 = 36°$$

2. The reason for Statement 1 is: Given

Statement 2 is: AO = BO
Both are radii and radii are equal.

The reason for Statement 3 is: Def. of isosc. Δ
An isosceles Δ has two equal sides.

Statement 4 is: $\overline{AB}$ is the base of ΔAOB

Statement 5 is: $\overline{CE}$ passes through O.

3. By Theorem 7.13,

$$(AP)(PB) = (CP)(PD).$$

Substituting we have:

$$3(PB) = (4)(6)$$
$$3PB = 24$$
$$PB = 8 \text{ cm}$$

SECTION EXERCISES

1. $\angle AEB = \frac{1}{2}(\overset{\frown}{AB} + \overset{\frown}{CD}) = \frac{1}{2}(58° + 130°)$
$$= \frac{1}{2}(188°) = 94°.$$

3. Since equal chords form equal arcs, $\overset{\frown}{AB} = 60°$.

5. Since a line through the center of a circle perpendicular to a chord bisects the chord, AE = CE. Thus, CE = 12 in.

7. Since $\overline{BD}$ passes through the center of the circle and bisects AC (we are given AE = CE = 5 ft), it is perpendicular to chord $\overline{AC}$ making $\angle AED = 90°$.

9. By Theorem 7.13, (AE)(EC) = (BE)(ED). Substituting 5 for AE, 6 for EC, and 3 for BE we have (5)(6) = (3)(ED) which gives 30 = 3ED or ED = 10 cm.

11. By Theorem 7.10, since AB = CD = 14 ft, OE = OF so that OE = 11 ft.

13. Since OE = OF = 5 cm, by Theorem 7.11, AB = CD. Since $\overline{OE} \perp \overline{AB}$ and $\overline{OF} \perp \overline{CD}$, $\overline{OE}$ bisects $\overline{AB}$ and $\overline{OF}$ bisects $\overline{CD}$ by Theorem 7.8. Thus AE = DF, and since AE = 4 cm, DF = 4 cm.

17. $\angle P = \frac{1}{2}(\overset{\frown}{AB} - \overset{\frown}{CD}) = \frac{1}{2}(130° - 50°) = \frac{1}{2}(80°)$
$= 40°$

15. Since $\overset{\frown}{AGB} = \overset{\frown}{DHC}$, by Theorem 7.7, AB = DC. Since AB = DC, by Theorem 7.10, OE = OF. Since OE = 15 cm, OF = 15 cm.

19. $\angle P = \frac{1}{2}(\overset{\frown}{AB} - \overset{\frown}{CD})$. Substitute 120° for $\overset{\frown}{AB}$ and 45° for $\angle P$ and solve for $\overset{\frown}{CD}$.

$45° = \frac{1}{2}(120° - \overset{\frown}{CD})$

$90° = 120° - \overset{\frown}{CD}$ Multiply both sides by 2

$-30° = -\overset{\frown}{CD}$ Subtract 120° from both sides

$30° = \overset{\frown}{CD}$ Multiply both sides by -1

21. By Theorem 7.15, (AP)(CP) = (PB)(PD). Substitute 12 for AP, 5 for CP, and 15 for PB.

$(12)(5) = (15)(PD)$

$\frac{(12)(5)}{15} = PD$

$4 = PD$

Thus, PD = 4 ft.

23. By Theorem 7.15, (AP)(CP) = (BP)(DP). Since AP = AC + CP = 5 + 4 = 9 cm, and BP = BD + DP = BD + 3, substituting we have:

$(9)(4) = (BD + 3)(3)$

$36 = 3BD + 9$

$27 = 3BD$

$9 = BD$

Thus, BD = 9 cm.

25. Since $\angle DAB = 30°$, $\overset{\frown}{BD} = 60°$. By Theorem 7.5, $\angle 1 = \frac{1}{2}(\overset{\frown}{BD} + \overset{\frown}{AC})$ so $40° = \frac{1}{2}(60° + \overset{\frown}{AC})$. Then $80° = 60° + \overset{\frown}{AC}$ so that $\overset{\frown}{AC} = 20°$. Since $\angle ABC = \frac{1}{2}\overset{\frown}{AC}$, $\angle ABC = \frac{1}{2}(20°) = 10°$.

27. Proof:

STATEMENTS	REASONS
1. $\overset{\frown}{BC} + \overset{\frown}{AD} = 180°$	1. Given
2. $\angle AED = 90°$	2. $\angle$ formed by chords is $\frac{1}{2}$ sum arc + arc of vertical $\angle$ (Theorem 7.5)
3. $\overset{\frown}{AB} + \overset{\frown}{CD} + \overset{\frown}{BC} + \overset{\frown}{AD} = 360°$	3. A circle is an arc of 360°.
4. $\overset{\frown}{AB} + \overset{\frown}{CD} = 180°$	4. Add.-subtr. law and 1 and 3
5. $\angle AEB = 90°$	5. Same as 2
6. $\angle AED$ and $\angle AEB$ are adjacent angles	6. Def of adj $\angle$'s
7. $\overline{AC} \perp \overline{BD}$	7. Def of $\perp$ lines

29.   Given: Chords $\overline{AB}$ and $\overline{CD}$, AB = CD, and $\overline{AB}$ intersects $\overline{CD}$ at P

Construction: Draw chords $\overline{BC}$, $\overline{AD}$, and $\overline{BD}$

Prove: AP = CP and BP = DP

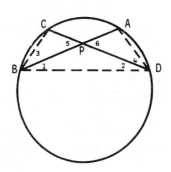

Proof: STATEMENTS

1. $\overline{AB}$ and $\overline{CD}$ are chords with AB = CD
2. $\overarc{BCA}$ = $\overarc{CAD}$
3. $\overarc{BCA}$ = $\overarc{BC}$ + $\overarc{CA}$ and $\overarc{CAD}$ = $\overarc{CA}$ + $\overarc{AD}$
4. $\overarc{BC}$ + $\overarc{CA}$ = $\overarc{CA}$ + $\overarc{AD}$
5. $\overarc{BC}$ = $\overarc{AD}$
6. ∠1 = ∠2
7. In ΔBPD, BP = DP
8. ∠3 = ∠4
9. ∠5 = ∠6
10. ΔCPB $\cong$ ΔAPD
11. AP = CP

REASONS

1. Given
2. = chords have = arcs
3. Arc add. post.
4. Substitution law
5. Arc add. post.
6. ∠ intercepting = arcs are =
7. Sides opp. = ∠'s are =
8. Both intercept $\overarc{AC}$
9. Vertical ∠'s are =
10. ASA = ASA
11. cpoctae

31.   Given: $\overarc{AB}$ = $\overarc{CD}$

Prove: AB = CD

Construction: Draw radii $\overline{AO}$, $\overline{BO}$, $\overline{CO}$, and $\overline{DO}$

Proof: STATEMENTS

1. $\overarc{AB}$ = $\overarc{CD}$
2. $\overline{AO}$, $\overline{BO}$, $\overline{CO}$, and $\overline{DO}$ are radii
3. AO = BO = CO = DO
4. ∠BOA = ∠COD
5. ΔBOA $\cong$ ΔCOD
6. AB = CD

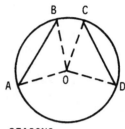

REASONS

1. Given
2. By construction
3. Radii are =
4. Def of measure of an arc
5. SAS = SAS
6. cpoctae

33. Given: $\overline{AB}$ and $\overline{CD}$ are chords with $\overline{OE} \perp \overline{AB}$, $\overline{OF} \perp \overline{CD}$, and OE = OF

Prove: AB = CD

Construction: Draw radii $\overline{AO}$, $\overline{BO}$, $\overline{CO}$, and $\overline{DO}$

Proof: STATEMENTS

1. $\overline{AB}$ and $\overline{CD}$ are chords
2. $\overline{OE} \perp \overline{AB}$ and $\overline{OF} \perp \overline{CD}$
3. ∠AEO, ∠BEO, ∠CFO, and ∠DFO are right angles
4. OE = OF
5. AO = BO = CO = DO
6. ΔAEO, ΔBEO, ΔCFO, and ΔDFO are right triangles
7. ΔAEO $\cong$ ΔCFO and ΔBEO $\cong$ ΔDFO
8. AE = CF and BE = DF

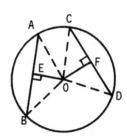

REASONS

1. Given
2. Given
3. $\perp$ lines form rt. ∠'s
4. Given
5. Radii are =
6. Def. of rt. Δ
7. HL = HL
8. cpoctae

9. AE + BE = CF + DF

10. AB = AE + BE and CD = CF + DF

11. AB = CD

9. Add.-subtr. law

10. Seg. add. post.

11. Substitution law

35. Suppose AB = 10 inches, P is the midpoint of $\overparen{AB}$, $\overline{PQ} \perp \overline{AB}$, and PQ = 1 inch as shown in the figure to the right. We want to find PO. Extend PO to form segment PR. By Theorem 7.13, (PQ)(QR) = (AQ)(BQ). Substitute 5 for AQ and BQ (a ⊥ line bisects the chord) and 1 for PQ.

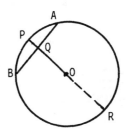

$$(1)(QR) = (5)(5)$$

$$QR = 25$$

Then PQ + QR = 1 + 25 = 26 is the length of a diameter making the radius $\frac{1}{2}(26)$ = 13 inches.

Section 3.3

7.3

PRACTICE EXERCISES

1. Using Figure 7.28, as in Example 1, we have

$$(OS)^2 = (SA)^2 + (OA)^2$$

$$(SA)^2 = (OS)^2 - (OA)^2$$

$$= [OB + SB]^2 - (OA)^2$$

$$= [4000 + 95]^2 - (4000)^2$$

$$= [4095]^2 - (4000)^2$$

$$= 769,025$$

Taking the square root with a calculator we obtain

$$SA \approx 876.9407$$

or, to the nearest mile, the horizon is about 877 miles away.

2. By Theorem 7.18,

$$\angle APD = \frac{1}{2}(\overparen{ACD} - \overparen{ABD}).$$

Since $\overparen{ACD}$ = 236°, and $\overparen{ACD} + \overparen{ABD}$ = 360°, $\overparen{ABD}$ = 360° - 236° = 124°. Substituting we have:

$$\angle APD = \frac{1}{2}(236° - 124°)$$

$$= \frac{1}{2}(112°)$$

$$= 56°$$

SECTION EXERCISES

1. By Theorem 7.16, $\angle PAD = \frac{1}{2}\overparen{AD} = \frac{1}{2}(70°) = 35°$

3. Since $\angle 1$ = 36°, by Theorem 7.2, $\angle 1 = \frac{1}{2}\overparen{AD}$. Thus, 36° = $\frac{1}{2}\overparen{AD}$ making $\overparen{AD}$ = 72°. By Theorem 7.16, $\angle PAD = \frac{1}{2}\overparen{AD} = \frac{1}{2}(72°) = 36°$.

5. By Theorem 7.16, $\angle PAD = \frac{1}{2}\overparen{AD}$ and by Theorem 7.2, $\angle 1 = \frac{1}{2}\overparen{AD}$. Thus, $\angle 1 = \angle PAD = 40°$.

7. By Theorem 7.17, $\angle APD = \frac{1}{2}(\overparen{AB} - \overparen{AD}) = \frac{1}{2}(140° - 70°) = \frac{1}{2}(70°) = 35°$.

9. By Theorem 7.2, $\angle 1 = \frac{1}{2}\overset{\frown}{AD}$ and $\angle 3 = \frac{1}{2}\overset{\frown}{AB}$. Then $36° = \frac{1}{2}\overset{\frown}{AD}$ and $70° = \frac{1}{2}\overset{\frown}{AB}$ so that $\overset{\frown}{AD} = 72°$ and $\overset{\frown}{AB} = 140°$. By Theorem 7.17, $\angle APD = \frac{1}{2}(\overset{\frown}{AB} - \overset{\frown}{AD}) = \frac{1}{2}(140° - 72°)$ $= \frac{1}{2}(68°) = 34°$.

11. By Theorem 7.17, $\angle APD = \frac{1}{2}(\overset{\frown}{AB} - \overset{\frown}{AD})$. Thus, $40° = \frac{1}{2}(138° - \overset{\frown}{AD})$ so that $80° = 138° - \overset{\frown}{AD}$ which means $-58° = -\overset{\frown}{AD}$ or $\overset{\frown}{AD} = 58°$. By Theorem 7.2 $\angle 1 = \frac{1}{2}\overset{\frown}{AD} = \frac{1}{2}(58°) = 29°$.

13. Since $\overset{\frown}{ADC} = 130°$ and $\overset{\frown}{ABC} = 360° - \overset{\frown}{ADC}$, $\overset{\frown}{ABC} = 360° - 130° = 230°$. By Theorem 7.18, $\angle APC = \frac{1}{2}(\overset{\frown}{ABC} - \overset{\frown}{ADC}) = \frac{1}{2}(230° - 130°)$ $= \frac{1}{2}(100°) = 50°$.

15. Since $\angle 1 = 35°$ and $\angle 2 = 30°$, by Theorem 7.2, $\overset{\frown}{AD} = 70°$ and $\overset{\frown}{CD} = 60°$. Then $\overset{\frown}{ADC} = \overset{\frown}{AD} + \overset{\frown}{CD} = 70° + 60° = 130°$, making $\overset{\frown}{ABC} = 360° - \overset{\frown}{ADC} = 360° - 130° = 230°$. By Theorem 7.18, $\angle APC = \frac{1}{2}(\overset{\frown}{ABC} - \overset{\frown}{ADC})$ $= \frac{1}{2}(230° - 130°) = \frac{1}{2}(100°) = 50°$.

17. By Theorem 7.19, AP = CP so that CP = 17 cm.

19. By Theorem 7.20, AP is the mean proportional between BP and DP. Thus,

$$\frac{BP}{AP} = \frac{AP}{DP}$$

$$\frac{18}{12} = \frac{12}{DP} \qquad \text{Substitute 18 for BP and 12 for AP}$$

$$18DP = (12)(12) \quad \text{Means-extremes property}$$

$$DP = \frac{(12)(12)}{18} = 8 \text{ cm}$$

21. Let BD = x, then BP = x + DP = x + 10. By Theorem 7.20, AP is the mean proportional between BP and DP. Thus,

$$\frac{BP}{AP} = \frac{AP}{DP}$$

$$\frac{x + 10}{15} = \frac{15}{10} \qquad \text{Substitute } x + 10 \text{ for BP, 15 for AP, and 10 for DP}$$

$$10(x + 10) = (15)(15) \quad \text{Means-extremes property}$$

$$10x + 100 = 225 \qquad \text{Distributive law}$$

$$10x = 125 \qquad \text{Subtract 100 from both sides}$$

$$x = 12.5 \qquad \text{Divide both sides by 10}$$

Thus, BD = 12.5 yd.

23. There are two internal tangents, m and n, to circles in the given positions as shown in the figure to the right.

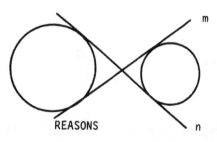

25. Proof:

STATEMENTS	REASONS
1. $\overset{\leftrightarrow}{PA}$ and $\overset{\leftrightarrow}{PB}$ are tangents to the circle	1. Given
2. $\angle P = \frac{1}{2}(\overset{\frown}{ADB} - \overset{\frown}{ACB})$	2. Theorem 7.18
3. $\overset{\frown}{ADB} + \overset{\frown}{ACB} = 360°$	3. Circle measures 360°
4. $\overset{\frown}{ADB} = 360° - \overset{\frown}{ACB}$	4. Arc add. post.

5. $\angle P = \frac{1}{2}([360° - \overarc{ACB}] - \overarc{ACB})$ 5. Substitution law

6. $\angle P = \frac{1}{2}(360° - 2\overarc{ACB})$ 6. Distributive law

7. $\angle P = 180° - \overarc{ACB}$ 7. Distributive law

8. $\angle P + \overarc{ACB} = 180°$ 8. Add.-subtr. law

27. <u>Construction:</u>   Extend $\overleftrightarrow{AB}$ and $\overleftrightarrow{CD}$ to meet at point P

<u>Proof:</u>   STATEMENTS   REASONS

1. $\overleftrightarrow{AB}$ and $\overleftrightarrow{CD}$ are common external tangents to circles that are not congruent   1. Given

2. $\overleftrightarrow{AB}$ and $\overleftrightarrow{CD}$ meet at P   2. By construction since O's are not $\cong$

3. AP = CP and BP = DP   3. Theorem 7.19

4. AB = AP - BP and CD = CP - DP   4. Seg. add. post.

5. AP - BP = CP - DP   5. Add.-subtr. law

6. AB = CD   6. Substitution law

29.   <u>Given:</u> $\overleftrightarrow{AP}$ and $\overleftrightarrow{BP}$ are tangents
   <u>Prove:</u> $\angle APB = \frac{1}{2}(\overarc{ADB} - \overarc{ACB})$

<u>Construction:</u> Choose point D on major arc AB and draw secant $\overrightarrow{PD}$ intersecting the circle at C and D.

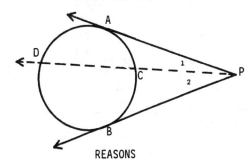

<u>Proof:</u>   STATEMENTS   REASONS

1. $\overleftrightarrow{AP}$ and $\overleftrightarrow{BP}$ are tangents   1. Given

2. $\overrightarrow{PD}$ is a secant   2. By construction

3. $\angle 1 = \frac{1}{2}(\overarc{AD} - \overarc{AC})$ and $\angle 2 = \frac{1}{2}(\overarc{DB} - \overarc{BC})$ 3. Theorem 7.17

4. $\angle APB = \angle 1 + \angle 2$ 4. $\angle$ add. post.

5. $\angle 1 + \angle 2 = \frac{1}{2}(\overarc{AD} - \overarc{AC}) + \frac{1}{2}(\overarc{DB} - \overarc{BC})$ 5. Add.-subtr. law

6. $\angle 1 + \angle 2 = \frac{1}{2}[\overarc{AD} + \overarc{DB} - (\overarc{AC} + \overarc{BC})]$ 6. Simplify

7. $\overarc{AD} + \overarc{DB} = \overarc{ADB}$ and $\overarc{AC} + \overarc{BC} = \overarc{ACB}$ 7. Arc add. post.

8. $\angle APB = \frac{1}{2}(\overarc{ADB} - \overarc{ACB})$ 8. Substitution law

31. Use Construction 7.1.

33. Use Construction 7.3.

35. Use construction 7.4

37. Follow the solution to Example 1. Using the same notation and figure we have:

$(SA)^2 = (OS)^2 - (OA)^2$

$= [OB + SB]^2 - (OA)^2$

$= [4000 + 1]^2 - (4000)^2$

$$= (4001)^2 - (4000)^2$$
$$= 8001$$

Taking the square root of both sides we have SA = 89.4 miles, correct to the nearest tenth of a mile.

39. We have BC = 5 ft and AB = 4 ft. We must find CD which is given by:

$$CD = \sqrt{(AC)(BC)}$$
$$= \sqrt{(9)(5)} \qquad \begin{array}{l} AC = AB + BC \\ = 5 + 4 = 9 \text{ ft} \end{array}$$
$$= \sqrt{45}$$

Thus, CD = 6.7 ft, correct to the nearest tenth of a foot.

Section 3.4

7.4

PRACTICE EXERCISES

1. First divide the circle into 8 equal arcs using the same method as was shown in Example 1. Then use Construction 7.1 to construct the tangent to the circle at each of these eight points on the circle. The points of intersection of these tangents form the vertices of the desired circumscribed octagon.

2. Since the measure of each angle of a regular n-gon is given by

$$a = \frac{360°}{n} \ ,$$

if a = 24°, substitute and solve for n.

$$24° = \frac{360°}{n}$$
$$(24°)n = 360°$$
$$n = \frac{360°}{24°} = 15$$

Thus, the regular polygon has 15 sides.

SECTION EXERCISES

1. By Theroem 7.23, $\angle A$ and $\angle C$ are supplementary. Thus, $\angle A + \angle C = 180°$; $86° + \angle C = 180°$; $\angle C = 180° - 86° = 94°$.

3. Since $\angle A$ and $\angle C$ are supplementary (by Theorem 7.23), $\angle A + \angle C = 180°$. Substituting into $\angle A + \angle B + \angle C = 276°$ we have $180° + \angle B = 276°$ making $\angle B = 276° - 180° = 96°$.

5. With $\overline{AB} \parallel \overline{DC}$ and AB = DC, opposite sides of the quadrilateral are parallel and equal making the quadrilateral a rectangle. Since all angles are 90°, $\angle A = 90°$.

7. Since $\angle A = \angle C$ and $\angle A + \angle C = 180°$ (by Theorem 7.23), $2\angle C = 180°$ making $\angle C = 90°$.

9. The endpoints of a diameter and the points of intersection of the circle with the perpendicular bisector of the diameter give four points that divide the circle into four equal arcs. By Theorem 7.25, the chords formed by these arcs form a regular 4-gon, that is, form a square.

11. Since the length of a side of a regular inscribed hexagon is equal to a radius, mark off six points on the circle with a compass set at the length of the radius. By Theorem 7.25, these points form the vertices of the desired inscribed regular hexagon.

13. Since the length of a side of a regular inscribed hexagon is equal to the radius, by marking off six points on the circle with a compass set at the length of the radius, and joining every other point we form an equilateral triangle that is inscribed in the circle (by Theorem 7.25).

15. Use Construction 4.3 and Construction 7.6

17. Use Construction 3.4 and Construction 7.5.

19. By Theorem 7.29, each central angle measures $\frac{360°}{n}$ where n = 3. Thus, each angle is $\frac{360°}{3} = 120°$.

21. By Theorem 7.29, each central angle measures $\frac{360°}{n}$ where n = 5. Thus, each angle is $\frac{360°}{5} = 72°$.

23. By Theorem 7.29, each central angle measures $\frac{360°}{n}$ where n = 9. Thus, each angle is $\frac{360°}{9} = 40°$.

25. By Theorem 7.29, $45° = \frac{360°}{n}$. Thus, 45n = 360 so n = $\frac{360}{45}$ = 8. The polygon has 8 sides (an octagon).

27. By Theorem 7.29, $20° = \frac{360°}{n}$. Thus, 20n = 360 so n = $\frac{360}{20}$ = 18. The polygon has 18 sides.

29. Given: ABCD is a parallelogram inscribed in a circle

Prove: ABCD is a rectangle

Proof:

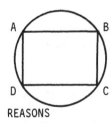

STATEMENTS	REASONS
1. ABCD is a parallelogram	1. Given
2. AB = DC and AD = BC	2. Opp sides of ▱ are =
3. $\overset{\frown}{AB}$ = $\overset{\frown}{DC}$ and $\overset{\frown}{AD}$ = $\overset{\frown}{BC}$	3. = chords form = arcs
4. $\overset{\frown}{AB}$ + $\overset{\frown}{AD}$ = $\overset{\frown}{DC}$ + $\overset{\frown}{BC}$	4. Add.-subtr. law
5. $\overset{\frown}{BAD}$ = $\overset{\frown}{AB}$ + $\overset{\frown}{AD}$ and $\overset{\frown}{BCD}$ = $\overset{\frown}{DC}$ + $\overset{\frown}{BC}$	5. Arc add. post.
6. $\overset{\frown}{BAD}$ = $\overset{\frown}{BCD}$	6. Substitution law
7. $\angle A = \frac{1}{2}\overset{\frown}{BAD}$ and $\angle C = \frac{1}{2}\overset{\frown}{BCD}$	7. Insc. $\angle = \frac{1}{2}$ intercepted arc
8. $\angle A = \angle C$	8. From 6 and 7 using substitution
9. $\angle A$ and $\angle C$ are supplementary	9. Opp $\angle$'s of inscribed quad. are supp.
10. $\angle A + \angle C = 180°$	10. Def. of supp. $\angle$'s
11. $\angle A + \angle A = 180°$	11. Substitution law
12. $2\angle A = 180°$	12. Distributive law
13. $\angle A = 90°$	13. Mult.-div. law

14. ∠A is a right angle   14. Def. of rt. ∠

15. ABCD is a rectangle   15. Def. of ▭

31. The proof follows from the fact that each side is an equal chord of the <u>circumscribed</u> circle; hence the same distance from the center of the circle so that all radii of the inscribed circle must be equal.

33. The proof follows by circumscribing a circle around the regular polygon and using the fact that equal chords (the equal sides of the regular polygon) have equal central angles.

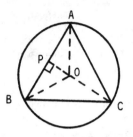

35. Consider an equilateral triangle inscribed in a circle with radius 4 cm as shown to the right. Draw altitude $\overline{OP}$ to side $\overline{AB}$. In right triangle $\triangle PBO$, $\angle PBO = 30°$, $\angle POB = 60°$, and hypotenuse $\overline{BO}$ (radius $\overline{BO}$) = 4 cm. Thus, by Theorem 6.14,

$$\overline{PB} = \frac{\sqrt{3}}{2}\,\overline{BO} = \frac{\sqrt{3}}{2}(4) = 2\sqrt{3}. \quad \text{Since } AB = 2PB,$$
$AB = 2(2\sqrt{3}) = 4\sqrt{3}$ cm.

Section 3.5

7.5

PRACTICE EXERCISES

1. Consider the figure to the right showing an inscribed square with side s. The apothem is $\frac{1}{2}$s. Using

$$A = \frac{1}{2}ap$$

we have

$$A = \frac{1}{2}\left(\frac{1}{2}s\right)(4s) = \frac{1}{4}s(4s) = \frac{1}{4}(4)(s^2) = s^2.$$

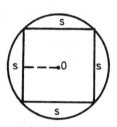

But the area of a square from before is given by

$$A = s^2.$$

Thus, the two formulas give the same result.

SECTION EXERCISES

1. By Postulate 7.7, the area of the colored sector is:

$$A = \frac{m}{360}\,\pi r^2$$
$$= \frac{90}{360}\,\pi(5)^2 \quad \text{Substitute 90 for m and 5 for r}$$
$$= \frac{1}{4}\pi(25) = \frac{25}{4}\,\pi \text{ cm}^2$$

By Postulate 7.8, the length of the arc of the sector is:

$$L = \frac{m}{180}\,\pi r$$
$$= \frac{90}{180}\,\pi(5) \quad \text{Substitute 90 for m and 5 for r}$$

3. By Postulate 7.7, the area of the colored sector is:

$$A = \frac{m}{360}\,\pi r^2$$
$$= \frac{45}{360}\,\pi(4)^2 \quad \text{Substitute 45 for m and 4 for r}$$
$$= \frac{1}{8}\,\pi(16) = 2\pi \text{ cm}^2$$

By Postulate 7.8, the length of the arc of the sector is:

$$L = \frac{m}{180}\,\pi r$$
$$= \frac{45}{180}\,\pi(4) \quad \text{Substitute 45 for m and 4 for r}$$

$$= \frac{1}{2}\pi(5) = \frac{5}{2}\pi \text{ cm}$$

$$= \frac{1}{4}\pi(4) = \pi \text{ cm}$$

5. The area of the colored segment is the area of the sector minus the area of the triangle. The area of the sector is:

$$A = \frac{m}{360}\pi r^2 = \frac{90}{360}\pi(4)^2 = \frac{1}{4}\pi(16)$$
$$= 4\pi \text{ yd}^2$$

The area of the triangle is:

$$A = \frac{1}{2}bh = \frac{1}{2}(4)(4) = 8 \text{ yd}^2$$

Thus, the area of the colored segment is:

$$4\pi - 8 \approx 4.6 \text{ yd}^2$$

7. The area of the colored segment is the area of the sector minus the area of the triangle. The area of the sector is:

$$A = \frac{m}{360}\pi r^2 = \frac{60}{360}\pi(12)^2 = \frac{1}{6}\pi(144)$$
$$= 24\pi \text{ ft}^2$$

The area of the triangle can be found by first drawing an altitude to the base which is also 12 ft, the same as the radius of the circle. This forms a 30°-60°-right triangle. The leg opposite the 60°-angle is the altitude and has length

$$\frac{\sqrt{3}}{2}(12) = 6\sqrt{3} \text{ ft}$$ by Theorem 6.14. Thus,

the area of the triangle is:

$$A = \frac{1}{2}bh = \frac{1}{2}(12)(6\sqrt{3}) = 36\sqrt{3} \text{ ft.}$$

Thus, the area of the colored segment is:

$$24\pi - 36\sqrt{3} \approx 13.0 \text{ ft}^2$$

9. The easiest method to use is to subtract the area of the 30°-60°-right triangle from the area of the semicircle. Since the hypotenuse of the triangle is 16 cm (twice the radius of the circle). One leg is 8 cm and the other is $\frac{\sqrt{3}}{2}(16) = 8\sqrt{3}$ cm. The legs are the base and height of the triangle so its area is:

$$A = \frac{1}{2}bh = \frac{1}{2}(8)(8\sqrt{3}) = 32\sqrt{3} \text{ cm}^2$$

The area of the semicircle is:

$$A = \frac{1}{2}\pi r^2 = \frac{1}{2}\pi(8)^2 = 32\pi \text{ cm}^2$$

Thus, the area of the colored region is:

$$32\pi - 32\sqrt{3} \approx 45.1 \text{ cm}^2$$

11. Since the diameter is 8.2 cm, the radius is $\frac{8.2}{2} = 4.1$ cm. Substitute 4.1 for r and 30 for m in

$$A = \frac{m}{360}\pi r^2 = \frac{30}{360}\pi(4.1)^2$$
$$= \frac{1}{12}\pi(4.1)^2$$
$$\approx 4.4 \text{ cm}^2.$$

13. Substitute 24π for A and 60 for m into

$$A = \frac{m}{360}\pi r^2$$ and solve for r.

$$24\pi = \frac{60}{360}\pi r^2$$

$$24 = \frac{1}{6}r^2 \qquad \text{Divide both sides by } \pi$$

$$144 = r^2 \qquad \text{Multiply both sides by 6}$$

$$\pm\sqrt{144} = r \qquad \text{Take square root of both sides}$$

$$\pm 12 = r$$

Discard the negative value, -12. Thus, the radius is 12 yd making the diameter twice this value or 24 yd.

15. Substitute 80 for p and 10 for a into
$$A = \frac{1}{2}ap.$$

$$A = \frac{1}{2}ap = \frac{1}{2}(10)(80) = (10)(40) = 400 \text{ yd}^2$$

17. Consider the regular hexagon with sides
    16 ft shown to the right. Draw an apothem
    $\overline{OA}$ and segment $\overline{OB}$ as shown.

    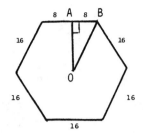

    Then AB = 8 and $\triangle AOB$ is a 30°-60°-right
    triangle. By Theorem 6.14,

    $$OA = \sqrt{3}AB = \sqrt{3}(8) = 8\sqrt{3} \text{ ft.}$$

    The perimeter of the hexagon is 6(16) = 96 ft.

    Thus, $a = 8\sqrt{3}$ and   p = 96 in $A = \frac{1}{2}ap$.

    $$A = \frac{1}{2}ap = \frac{1}{2}(8\sqrt{3})(96) = 4\sqrt{3}(96)$$
    $$= 384\sqrt{3} \text{ ft}^2$$

19. Let s be the side of a regular hexagon.
    Then the perimeter of the hexagon is
    p = 65. The apothem can also be expressed
    in terms of s. Consider the figure to the
    right. By Theorem 6.14,

    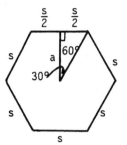

    $a = \sqrt{3}(\frac{s}{2}) = \frac{\sqrt{3}}{2} s$.

    Substitute 6s for p, $\frac{\sqrt{3}}{2}$ s for a, and
    $1350\sqrt{3}$ for A in $A = \frac{1}{2}ap$ and solve for s.

    $$1350\sqrt{3} = \frac{1}{2}(\frac{\sqrt{3}}{2} s)(6s)$$

    $$1350\sqrt{3} = \frac{6\sqrt{3}}{4} s^2$$

    $$\frac{4}{6\sqrt{3}} (1350\sqrt{3}) = s^2$$

    $$\frac{(4)(1350)}{6} = s^2$$

    $$900 = s^2$$

    $$\pm\sqrt{900} = s$$

    $$\pm 30 = s$$

    Discard the negative value, -30. Thus,
    each side of the regular hexagon is 30 cm.

21. The area of a regular 16-gon with apothem
    12 ft can be approximated by the area of
    the inscribed circle with radius 12 ft.

    $$A = \pi r^2 = \pi(12)^2 \approx 452.2 \text{ ft}^2$$

23. The area of the colored region is the area
    of the equilateral triangle minus the areas
    of the three congruent sectors. First find
    the altitude of the triangle. An altitude
    forms a 30°-60°-right triangle and by
    Theorem 6.14, the length of the altitude is
    $\frac{\sqrt{3}}{2}$ (hypotenuse) = $\frac{\sqrt{3}}{2}(4) = 2\sqrt{3}$ cm. Thus,
    the area of the triangle is:

    $$A = \frac{1}{2}bh = \frac{1}{2}(4)(2\sqrt{3}) = 4\sqrt{3} \text{ cm}^2$$

    The area of each sector is:

    $$A = \frac{m}{360} \pi r^2 = \frac{60}{360} \pi(2)^2 = \frac{1}{6} \pi(4) = \frac{2}{3} \pi \text{ cm}^2$$

    Thus, the area of the colored region is:

    $$4\sqrt{3} - 3(\frac{2}{3} \pi) = 4\sqrt{3} - 2\pi \approx 0.6 \text{ cm}^2$$

25. The proof is a direct result of Theorem 7.10.

27. The track is divided into four sections that can be found by subtracting the area of one equilateral triangle from the area of another equilateral triangle (the parts with central angle 60°) and into four sections that can be found by subtracting the area of one sector from another sector (the parts with central angle 30°). The altitude of the larger equilateral triangle is $\frac{\sqrt{3}}{2}$ (70) and the altitude of the smaller equilateral triangle is $\frac{\sqrt{3}}{2}$ (60). Thus, the area of the triangles are:

$$A = \frac{1}{2}(70)(\frac{\sqrt{3}}{2}(70)) \quad \text{and} \quad A = \frac{1}{2}(60)(\frac{\sqrt{3}}{2}(60))$$

$$= \frac{(70)^2}{4}\sqrt{3} \qquad\qquad\qquad = \frac{(60)^2}{4}\sqrt{3}$$

The area of this portion of the track is:

$$\frac{(70)^2}{4}\sqrt{3} - \frac{(60)^2}{4}\sqrt{3} = [(70)^2 - (60)^2]\frac{\sqrt{3}}{4}$$

The four sections of the track of this form have area 4 times this value which is

$$\sqrt{3}[(70)^2 - (60)^2].$$

The areas of the sectors are:

$$A = \frac{m}{360}\pi r^2 \qquad \text{and} \qquad A = \frac{m}{360}\pi r^2$$

$$= \frac{30}{360}\pi(70)^2 \qquad\qquad = \frac{30}{360}\pi(60)^2$$

$$= \frac{(70)^2}{12}\pi \qquad\qquad\quad = \frac{(60)^2}{12}\pi$$

The area of this portion of the track is:

$$\frac{(70)^2}{12}\pi - \frac{(60)^2}{12}\pi = [(70)^2 - (60)^2]\frac{\pi}{12}$$

The four sections of the track of this form have area 4 times this value which is:

$$4(\frac{\pi}{12})[(70)^2 - (60)^2] = \frac{\pi}{3}[(70)^2 - (60)^2]$$

The total track area is then

$$\sqrt{3}[(70)^2 - (60)^2] + \frac{\pi}{3}[(70)^2 - (60)^2]$$

$$= (\sqrt{3} + \frac{\pi}{3})[(70)^2 - (60)^2]$$

$$= 3612.3 \text{ yd}^2$$

Section 3.6

CHAPTER 7   REVIEW EXERCISES

1. The diameter is twice the radius or 2(2.6) = 5.2 cm.

2. The radius is half the diameter or $\frac{1}{2}(\frac{4}{5}) = \frac{2}{5}$ yd.

3. Since the diameter is 9.2 ft, the radius is $\frac{1}{2}(9.2)$ = 4.6 ft. The circumference is
$$C = \pi d = (3.14)(9.2) \approx 28.9 \text{ ft.}$$

4. The altitude of an equilateral triangle 10 inches on a side is a leg of a 30°-60°-rt triangle with length $\frac{\sqrt{3}}{2}$ (hypotenuse) $= \frac{\sqrt{3}}{2}(10) = 5\sqrt{3}$ inches. Thus, the area of

The area is
$$A = \pi r^2 = (3.14)(4.6)^2 \approx 66.4 \text{ ft}^2.$$

the triangle is
$$A = \tfrac{1}{2}bh = \tfrac{1}{2}(10)(5\sqrt{3}) = 25\sqrt{3} \text{ in}^2.$$

The area of the circle removed with radius 1.5 inches is
$$A = \pi r^2 = \pi(1.5)^2.$$

The area of the remaining part is the difference
$$25\sqrt{3} - \pi(1.5)^2 \approx 36.2 \text{ in}^2.$$

5. (a) central angle   (b) inscribed angle
   (c) $\overset{\frown}{AB}$ has the same measure as central angle $\angle AOB$ which is 50°.   (d) $\overset{\frown}{ACB}$ = 360° - $\overset{\frown}{AB}$
   = 360° - 50° = 310°   (e) $\angle ACB = \tfrac{1}{2} \overset{\frown}{AB}$
   = $\tfrac{1}{2}(50°)$ = 25°

6. <u>Given</u>: $\angle 1$ and $\angle 2$ are vertical angles with vertex at center 0

   <u>Prove</u>: $\overset{\frown}{AB} = \overset{\frown}{CD}$

   <u>Proof</u>:   STATEMENTS

   1. $\angle 1$ and $\angle 2$ are vertical angles with vertex at center 0
   2. $\angle 1 = \angle 2$
   3. $\overset{\frown}{AB} = \angle 1$ and $\overset{\frown}{CD} = \angle 2$
   4. $\overset{\frown}{AB} = \overset{\frown}{CD}$

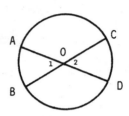

   REASONS

   1. Given
   2. Vert. $\angle$'s are =
   3. Def. of measure of an arc
   4. Substitution law

7. $\angle BPC = \tfrac{1}{2}(\overset{\frown}{BC} + \overset{\frown}{AD}) = \tfrac{1}{2}(56° + 132°)$
   = $\tfrac{1}{2}(188°)$ = 94°

8. Since CD = DA, $\overset{\frown}{CD} = \overset{\frown}{DA}$. Since $\overset{\frown}{CD}$ = 135°,
   $\overset{\frown}{DA}$ = 135°

9. By Theorem 7.8, CP = AP since the segment $\overline{BD}$ bisects chord $\overline{AC}$. Thus, CP = 17 cm.

10. By Theorem 7.13, (CP)(AP) = (BP)(PD). Substituting we have (6)(5) = (3)(PD) making PD = $\dfrac{(6)(5)}{3}$ = 10 ft.

11. By Theorem 7.10, the distances to the center are equal.

12. $\angle P = \tfrac{1}{2}(\overset{\frown}{BD} - \overset{\frown}{AC}) = \tfrac{1}{2}(68° - 28°) = \tfrac{1}{2}(40°)$
    = 20°

13. $\angle P = \tfrac{1}{2}(\overset{\frown}{BD} - \overset{\frown}{AC})$ so substituting we have
    $24° = \tfrac{1}{2}(\overset{\frown}{BD} - 30°)$ which gives $48° = \overset{\frown}{BD} - 30°$
    or $\overset{\frown}{BD}$ = 78°.

14. By Theorem 7.15, (PB)(PA) = (PD)(PC). Substituting we have (12)(3) = (PD)(4) so that PD = $\dfrac{(12)(3)}{4}$ = (3)(3) = 9 ft.

15. <u>Proof</u>   STATEMENTS

    1. ABCD is a rectangle
    2. AB = DC
    3. $\overset{\frown}{AB} = \overset{\frown}{CD}$

    REASONS

    1. Given
    2. Opp. sides of rect. are =
    3. = chords have = arcs

16. Proof:

STATEMENTS	REASONS
1. $\overline{AD} \perp \overline{BC}$ and $\overline{AD}$ contains the center O	1. Given
2. $\overline{AD}$ bisects $\overline{BC}$	2. Line through center $\perp$ chord bisects the chord
3. BD = DC	3. Def. of bisector
4. $\angle ADB$ and $\angle ADC$ are right angles	4. $\perp$ lines form rt. $\angle$'s
5. $\triangle ADB$ and $\triangle ADC$ are right triangles	5. Def. of rt $\triangle$
6. AD = AD	6. Reflexive law
7. $\triangle ADB \cong \triangle ADC$	7. LL = LL
8. AB = AC	8. cpoctae
9. $\overparen{AB} = \overparen{AC}$	9. = chords have = arcs

17. $\angle PAB = \frac{1}{2} \overparen{AB} = \frac{1}{2}(66°) = 33°$ by Theorem 7.16.

18. Since $\angle ADB = 35°$, $\overparen{AB} = 2(35°) = 70°$ by Theorem 7.2. By Theorem 7.16, $\angle PAB = \frac{1}{2} \overparen{AB}$ $= \frac{1}{2}(70°) = 35°$.

19. $\angle APD = \frac{1}{2}(\overparen{AD} - \overparen{AB}) = \frac{1}{2}(130° - 64°)$ $= \frac{1}{2}(66°) = 33°$ by Theorem 7.17.

20. Since $\overparen{ABC} = 130°$, $\overparen{ADC} = 360° - 130° = 230°$. By Theorem 7.18, $\angle APC = \frac{1}{2}(\overparen{ADC} - \overparen{ABC})$ $= \frac{1}{2}(230° - 130°) = \frac{1}{2}(100°) = 50°$.

21. By Theorem 7.19, AP = CP. Since AP = 38 cm, CP = 38 cm.

22. By Theorem 7.20, AP is the mean proportional between DP and BP. Thus,

$$\frac{DP}{AP} = \frac{AP}{BP}$$

$$\frac{30}{20} = \frac{20}{BP} \qquad \text{Substitute 30 for DP and 20 for AP}$$

$$(30)(BP) = (20)(20) \quad \text{Means-extremes property}$$

$$BP = \frac{(20)(20)}{30} = 13.\overline{3} \text{ ft}$$

Remember that $13.\overline{3}$ corresponds to $13\frac{1}{3}$.

23. Proof:

STATEMENTS	REASONS
1. $\overparen{BD} = 2\overparen{AC}$	1. Given
2. $\angle B = \frac{1}{2}\overparen{AC}$	2. Insc. $\angle$ has measure $\frac{1}{2}$ arc
3. $\angle P = \frac{1}{2}(\overparen{BD} - \overparen{AC})$	3. Theorem 7.14
4. $\angle P = \frac{1}{2}(2\overparen{AC} - \overparen{AC})$	4. Substitution law
5. $\angle P = \frac{1}{2}\overparen{AC}$	5. Distributive law
6. $\angle P = \angle B$	6. Sym. and trans. laws
7. PC = BC	7. Sides opp. = $\angle$'s are =

24. Proof:

STATEMENTS	REASONS
1. $\overline{AD}$ and $\overline{DC}$ are tangents	1. Given
2. AD = DC	2. Theorem 7.19
3. ABCD is a parallelogram	3. Given
4. ABCD is a rhombus	4. Def. of rhombus

25. <u>Proof:</u>

STATEMENTS	REASONS
1. $\overline{AB}$ is a common internal tangent	1. Given
2. $\overleftrightarrow{OP}$ is the line of centers	2. Given
3. $\overline{OA} \perp \overline{AB}$ and $\overline{PB} \perp \overline{AB}$	3. Radius to pt of tangency is $\perp$ to tangent
4. $\angle OAC$ and $\angle CBP$ are right angles	4. $\perp$ lines form rt $\angle$'s
5. $\angle OAC = \angle CBP$	5. All rt. $\angle$'s are =
6. $\angle OCA = \angle BCP$	6. Vert. $\angle$'s are =
7. $\triangle OAC \sim \triangle CBP$	7. AA $\sim$ AA
8. $\angle O = \angle P$	8. Corr. $\angle$'s in $\sim$ $\triangle$'s are =

26. <u>Given:</u>   Circles centered at O and P are tangent externally at D. l is their common internal tangent, A is on l, $\overline{AC}$ is tangent to circle centered at O, and $\overline{AB}$ is tangent to circle centered at P.

<u>Prove:</u>   AC = AB

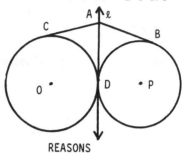

<u>Proof:</u>

STATEMENTS	REASONS
1. l is common internal tangent to circles at D with A on l	1. Given
2. $\overline{AC}$ is tangent to circle centered at O and $\overline{AB}$ is tangent to circle centered at P	2. Given
3. AC = AD and AD = AB	3. Tangents to circle from same pt are =
4. AC = AB	4. Trans. law

27. Use Construction 7.1

28. Using the same figure as Example 1 in Section 7.3, we have

$$(SA)^2 = (OS)^2 - (OA)^2$$
$$= [OB + SB]^2 - (OA)^2$$
$$= [4000 + 5] - (4000)^2$$
$$= (4005)^2 - (4000)^2$$
$$= 40,025$$

Taking the square root of both sides and discarding the negative value gives SA $\approx$ 200.1 mi, correct to the nearest tenth of a mile.

29. By Theorem 7.23, $\angle D$ and $\angle B$ are supplementary. Thus, $\angle D + \angle B = 180°$ so that $88° + \angle B = 180°$ making $\angle B = 180° - 88° = 92°$.

30. Since $\overline{AD} \parallel \overline{BC}$ and AD = BC, by Theorem 4.25, ABCD is a parallelogram. By Theorem 7.24, ABCD is a rectangle so that $\angle D = 90°$.

31. Divide the circle into four equal arcs using the endpoints of a diameter and the points of intersection of the perpendicular bisector of the diameter and the circle. The perpendicular bisector of a side of the square determines the bisector of the arc formed by the side which is used to mark off 8 equal arcs to form the regular octagon.

32. Construct the regular hexagon by inscribing it in a circle marking off arcs using the radius of the circle. Then use Construction 7.6 to inscribe a circle in the hexagon.

33. Each central angle of a regular 18-gon has measure $\frac{360°}{18} = 20°$.

34. Solve $10° = \frac{360°}{n}$ for n to obtain n = 36 sides.

35. The hexagon has sides equal in length to the radius of the circle which is 14 cm.

36. The proof involves showing that two triangles are congruent by SSS = SSS since radii are equal as are the sides of the regular polygon. Then use cpoctae to show the interior angles are bisected.

37. $A = \frac{m}{360} \pi r^2 = \frac{18}{360} \pi (11.4)^2 \approx 20.4$ in².

38. The area of the desired segment is the area of the sector minus the area of an equilateral triangle with base 10 cm and altitude $\frac{\sqrt{3}}{2}(10)$ cm.

Area of triangle = $\frac{1}{2}(10)(\frac{\sqrt{3}}{2}(10)) = 25\sqrt{3}$ cm²

Area of sector = $\frac{60}{360} \pi (10)^2 = \frac{50}{3} \pi$ cm²

Area of segment = $\frac{50}{3}\pi - 25\sqrt{3} \approx 9.0$ cm²

39. The apothem of the hexagon is $\frac{\sqrt{3}}{2}(30)$ $= 15\sqrt{3}$ yd.

The perimeter of the hexagon is 6(30) = 180 yd.

The area of the regular hexagon is:

$A = \frac{1}{2}ap = \frac{1}{2}(15\sqrt{3})(180) \approx 2338.3$ yd².

40. The area of a regular 30-gon with apothem 15.5 ft can be approximated by the area of a circle with radius 15.5 ft.

$A = \pi (15.5)^2 \approx 754.4$ ft²

41. Each "leaf" of the colored region can be thought of as two segments formed by an arc of 90° with radius 2 yd. Thus, each segment is the area of the sector minus the right triangle with legs 2 yd:

$\frac{90}{360} \pi (2)^2 - \frac{1}{2}(2)(2) = \pi - 2$

Each "leaf" is two of these segments with area:

$2(\pi - 2) = 2\pi - 4$

The total area of the colored region is four of these leafs which is

$4(2\pi - 4) = 8\pi - 16$ yd²

42. The length of an arc is given by $L = \frac{m}{180} \pi r$. Substitute 40 for m and 5.2 for r.

$L = \frac{40}{180} \pi (5.2) \approx 3.6$ ft

Section 3.6
CHAPTER 7 TEST

1. $C = \pi d = (3.14)(12.6) \approx 39.6$ cm ; $A = \pi r^2$
   $= \pi(6.3)^2 = (3.14)(6.3)^2 \approx 124.6$ cm^2

2. $\angle BAD = \frac{1}{2}\overarc{BD} = \frac{1}{2}(130°) = 65°$

3. $\angle P = \frac{1}{2}(\overarc{BD} - \overarc{AC})$. Since $\angle BOD = 130°$,
   $\overarc{BD} = 130°$. Since $\angle ADC = 30°$, $\overarc{AC} = 2(30°)$
   $= 60°$. Thus, $\angle P = \frac{1}{2}(130° - 60°) = \frac{1}{2}(70°)$
   $= 35°$.

4. $(DE)(AE) = (BE)(EC)$ so $(DE)(4) = (6)(2)$
   making DE $= \frac{(6)(2)}{4} = 3$ cm.

5. $\angle AEC = \frac{1}{2}(\overarc{AC} + \overarc{BD}) = \frac{1}{2}(60° + 130°) = \frac{1}{2}(190°)$
   $= 95°$.

6. Since MW = NW and MW = 4 cm, NW = 4 cm.

7. $(PQ)(PR) = (PT)(PS)$ so substituting we
   have $(12)(6) = (9)(PS)$ which gives
   PS $= \frac{(12)(6)}{9} = 8$ cm.

8. Since PA = PB and PA = 15 ft, PB = 15 ft.

9. Use Construction 7.2.

10. Since $\angle B$ and $\angle D$ are supplementary, and
    $\angle B = 100°$, $\angle D = 80°$.

11. Use Construction 3.4 and Construction 7.6.

12. The measure of each central angle of a
    regular octagon is $\frac{360°}{8} = 45°$.

13. $A = \frac{1}{2}ap = \frac{1}{2}(7)(56) = 196$ yd^2

14. The area of the segment is found by
    subtracting the area of an equilateral
    triangle with base 8 cm and height
    $\frac{\sqrt{3}}{2}(8)$ cm from the area of a sector with
    radii 8 cm and arc 60°.

    Area of triangle $= \frac{1}{2}(8)(\frac{\sqrt{3}}{2}(8)) = 16\sqrt{3}$ cm^2

    Area of sector $= \frac{60}{360}\pi(8)^2 = \frac{32}{3}\pi$ cm^2

    Area of segment $= \frac{32}{3}\pi - 16\sqrt{3} \approx 5.8$ cm^2

15. The proof follows easily from the fact that
    the tangents to the diameter are perpendicular
    to the diameter, and lines perpendicular to
    the same line are parallel.

TRIGONOMETRY

PART 4 – THE TRIGONOMETRIC FUNCTIONS

THE TRIGONOMETRIC FUNCTIONS

Using trigonometry it often is possible to calculate distances that may not be directly measurable. In Section 4-5 we show how we can measure the distance from the Goodyear blimp to a point on the football field.

Many applied problems in science and technology require the use of triangles, especially right triangles, for their solution. Included among these are problems in air navigation, surveying, the motion of rockets and missiles, structural design, and optics. Problems involving forces acting on objects and the measurement of distances between various parts of the solar system and universe can also be solved. Even certain types of electric circuits can be analyzed by the use of triangles.

In **trigonometry** we develop methods for measuring the sides and angles of triangles as well as solving related applied problems. Because of the great number of applications it has in many areas, trigonometry is considered one of the most practical and relevant branches of mathematics.

In this chapter we introduce the basic trigonometric functions and show a number of applications of right triangles from many areas of science and technology. In later chapters we will use the trigonometric functions with other types of triangles and their applications.

Also in later chapters we will see how the trigonometric functions are applied without reference to triangles. Such applications are found in electronics, mechanical vibrations, acoustics, optics, and other fields.

Section 4.1

4-1 ANGLES

In the review of geometry in Chapter 2, we stated a basic definition of an *angle.* In this section we extend this definition and give other important definitions related to angles.

An **angle** *is generated by rotating a ray about its fixed endpoint from an* **initial position** *to a* **terminal position.** *The initial position is called the* **initial side** *of the angle, the terminal position is called the* **terminal side,** *and the fixed endpoint is the* **vertex.** The angle itself is the amount of rotation from the initial side to the terminal side.

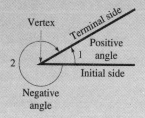

Fig. 4-1

*If the rotation of the terminal side from the initial side is **counterclockwise**, the angle is defined as **positive**. If the rotation is **clockwise**, the angle is **negative**.* In Fig. 4-1, $\angle 1$ is positive and $\angle 2$ is negative.

There are many symbols used to designate angles. Among the most widely used are certain Greek letters such as θ (theta), ϕ (phi), α (alpha), and β (beta). Capital letters representing the vertex (e.g., $\angle A$ or simply A) and other literal symbols, such as x and y, are also used commonly.

In Chapter 2 we introduced two measurements of an angle. These are the *degree* and the *radian*. Since degrees and radians are both used on calculators and computers, we will briefly review the relationship between them in this section. However, we will not make use of radians until Chapter 8.

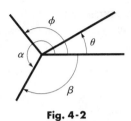

Fig. 4-2

From Section 2-1 we recall that *a* **degree** *is* 1/360 *of one complete rotation.* In Fig. 4-2, $\angle \theta = 30°$, $\angle \phi = 140°$, $\angle \alpha = 240°$, and $\angle \beta = -120°$. Note that β is drawn in a clockwise direction to show that it is negative. The other angles are drawn in a counterclockwise direction to show that they are positive angles.

In Chapter 2 we used degrees and decimal parts of a degree. Most calculators use degrees in this decimal form. Another traditional way is to divide a degree into 60 equal parts called **minutes;** each minute is divided into 60 equal parts called **seconds.** The symbols ′ and ″ are used to designate minutes and seconds, respectively.

In Fig. 4-2 we note that angles α and β have the same initial and terminal sides. *Such angles are called* **coterminal angles.** An understanding of coterminal angles is important in certain concepts of trigonometry.

EXAMPLE 1 Determine the values of two angles that are coterminal with an angle of 145.6°.

Since there are 360° in a complete rotation, we can find one coterminal angle by considering the angle that is 360° larger than the given angle. This gives us an angle of 505.6°. Another method of finding a coterminal angle is to subtract 145.6° from 360° and then consider the resulting angle to be negative. This means that the original angle and the derived angle would make up one complete rotation, when put together. This method leads us to the angle of $-214.4°$ (see Fig. 4-3). These methods could be employed repeatedly to find other coterminal angles. ‒‒‒‒‒‒‒‒‒■

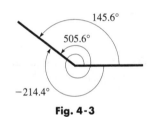

Fig. 4-3

Angle Conversions

NOTE▶ Although we will use only degrees as a measure of an angle in this chapter, when using a calculator we must *be careful to have the calculator set in the correct mode.* Therefore, to be sure that the calculator is using degrees, set the *mode* feature to degrees. In later chapters we will have use for a setting of radians. We can change from one measure to the other by using a calculator feature or using the definition of a radian in Section 2-4 that π rad $= 180°$.

Before the extensive use of calculators it was common to use degrees and minutes in tables, whereas calculators use degrees and decimal parts of a degree. Changing from one form to another can be done directly on a calculator by use of the *dms (degree-minute-second)* feature. The following examples illustrate angle conversions by using the definitions of the different measures of an angle and by using the appropriate calculator features.

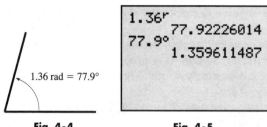

Fig. 4-4   **Fig. 4-5**

EXAMPLE 2   Express 1.36 rad in degrees.

We know that π rad = 180°, which means 1 rad = 180°/π. Therefore,

$$1.36 \text{ rad} = 1.36\left(\frac{180°}{\pi}\right) = 77.9° \qquad \text{to nearest 0.1°}$$

This angle is shown in Fig. 4-4. We again note that degrees and radians are simply two different ways of measuring an angle.

In Fig. 4-5, a graphing calculator display shows the conversions of 1.36 rad to degrees (calculator in degree mode) and 77.9° to radians (calculator in radian mode). ∎

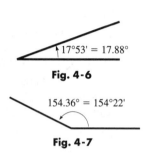

Fig. 4-6

154.36° = 154°22′

Fig. 4-7

EXAMPLE 3   To change 17°53′ to decimal form, we use the fact that $1° = 60'$. Therefore, $53' = \left(\frac{53}{60}\right)° = 0.88°$ to nearest 0.01°

This means that 17°53′ = 17.88°. This angle is shown in Fig. 4-6.

To change 154.36° to an angle measured to the nearest minute, we have

$$0.36° = 0.36(60') = 22'$$

This means that 154.36° = 154°22′. See Fig. 4-7. ∎

Standard Position of an Angle

If the initial side of the angle is the positive x-axis and the vertex is the origin, the angle is said to be in **standard position.** The angle is then determined by the position of the terminal side. *If the terminal side is in the first quadrant, the angle is called a* **first-quadrant angle.** Similar terms are used when the terminal side is in the other quadrants. *If the terminal side coincides with one of the axes, the angle is a* **quadrantal angle.** For an angle in standard position, the terminal side can be determined if we know any point, except the origin, on the terminal side.

EXAMPLE 4   A standard position angle of 60° is a first-quadrant angle with its terminal side 60° from the *x*-axis. See Fig. 4-8(a).

A second-quadrant angle of 130° is shown in Fig. 4-8(b).

A third-quadrant angle of 225° is shown in Fig. 4-8(c).

A fourth-quadrant angle of 340° is shown in Fig. 4-8(d).

A standard position angle of −120° is shown in Fig. 4-8(e). Since the terminal side is in the third quadrant, it is a third-quadrant angle.

A standard position angle of 90° is a quadrantal angle since its terminal side is the positive *y*-axis. See Fig. 4-8(f).

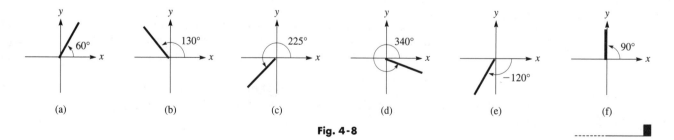

(a)   (b)   (c)   (d)   (e)   (f)

Fig. 4-8 ∎

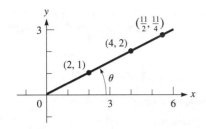

Fig. 4-9

EXAMPLE 5   In Fig. 4-9, θ is in standard position, and the terminal side is uniquely determined by knowing that it passes through the point $(2, 1)$. The same terminal side passes through $(4, 2)$ and $(\frac{11}{2}, \frac{11}{4})$, among other points. Knowing that the terminal side passes through any one of these points makes it possible to determine the terminal side of the angle. ∎

EXERCISES *4-1*

In Exercises 1–4, draw the given angles.

1. 60°, 120°, −90°   **2.** 330°, −150°, 450°

3. 50°, −360°, −30°   **4.** 45°, 245°, −250°

In Exercises 5–12, determine one positive and one negative coterminal angle for each angle given.

5. 45°   **6.** 73°

7. −150°   **8.** 162°

9. 70°30′   **10.** 153°47′

11. 278.1°   **12.** −197.6°

In Exercises 13–16, by means of the definition of a radian, change the given angles in radians to equal angles expressed in degrees to the nearest 0.01°.

13. 0.265 rad   **14.** 0.838 rad

15. 1.447 rad   **16.** 3.642 rad

In Exercises 17–20, use a calculator conversion sequence to change the given angles in radians to equal angles expressed in degrees to the nearest 0.01°.

17. 0.329 rad   **18.** 2.089 rad

19. 4.110 rad   **20.** 0.067 rad

In Exercises 21–24, use a calculator conversion sequence to change the given angles to equal angles expressed in radians to three significant digits.

21. 56.0°   **22.** 137.4°

23. 284.8°   **24.** −17.5°

In Exercises 25–28, change the given angles to equal angles expressed to the nearest minute.

25. 47.50°   **26.** 315.80°

27. −5.62°   **28.** 142.87°

In Exercises 29–32, change the given angles to equal angles expressed in decimal form to the nearest 0.01°.

29. 15°12′   **30.** 157°39′

31. 301°16′   **32.** −4°47′

In Exercises 33–40, draw angles in standard position such that the terminal side passes through the given point.

33. $(4, 2)$ **34.** $(−3, 8)$

35. $(−3, −5)$ **36.** $(6, −1)$

37. $(−7, 5)$ **38.** $(−4, −2)$

39. $(2, −5)$ **40.** $(1, 6)$

In Exercises 41 and 42, change the given angles to equal angles expressed in decimal form to the nearest 0.001°. In Exercises 43 and 44, change the given angles to equal angles expressed to the nearest second.

41. 21°42′36″   **42.** 7°16′23″

43. 86.274°   **44.** 57.019°

Section 4.2

4-2 DEFINING THE TRIGONOMETRIC FUNCTIONS

In Chapter 2 we reviewed many of the basic geometric figures and their properties. Important to the definitions and development in this section are the right triangle, the Pythagorean theorem, and the properties of similar triangles. We now briefly review similar triangles and their properties.

As stated in Section 2-2, *two triangles are* **similar** *if they have the same shape (but not necessarily the same size).* Similar triangles have the following important properties.

Properties of Similar Triangles

1. *Corresponding angles are equal.*

2. *Corresponding sides are proportional.*

The **corresponding sides** *are the sides, one in each triangle, that are between the same pair of equal* **corresponding angles.**

EXAMPLE 1   In Fig. 4-10 the triangles are similar and are lettered so that corresponding sides and angles have the same letters. That is, angles A_1 and A_2, angles B_1 and B_2, and angles C_1 and C_2 are pairs of corresponding angles. The pairs of corresponding sides are a_1 and a_2, b_1 and b_2, and c_1 and c_2. From the properties of similar triangles, we know that the corresponding angles are equal, or

$$\angle A_1 = \angle A_2, \quad \angle B_1 = \angle B_2, \quad \angle C_1 = \angle C_2$$

Also, the corresponding sides are proportional, which we can show as

$$\frac{a_1}{a_2} = \frac{b_1}{b_2}, \quad \frac{a_1}{a_2} = \frac{c_1}{c_2}, \quad \frac{b_1}{b_2} = \frac{c_1}{c_2}$$

Fig. 4-10

In Example 1, if we multiply both sides of

$$\frac{a_1}{a_2} = \frac{b_1}{b_2} \quad \text{by} \quad \frac{a_2}{b_1}, \quad \text{we get} \quad \frac{a_1}{a_2}\left(\frac{a_2}{b_1}\right) = \frac{b_1}{b_2}\left(\frac{a_2}{b_1}\right)$$

which when simplified gives

$$\frac{a_1}{b_1} = \frac{a_2}{b_2}$$

This shows us that *when two triangles are similar*

the ratio of one side to another side in one triangle is the same as the ratio of the corresponding sides in the other triangle.

Using this we now proceed to the definitions of the trigonometric functions.

We now place an angle θ in standard position and drop perpendicular lines from points on the terminal side to the x-axis, as shown in Fig. 4-11. In doing this we set up similar triangles, each with one vertex at the origin and one side along the x-axis.

EXAMPLE 2   In Fig. 4-11 we can see that triangles ORP and OSQ are similar since their corresponding angles are equal (each has the same angle at O, a right angle, and therefore equal angles at P and Q). This means that ratios of the lengths of corresponding sides are equal. For example,

$$\frac{RP}{OR} = \frac{SQ}{OS} \quad \text{which is the same as} \quad \frac{y}{x} = \frac{b}{a}$$

For any position (except at the origin) of Q on the terminal side of θ, the ratio b/a of its ordinate to its abscissa will equal y/x.

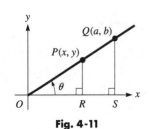

Fig. 4-11

For any angle θ in standard position, six different ratios may be set up. Because of the property of similar triangles, any given ratio has the same value for any point on the terminal side that is chosen. For a different angle, with a different terminal side, the ratio will have a different value. Thus, the values of the ratios depend on the position of the terminal side, which means that *the values of the ratios depend on the size of the angle, and there is only one value for each ratio for a given angle.* Recalling the meaning of a function, we see that *the ratios are functions of the angle. These functions are called the* **trigonometric functions,** and they are defined as follows (see Fig. 4-12):

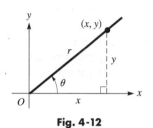

Fig. 4-12

$$
\begin{array}{ll}
\textit{sine of } \theta\text{: } \sin \theta = \dfrac{y}{r} & \textit{cosine of } \theta\text{: } \cos \theta = \dfrac{x}{r} \\[2mm]
\textit{tangent of } \theta\text{: } \tan \theta = \dfrac{y}{x} & \textit{cotangent of } \theta\text{: } \cot \theta = \dfrac{x}{y} \\[2mm]
\textit{secant of } \theta\text{: } \sec \theta = \dfrac{r}{x} & \textit{cosecant of } \theta\text{: } \csc \theta = \dfrac{r}{y}
\end{array}
\tag{4-1}
$$

Here, *the distance r from the origin to the point is called the* **radius vector.** Also note that we have used the abbreviations that are used most of the time when working with these functions.

In this chapter we shall restrict our attention to the trigonometric functions of acute angles (angles between 0° and 90°). However, *the definitions in Eqs. (4-1) are general and may be used for angles of any magnitude.* Discussion of the trigonometric functions of angles in general, along with other important properties, is found in Chapters 8 and 20.

We should note that a given function is not defined if the denominator is zero. The denominator is zero in $\tan \theta$ and $\sec \theta$ for $x = 0$, and in $\cot \theta$ and $\csc \theta$ for $y = 0$. In all cases we will assume that $r > 0$. If $r = 0$, there would be no terminal side and therefore no angle. These restrictions affect the domain of these functions. We will discuss the domains and ranges of the trigonometric functions in Chapter 10, when we consider the graphs of these functions.

Evaluating the Trigonometric Functions

When evaluating the trigonometric functions we use the definitions in Eqs. (4-1). We also often use the *Pythagorean theorem,* which we discussed in Section 2-2. For reference, we restate it here. For the right triangle in Fig. 4-13, with hypotenuse c and legs a and b, we have

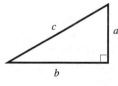

Fig. 4-13

$$
c^2 = a^2 + b^2
\tag{4-2}
$$

Following are examples of evaluating the trigonometric functions of an angle when a point on the terminal side of the angle is given or can be found.

EXAMPLE 3 Find the values of the trigonometric functions of the angle θ with its terminal side passing through the point $(3, 4)$.

By placing the angle in standard position, as shown in Fig. 4-14, and drawing the terminal side through $(3, 4)$, we find by use of the Pythagorean theorem that

$$r = \sqrt{3^2 + 4^2} = \sqrt{25} = 5$$

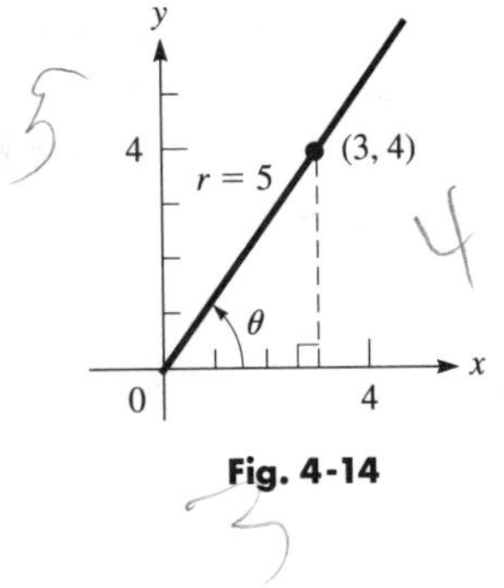

Using the values $x = 3$, $y = 4$, and $r = 5$, we find that

$$\sin \theta = \frac{4}{5} \qquad \cos \theta = \frac{3}{5} \qquad \tan \theta = \frac{4}{3}$$

$$\cot \theta = \frac{3}{4} \qquad \sec \theta = \frac{5}{3} \qquad \csc \theta = \frac{5}{4}$$

We have left each of these results in the form of a fraction, which is considered to be an *exact form* in that there has been no approximation made. In writing decimal values, we find that $\tan \theta = 1.333$ and $\sec \theta = 1.667$, where these values have been rounded off and are therefore *approximate*. ──────────■

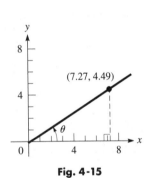

Fig. 4-14

EXAMPLE 4 Find the values of the trigonometric functions of the angle whose terminal side passes through $(7.27, 4.49)$. The coordinates are approximate.

We show the angle and the given point in Fig. 4-15. From the Pythagorean theorem, we have

$$r = \sqrt{7.27^2 + 4.49^2} = 8.545$$

(Here we show a rounded-off value of r. It is not actually necessary to record the value of r since its value can be stored in the memory of a calculator. The reason for recording it here is to show the values used in the calculation of each of the trigonometric functions.) Therefore, we have the following values:

$$\sin \theta = \frac{4.49}{8.545} = 0.525 \qquad \cos \theta = \frac{7.27}{8.545} = 0.851$$

$$\tan \theta = \frac{4.49}{7.27} = 0.618 \qquad \cot \theta = \frac{7.27}{4.49} = 1.62$$

$$\sec \theta = \frac{8.545}{7.27} = 1.18 \qquad \csc \theta = \frac{8.545}{4.49} = 1.90$$

Since the coordinates are approximate, the results are rounded off.

The display in a graphing calculator window is shown in Fig. 4-16. (The key sequences are indicated by the display.) The first result shown is the value of r, and the calculator stores this result under *ans*. In order to evaluate all of the trigonometric functions, we then store the value of r as the value of x. (It is not necessary to enter *ans*. The first key to use for line 3 is *sto.*) This is shown in the third and fourth lines of the display. To find $\sin \theta$ we continue with the fifth line of the display, and the result is shown on the sixth line. To get values of the other functions, we can use the value of r stored as x (here, x is chosen for convenience of calculator use—it is *not* the same as the x-coordinate of the point.) ──────────■

```
√(7.27²+4.49²)
           8.544764479
Ans→X
           8.544764479
4.49/X
            .5254679648
```

Fig. 4-16

In Example 4, we expressed the result as sin $\theta = 0.525$. A common error is to omit the angle and give the value as sin $= 0.525$. This is a meaningless expression, for *we must show the angle* for which we have the value of a function.

CAUTION ▶

If one of the trigonometric functions is known, it is possible to find the values of the other functions. The following example illustrates the method.

■ EXAMPLE 5 If we know that sin $\theta = 3/7$ and that θ is a first-quadrant angle, we know the ratio of the ordinate to the radius vector (y to r) is 3 to 7. Therefore, the point on the terminal side for which $y = 3$ can be found by use of the Pythagorean theorem. The x-value for this point is

$$x = \sqrt{7^2 - 3^2} = \sqrt{49 - 9} = \sqrt{40} = 2\sqrt{10}$$

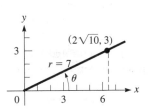

Fig. 4-17

Therefore, the point $(2\sqrt{10}, 3)$ is on the terminal side, as shown in Fig. 4-17.

Therefore, using the values $x = 2\sqrt{10}$, $y = 3$, and $r = 7$, we have the other trigonometric functions of θ. They are

$$\cos \theta = \frac{2\sqrt{10}}{7}, \quad \tan \theta = \frac{3}{2\sqrt{10}}, \quad \cot \theta = \frac{2\sqrt{10}}{3}, \quad \sec \theta = \frac{7}{2\sqrt{10}}, \quad \csc \theta = \frac{7}{3}$$

These values are *exact*. *Approximate* decimal values found on a calculator are

$$\cos \theta = 0.9035, \quad \tan \theta = 0.4743, \quad \cot \theta = 2.108$$
$$\sec \theta = 1.107, \quad \csc \theta = 2.333 \quad \text{--------■}$$

─────────── **EXERCISES** $4\text{-}2$ ───────────

In Exercises 1–16, find values of the trigonometric functions of the angle (in standard position) whose terminal side passes through the given points. For Exercises 1–12, give answers in exact form. For Exercises 13–16, the coordinates are approximate.

1. (6, 8)   **2.** (5, 12)   **3.** (15, 8)   **4.** (24, 7)

5. (9, 40)   **6.** (16, 30)   **7.** $(1, \sqrt{15})$ **8.** $(\sqrt{3}, 2)$

9. (1, 1)   **10.** (6, 5)   **11.** (5, 2)   **12.** $(1, \frac{1}{2})$

13. (3.25, 5.15)   **14.** (0.687, 0.943)

15. (0.08623, 0.01327)   **16.** (37.65, 21.87)

In Exercises 17–24, find the values of the indicated functions. In Exercises 17–20, give answers in exact form. In Exercises 21–24, the values are approximate.

17. Given cos $\theta = 12/13$, find sin θ and cot θ.

18. Given sin $\theta = 1/2$, find cos θ and csc θ.

19. Given tan $\theta = 1$, find sin θ and sec θ.

20. Given sec $\theta = 4/3$, find tan θ and cos θ.

21. Given sin $\theta = 0.750$, find cot θ and csc θ.

22. Given cos $\theta = 0.326$, find sin θ and tan θ.

23. Given cot $\theta = 0.254$, find cos θ and tan θ.

24. Given csc $\theta = 1.20$, find sec θ and cos θ.

In Exercises 25–28, each point listed is on the terminal side of an angle. Show that each of the indicated functions is the same for each of the points.

25. (3, 4), (6, 8), (4.5, 6), sin θ and tan θ

26. (5, 12), (15, 36), (7.5, 18), cos θ and cot θ

27. (2, 1), (4, 2), (8, 4), tan θ and sec θ

28. (3, 2), (6,4), (9, 6), csc θ and cos θ

In Exercises 29–32, answer the given questions.

29. If tan $\theta = 3/4$, what is the value of $\sin^2 \theta + \cos^2 \theta$? [$\sin^2 \theta = (\sin \theta)^2$]

30. What is x if (2, 5) and (7, x) are on the same terminal side?

31. From the definitions of the trigonometric functions, it can be seen that csc θ is the reciprocal of sin θ. What function is the reciprocal of cos θ?

W 32. Refer to the definitions of the trigonometric functions in Eqs. (4-1). Is the quotient of one of the functions divided by cos θ equal to tan θ? Explain.

Section 4.3

4-3 VALUES OF THE TRIGONOMETRIC FUNCTIONS

We have been able to calculate the trigonometric functions if we knew one point on the terminal side of the angle. However, in practice it is more common to know the angle in degrees, for example, and to be required to find the functions of this angle. Therefore, we must be able to determine the trigonometric functions of angles in degrees.

One way to determine the functions of a given angle is to make a scale drawing. That is, we draw the angle in standard position using a protractor and then measure the lengths of the values of *x, y,* and *r* for some point on the terminal side. By using the proper ratios we may determine the functions of this angle.

We may also use certain geometric facts to determine the functions of some particular angles. The following two examples illustrate this procedure.

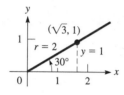

Fig. 4-18

EXAMPLE 1   From geometry we find that the side opposite a 30° angle in a right triangle is one-half of the hypotenuse. Using this fact and letting $y = 1$ and $r = 2$ (see Fig. 4-18), we calculate that $x = \sqrt{2^2 - 1^2} = \sqrt{3}$ from the Pythagorean theorem. Therefore, with $x = \sqrt{3}$, $y = 1$, and $r = 2$, we have

$$\sin 30° = \frac{1}{2} \qquad \cos 30° = \frac{\sqrt{3}}{2} \qquad \tan 30° = \frac{1}{\sqrt{3}}$$

In a similar way we may determine the values of the functions of 60° to be

$$\sin 60° = \frac{\sqrt{3}}{2} \qquad \cos 60° = \frac{1}{2} \qquad \tan 60° = \sqrt{3}$$

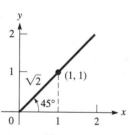

Fig. 4-19

EXAMPLE 2   Find sin 45°, cos 45°, and tan 45°.

From geometry we know that in an isosceles right triangle the angles are 45°, 45°, and 90°. We know that the sides are in proportion 1, 1, $\sqrt{2}$, respectively. Putting the 45° angle in standard position, we find $x = 1, y = 1$, and $r = \sqrt{2}$ (see Fig. 4-19). From this we determine

$$\sin 45° = \frac{1}{\sqrt{2}} \qquad \cos 45° = \frac{1}{\sqrt{2}} \qquad \tan 45° = 1$$

As in Example 1, we have given the exact values. Decimal approximations are given in the table that follows.

Summarizing the results for 30°, 45°, and 60°, we have:

θ	30°	45°	60°	*(decimal approximations)* 30°	45°	60°
$\sin \theta$	$\dfrac{1}{2}$	$\dfrac{1}{\sqrt{2}}$	$\dfrac{\sqrt{3}}{2}$	0.500	0.707	0.866
$\cos \theta$	$\dfrac{\sqrt{3}}{2}$	$\dfrac{1}{\sqrt{2}}$	$\dfrac{1}{2}$	0.866	0.707	0.500
$\tan \theta$	$\dfrac{1}{\sqrt{3}}$	1	$\sqrt{3}$	0.577	1.000	1.732

NOTE ▶   It is helpful to be familiar with these values, as they are used in later sections.

The scale-drawing method for finding values of the trigonometric functions gives only approximate results, and geometric methods work only for a limited number of angles. However, it is possible to find these values to any required degree of accuracy through more advanced mathematical methods (using calculus and what are known as *power series*).

The values of the trigonometric functions sin θ, cos θ, and tan θ are programmed into graphing calculators. For all of our work in the remainder of this chapter, *be sure that your calculator is set for degrees* (not radians). The following examples illustrate the use of a calculator in finding trigonometric values.

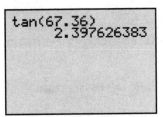

Not all calculators will require parentheses around 67.36.

Fig. 4-20

■**EXAMPLE 3** Using a graphing calculator to find the value of tan 67.36°, we first enter the function and then the angle, just as we have written it. The resulting display is shown in Fig. 4-20.

Therefore, we see that tan 67.36° = 2.397626383. ▪

Not only are we able to find values of the trigonometric functions if we know the angle, but we can also find the angle if we know that value of a function. In doing this, we are actually using another important type of mathematical function, an **inverse trigonometric function.** They are discussed in detail in Chapter 20. For the purpose of using a calculator at this point, it is sufficient to recognize and understand the notation that is used.

The notation for "the angle whose sine is x" is $\sin^{-1} x$. This is called the *inverse sine function.* Equivalent meanings are given to $\cos^{-1} x$ (the angle whose cosine is x) and $\tan^{-1} x$ (the angle whose tangent is x). (The -1 used with a *function* indicates an *inverse function* and is *not* a negative exponent.) On a calculator the $\sin^{-1}$ key is used to find the angle when the sine of that angle is known. The following example illustrates the use of the equivalent $\cos^{-1}$ key.

INVERSE TRIGONOMETRIC FUNCTIONS

CAUTION ▶

Another notation that is used for $\sin^{-1} x$ is arcsin x.

Fig. 4-21

■**EXAMPLE 4** If cos θ = 0.3527, which means that $\theta = \cos^{-1}$ 0.3527 (θ is the angle whose cosine is 0.3527), we can use a graphing calculator to find θ. The display for this is shown in Fig. 4-21.

Therefore, we see that θ = 69.35° (rounded off). ▪

When using the trigonometric functions, the angle is often *approximate*. Angles of 2.3°, 92.3°, and 182.3° are angles with equal accuracy, which shows that *the accuracy of an angle does not depend on the number of digits shown.* The measurement of an angle and the accuracy of its trigonometric functions are shown in the following table.

Angles and Accuracy of Trigonometric Functions

Measurement of Angle to Nearest	Accuracy of Trigonometric Function
1°	2 significant digits
0.1° or 10′	3 significant digits
0.01° or 1′	4 significant digits

We rounded off the result in Example 4 according to this table.

It is generally possible to set up the solution of a problem in terms of the sine, cosine, or tangent. However, there are times when a value of the cotangent, secant, or cosecant is given or is needed. We will now show how values of these functions are found using a calculator.

RECIPROCAL FUNCTIONS

From the definitions of the trigonometric functions, we see that $\csc \theta = r/y$ and $\sin \theta = y/r$. This means that *the value of* $\csc \theta$ *is the reciprocal of the value of* $\sin \theta$. Therefore, by use of the reciprocal key, x^{-1} (here, the -1 *is* an exponent) of a calculator, the values of these functions can be found. (Remember, by the definition of a reciprocal, $x^{-1} = 1/x$).

NOTE ▶

■EXAMPLE 5   To find the value of sec 27.82°, we use the fact that

$$\sec 27.82° = \frac{1}{\cos 27.82°} \quad \text{or} \quad \sec 27.82° = (\cos 27.82°)^{-1}$$

Therefore, we are to find the reciprocal of the value of cos 27.82°. This value can be found using either the first two lines, or the third and fourth lines, of the calculator display shown in Fig. 4-22.

From the display, we see that sec 27.82° = 1.131, with the results rounded off according to the table at the bottom of page 113.   ------------■

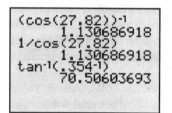

Fig. 4-22

■EXAMPLE 6   To find the value of θ if cot θ = 0.354, we use the fact that

$$\tan \theta = \frac{1}{\cot \theta} = \frac{1}{0.354}$$

The value found by using a graphing calculator is shown in the fifth and sixth lines of Fig. 4-22.

Therefore, $\theta = 70.5°$ (rounded off).   ------------■

In the following example, we see how to find the value of one function if we know the value of another function of the same angle.

■EXAMPLE 7   Find sin θ if sec θ = 2.504.

Since the value of sec θ is known, we know that cos θ = 2.504^{-1} (or 1/2.504). This in turn tells us that $\theta = \cos^{-1}(2.504^{-1})$. Since we are to find the value of sin θ, we can see that

$$\sin \theta = \sin(\cos^{-1}(2.504^{-1}))$$

Therefore, we have the calculator display shown in Fig. 4-23.

This means that sin θ = 0.9168 (rounded off).   ------------■

Fig. 4-23

Calculators have been used extensively since the 1970s. Until then the values of the trigonometric functions were generally found by the use of tables (where linear interpolation was used to find values to one more place than was shown in the table). Many standard sources with tables are still available with a precision to at least 10′ or 0.1° (these tables give values with a precision to about five decimal places). However, a calculator is much easier to use than a table, and it can give values to a much greater accuracy. Therefore, we will not use tables in this text.

The following example illustrates the use of the value of a trigonometric function in an applied problem. We consider various types of applications later in the chapter.

EXAMPLE 8   When a rocket is launched, its horizontal velocity v_x is related to the velocity v with which it is fired by the equation $v_x = v \cos \theta$ (which means $v(\cos \theta)$, but does *not* mean $\cos \theta\, v$, which is the same as $\cos (\theta\, v)$). Here, θ is the angle between the horizontal and the direction in which it is fired (see Fig. 4-24). Find v_x if $v = 1250$ m/s and $\theta = 36.0°$.

Substituting the given values of v and θ in $v_x = v \cos \theta$, we have

$$v_x = 1250 \cos 36.0°$$
$$= 1010 \text{ m/s}$$

Therefore, the horizontal velocity is 1010 m/s.

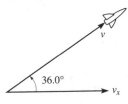

Fig. 4-24

EXERCISES *4-3*

In Exercises 1–4, use a protractor to draw the given angle. Measure off 10 units (centimeters are convenient) along the radius vector. Then measure the corresponding values of x and y. From these values determine the trigonometric functions of the angle.

1. 40°   2. 75°   3. 15°   4. 53°

In Exercises 5–20, find the values of the trigonometric functions. Round off results according to the table following Example 4.

5. $\sin 22.4°$ 6. $\cos 72.5°$
7. $\tan 57.6°$ 8. $\sin 36.0°$
9. $\cos 15.71°$ 10. $\tan 8.653°$
11. $\sin 84°$ 12. $\cos 47°$
13. $\cot 67.78°$ 14. $\csc 22.81°$
15. $\sec 50.4°$ 16. $\cot 41.8°$
17. $\csc 49.3°$ 18. $\sec 7.8°$
19. $\cot 85.96°$ 20. $\csc 76.30°$

In Exercises 21–36, find θ for each of the given trigonometric functions. Round off results according to the table following Example 4.

21. $\cos \theta = 0.3261$ 22. $\tan \theta = 2.470$
23. $\sin \theta = 0.9114$ 24. $\cos \theta = 0.0427$
25. $\tan \theta = 0.207$ 26. $\sin \theta = 0.109$
27. $\cos \theta = 0.65007$ 28. $\tan \theta = 5.7706$
29. $\csc \theta = 1.245$ 30. $\sec \theta = 2.045$
31. $\cot \theta = 0.1443$ 32. $\csc \theta = 1.012$
33. $\sec \theta = 3.65$ 34. $\cot \theta = 2.08$
35. $\csc \theta = 3.262$ 36. $\cot \theta = 0.1519$

In Exercises 37 and 38, use a calculator to verify the given relationships. $[\sin^2 \theta = (\sin \theta)^2]$

37. $\dfrac{\sin 43.7°}{\cos 43.7°} = \tan 43.7°$ 38. $\sin^2 77.5° + \cos^2 77.5° = 1$

(W) *In Exercises 39 and 40, explain why the given statements are true for an acute angle θ.*

39. $\sin \theta$ is always between 0 and 1.
40. $\tan \theta$ can equal any positive real number.

In Exercises 41–44, find the values of the indicated trigonometric functions.

41. Find $\sin \theta$, given $\tan \theta = 1.936$.
42. Find $\cos \theta$, given $\sin \theta = 0.6725$.
43. Find $\tan \theta$, given $\sec \theta = 1.3698$.
44. Find $\csc \theta$, given $\cos \theta = 0.1063$.

In Exercises 45–48, solve the given problems.

45. The sound produced by a jet engine was measured at a distance of 100 m in all directions. The loudness d of the sound (in decibels) was found to be $d = 70.0 + 30.0 \cos \theta$, where the 0° line was directed in front of the engine. Calculate d for $\theta = 54.5°$.

46. A brace is used in the structure shown in Fig. 4-25. Its length is $l = a(\sec \theta + \csc \theta)$. Find l if $a = 28.0$ cm and $\theta = 34.5°$.

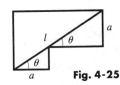

Fig. 4-25

47. The current i in a certain electric circuit is given by the equation $i = I \sin(\theta - 5.0°)$. Find i for $I = 1.80$ A and $\theta = 46.3°$.

48. A submarine dives such that the horizontal distance h and vertical distance v are related by $v = h \tan \theta$. Here θ is the angle of the dive, as shown in Fig. 4-26. Find θ if $h = 2.35$ mi and $v = 1.52$ mi.

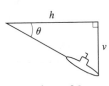

Fig. 4-26

Section 4.4

4-4 THE RIGHT TRIANGLE

From geometry we know that a triangle, by definition, consists of three sides and has three angles. If one side and any other two of these six parts of the triangle are known, it is possible to determine the other three parts. One of the three known parts must be a side, for if we know only the three angles, we can conclude only that an entire set of similar triangles has those particular angles.

EXAMPLE 1   Assume that one side and two angles are known, such as the side of 5 and the angles of 35° and 90° in the triangle in Fig. 4-27. Then we may determine the third angle α by the fact that the sum of the angles of a triangle is always 180°. Of all possible similar triangles having the three angles of 35°, 90°, and 55° (which is α), we have the one with the particular side of 5 between angles of 35° and 90°. Only one triangle with these parts is possible (in the sense that all triangles with the given parts are *congruent* and have equal corresponding angles and sides).

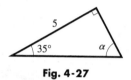

Fig. 4-27

To **solve a triangle** *means that, when we are given three parts of a triangle (at least one a side), we are to find the other three parts.* In this section we are going to demonstrate the method of solving a right triangle. *Since one angle of the triangle will be 90°, it is necessary to know one side and one other part.* Also, we know that the sum of the three angles of a triangle is 180°, and this in turn tells us that *the sum of the other two angles, both acute, is 90°. Any two acute angles whose sum is 90° are said to be* **complementary.**

For consistency, when we are labeling the parts of the right triangle *we shall use the letters A and B to denote the acute angles and C to denote the right angle. The letters a, b, and c will denote the sides opposite these angles, respectively. Thus, side c is the hypotenuse of the right triangle.* See Fig. 4-28.

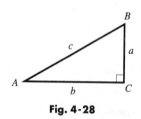

Fig. 4-28

In solving right triangles we shall find it convenient to express the trigonometric functions of the acute angles in terms of the sides. By placing the vertex of angle A at the origin and the vertex of right angle C on the positive x-axis, as shown in Fig. 4-29, we have the following ratios for angle A in terms of the sides of the triangle.

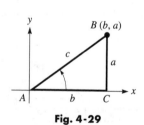

Fig. 4-29

$$\sin A = \frac{a}{c} \qquad \cos A = \frac{b}{c} \qquad \tan A = \frac{a}{b}$$
$$\cot A = \frac{b}{a} \qquad \sec A = \frac{c}{b} \qquad \csc A = \frac{c}{a}$$

(4-3)

If we should place the vertex of B at the origin, instead of the vertex of angle A, we would obtain the following ratios for the functions of angle B (see Fig. 4-30):

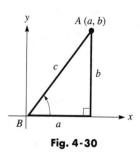

Fig. 4-30

$$\sin B = \frac{b}{c} \qquad \cos B = \frac{a}{c} \qquad \tan B = \frac{b}{a}$$
$$\cot B = \frac{a}{b} \qquad \sec B = \frac{c}{a} \qquad \csc B = \frac{c}{b}$$

(4-4)

Equations (4-3) and (4-4) show that we may generalize our definitions of the trigonometric functions of an acute angle of a right triangle (we have chosen $\angle A$ in Fig. 4-31) to be as follows:

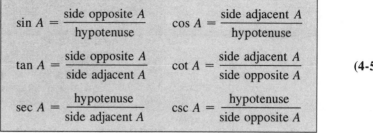

$$
\begin{array}{ll}
\sin A = \dfrac{\text{side opposite } A}{\text{hypotenuse}} & \cos A = \dfrac{\text{side adjacent } A}{\text{hypotenuse}} \\[2mm]
\tan A = \dfrac{\text{side opposite } A}{\text{side adjacent } A} & \cot A = \dfrac{\text{side adjacent } A}{\text{side opposite } A} \\[2mm]
\sec A = \dfrac{\text{hypotenuse}}{\text{side adjacent } A} & \csc A = \dfrac{\text{hypotenuse}}{\text{side opposite } A}
\end{array}
\qquad (4\text{-}5)
$$

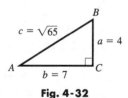

Fig. 4-31

Which side is adjacent or opposite depends on the angle being considered. In Fig. 4-31 the side opposite A is adjacent to B, and the side adjacent to A is opposite B.

Using the definitions in this form, we can solve right triangles without placing the angle in standard position. The angle need only be a part of any right triangle.

We note from the above discussion that $\sin A = \cos B$, $\tan A = \cot B$, and $\sec A = \csc B$. From this we conclude that *cofunctions of acute complementary angles are equal.* The sine function and cosine function are cofunctions, the tangent function and cotangent function are cofunctions, and the secant function and cosecant functions are cofunctions. This property of the values of the trigonometric functions is illustrated in the following example.

EXAMPLE 2 Given $a = 4$, $b = 7$, and $c = \sqrt{65}$, find $\sin A$, $\cos A$, and $\tan A$ (see Fig. 4-32) in exact form and in approximate decimal form (to three significant digits).

$$
\sin A = \frac{\text{side opposite angle } A}{\text{hypotenuse}} = \frac{4}{\sqrt{65}} = 0.496
$$

$$
\cos A = \frac{\text{side adjacent angle } A}{\text{hypotenuse}} = \frac{7}{\sqrt{65}} = 0.868
$$

$$
\tan A = \frac{\text{side opposite angle } A}{\text{side adjacent angle } A} = \frac{4}{7} = 0.571
$$

EXAMPLE 3 Finding $\sin B$, $\cos B$, and $\tan B$ for the triangle in Fig. 4-32, we have

$$
\sin B = \frac{\text{side opposite angle } B}{\text{hypotenuse}} = \frac{7}{\sqrt{65}} = 0.868
$$

$$
\cos B = \frac{\text{side adjacent angle } B}{\text{hypotenuse}} = \frac{4}{\sqrt{65}} = 0.496
$$

$$
\tan B = \frac{\text{side opposite angle } B}{\text{side adjacent angle } B} = \frac{7}{4} = 1.75
$$

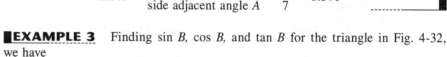

Fig. 4-32

In Fig. 4-32 we note that A and B are complementary angles. Comparing with values found in Example 2, we see that $\sin A = \cos B$ and $\cos A = \sin B$.

We are now ready to solve right triangles. The method is given and illustrated on the next page.

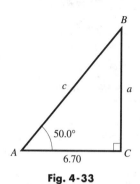

Procedure for Solving a Right Triangle

1. *Sketch a right triangle and label the known and unknown sides and angles.*
2. *Express each of the three unknown parts in terms of the known parts and solve for the unknown parts.*
3. *Check the results.* The sum of the angles should be 180°. If only one side is given, check the computed side with the Pythagorean theorem. If two sides are given, check the angles and computed side by using appropriate trigonometric functions.

Fig. 4-33

EXAMPLE 4 Solve the right triangle with $A = 50.0°$ and $b = 6.70$.

We first sketch the right triangle shown in Fig. 4-33. (In making the sketch, we should be careful to follow proper labeling of the triangle as outlined on the previous page.) We then express unknown side a in terms of known side b and known angle A and solve for a. We will then do the same for unknown side c and unknown angle B.

Finding side a, we know that $\tan A = \dfrac{a}{b}$, which means that $a = b \tan A$. Thus,

$$a = 6.70 \tan 50.0° = 7.98$$ lines 1 & 2 of calculator display in Fig. 4-34

```
6.7tan(50)
        7.98474907
6.7/cos(50)
       10.42334964
90-50
                40
```

Fig. 4-34

Next, solving for side c, we have $\cos A = \dfrac{b}{c}$, which means $c = \dfrac{b}{\cos A}$.

$$c = \frac{6.70}{\cos 50.0°} = 10.4$$ lines 3 & 4 of calculator display in Fig. 4-34

Now solving for B, we know that $A + B = 90°$, or

$$B = 90° - A$$
$$= 90° - 50.0° = 40.0°$$ lines 5 & 6 of calculator display in Fig. 4-34

Therefore, $a = 7.98$, $c = 10.4$, and $B = 40.0°$.

Checking the angles: $A + B + C = 50.0° + 40.0° + 90° = 180°$
Checking the sides: $10.4^2 = 108.16$
$7.98^2 + 6.70^2 = 108.57$

```
6.7tan(50)
        7.98474907
Ans→A
        7.98474907
6.7/cos(50)
       10.42334964
Ans→C
       10.42334964
A²+6.7²
       108.6462177
C²
       108.6462177
```

Fig. 4-35

Since the computed values were rounded off, the values 108.16 and 108.57 show that the values for sides a and c check.

As we calculate the values of the unknown parts, if we store each in the calculator memory, we can get a better check of the solution. In Fig. 4-35 we see the solution for each side, its storage in memory, and the check of these values. The lines above the display are those that are replaced as the solution proceeds. From this calculator display we see that the values for sides a and c check very accurately. ∎

NOTE ▸ In finding the unknown parts, we first expressed them in terms of the known parts. We do this because *it is best to use given values in calculations.* If we use one computed value to find another computed value, any error in the first would be carried to the value of the second. For example, in Example 4, if we were to find the value of c by using the value of a, any error in a would cause c to be in error as well.

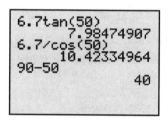

See Appendix C for a graphing calculator program SLVRTTRI. It can be used to solve a right triangle, given the two legs.

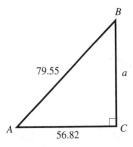

Fig. 4-36

We should also point out that, by inspection, we can make a rough check on the sides and angles of any triangle.

The longest side is always opposite the largest angle, and the shortest side is always opposite the smallest angle.

In a right triangle, *the hypotenuse is always the longest side.* We see that this is true for the sides and angles for the triangle in Example 4, where c is the longest side (opposite the 90° angle), and b is the shortest side and is opposite the angle of 40°.

■EXAMPLE 5   Solve the right triangle with $b = 56.82$ and $c = 79.55$.

We sketch the right triangle as shown in Fig. 4-36. Since two sides are given, we will use the Pythagorean theorem to find the third side a. Also, we will use the cosine to find $\angle A$.

Since $c^2 = a^2 + b^2$, $a^2 = c^2 - b^2$. Therefore,

$$a = \sqrt{c^2 - b^2} = \sqrt{79.55^2 - 56.82^2}$$
$$= 55.67 \qquad \text{lines 1 \& 2 shown in Fig. 4-37}$$

Since $\cos A = \dfrac{b}{c}$, we have

$$\cos A = \frac{56.82}{79.55}, \qquad A = \cos^{-1}\left(\frac{56.82}{79.55}\right) = 44.42° \qquad \text{lines 3–5 shown in Fig. 4-37}$$

It is not necessary to actually calculate the ratio 56.82/79.55. In the same way, we find the value of angle B.

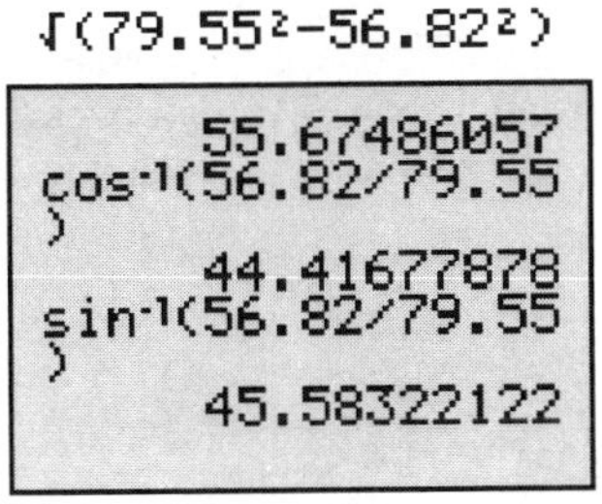

$$\sin B = \frac{56.82}{79.55}, \qquad B = \sin^{-1}\left(\frac{56.82}{79.55}\right) = 45.58° \qquad \text{lines 6–8 shown in Fig. 4-37}$$

√(79.55²-56.82²)

```
              55.67486057
cos⁻¹(56.82/79.55
)
              44.41677878
sin⁻¹(56.82/79.55
)
              45.58322122
```

Fig. 4-37

Although we used a different function, we did use exactly the same ratio to find B as we used to find A. Therefore, many texts would find B from the fact that $A + B = 90°$, or $B = 90° - A = 90° - 44.42° = 45.58°$. This is also acceptable since any possible error should be discovered when the solution is checked.

We have now found that

$$a = 55.67 \qquad A = 44.42° \qquad B = 45.58°$$

Checking the sides and angles, we first note that side a is the shortest side and is opposite the smallest angle, $\angle A$. Also, the hypotenuse is the longest side. Next, using the sine function (we could use the cosine or tangent) to check the sides, we have

As we noted earlier, the symbol $\approx$ means "equals approximately."

$$\sin 44.42° = \frac{55.67}{79.55}, \text{ or } 0.6999 \approx 0.6998 \qquad \sin 45.58° = \frac{56.82}{79.55}, \text{ or } 0.7142 \approx 0.7143$$

This shows that the values check. As we noted at the end of Example 4, we would get a more accurate check if we save the calculator values as they are found and use them for the check.   --------■

■EXAMPLE 6   Given that $\angle A$ and side a are known, express the unknown parts of the right triangle in terms of A and a.

We sketch a right triangle as shown in Fig. 4-38, and set up the required expressions as follows:

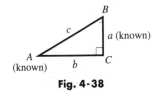

Fig. 4-38

Since $\dfrac{a}{b} = \tan A$, we have $b = \dfrac{a}{\tan A}$. Since $\dfrac{a}{c} = \sin A$, we have $c = \dfrac{a}{\sin A}$.

Since A is known, $B = 90° - A$.   --------■

EXERCISES *4-4*

In Exercises 1–4, draw appropriate figures and verify through observation that only one triangle may contain the given parts (that is, any other which may be drawn will be congruent).

1. A 60° angle included between sides of 3 in. and 6 in.

2. A side of 4 in. included between angles of 40° and 50°

3. A right triangle with a hypotenuse of 5 cm and a leg of 3 cm

4. A right triangle with a 70° angle between the hypotenuse and a leg of 5 cm

In Exercises 5–24, solve the right triangles with the given parts. Round off results. Refer to Fig. 4-39.

5. $A = 77.8°$, $a = 6700$

6. $A = 18.4°$, $c = 0.0897$

7. $a = 150$, $c = 345$

8. $a = 93.2$, $c = 124$

9. $B = 32.1°$, $c = 23.8$

10. $B = 64.3°$, $b = 0.652$

11. $b = 82$, $c = 88$ **12.** $a = 5920$, $b = 4110$

13. $A = 32.10°$, $c = 56.85$ **14.** $B = 12.60°$, $c = 18.42$

15. $a = 56.73$, $b = 44.09$ **16.** $a = 9.908$, $c = 12.63$

17. $B = 37.5°$, $a = 0.862$ **18.** $A = 52°$, $b = 8.4$

19. $B = 74.18°$, $b = 1.849$ **20.** $A = 51.36°$, $a = 369.2$

21. $a = 591.87$, $b = 264.93$ **22.** $b = 2.9507$, $c = 5.0864$

23. $A = 12.975°$, $b = 14.592$ **24.** $B = 84.942°$, $a = 7413.5$

In Exercises 25–28, find the part of the triangle labeled either x or A in the indicated figure.

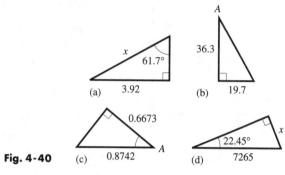

Fig. 4-40   (a)   (b)   (c)   (d)

25. Fig. 4-40(a)   **26.** Fig. 4-40(b)

27. Fig. 4-40(c)   **28.** Fig. 4-40(d)

In Exercises 29–32, refer to Fig. 4-39. In Exercises 29–31, the listed parts are assumed known. Express the other parts in terms of these known parts.

29. A, c **30.** a, b **31.** B, a

(W) 32. In Fig. 4-39, is there any combination of two given parts (not including $\angle C$) that does not give a unique solution of the triangle? Explain.

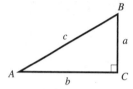

Fig. 4-39

Section 4.5

4-5 APPLICATIONS OF RIGHT TRIANGLES

SOLVING A WORD PROBLEM

EXAMPLE 1   The Sears Tower in Chicago can be seen from a point on the ground known to be 5200 ft from the base of the tower. The **angle of elevation** (*the angle between the horizontal and the line of sight, when the object is **above** the horizontal*) from the observer to the top of the tower is 16°. Based on this information, how high is the Sears Tower?

By drawing an appropriate figure, as shown in Fig. 4-41, we show the given information and that which is required. Here we have let h be the height of the tower, O the position of the observer, and B the point at the base of Sears Tower. From the figure we see that

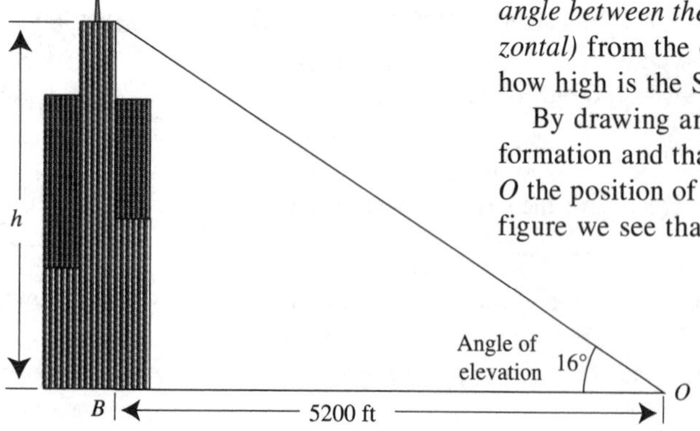

$$\frac{h}{5200} = \tan 16° \qquad \frac{\text{required opposite side}}{\text{given adjacent side}} = \text{tangent of given angle}$$

$$h = 5200 \tan 16°$$

$$= 1500 \text{ ft}$$

Here we have rounded off the result since the data are good only to two significant digits. (The Sears Tower was completed in 1974 and is the tallest building in the world. Its height is actually 1454 ft.) ∎

Fig. 4-41

Angle of elevation   16°

B ◄——— 5200 ft ———► O

h

See the chapter introduction.

SOLVING A WORD PROBLEM

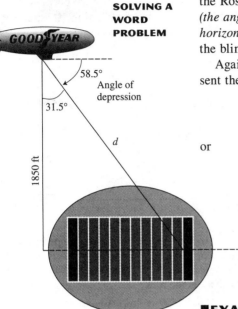

58.5°
Angle of depression
31.5°

d

1850 ft

Fig. 4-42

SOLVING A WORD PROBLEM

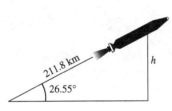

211.8 km
h
26.55°

Fig. 4-43

SOLVING A WORD PROBLEM

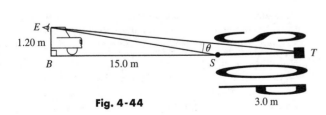

E
1.20 m
B 15.0 m *S* θ *T*
3.0 m

Fig. 4-44

EXAMPLE 2 The Goodyear blimp is 1850 ft above the ground and south of the Rose Bowl in California during a Super Bowl game. The **angle of depression** *(the angle between the horizontal and the line of sight, when the object is **below** the horizontal)* of the north goal line from the blimp is 58.5°. How far is the observer in the blimp from the goal line?

Again we sketch an appropriate figure as shown in Fig. 4-42. Here we let *d* represent the required distance. From the figure we see that

$$\frac{1850}{d} = \cos 31.5° \qquad \frac{\text{given adjacent side}}{\text{required hypotenuse}} = \text{cosine of known angle}$$

or

$$d = \frac{1850}{\cos 31.5°}$$
$$= 2170 \text{ ft}$$

Here we have rounded off the result to three significant digits, the accuracy of the given information. (The Super Bowl games in 1977, 1980, 1987, and 1993 were played in the Rose Bowl.)

EXAMPLE 3 A missile is launched at an angle of 26.55° with respect to the horizontal. If it travels in a straight line over level terrain for 2.000 min and its average speed is 6355 km/h, what is its altitude at this time?

In Fig. 4-43 we let *h* represent the altitude of the missile after 2.000 min (altitude is measured on a perpendicular line). Also, we determine that in this time the missile has flown 211.8 km in a direct line from the launching site. This is found from the fact that it travels at 6355 km/h for $\frac{1}{30.00}$ h (2.000 min), and distance = speed × time. We therefore have $(6355 \text{ km/h}) \left(\frac{1}{30.00} \text{ h}\right) = 211.8$ km. This means

$$\frac{h}{211.8} = \sin 26.55° \qquad \frac{\text{required opposite side}}{\text{known hypotenuse}} = \text{sine of given angle}$$
$$h = 211.8(\sin 26.55°)$$
$$= 94.67 \text{ km}$$

EXAMPLE 4 A driver coming to an intersection sees the word STOP in the roadway. From the measurements shown in Fig. 4-44, find the angle θ that the letters make at the driver's eye.

From the figure we know sides *BS* and *BE* in triangle *BES,* and sides *BT* and *BE* in triangle *BET.* This means we can find ∠*TEB* and ∠*SEB* by use of the tangent. We then find θ from the fact that θ = ∠*TEB* − ∠*SEB.*

$$\tan∠TEB = \frac{18.0}{1.20}, \qquad ∠TEB = 86.2°$$
$$\tan∠SEB = \frac{15.0}{1.20}, \qquad ∠SEB = 85.4°$$
$$θ = 86.2° − 85.4° = 0.8°$$

Lasers were first produced in the late 1950s.

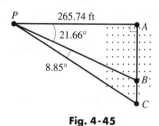

Fig. 4-45

EXAMPLE 5   Using lasers, a surveyor makes the measurements shown in Fig. 4-45, where points *B* and *C* are in a marsh. Find the distance between *B* and *C*. Since the distance *BC* = *AC* − *AB*, *BC* is found by finding *AC* and *AB* and subtracting.

$$\frac{AB}{265.74} = \tan 21.66° \quad \text{or} \quad AB = 265.74 \tan 21.66°$$

$$\frac{AC}{265.74} = \tan(21.66° + 8.85°) \quad \text{or} \quad AC = 265.74 \tan 30.51°$$

$$BC = AC - AB = 265.74 \tan 30.51° - 265.74 \tan 21.66°$$
$$= 51.06 \text{ ft}$$

EXERCISES *4-5*

In the following exercises, solve the given problems. Sketch an appropriate figure unless the figure is given.

1. A straight 120-ft culvert is built down a hillside that makes an angle of 54.0° with the horizontal. Find the height of the hill.

2. A point near the top of the Leaning Tower of Pisa is 50.5 m from a point at the base of the tower (measured along the tower). This top point is also directly above a point on the ground 4.25 m from the same base point. What angle does the tower make with the ground? See Fig. 4-46.

Fig. 4-46

3. A tree has a shadow 22.8 ft long when the angle of elevation of the sun is 62.6°. How tall is the tree?

4. The straight arm of a robot is 1.25 m long and makes an angle of 13.0° above a horizontal conveyor belt. How high above the belt is the end of the arm? See Fig. 4-47.

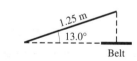

Fig. 4-47

5. The headlights of an automobile are set such that the beam drops 2.00 in. for each 25.0 ft in front of the car. What is the angle between the beam and the road?

6. A bullet was fired such that it just grazed the top of a table. It entered a wall, which is 12.60 ft from the graze point in the table, at a point 4.63 ft above the tabletop. At what angle was the bullet fired above the horizontal? See Fig. 4-48.

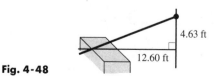

Fig. 4-48

7. A robot is on the surface of Mars. The angle of depression from a camera in the robot to a rock on the surface of Mars is 13.33°. The camera is 196.0 cm above the surface. How far from the camera is the rock?

8. From a small boat 2500 ft downstream from the Horseshoe Falls (Canadian) at Niagara Falls, the angle of elevation of the top of the Falls is 4.0°. How high are the Falls? See Fig. 4-49.

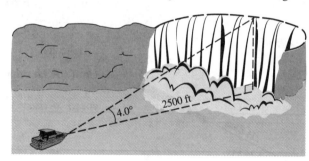

Fig. 4-49

9. In designing a new building, a doorway is 2.65 ft above the ground. A ramp for the disabled, at an angle of 6.0° with the ground, is to be built to the doorway. How long will the ramp be?

10. On a test flight, during the landing of the space shuttle, the ship was 325 ft above the end of the landing strip. It then came in on a constant angle of 7.5° with the landing strip. How far from the end of the landing strip did it first touch ground?

11. A rectangular piece of plywood 4.00 ft by 8.00 ft is cut from one corner to an opposite corner. What are the angles between edges of the resulting pieces?

12. A guardrail is to be constructed around the top of a circular observation tower. The diameter of the observation area is 12.3 m. If the railing is constructed with 30 equal straight sections, what should be the length of each section?

13. The angle of inclination of a road is often expressed as *percent grade,* which is the vertical rise divided by the horizontal run (expressed as a percent). See Fig. 4-50. A 6.0% grade corresponds to a road that rises 6.0 ft for every 100 ft along the horizontal. Find the angle of inclination that corresponds to a 6.0% grade.

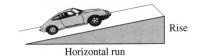

Fig. 4-50   Horizontal run   Rise

14. A tabletop is in the shape of a regular octagon (8 sides). What is the greatest distance across the table if one edge of the octagon is 0.750 m?

15. To get a good view of a person in front of a teller's window, it is determined that a surveillance camera at a bank should be directed at a point 15.5 ft to the right and 6.75 ft below the camera. See Fig. 4-51. At what angle of depression should the camera be directed?

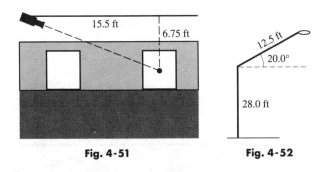

Fig. 4-51   **Fig. 4-52**

16. A street light is designed as shown in Fig. 4-52. How high above the street is the light?

17. A straight driveway is 85.0 ft long, and the top is 12.0 ft above the bottom. What angle does it make with the horizontal?

18. Part of the Tower Bridge in London is a drawbridge. This part of the bridge is 76.0 m long. When each half is raised, the distance between them is 8.0 m. What angle does each half make with the horizontal? See Fig. 4-53.

Fig. 4-53

19. A square wire loop is rotating in the magnetic field between two poles of a magnet in order to induce an electric current. The axis of rotation passes through the center of the loop and is midway between the poles, as shown in the side view in Fig. 4-54. How far is the edge of the loop from either pole if the side of the square is 7.30 cm and the poles are 7.66 cm apart when the angle between the loop and the vertical is 78.0°?

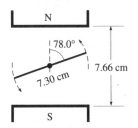

Fig. 4-54

20. From a space probe circling Io, one of Jupiter's moons, at an altitude of 552 km, it was observed that the angle of depression of the horizon was 39.7°. What is the radius of Io?

21. A manufacturing plant is designed to be in the shape of a regular pentagon with 92.5 ft on each side. A security fence surrounds the building to form a circle, and each corner of the building is to be 25.0 ft from the closest point on the fence. How much fencing is required?

22. A surveyor on the New York City side of the Hudson River wishes to find the height of a cliff *(palisade)* on the New Jersey side. Figure 4-55 shows the measurements which were made. How high is the cliff? (In the figure, the triangle containing the height *h* is vertical and perpendicular to the river.)

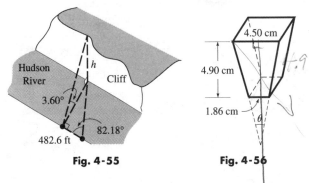

Fig. 4-55   **Fig. 4-56**

23. Find the angle θ in the taper shown in Fig. 4-56. (The front face is an isosceles trapezoid.)

24. What is the circumference of the Arctic Circle (latitude 66°32′N)? The radius of the earth is 3960 mi.

25. A stairway 1.0 m wide goes from the bottom of a cylindrical storage tank to the top at a point halfway around the tank. The handrail on the outside of the stairway makes an angle of 31.8° with the horizontal, and the radius of the tank is 11.8 m. Find the length of the handrail. See Fig. 4-57.

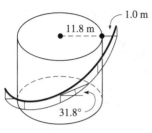

Fig. 4-57

Fig. 4-58

26. An antenna is on the top of the World Trade Center. From a point on the river 7800 ft from the Center, the angles of elevation of the top and bottom of the antenna are 12.1° and 9.9°, respectively. How tall is the antenna? (Disregard the small part of the antenna near the base that cannot be seen.) The World Trade Center is shown in Fig. 4-58.

27. Some of the streets of San Francisco are shown in Fig. 4-59. The distances between intersections *A* and *B*, *A* and *D*, and *C* and *E* are shown. How far is it between intersections *C* and *D*?

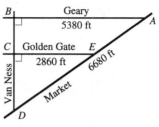

Fig. 4-59

28. A supporting girder structure is shown in Fig. 4-60. Find the length *x*.

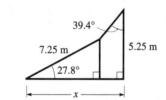

Fig. 4-60

Section 4.6

CHAPTER EQUATIONS

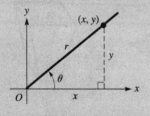

$$\sin \theta = \frac{y}{r} \qquad \cos \theta = \frac{x}{r}$$

$$\tan \theta = \frac{y}{x} \qquad \cot \theta = \frac{x}{y}$$ (4-1)

$$\sec \theta = \frac{r}{x} \qquad \csc \theta = \frac{r}{y}$$

Pythagorean theorem

$$c^2 = a^2 + b^2$$ (4-2)

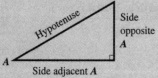

$$\sin A = \frac{\text{side opposite } A}{\text{hypotenuse}} \qquad \cos A = \frac{\text{side adjacent } A}{\text{hypotenuse}}$$

$$\tan A = \frac{\text{side opposite } A}{\text{side adjacent } A} \qquad \cot A = \frac{\text{side adjacent } A}{\text{side opposite } A}$$ (4-5)

$$\sec A = \frac{\text{hypotenuse}}{\text{side adjacent } A} \qquad \csc A = \frac{\text{hypotenuse}}{\text{side opposite } A}$$

REVIEW EXERCISES

In Exercises 1–4, find the smallest positive angle and the smallest negative angle (numerically) coterminal with but not equal to the given angle.

1. 17.0° **2.** 248.3° **3.** −217.5° **4.** −7.6°

In Exercises 5–8, express the given angles in decimal form.

5. 31°54′ **6.** 174°45′ **7.** 38°6′ **8.** 321°27′

In Exercises 9–12, express the given angles to the nearest minute.

9. 17.5° **10.** 65.4° **11.** 49.7° **12.** 126.25°

In Exercises 13–16, determine the trigonometric functions of the angles (in standard position) whose terminal side passes through the given points. Give answers in exact form.

13. (24, 7) **14.** (5, 4) **15.** (4, 4) **16.** (1.2, 0.5)

In Exercises 17–20, find the indicated trigonometric functions. Give answers in decimal form, rounded off to three significant digits.

17. Given $\sin \theta = \frac{5}{13}$, find $\cos \theta$ and $\cot \theta$.
18. Given $\cos \theta = \frac{3}{8}$, find $\sin \theta$ and $\tan \theta$.
19. Given $\tan \theta = 2$, find $\cos \theta$ and $\csc \theta$.
20. Given $\cot \theta = 4$, find $\sin \theta$ and $\sec \theta$.

In Exercises 21–28, find the values of the trigonometric functions. Round off results.

21. sin 72.1° **22.** cos 40.3°
23. tan 61.64° **24.** sin 49.09°
25. sec 18.4° **26.** csc 82.4°
27. (cot 7.06°)(sin 7.06°) − cos 7.06°
28. (sec 79.36°)(sin 79.36°) − tan 79.36°

In Exercises 29–36, find θ for each of the given trigonometric functions. Round off results.

29. cos θ = 0.950 **30.** sin θ = 0.63052
31. tan θ = 1.574 **32.** cos θ = 0.1345
33. csc θ = 4.713 **34.** cot θ = 0.7561
35. sec θ = 2.54 **36.** csc θ = 1.92

In Exercises 37–48, solve the right triangles with the given parts. Refer to Fig. 4-61.

37. A = 17.0°, b = 6.00
38. B = 68.1°, a = 1080
39. a = 81.0, b = 64.5
40. a = 1.06, c = 3.82

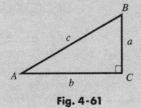

Fig. 4-61

41. A = 37.5°, a = 12.0 **42.** B = 15.7°, c = 12.6
43. b = 6.508, c = 7.642 **44.** a = 72.14, b = 14.37
45. A = 49.67°, c = 0.8253 **46.** B = 4.38°, b = 5.682
47. a = 11.652, c = 15.483 **48.** a = 724.39, b = 852.44

In Exercises 49–76, solve the given applied problems.

49. The voltage e at any instant in a coil of wire that is turning in a magnetic field is given by $e = E \cos \alpha$, where E is the maximum voltage and α is the angle the coil makes with the field. Find the acute angle α if $e = 56.9$ V and $E = 339$ V.

50. A formula for the area of a quadrilateral is $A = \frac{1}{2} d_1 d_2 \sin \theta$, where d_1 and d_2 are the lengths of the diagonals and θ is the angle between them. Find the area of a four-sided carpet remnant with diagonals 3.25 ft and 4.38 ft and $\theta = 72.0°$.

51. For a car rounding a curve, the road should be banked at an angle θ according to the equation $\tan \theta = \dfrac{v^2}{gr}$. Here, v is the speed of the car and r is the radius of the curve in the road. See Fig. 4-62. Find θ for $v = 80.7$ ft/s (55.0 mi/h), $g = 32.2$ ft/s^2, and $r = 950$ ft.

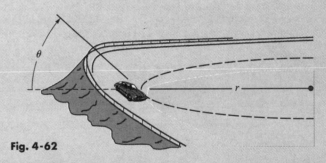

Fig. 4-62

52. The *apparent power S* in an electric circuit in which the power is P and the impedance phase angle is θ is given by $S = P \sec \theta$. Given $P = 12.0$ V·A and $\theta = 29.4°$, find S.

53. A surveyor measures two sides and the included angle of a triangular tract of land to be $a = 31.96$ m, $b = 47.25$ m, and $C = 64.09°$. (a) Show that a formula for the area A of the tract is $A = \frac{1}{2} ab \sin C$. (b) Find the area of the tract.

54. A water channel has the cross section of an isosceles trapezoid. See Fig. 4-63. (a) Show that a formula for the area of the cross section is $A = bh + h^2 \cot \theta$. (b) Find A if $b = 12.6$ ft, $h = 4.75$ ft, and $\theta = 37.2°$.

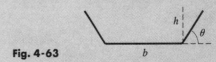

Fig. 4-63

Part 4 4.6 Chapter Equations, Exercises, Test **233**

55. In tracking an airplane on radar, it is found that the plane is 27.5 km on a direct line from the control tower, with an angle of elevation of 10.3°. What is the altitude of the plane?

56. A straight emergency chute for an airplane is 16.0 ft long. In being tested, the end of the chute is 8.5 ft above the ground. What angle does the chute make with the ground?

57. The window of a house is shaded as shown in Fig. 4-64. What percent of the window is shaded when the angle of elevation θ of the sun is 65°?

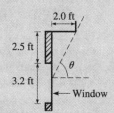

2.0 ft

2.5 ft

3.2 ft

θ

Window

Fig. 4-64

58. The windshield on an automobile is inclined 42.5° with respect to the horizontal. Assuming that the windshield is flat and rectangular, what is its area if it is 4.80 ft wide and the bottom is 1.50 ft in front of the top?

59. A water slide at an amusement park is 85 ft long and is inclined at an angle of 52° with the horizontal. How high is the top of the slide above the water level?

60. The distance from the ground level to the underside of a cloud is called the *ceiling*. See Fig. 4-65. A ground observer 950 m from a searchlight aimed vertically notes that the angle of elevation of the spot of light on a cloud is 76°. What is the ceiling?

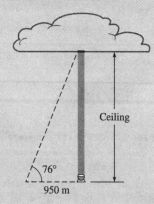

Ceiling

76°

950 m

Fig. 4-65

61. The vertical cross section of an attic room in a house is shown in Fig. 4-66. Find the distance *d* across the floor.

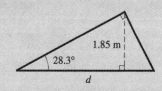

1.85 m

28.3°

d

Fig. 4-66

62. The impedance *Z* and resistance *R* in an alternating-current circuit may be represented by letting the impedance be the hypotenuse of a right triangle and the resistance be the side adjacent to the phase angle θ. If *R* = 1750 Ω and θ = 17.38°, find *Z*.

63. A typical aqueduct built by the Romans dropped on average at an angle of about 0.03° to allow gravity to move the water from the source to the city. For such an aqueduct of 65 km in length, how much higher was the source than the city?

64. A Coast Guard boat 2.75 km from a straight beach can travel at 37.5 km/h. By traveling along a line that is at 69.0° with the beach, how long will it take it to reach the beach? See Fig. 4-67.

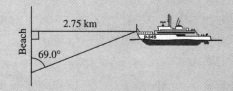

Beach

2.75 km

69.0°

P-345

Fig. 4-67

65. In the structural support shown in Fig. 4-68, find *x*.

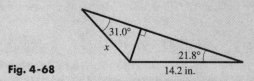

31.0°

x

21.8°

14.2 in.

Fig. 4-68

66. A person standing on a level plain hears the sound of a plane, looks in the direction of the sound, but the plane is not there (familiar?). When the sound was heard, it was coming from a point at an angle of elevation of 25°, and the plane was traveling at 450 mi/h (660 ft/s) at a constant altitude of 2800 ft along a straight line. If the plane later passes directly over the person, at what angle of elevation should the person have looked directly to see the plane when the sound was heard? (The speed of sound is 1130 ft/s.) See Fig. 4-69.

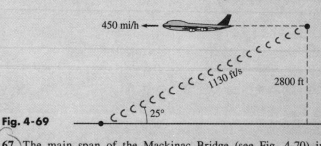

450 mi/h

1130 ft/s

2800 ft

25°

Fig. 4-69

67. The main span of the Mackinac Bridge (see Fig. 4-70) in northern Michigan is 1160 m long. The angle *subtended* by the span at the eye of an observer in a helicopter is 2.2°. Show that the distance calculated from the helicopter to the span is about the same if the line of sight is perpendicular to the end or to the middle of the span.

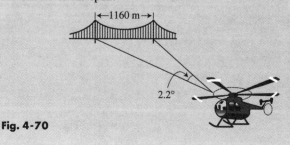

1160 m

2.2°

Fig. 4-70

68. Each side piece of the trellis shown in Fig. 4-71 makes an angle of 80.0° with the ground. Find the length of each side piece and the area covered by the trellis.

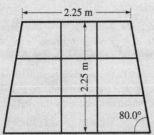

Fig. 4-71

(W) **69.** The surface of a soccer ball consists of 20 regular hexagons (6 sides) interlocked around 12 regular pentagons (5 sides). See Fig. 4-72. (a) If the side of each hexagon and pentagon is 45.0 mm, what is the surface area of the soccer ball? (b) Find the surface area, given that the diameter of the ball is 222 mm. (c) Assuming that the given values are accurate, account for the difference in the values found in parts (a) and (b).

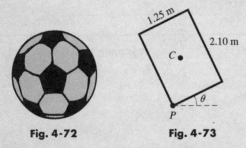

Fig. 4-72   **Fig. 4-73**

70. Through what angle θ must the crate shown in Fig. 4-73 be tipped in order that its center of gravity C is directly above the pivot point P?

71. A laser beam is transmitted with a "width" of 0.00200°. What is the diameter of a spot of the beam on an object 52,500 km distant? See Fig. 4-74.

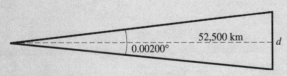

Fig. 4-74

72. Find the gear angle θ in Fig. 4-75 if $t = 0.180$ in.

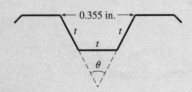

Fig. 4-75

73. A hang glider is directly above the shore of a lake. An observer on a hill is 375 m along a straight line from the shore. From the observer, the angle of elevation of the hang glider is 42.0°, and the angle of depression of the shore is 25.0°. How far above the shore is the hang glider?

74. A ground observer sights a weather balloon to the east at an angle of elevation of 15.0°. A second observer 2.35 mi to the east of the first also sights the balloon to the east at an angle of elevation of 24.0°. How high is the balloon? See Fig. 4-76.

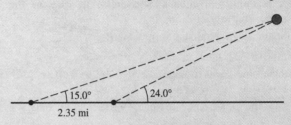

Fig. 4-76

75. A uniform strip of wood 5.0 cm wide frames a trapezoidal window as shown in Fig. 4-77. Find the left dimension l of the outside of the frame.

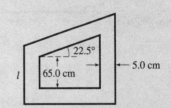

Fig. 4-77

76. A crop-dusting plane flies over a level field at a height of 25 ft. If the dust leaves the plane through a 30° angle and hits the ground after the plane travels 75 ft, how wide a strip is dusted? See Fig. 4-78.

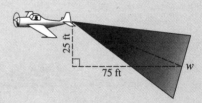

Fig. 4-78

Writing Exercise

77. Two students were discussing a problem in which a distant object was seen through an angle of 2.3°. One found the length of the object (perpendicular to the line of sight) using the tangent of the angle, and the other had the same answer using the sine of the angle. Write a paragraph explaining how this is possible.

PRACTICE TEST

1. Express 37°39′ in decimal form.

2. Find θ to the nearest 0.01° if $\cos \theta = 0.3726$.

3. A ship's captain, desiring to travel due south, discovers due to an improperly functioning instrument, the ship has gone 22.62 km in a direction 4.05° east of south. How far from its course (to the east) is the ship?

4. Find $\tan \theta$ in fractional form if $\sin \theta = \frac{2}{3}$.

5. Find $\csc \theta$ if $\tan \theta = 1.294$.

6. Solve the right triangle in Fig. 4-79 if $A = 37.4°$ and $b = 52.8$.

7. Solve the right triangle in Fig. 4-79 if $a = 2.49$ and $c = 3.88$.

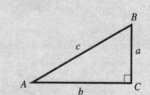

Fig. 4-79

8. In finding the wavelength λ (the Greek lambda) of light, the equation $\lambda = d \sin \theta$ is used. Find λ if $d = 30.05 \ \mu$m and $\theta = 1.167°$. (μ is the prefix for 10^{-6}.)

9. Determine the trigonometric functions of an angle in standard position if its terminal side passes through $(5, 2)$. Give answers in exact and decimal forms.

10. A surveyor sights two points directly ahead. Both are at an elevation 18.525 m lower than the observation point. How far apart are the points if the angles of depression are 13.500° and 21.375°, respectively? See Fig. 4-80.

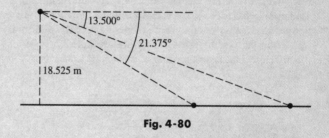

Fig. 4-80

Section 4.1
Exercises 4-1, page 107

1.   **3.**

5. 405°, −315°   **7.** 210°, −510°   **9.** 430° 30′, −289° 30′

11. 638.1°, −81.9°   **13.** 15.18°   **15.** 82.91°   **17.** 18.85°

19. 235.49°   **21.** 0.977   **23.** 4.97   **25.** 47° 30′

27. −5° 37′   **29.** 15.20°   **31.** 301.27°

33.   **35.**   **37.** (−7, 5), (−3, −5)

39.   **41.** 21.710°

                 43. 86° 16′ 26″

Section 4.2
Exercises 4-2, page 111

1. $\sin \theta = \dfrac{4}{5}$, $\cos \theta = \dfrac{3}{5}$, $\tan \theta = \dfrac{4}{3}$, $\cot \theta = \dfrac{3}{4}$, $\sec \theta = \dfrac{5}{3}$, $\csc \theta = \dfrac{5}{4}$

3. $\sin \theta = \dfrac{8}{17}$, $\cos \theta = \dfrac{15}{17}$, $\tan \theta = \dfrac{8}{15}$, $\cot \theta = \dfrac{15}{8}$, $\sec \theta = \dfrac{17}{15}$, $\csc \theta = \dfrac{17}{8}$

5. $\sin \theta = \dfrac{40}{41}$, $\cos \theta = \dfrac{9}{41}$, $\tan \theta = \dfrac{40}{9}$, $\cot \theta = \dfrac{9}{40}$, $\sec \theta = \dfrac{41}{9}$, $\csc \theta = \dfrac{41}{40}$

7. $\sin \theta = \dfrac{\sqrt{15}}{4}$, $\cos \theta = \dfrac{1}{4}$, $\tan \theta = \sqrt{15}$, $\cot \theta = \dfrac{1}{\sqrt{15}}$, $\sec \theta = 4$, $\csc \theta = \dfrac{4}{\sqrt{15}}$

9. $\sin \theta = \dfrac{1}{\sqrt{2}}$, $\cos \theta = \dfrac{1}{\sqrt{2}}$, $\tan \theta = 1$, $\cot \theta = 1$, $\sec \theta = \sqrt{2}$, $\csc \theta = \sqrt{2}$

11. $\sin \theta = \dfrac{2}{\sqrt{29}}$, $\cos \theta = \dfrac{5}{\sqrt{29}}$, $\tan \theta = \dfrac{2}{5}$, $\cot \theta = \dfrac{5}{2}$, $\sec \theta = \dfrac{\sqrt{29}}{5}$, $\csc \theta = \dfrac{\sqrt{29}}{2}$

13. $\sin \theta = 0.846$, $\cos \theta = 0.534$, $\tan \theta = 1.58$, $\cot \theta = 0.631$, $\sec \theta = 1.87$, $\csc \theta = 1.18$

15. $\sin \theta = 0.1521$, $\cos \theta = 0.9884$, $\tan \theta = 0.1539$, $\cot \theta = 6.498$, $\sec \theta = 1.012$, $\csc \theta = 6.575$

17. $\dfrac{5}{13}, \dfrac{12}{5}$ **19.** $\dfrac{1}{\sqrt{2}}, \sqrt{2}$ **21.** 0.882, 1.33

23. 0.246, 3.94   **25.** $\sin \theta = \dfrac{4}{5}$, $\tan \theta = \dfrac{4}{3}$

27. $\tan \theta = \dfrac{1}{2}$, $\sec \theta = \dfrac{\sqrt{5}}{2}$ **29.** 1   **31.** $\sec \theta$

Section 4.3
Exercises 4-3, page 115

1. $\sin 40° = 0.64$, $\cos 40° = 0.77$, $\tan 40° = 0.84$, $\cot 40° = 1.19$, $\sec 40° = 1.31$, $\csc 40° = 1.56$

3. $\sin 15° = 0.26$, $\cos 15° = 0.97$, $\tan 15° = 0.27$, $\cot 15° = 3.73$, $\sec 15° = 1.04$, $\csc 15° = 3.86$

5. 0.381   **7.** 1.58   **9.** 0.9626   **11.** 0.99

13. 0.4085   **15.** 1.57   **17.** 1.32   **19.** 0.07063

21. 70.97°   **23.** 65.70°   **25.** 11.7°   **27.** 49.453°

29. 53.44°   **31.** 81.79°   **33.** 74.1°   **35.** 17.85°

37. 0.9556 = 0.9556   **39.** y is always less than r.

41. 0.8885   **43.** 0.93614   **45.** 87 dB   **47.** 1.19 A

Section 4.4
Exercises 4-4, page 120

1.   **3.**

5. $B = 12.2°$, $b = 1450$, $c = 6850$

7. $A = 25.8°$, $B = 64.2°$, $b = 311$

9. $A = 57.9°$, $a = 20.2$, $b = 12.6$

11. $A = 21°$, $a = 32$, $B = 69°$

13. $a = 30.21$, $B = 57.90°$, $b = 48.16$

15. $A = 52.15°$, $B = 37.85°$, $c = 71.85$

17. $A = 52.5°$, $b = 0.661$, $c = 1.09$

19. $A = 15.82°$, $a = 0.5239$, $c = 1.922$

21. $A = 65.886°$, $B = 24.114°$, $c = 648.46$

23. $a = 3.3621$, $B = 77.025°$, $c = 14.974$

25. 4.45   **27.** 40.24°

29. $a = c \sin A$, $b = c \cos A$, $B = 90° - A$

31. $A = 90° - B$, $b = a \tan B$, $c = \dfrac{a}{\cos B}$

Section 4.5
Exercises 4-5, page 122

1. 97 ft   **3.** 44.0 ft   **5.** 0.4°   **7.** 850.1 cm

9. 25.4 ft   **11.** 26.6°, 63.4°, 90.0°   **13.** 3.4°   **15.** 23.5°

17. 8.1°   **19.** 3.07 cm   **21.** 651 ft   **23.** 30.2°

25. 47.3 m   **27.** 2100 ft

Section 4.6
Review Exercises for Chapter 4, page 125

1. 377.0°, −343.0°   **3.** 142.5°, −577.5°   **5.** 31.9°

7. 38.1°   **9.** 17° 30′   **11.** 49° 42′

13. $\sin \theta = \dfrac{7}{25}$, $\cos \theta = \dfrac{24}{25}$, $\tan \theta = \dfrac{7}{24}$, $\cot \theta = \dfrac{24}{7}$,

   $\sec \theta = \dfrac{25}{24}$, $\csc \theta = \dfrac{25}{7}$

15. $\sin \theta = \dfrac{1}{\sqrt{2}}$, $\cos \theta = \dfrac{1}{\sqrt{2}}$, $\tan \theta = 1$, $\cot \theta = 1$,

   $\sec \theta = \sqrt{2}$, $\csc \theta = \sqrt{2}$

17. 0.923, 2.40   **19.** 0.447, 1.12   **21.** 0.952

23. 1.853   **25.** 1.05   **27.** 0   **29.** 18.2°   **31.** 57.57°

33. 12.25°   **35.** 66.8°   **37.** $a = 1.83$, $B = 73.0°$, $c = 6.27$

39. $A = 51.5°$, $B = 38.5°$, $c = 104$

41. $B = 52.5°$, $b = 15.6$, $c = 19.7$

43. $A = 31.61°$, $a = 4.006$, $B = 58.39°$

45. $a = 0.6292$, $B = 40.33°$, $b = 0.5341$

47. $A = 48.813°$, $B = 41.187°$, $b = 10.196$

49. 80.3°   **51.** 12.0°

53. (a) $A = \frac{1}{2}bh = \frac{1}{2}b(a \sin C) = \frac{1}{2}ab \sin C$ (b) 679.2 m^2

55. 4.92 km   **57.** 56%   **59.** 67 ft   **61.** 4.43 m

63. 34 m   **65.** 10.2 in.

67. middle: $\dfrac{580}{\tan 1.1°} = 30{,}200$ m; end: $\dfrac{1160}{\tan 2.2°} = 30{,}200$ m

69. (a) 147,000 mm^2 (b) 155,000 mm^2
   (c) Curved surfaces covering each pentagon or hexagon would have greater area than plane area.

71. 1.83 km   **73.** 464 m   **75.** 73.3 cm

THE TRIGONOMETRIC FUNCTIONS

4.1 Angles Section 4.1

1. (a) 60°

(b) 120°

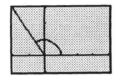

(c) −90°

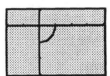

5. positive: $45° + 360° = 405°$
negative: $45° - 360° = -315°$

9. positive: $70°30' + 360 = 430°30'$
negative: $70°30' - 360° = -289°30'$

13. To change 0.265 rad to degrees multiply by $\dfrac{180}{\pi}$, 0.265 rad $\left(\dfrac{180°}{\pi\ \text{rad}}\right) \approx 15.18°$

17. $0.329\ \text{rad} \approx 18.85°$

 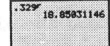

21. $56.0° = 0.977\ \text{rad}$ to three significant digits

 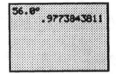

25. $47° + 0.5° \cdot \dfrac{60'}{1°} = 47° + 30' = 47°30'$

29. $15°12' = 15° + 12' \cdot \dfrac{1°}{60'} = 15.2°$

33. Angle in standard position terminal side passing through $(4, 2)$.

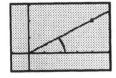

37. Angle in standard position terminal side passing through $(-7, 5)$.

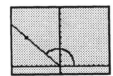

41. $21°42'36'' = 21° + 42' \cdot \dfrac{1°}{60'} + 36'' \cdot \dfrac{1°}{60''} \cdot \dfrac{1°}{60'} = 21.710°$

Section 4.2

4.2   Defining the Trigonometric Functions

1. $r = \sqrt{6^2 + 8^2} = \sqrt{36 + 64} = \sqrt{100} = 10$

$$\sin \theta = \frac{y}{r} = \frac{8}{10} = \frac{4}{5}$$

$$\cos \theta = \frac{x}{r} = \frac{6}{10} = \frac{3}{5}$$

$$\tan \theta = \frac{y}{x} = \frac{8}{6} = \frac{4}{3}$$

$$\csc \theta = \frac{r}{y} = \frac{10}{8} = \frac{5}{4}$$

$$\sec \theta = \frac{r}{x} = \frac{10}{6} = \frac{5}{3}$$

$$\cot \theta = \frac{x}{y} = \frac{6}{8} = \frac{3}{4}$$

5. $r = \sqrt{9^2 + 40^2} = 41$

$$\sin \theta = \frac{y}{r} = \frac{40}{41}$$

$$\cos \theta = \frac{x}{r} = \frac{9}{41}$$

$$\tan \theta = \frac{y}{x} = \frac{40}{9}$$

$$\csc \theta = \frac{r}{y} = \frac{41}{40}$$

$$\sec \theta = \frac{r}{x} = \frac{41}{9}$$

$$\cot \theta = \frac{x}{y} = \frac{9}{40}$$

9. $r = \sqrt{1^2 + 1^2} = \sqrt{2}$

$$\sin \theta = \frac{y}{r} = \frac{1}{\sqrt{2}} = \frac{\sqrt{2}}{2}$$

$$\cos \theta = \frac{x}{r} = \frac{1}{\sqrt{2}} = \frac{\sqrt{2}}{2}$$

$$\tan \theta = \frac{y}{x} = \frac{1}{1} = 1$$

$$\csc \theta = \frac{r}{y} = \frac{\sqrt{2}}{1} = \sqrt{2}$$

$$\sec \theta = \frac{r}{x} = \frac{\sqrt{2}}{1} = \sqrt{2}$$

$$\cot \theta = \frac{x}{y} = \frac{1}{1} = 1$$

13. $r = \sqrt{3.25^2 + 5.15^2} = \sqrt{37.085} \approx 6.09$

to three significant ditits

$$\sin \theta = \frac{y}{r} = \frac{5.15}{6.09} = 0.846$$

$$\cos \theta = \frac{x}{r} = \frac{3.25}{6.09} = 0.534$$

$$\tan \theta = \frac{y}{x} = \frac{5.15}{3.25} = 1.58$$

$$\csc \theta = \frac{r}{y} = \frac{6.09}{5.15} = 1.18$$

$$\sec \theta = \frac{r}{x} = \frac{6.09}{3.25} = 1.87$$

$$\cot \theta = \frac{x}{y} = \frac{3.25}{5.15} = 0.631$$

17. $\cos \theta = \frac{12}{13} \Rightarrow x = 12$ and $r = 13$ with θ in QI.

$$r^2 = x^2 + y^2 \Rightarrow 169 = 144 + y^2 \Rightarrow y^2 = 25$$
$$y = 5$$

$$\sin \theta = \frac{y}{r} = \frac{5}{13}, \ \cot \theta = \frac{x}{y} = \frac{12}{5}.$$

21. $\sin \theta = 0.750 \Rightarrow y = 0.750$ and $r = 1$ with θ in QI.
$$r^2 = x^2 + y^2 \Rightarrow 1^2 = x^2 + 0.750^2 \Rightarrow x^2 = 0.4375 \Rightarrow x = 0.661$$

$$\cot \theta = \frac{x}{y} = \frac{0.661}{0.750} = 0.881,$$

$$\csc \theta = \frac{r}{y} = \frac{1}{0.750} = 1.333.$$

25. For $(3, 4)$, $r = 5$, $\sin \theta = \dfrac{y}{r} = \dfrac{4}{5}$ and $\tan \theta = \dfrac{y}{x} = \dfrac{4}{3}$.

For $(6, 8)$, $r = 10$, $\sin \theta = \dfrac{y}{r} = \dfrac{8}{10} = \dfrac{4}{5}$ and $\tan \theta = \dfrac{y}{x} = \dfrac{8}{6} = \dfrac{4}{3}$.

For $(4.5, 6)$, $r = 7.5$, $\sin \theta = \dfrac{y}{r} = \dfrac{6}{7.5} = \dfrac{4}{5}$ and $\tan \theta = \dfrac{y}{x} = \dfrac{6}{4.5} = \dfrac{4}{3}$.

29. $\sin^2 \theta + \cos^2 \theta = \left(\dfrac{3}{5}\right)^2 + \left(\dfrac{4}{5}\right)^2 = \dfrac{9}{25} + \dfrac{16}{25} = \dfrac{25}{25} = 1$

Section 4.3

4.3   Values of the Trigonometric Functions

1. Answers may vary. One set of measurements gives $x = 7.6$ and $y = 6.5$.

$$\sin 40° = \frac{6.5}{10} = 0.65 \qquad\qquad \csc 40° = \frac{10}{6.5} = 1.54$$

$$\cos 40° = \frac{7.6}{10} = 0.76 \qquad\qquad \sec 40° = \frac{10}{7.6} = 1.32$$

$$\tan 40° = \frac{6.5}{7.6} = 0.86 \qquad\qquad \cot 40° = \frac{7.6}{6.5} = 1.17$$

5. $\sin 22.4° = 0.381$

9. $\cos 15.71° = 0.9626$

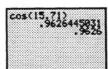

13. $\cot 67.78° = 0.4085$

17. $\csc 49.3° = 1.32$

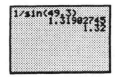

21. $\cos 70.97° = 0.3261$

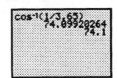

25. $\tan 11.7° = 0.207$

29. $\csc 53.44° = 1.245$

33. $\sec 74.1° = 3.65$

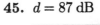

37.

$$\frac{\sin 43.7°}{\cos 43.7°} = \tan 43.7° = 0.96$$

41. Given $\tan \theta = 1.936$, $\sin \theta = 0.8885$

45. $d = 87$ dB

Section 4.4

4.4 The Right Triangle

1. A 60° angle between sides of 3 in and 6 in determines the unique triangle shown in the figure below.

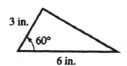

5. $\sin 77.8° = \dfrac{6700}{c} \Rightarrow c = 6850$, $\angle B = 90° - 77.8° = 12.2°$

   $\tan 77.8° = \dfrac{6700}{b} \Rightarrow b = 1450$

9. $\angle A = 90° - 32.1° = 57.9°$, $\sin 32.1° = \dfrac{b}{23.8} \Rightarrow b = 12.6$

   $\cos 32.1° = \dfrac{a}{23.8} \Rightarrow a = 20.2$

13. $\angle B = 90° - 32.1° = 57.9°$, $\sin 32.1° = \dfrac{a}{56.85} \Rightarrow a = 30.21$

    $\cos 32.1° = \dfrac{b}{56.85} \Rightarrow b = 48.16$

17. $\angle A = 90° - 37.5° = 52.5°$, $\tan 37.5° = \dfrac{b}{0.862} \Rightarrow b = 0.661$

    $\cos 37.5° = \dfrac{0.862}{c} \Rightarrow c = 1.09$

21. $\tan A = \dfrac{591.87}{264.93} \Rightarrow A = 65.89°$ $\tan B = \dfrac{264.93}{591.87} \Rightarrow B = 24.11°$

    $c = \sqrt{264.93^2 + 591.87^2} = 648.46$

25. $\sin 61.7° = \dfrac{3.92}{x} \Rightarrow x = \dfrac{3.92}{\sin 61.7°} = 4.45$

29. $\angle B = 90° - \angle A$, $\sin A = \dfrac{a}{c} \Rightarrow a = c \sin A$, $\cos A = \dfrac{b}{c} \Rightarrow b = c \cos A$

Section 4.5

4.5 Applications of Right Triangles

1. $\sin 54° = \dfrac{h}{120} \Rightarrow h = 120 \sin 54° = 97$ ft

5. $25.0 \text{ ft} \cdot \dfrac{12 \text{ in}}{1 \text{ ft}} = 300 \text{ in}$, $\theta = \tan^{-1} \dfrac{2.00}{300} = 0.4°$

9. $\sin 6.0° = \dfrac{2.65}{x} \Rightarrow x = \dfrac{2.65}{\sin 6.0°} = 25.4$ ft

13. $\theta = \tan^{-1} \dfrac{6.0}{100} = 3.4°$

17. $\theta = \sin^{-1} \dfrac{12.0}{85.0} = 8.1°$

21. Each angle of the pentagon is $\frac{360°}{5} = 72°$. Radii drawn from the center of the pentagon (which is also the center of the circle) through adjacent vertices of the pentagon outward to the fence form an isosceles triangle with base 92.5 and equal sides x. A $\perp$ bisector from the center of the pentagon to the base this isosceles triangle forms a right triangle with hypotenuse x and base 46.25. The base angle of this right triangle is $\frac{180° - 72°}{2} = 54°$. Thus,

$$\cos(54°) = \frac{46.25}{x} \Rightarrow x = \frac{46.25}{\cos 54°} \text{ and } C = 2\pi(x + 25)$$

$$C = 2\pi\left(\frac{46.25}{\cos 54°} + 25\right) = 651 \text{ ft}$$

25. $\frac{1}{2}C = \frac{1}{2}[2\pi(11.8 + 1)] = 12.8\pi \qquad \cos 31.8° = \frac{12.8\pi}{l} \Rightarrow l = 47.3 \text{ m}$

Section 4.6

Chapter 4 Review Exercises

1. $17.0° + 360.0° = 377.0°, \quad 17.0 - 360.0° = -343.0°$ **5. and 9.** $31°54' = 31.9°, 17.5° = 17°30'$

```
31°54'
                  31.9
17.5▸DMS
           17°30'0"
```

13. $r = \sqrt{x^2 + y^2} = \sqrt{24^2 + 7^2} = \sqrt{625} = 25$

$$\sin\theta = \frac{y}{r} = \frac{7}{25} \qquad\qquad \csc\theta = \frac{r}{y} = \frac{25}{7}$$

$$\cos\theta = \frac{x}{r} = \frac{24}{25} \qquad\qquad \sec\theta = \frac{r}{x} = \frac{25}{24}$$

$$\tan\theta = \frac{y}{x} = \frac{7}{24} \qquad\qquad \cot\theta = \frac{x}{y} = \frac{24}{7}$$

17. $r^2 = x^2 + y^2 \Rightarrow 13^2 = x^2 + 5^2 \Rightarrow x = 12$

$$\cos\theta = \frac{x}{r} = \frac{12}{13} = 0.923$$

$$\cot\theta = \frac{x}{y} = \frac{12}{5} = 2.40$$

21. $\sin 72.1° = 0.952$ **25.** $\sec 18.4° = 1.05$ **29.** $\cos 18.2° = 0.950$ **33.**

$$\csc 12.25° = 4.713$$

```
sin(72.1)
    .9515944039
          .952
```

```
1/cos(18.4)
    1.053878471
            1.05
```

```
cos⁻¹(.950)
    18.19487234
          18.19
```

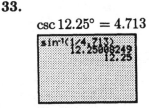

```
sin⁻¹(1/4.713)
    12.25006243
          12.25
```

37. $\angle B = 90.0° - 17.0° = 73.0°$ $\tan 17.0° = \frac{a}{6.00} \Rightarrow a = 1.83$

$$\cos 17.0° = \frac{6.00}{c} \Rightarrow c = \frac{6.00}{\cos 17.0°} = 6.27$$

41. $\angle B = 90.0° - 37.5° = 52.5°$ $\tan 37.5° = \dfrac{12.0}{b} \Rightarrow b = 15.6$

$\sin 37.5° = \dfrac{12.0}{c} \Rightarrow c = \dfrac{12.0}{\sin 37.5°} = 19.7$

45. $\angle B = 90.00° - 49.67° = 40.33°$ $\sin 49.67° = \dfrac{a}{0.8253} \Rightarrow a = 0.6292$

$\cos 49.67° = \dfrac{b}{0.8253} \Rightarrow b = 0.5341$

49. $e = E \cos \alpha \Rightarrow 56.9 = 339 \cos \alpha \Rightarrow \alpha = \cos^{-1} \dfrac{56.9}{339} = 80.3°$

53. (a) A triangle with angle θ included between sides a and b, the base, has an altitude of $a \sin \theta$. The area, A, is $A = \dfrac{1}{2} \cdot b \cdot a \sin \theta$.

(b) The area of the tract is $A = \dfrac{1}{2} \cdot 31.96 \cdot 47.25 \sin 64.09° = 679.2 \text{ m}^2$.

57. $\tan(90° - 65°) = \dfrac{2.0}{2.5 + x} \Rightarrow x = \dfrac{2.0}{\tan 25°} - 2.5 = 1.8$

$\dfrac{1.8}{3.2} = 0.5625$, 56% of the window is shaded.

61. $d = a + b = \dfrac{1.85}{\tan 28.3°} + \dfrac{1.85}{\tan(90.0° - 28.3°)} = 4.43 \text{ m}$

65. $\sin 31.0° = \dfrac{d}{x} \Rightarrow \sin 31.0° = \dfrac{14.2 \sin 21.8°}{x} \Rightarrow x = \dfrac{14.2 \sin 21.8°}{\sin 31.0°} = 10.2 \text{ in}$

69. Each angle of a regular pentagon is $\dfrac{(5-2) \cdot 180}{5} = 108°$. A regular pentagon with a side of 45.0 mm consists of 5 triangles of base 45.0 and altitude of $22.5 \tan 54°$. The area of 12 such pentagons is $12 \cdot 5 \cdot \dfrac{1}{2} \cdot 45.0 \cdot 22.5 \tan 54°$ or 41,807.60083 mm^2. Each angle of a regular hexagon is $\dfrac{(6-2) \cdot 180}{6} = 120°$. A regular hexagon with a side of 45.0 mm consists of 6 triangles of base 45.0 and an altitude of $22.5 \tan 60°$. The area of 20 such hexagons is

$$20 \cdot 6 \cdot \dfrac{1}{2} \cdot 45 \cdot 22.5 \tan 60° = 105,222.0866 \text{ mm}^2.$$

Thus, the area of 12 regular pentagons of side 45.0 mm and 20 regular hexagons of side 45.0 mm is 147,029.6874 mm^2 (147,000 mm^2 rounded off). Since this is the area of a flat surface it approximates the area of the spherical soccer ball which is given by

$$4\pi r^2 = 4\pi \cdot \left(\dfrac{222}{2}\right)^2 = 154,830.2523 \text{ mm}^2 \ (155,000 \text{ mm}^2 \text{ rounded off}).$$

73. $h = a + b = 375 \sin 25° + d \tan 42°$

$\quad\quad\quad\; = 375 \sin 25° + 375 \cos 25° \tan 42°$

$\quad\quad\quad\; = 464 \text{ m}$

77. For small angles, such as 2.3°, the sine and tangent are approximately equal.

$$\sin 2.3° = 0.0401317925 \approx \tan 2.3° = 0.040164149.$$

6. $B = 90° - 37.4° = 52.6°$

$$\frac{a}{52.8} = \tan 37.4°$$
$$a = 52.8 \tan 37.4°$$
$$= 40.4$$

$$\frac{52.8}{c} = \cos 37.4°$$
$$c = \frac{52.8}{\cos 37.4°}$$
$$= 66.5$$

$A = 37.4°$
$b = 52.8$

7. $2.49^2 + b^2 = 3.88^2$
$b = \sqrt{3.88^2 - 2.49^2} = 2.98$
$\sin A = \dfrac{2.49}{3.88}$
$A = 39.9°$　　$B = 50.1°$

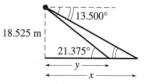

```
√(3.88²-2.49²)
        2.975617583
sin⁻¹(2.49/3.88)
        39.92262926
90-Ans
        50.07737074
```

$c = 3.88$　　$a = 2.49$

A　　b　　B

8. $\lambda = d \sin \theta$
$= 30.05 \sin 1.167°$
$= 0.6120 \ \mu m$

9. $r = \sqrt{5^2 + 2^2} = \sqrt{29}$

$\sin \theta = \dfrac{2}{\sqrt{29}} = 0.3714$　　$\csc \theta = \dfrac{\sqrt{29}}{2} = 2.693$

$\cos \theta = \dfrac{5}{\sqrt{29}} = 0.9285$　　$\sec \theta = \dfrac{\sqrt{29}}{5} = 1.077$

$\tan \theta = \dfrac{2}{5} = 0.4000$　　$\cot \theta = \dfrac{5}{2} = 2.500$

y　　$(5, 2)$
r　　$y = 2$
θ
0　　$x = 5$　　x

10. Distance between points is $x - y$.

$$\frac{18.525}{x} = \tan 13.500°$$
$$\frac{18.525}{y} = \tan 21.375°$$

$$x - y = \frac{18.525}{\tan 13.500°} - \frac{18.525}{\tan 21.375°} = 29.831 \text{ m}$$

$13.500°$

18.525 m

$21.375°$

y

x

Part 4

Chapter 4

1. $39' = \left(\frac{39}{60}\right)° = 0.65°$
$37°39' = 37.65°$

2. $\cos \theta = 0.3726; \ \theta = 68.12°$

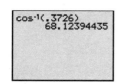

```
cos⁻¹(.3726)
        68.12394435
```

3. Let x = distance from
　　course to east

$$\frac{x}{22.62} = \sin 4.05°$$
$$x = 22.62 \sin 4.05°$$
$$= 1.598 \text{ km}$$

22.62 km
$4.05°$
S　x

4. $\sin \theta = \dfrac{2}{3}$
$x = \sqrt{3^2 - 2^2} = \sqrt{5}$
$\tan \theta = \dfrac{2}{\sqrt{5}}$

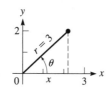

y
2
$r = 3$
θ
0　x　3　x

5. $\tan \theta = 1.294; \ \csc \theta = 1.264$

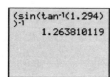

```
(sin(tan⁻¹(1.294)
)⁻¹
        1.263810119
```

PART 5 – TRIGONOMETRIC FUNCTIONS OF ANY ANGLES

TRIGONOMETRIC FUNCTIONS OF ANY ANGLE

When we were dealing with the trigonometric functions in Chapter 4, we restricted ourselves to right triangles and functions of acute angles measured in degrees. Since we did define the functions in general, we can use these same definitions for finding the functions of any possible angle.

In this chapter we will evaluate the trigonometric functions of angles of any magnitude. Also, we shall develop the use of radian measure, as well as use angles measured in degrees.

There are numerous applications of triangles that are not right triangles and of radian measure. Many of the triangle applications in areas such as navigation and forces on structures are given in the next chapter. Applications of radian measure in areas such as mechanical vibrations, electric currents, and rotational motion are given in this chapter and in Chapter 10.

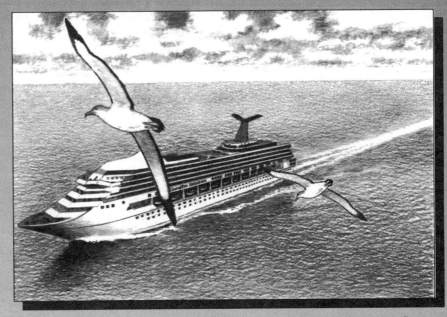

Cruise ships generally measure distances traveled in nautical miles. In Section 8-4 we will see how a nautical mile is defined as a distance along an arc of the earth's surface.

Section 5.1

8-1 SIGNS OF THE TRIGONOMETRIC FUNCTIONS

We recall the definitions of the trigonometric functions that were given in Section 4-2. *Here the point (x, y) is a point on the terminal side of angle θ, and r is the radius vector.* See Fig. 8-1.

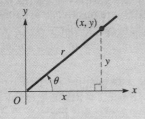

Fig. 8-1

$$\sin \theta = \frac{y}{r} \qquad \cos \theta = \frac{x}{r} \qquad \tan \theta = \frac{y}{x}$$

$$\cot \theta = \frac{x}{y} \qquad \sec \theta = \frac{r}{x} \qquad \csc \theta = \frac{r}{y} \qquad \text{(8-1)}$$

As we have noted, these definitions are valid for an angle of any magnitude. In this section we determine the *signs* of the trigonometric functions of angles with terminal sides in each of the four quadrants.

We see that we can find the functions if we know the values of the coordinates (x, y) on the terminal side of θ and the radius vector r. Of course, if either x or y is zero in the denominator, the function is undefined, and we will consider this further in the next section. *Remembering that r is always considered to be positive, we can see that the various functions will vary in sign in each of the quadrants, depending on the signs of x and y.*

If the terminal side of the angle is in the first or second quadrant, the value of $\sin \theta$ will be positive, but if the terminal side is in the third or fourth quadrant, $\sin \theta$ is negative. This is because *the sign of* $\sin \theta$ *depends on the sign of the y-coordinate* of the point on the terminal side, and y is positive if the point is above the x-axis, and y is negative if this point is below the x-axis. See Fig. 8-2.

	Quadrant			
	I	II	III	IV
$\sin \theta$	+	+	−	−

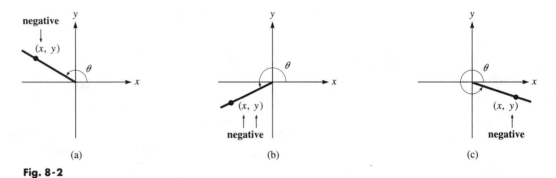

Fig. 8-2

EXAMPLE 1 The value of sin 20° is positive, since the terminal side of 20° is in the first quadrant. The value of sin 160° is positive, since the terminal side of 160° is in the second quadrant. The values of sin 200° and sin 340° are negative, since the terminal sides of these angles are in the third and fourth quadrants, respectively.

	Quadrant			
	I	II	III	IV
$\tan \theta$	+	−	+	−

The sign of $\tan \theta$ *depends on the ratio of y to x.* In the first quadrant both x and y are positive, and therefore the ratio y/x is positive. In the third quadrant both x and y are negative, and the ratio y/x is positive. In the second quadrant x is negative and y is positive, and in the fourth quadrant x is positive and y is negative. Therefore, in these quadrants, the ratio y/x is negative. See Fig. 8-2.

EXAMPLE 2 The values of tan 20° and tan 200° are positive, since the terminal sides of these angles are in the first and third quadrants, respectively. The values of tan 160° and tan 340° are negative, since the terminal sides of these angles are in the second and fourth quadrants, respectively.

	Quadrant			
	I	II	III	IV
$\cos \theta$	+	−	−	+

The sign of $\cos \theta$ *depends on the sign of x.* Since x is positive in the first and fourth quadrants, $\cos \theta$ is positive in these quadrants. Since x is negative in the second and third quadrants, $\cos \theta$ is negative in these quadrants. See Fig. 8-2.

EXAMPLE 3 The values of cos 20° and cos 340° are positive, since the terminal sides of these angles are in the first and fourth quadrants, respectively. The values of cos 160° and cos 200° are negative, since the terminal sides of these angles are in the second and third quadrants, respectively.

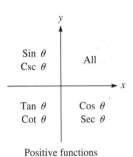

Sin θ | All
Csc θ |

Tan θ | Cos θ
Cot θ | Sec θ

Positive functions

Fig. 8-3

Since csc θ is defined in terms of y and r, as is sin θ, the sign of csc θ is the same as that of sin θ. For the same reason, cot θ has the same sign as tan θ, and sec θ has the same sign as cos θ. Therefore:

All functions of first-quadrant angles are positive. Sin θ and csc θ are positive for second-quadrant angles. Tan θ and cot θ are positive for third-quadrant angles. Cos θ and sec θ are positive for fourth-quadrant angles. All others are negative.

This is shown in Fig. 8-3.

This discussion does not include the *quadrantal angles,* those angles with terminal sides on one of the axes. They will be discussed in the next section.

■EXAMPLE 4   The following functions have *positive* values: sin 150°, sin (−200°), cos 8°, cos 300°, cos (−40°), tan 220°, tan (−100°), cot 260°, cot (−310°), sec 280°, sec (−37°), csc 140°, and csc (−190°). _____■

■EXAMPLE 5   The following functions have *negative* values: sin 190°, sin 325°, cos 95°, cos (−120°), tan 172°, tan 295°, cot 105°, cot (−60°), sec 135°, sec (−135°), csc 240°, and csc 355°. _____■

A calculator will always give the correct sign for a trigonometric function of a given angle. However, as we will see in the next section, a calculator will *not* always give the required angle for a given value of a function.

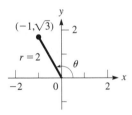

Fig. 8-4

■EXAMPLE 6   Determine the trigonometric functions of θ if the terminal side of θ passes through $(-1,\sqrt{3})$. See Fig. 8-4.

We know that $x = -1$, $y = \sqrt{3}$, and from the Pythagorean theorem we find that $r = 2$. Therefore, the trigonometric functions of θ are

$$\sin \theta = \frac{\sqrt{3}}{2} = 0.8660 \qquad \cos \theta = -\frac{1}{2} = -0.5000 \quad \tan \theta = -\sqrt{3} = -1.732$$

$$\cot \theta = -\frac{1}{\sqrt{3}} = -0.5774 \quad \sec \theta = -2 = -2.000 \qquad \csc \theta = \frac{2}{\sqrt{3}} = 1.155$$

The point $(-1,\sqrt{3})$ is in the second quadrant, and the signs of the functions of θ are those of a second-quadrant angle. _____■

━━━━━━ **EXERCISES** *8-1* ━━━━━━

In Exercises 1–8, determine the sign of the given trigonometric functions.

1. sin 36°, cos 120°   **2.** tan 320°, sec 185°

3. csc 98°, cot 82°   **4.** cos 260°, csc 290°

5. sec 150°, tan 220°   **6.** sin 335°, cot 265°

7. cos 348°, csc 238°   **8.** cot 110°, sec 309°

9. tan 460°, sin (−110°)   **10.** csc (−200°), cos 550°

11. cot (−2°), cos 710°   **12.** sin 539°, tan (−480°)

In Exercises 13–20, find the trigonometric functions of θ if the terminal side of θ passes through the given point.

13. (2, 1)   **14.** (−1, 1)

15. (−2, −3)   **16.** (4, −3)

17. (−5, 12)   **18.** (−3, −4)

19. (50, −20)   **20.** (9, 40)

In Exercises 21–32, determine the quadrant in which the terminal side of θ lies, subject to both given conditions.

21. sin θ > 0, cos θ < 0   **22.** tan θ > 0, cos θ < 0

23. sec θ < 0, cot θ < 0   **24.** cos θ > 0, csc θ < 0

25. csc θ < 0, tan θ < 0   **26.** sec θ > 0, csc θ > 0

27. sin θ < 0, tan θ > 0   **28.** cot θ < 0, sin θ < 0

29. tan θ < 0, cos θ > 0   **30.** sec θ > 0, csc θ < 0

31. sin θ > 0, cot θ < 0   **32.** tan θ > 0, csc θ < 0

Section 5.2

8-2 TRIGONOMETRIC FUNCTIONS OF ANY ANGLE

The trigonometric functions of acute angles (angles less than 90°) were discussed in Section 4-3, and in the previous section we determined the signs of the trigonometric functions in each of the four quadrants. In this section we show how we can find the trigonometric functions of an angle of any magnitude. This information will be very important in Chapter 9, when we discuss vectors and oblique triangles, and in Chapter 10, when we graph the trigonometric functions. Even *a calculator will not always give the required angle for a given value of a function.*

CAUTION ▶

Any angle in standard position is coterminal with some positive angle less than 360°. Since the terminal sides of coterminal angles are the same, the trigonometric functions of coterminal angles are the same. Therefore, we need consider only the problem of finding the values of the trigonometric functions of positive angles less than 360°.

■**EXAMPLE 1**   The following pairs of angles are coterminal.

$$390° \quad \text{and} \quad 30° \qquad -60° \quad \text{and} \quad 300°$$
$$900° \quad \text{and} \quad 180° \qquad -150° \quad \text{and} \quad 210°$$

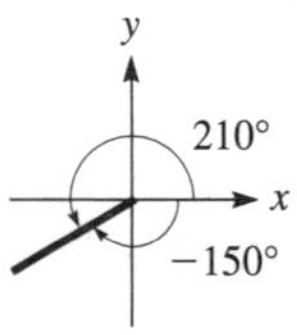

From this we conclude that the trigonometric functions of both angles in each of these pairs are equal. That is, for example,

$$\sin 390° = \sin 30° \quad \text{and} \quad \tan(-150°) = \tan 210°$$

See Fig. 8-5.

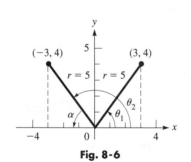

Fig. 8-5

Considering the definitions of the functions, we see that the values of the functions depend only on the values of *x, y,* and *r*. The absolute value of a function of a second-quadrant angle is equal to the value of the same function of a first-quadrant angle. For example, considering angles θ_1 and θ_2 in Fig. 8-6, for angle θ_2 with terminal side passing through $(-3, 4)$, $\tan \theta_2 = -4/3$, or $|\tan \theta_2| = 4/3$. For angle θ_1, with terminal side passing through $(3, 4)$, $\tan \theta_1 = 4/3$, and we see that $|\tan \theta_2| = \tan \theta_1$. Triangles containing angles θ_1 and α are congruent, which means $\theta_1 = \alpha$. Knowing that the absolute value of a function of θ_2 equals the same function of θ_1 means that

$$|F(\theta_2)| = |F(\theta_1)| = |F(\alpha)| \qquad \textbf{(8-2)}$$

Fig. 8-6

where *F* represents any of the trigonometric functions.

REFERENCE ANGLE

The angle labeled α is called the **reference angle.** *The reference angle of a given angle is the acute angle formed by the terminal side of the angle and the x-axis.*

Using Eq. (8-2) and the fact that $\alpha = 180° - \theta_2$, we may conclude that the value of any trigonometric function of any second-quadrant angle is found from

$$\boxed{F(\theta_2) = \pm F(180° - \theta_2) = \pm F(\alpha)} \qquad \textbf{(8-3)}$$

NOTE ▶

The *sign* used depends on whether the *function* is positive or negative in the second quadrant.

EXAMPLE 2 In Fig. 8-6, the trigonometric functions of θ are as follows:

$$\sin \theta_2 = \sin (180° - \theta_2) = \sin \alpha = \sin \theta_1 = \tfrac{4}{5} = 0.8000$$

$$\cos \theta_2 = -\cos \theta_1 = -\tfrac{3}{5} = -0.6000, \quad \tan \theta_2 = -\tfrac{4}{3} = -1.333$$

$$\cot \theta_2 = -\tfrac{3}{4} = -0.7500, \quad \sec \theta_2 = -\tfrac{5}{3} = -1.667, \quad \csc \theta_2 = \tfrac{5}{4} = 1.250 \quad \blacksquare$$

In the same way, we derive the formulas for trigonometric functions of any third- or fourth-quadrant angle. In Fig. 8-7 the reference angle α is found by subtracting 180° from θ_3 and the functions of α and θ_1 are numerically equal. In Fig. 8-8 the reference angle α is found by subtracting θ_4 from 360°.

$$F(\theta_3) = \pm F(\theta_3 - 180°) = \pm F(\alpha) \tag{8-4}$$

$$F(\theta_4) = \pm F(360° - \theta_4) = \pm F(\alpha) \tag{8-5}$$

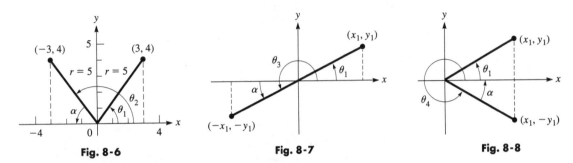

Fig. 8-6   **Fig. 8-7**   **Fig. 8-8**

EXAMPLE 3 If $\theta_3 = 210°$, the trigonometric functions of θ_3 are found by using Eq. (8-4) as follows. See Fig. 8-9.

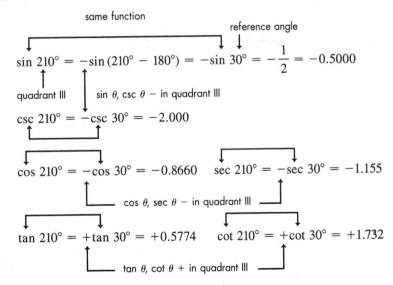

Fig. 8-9

Here we see that the reference angle is $210° - 180° = 30°$ and that we can express the value of a function of 210° in terms of the same function of 30°. We must be careful to attach the correct sign to the result. $\quad$ --------- $\blacksquare$

EXAMPLE 4 If $\theta_4 = 315°$, the trigonometric functions of θ_4 are found by using Eq. (8-5) as follows. See Fig. 8-10.

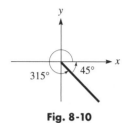

Fig. 8-10

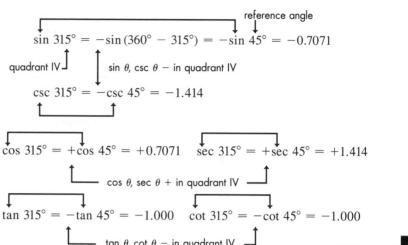

$$\sin 315° = -\sin(360° - 315°) = -\sin 45° = -0.7071$$

quadrant IV $\qquad$ sin θ, csc θ − in quadrant IV

$$\csc 315° = -\csc 45° = -1.414$$

$$\cos 315° = +\cos 45° = +0.7071 \qquad \sec 315° = +\sec 45° = +1.414$$

cos θ, sec θ + in quadrant IV

$$\tan 315° = -\tan 45° = -1.000 \qquad \cot 315° = -\cot 45° = -1.000$$

tan θ, cot θ − in quadrant IV

EXAMPLE 5 Other illustrations using Eqs. (8-3), (8-4), and (8-5) follow:

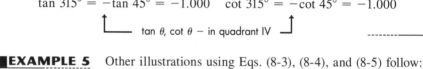

same function $\qquad$ reference angle

$$\sin 160° = +\sin(180° - 160°) = \sin 20° = 0.3420$$
$$\tan 110° = -\tan(180° - 110°) = -\tan 70° = -2.747$$
$$\cos 225° = -\cos(225° - 180°) = -\cos 45° = -0.7071$$
$$\cot 260° = +\cot(260° - 180°) = \cot 80° = 0.1763$$
$$\sec 304° = +\sec(360° - 304°) = \sec 56° = 1.788$$
$$\sin 357° = -\sin(360° - 357°) = -\sin 3° = -0.0523$$

determines $\qquad$ proper sign for function in quadrant
quadrant

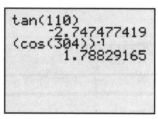

Fig. 8-11

A calculator can directly evaluate functions like those in Examples 3, 4, and 5. The function and angle are entered, and the calculator gives the value, with the proper sign. The reciprocal key is used to find cot θ, sec θ, and csc θ, as shown in Section 4-3. A calculator display for tan 110° and sec 304° of Example 5 is shown in Fig. 8-11.

In most examples we will round off values to four significant digits (as we did in Examples 3, 4, and 5). However, *if the angle is approximate, we must use the guidelines in Section 4-3 for rounding off values.*

NOTE ▶

EXAMPLE 6 A formula for finding the area of a triangle, knowing sides a and b and the included $\angle C$, is $A = \frac{1}{2}ab \sin C$. A surveyor uses this formula to find the area of a triangular tract of land for which $a = 173.2$ m, $b = 156.3$ m, and $C = 112.51°$. See Fig. 8-12.

To find the area, we substitute into the formula, which gives us

$$A = \tfrac{1}{2}(173.2)(156.3)\sin 112.51°$$
$$= 12,500 \text{ m}^2 \qquad \text{rounded to four significant digits}$$

When these numbers are entered into the calculator, the calculator automatically uses a positive value for sin 112.51°.

Fig. 8-12

Knowing how to use the reference angle is important when using a calculator, because *if we have the value of a function and want to find the angle,*

CAUTION ▶ *the calculator will not necessarily give us directly the required angle.*

It will give us an angle we can use, but whether or not it is the required angle for the problem will depend on the problem being solved.

When a value of a trigonometric function is entered into a calculator, it is programmed to give the angle as follows:

> *For positive values of a function, the calculator displays positive acute angles.*
> *For negative values of* $\sin \theta$ *and* $\tan \theta$*, the calculator displays negative acute angles for* $\sin^{-1}$ *and* $\tan^{-1}$*.*
> *For negative values of* $\cos \theta$*, the calculator displays angles between* $90°$ *and* $180°$ *for* $\cos^{-1}$*.*

The reason that the calculator displays these values is shown in Chapter 20, when the inverse trigonometric functions are discussed in detail.

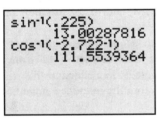

Fig. 8-13

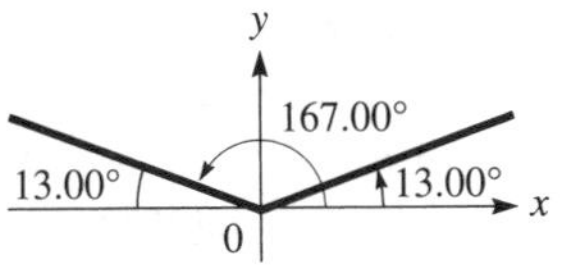

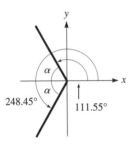

Fig. 8-15

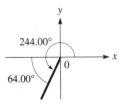

Fig. 8-16

■EXAMPLE 7 For $\sin \theta = 0.2250$, we see from the first two lines of the calculator display shown in Fig. 8-13 that $\theta = 13.00°$ (rounded off).

This result is correct, but we must remember that

$$\sin (180° - 13.00°) = \sin 167.00° = 0.2250$$

also. If we need only an acute angle, $\theta = 13.00°$ is correct. However, if a second-quadrant angle is required, we see that $\theta = 167.00°$ is the angle (see Fig. 8-14). These values can be checked by finding $\sin 13.00°$ and $\sin 167.00°$. ┄┄┄┄┄■

(Fig. 8-14 shown at left)

Fig. 8-14

■EXAMPLE 8 For $\sec \theta = -2.722$ and $0° \leq \theta < 360°$ (this means θ may equal $0°$ or be between $0°$ and $360°$), we see from the third and fourth lines of the calculator display in Fig. 8-13 that $\theta = 111.55°$ (rounded off).

The angle $111.55°$ is the second-quadrant angle, but $\sec \theta < 0$ in the third quadrant as well. The reference angle is $\alpha = 180° - 111.55° = 68.45°$, and the third-quadrant angle is $180° + 68.45° = 248.45°$. Therefore, the two angles between $0°$ and $360°$ for which $\sec \theta = -2.722$ are $111.55°$ and $248.45°$ (see Fig. 8-15). These angles can be checked by finding $\sec 111.55°$ and $\sec 248.45°$. ┄┄┄┄■

■EXAMPLE 9 Given that $\tan \theta = 2.050$ and $\cos \theta < 0$, find the angle θ for $0° \leq \theta < 360°$.

Since $\tan \theta$ is positive and $\cos \theta$ is negative, θ must be a third-quadrant angle. A calculator will display an angle of $64.00°$ (rounded off) for $\tan \theta = 2.050$. However, since we need a third-quadrant angle, *we must add* $64.00°$ *to* $180°$. Thus, the required angle is $244.00°$ (see Fig. 8-16). Check by finding $\tan 244.00°$.

If we are given that $\tan \theta = -2.050$ and $\cos \theta < 0$, the calculator will display an angle of $-64.00°$ for $\tan \theta = -2.050$. We would then have to *recognize that the reference angle is* $64.00°$ *and subtract it from* $180°$ *to get* $116.00°$, the required second-quadrant angle. This can be checked by finding $\tan 116.00°$. ┄┄┄■

NOTE ▶ We see that the calculator gives the reference angle (disregarding any minus signs) in all cases except when $\cos \theta$ is negative. To avoid confusion from the angle displayed by the calculator, *a good procedure is to find the reference angle first.* Then it can be used to determine the angle required by the problem.

We can find the reference angle by entering the absolute value of the function. The displayed angle will be the reference angle. Then the required angle θ is found by using the reference angle as desribed earlier, and as shown in Eqs. (8-6) for θ in the given quadrant. The angle should be checked as indicated in the earlier examples.

$$
\begin{aligned}
\theta &= \alpha & &\text{(first quadrant)} \\
\theta &= 180° - \alpha & &\text{(second quadrant)} \\
\theta &= 180° + \alpha & &\text{(third quadrant)} \\
\theta &= 360° - \alpha & &\text{(fourth quadrant)}
\end{aligned}
$$

(8-6)

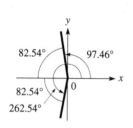

Fig. 8-17

■**EXAMPLE 10**   Given that cos $\theta = -0.1298$, find θ for $0° \le \theta < 360°$.

Since cos θ is negative, θ is either a second-quadrant angle or a third-quadrant angle. Using 0.1298, the calculator tells us that the reference angle is 82.54°.

To get the required second-quadrant angle, we subtract 82.54° from 180° and obtain 97.46°. To get the required third-quadrant angle, we add 82.54° to 180° to obtain 262.54°. See Fig. 8-17.

If we use −0.1298, the calculator displays the required second-quadrant angle of 97.46°. However, to get the third-quadrant angle we must then subtract 97.46° from 180° to get the reference angle of 82.54°. The reference angle is then added to 180° to obtain the result of 262.54°. Also note that it is better to store the reference angle in memory rather than recalculate it.   ■

Using Eqs. (8-3) through (8-5) we may find the value of any function when the terminal side of the angle lies *in* one of the quadrants. We now consider *the angle for which the terminal side is along one of the axes, a* **quadrantal angle.** Using the definitions of the functions (recalling that $r > 0$), we obtain the following values.

QUADRANTAL ANGLES

θ	$\sin \theta$	$\cos \theta$	$\tan \theta$	$\cot \theta$	$\sec \theta$	$\csc \theta$
0°	0.000	1.000	0.000	undef.	1.000	undef.
90°	1.000	0.000	undef.	0.000	undef.	1.000
180°	0.000	−1.000	0.000	undef.	−1.000	undef.
270°	−1.000	0.000	undef.	0.000	undef.	−1.000
360°	Same as the functions of 0° (same terminal side)

The values in the table may be verified by referring to the figures in Fig. 8-18.

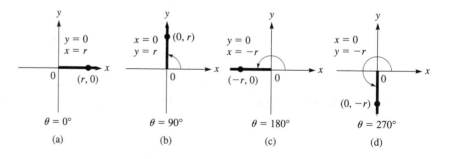

Fig. 8-18

EXAMPLE 11 Since $\sin \theta = y/r$, by looking at Fig. 8-18(a) we can see that $\sin 0° = 0/r = 0$.

Since $\tan \theta = y/x$, from Fig. 8-18(b) we see that $\tan 90° = r/0$, which is undefined due to the division by zero. If we use a calculator to find $\tan 90°$, the display would indicate an error (due to division by zero).

Since $\cos \theta = x/r$, from Fig. 8-18(c) we see that $\cos 180° = -r/r = -1$.

Since $\cot \theta = x/y$, from Fig. 8-18(d) we see that $\cot 270° = 0/-r = 0$. ∎

EXERCISES 8-2

In Exercises 1–6, express the given trigonometric function in terms of the same function of a positive acute angle.

1. $\sin 160°$, $\cos 220°$
2. $\tan 91°$, $\sec 345°$
3. $\tan 105°$, $\csc 302°$
4. $\cos 190°$, $\cot 290°$
5. $\cos 400°$, $\tan(-400°)$
6. $\tan 920°$, $\csc(-550°)$

In Exercises 7–36, the given angles are approximate. In Exercises 7–12, find the values of the given trigonometric functions by finding the reference angle and attaching the proper sign.

7. $\sin 195°$
8. $\tan 311°$
9. $\cos 106.3°$
10. $\sin 103.4°$
11. $\sec 328.33°$
12. $\cot 136.53°$

In Exercises 13–18, find the values of the given trigonometric functions directly from a calculator.

13. $\tan 152.4°$
14. $\cos 341.4°$
15. $\sin 310.36°$
16. $\tan 242.68°$
17. $\csc 194.82°$
18. $\sec 261.08°$

In Exercises 19–32, find θ for $0° \le \theta < 360°$.

19. $\sin \theta = -0.8480$
20. $\tan \theta = -1.830$
21. $\cos \theta = 0.4003$
22. $\sin \theta = 0.6374$
23. $\cot \theta = -0.212$
24. $\csc \theta = -1.09$
25. $\sin \theta = 0.870$, $\cos \theta < 0$
26. $\tan \theta = 0.932$, $\sin \theta < 0$
27. $\cos \theta = -0.12$, $\tan \theta > 0$
28. $\sin \theta = -0.192$, $\tan \theta < 0$
29. $\tan \theta = -1.366$, $\cos \theta > 0$
30. $\cos \theta = 0.5726$, $\sin \theta < 0$
31. $\sec \theta = 2.047$, $\cot \theta < 0$
32. $\cot \theta = -0.3256$, $\csc \theta > 0$

In Exercises 33–36, determine the function that satisfies the given conditions.

33. Find $\tan \theta$ when $\sin \theta = -0.5736$ and $\cos \theta > 0$.
34. Find $\sin \theta$ when $\cos \theta = 0.422$ and $\tan \theta < 0$.
35. Find $\cos \theta$ when $\tan \theta = -0.809$ and $\csc \theta > 0$.
36. Find $\cot \theta$ when $\sec \theta = 1.122$ and $\sin \theta < 0$.

In Exercises 37–40, insert the proper sign, $>$ or $<$ or $=$, between the given expressions.

37. $\sin 90°$ ___ $2 \sin 45°$
38. $\cos 360°$ ___ $2 \cos 180°$
39. $\tan 180°$ ___ $\tan 0°$
40. $\sin 270°$ ___ $3 \sin 90°$

In Exercises 41–44, evaluate the given expressions.

41. The current i in an alternating-current circuit is given by $i = i_m \sin \theta$, where i_m is the maximum current in the circuit. Find i if $i_m = 0.0259$ A and $\theta = 495.2°$.

42. A force F is related to force F_x directed along the x-axis by $F = F_x \sec \theta$, where θ is the standard position angle for F. Find F if $F_x = -29.2$ N and $\theta = 127.6°$. See Fig. 8-19.

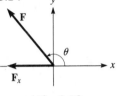
Fig. 8-19

43. For the slider mechanism shown in Fig. 8-20, $y \sin \alpha = x \sin \beta$. Find y if $x = 6.78$ in., $\alpha = 31.3°$, and $\beta = 104.7°$.

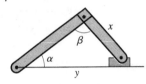

Fig. 8-20   **Fig. 8-21**

44. A laser follows the path shown in Fig. 8-21. The angle θ is related to the distances a, b, and c by $2ab \cos \theta = a^2 + b^2 - c^2$. Find θ if $a = 15.3$ cm, $b = 12.9$ cm, and $c = 24.5$ cm.

In Exercises 45–48, the trigonometric functions of negative angles are considered. In Exercises 46–48, use Eqs. (8-7).

(W) **45.** Using the definitions of the trigonometric functions, explain why $\sin(-\theta) = -\sin \theta$. See Fig. 8-22. Also verify the remaining equations derived in Eqs. (8-7).

$$\sin(-\theta) = -\sin \theta$$
$$\cos(-\theta) = \cos \theta$$
$$\tan(-\theta) = -\tan \theta$$
$$\cot(-\theta) = -\cot \theta \quad \textbf{(8-7)}$$
$$\sec(-\theta) = \sec \theta$$
$$\csc(-\theta) = -\csc \theta$$

Fig. 8-22

46. Find (a) $\sin(-60°)$ and (b) $\cos(-156°)$.
47. Find (a) $\tan(-100°)$ and (b) $\cot(-215°)$.
48. Find (a) $\sec(-310°)$ and (b) $\csc(-35°)$.

Section 5.3

8-3 RADIANS

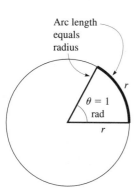

Arc length equals radius

$\theta = 1$ rad

Fig. 8-23

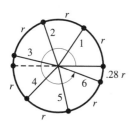

Fig. 8-24

For many problems in which trigonometric functions are used, particularly those involving the solution of triangles, degree measurements of angles are convenient and quite sufficient. However, division of a circle into 360 equal parts is by definition, and it is arbitrary and artificial (see the margin comment page 49).

In numerous other types of applications and in more theoretical discussions, the *radian* is a more meaningful measure of an angle. We defined the radian in Chapter 2 and reviewed it briefly in Chapter 4. In this section we discuss the radian in detail and start by reviewing its definition.

> A **radian** *is the measure of an angle with its vertex at the center of a circle and with an intercepted arc on the circle equal in length to the radius of the circle.* See Fig. 8-23.

Since the circumference of any circle in terms of its radius is given by $c = 2\pi r$, the ratio of the circumference to the radius is 2π. This means that the radius may be laid off 2π (about 6.28) times along the circumference, regardless of the length of the radius. Therefore, we see that radian measure is independent of the radius of the circle. The definition of a radian is based on an important property of a circle and is therefore a more natural measure of an angle. In Fig. 8-24 the numbers on each of the radii indicate the number of radians in the angle measured in standard position. The circular arrow shows an angle of 6 radians.

Since the radius may be laid off 2π times along the circumference, it follows that there are 2π radians in one complete rotation. Also, there are 360° in one complete rotation. Therefore, 360° is *equivalent* to 2π radians. It then follows that the relation between degrees and radians is 2π rad = 360°, or

CONVERTING ANGLES

$$\pi \text{ rad} = 180° \qquad\qquad \textbf{(8-8)}$$

DEGREES TO RADIANS

$$1° = \frac{\pi}{180} \text{ rad} = 0.01745 \text{ rad} \qquad\qquad \textbf{(8-9)}$$

RADIANS TO DEGREES

$$1 \text{ rad} = \frac{180°}{\pi} = 57.30° \qquad\qquad \textbf{(8-10)}$$

We see from Eqs. (8-8) through (8-10) that we convert angle measurements from degrees to radians or from radians to degrees as follows:

> **Procedure for Converting Angle Measurements**
> 1. *To convert an angle measured in degrees to the same angle measured in* radians, **multiply the number of degrees by $\pi/180°$.**
> 2. *To convert an angle measured in radians to the same angle measured in degrees,* **multiply the number of radians by $180°/\pi$.**

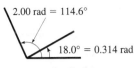

2.00 rad = 114.6°

18.0° = 0.314 rad

Fig. 8-25

EXAMPLE 1 (a) $18.0° = \left(\dfrac{\pi}{180°}\right)(18.0°) = \dfrac{\pi}{10.0} = \dfrac{3.14}{10.0} = 0.314$ rad

converting degrees to radians

degrees cancel   (See Fig. 8-25.)

converting radians to degrees

(b) 2.00 rad $= \left(\dfrac{180°}{\pi}\right)(2.00) = \dfrac{360°}{3.14} = 114.6°$ (See Fig. 8-25.)

In multiplying by $\pi/180°$ or $180°/\pi$, we are actually only multiplying by 1 because π rad $= 180°$. Although the unit of measurement is different, *the angle is the same.* See Appendix B on unit conversions.

Due to the nature of the definition of the radian, it is very common to express radians in terms of π. Expressing angles in terms of π is illustrated in the following example.

$\frac{3\pi}{4}$ rad = 135°

45° = $\frac{\pi}{4}$ rad

Fig. 8-26

EXAMPLE 2

converting degrees to radians

(a) $30° = \left(\dfrac{\pi}{180°}\right)(30°) = \dfrac{\pi}{6}$ rad

(b) $45° = \left(\dfrac{\pi}{180°}\right)(45°) = \dfrac{\pi}{4}$ rad   (See Fig. 8-26.)

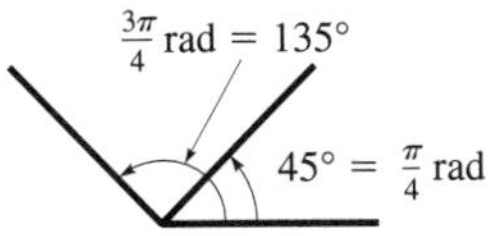

converting radians to degrees

(c) $\dfrac{\pi}{2}$ rad $= \left(\dfrac{180°}{\pi}\right)\left(\dfrac{\pi}{2}\right) = 90°$

(d) $\dfrac{3\pi}{4}$ rad $= \left(\dfrac{180°}{\pi}\right)\left(\dfrac{3\pi}{4}\right) = 135°$ (See Fig. 8-26.)

NOTE ▶

We wish now to make a very important point. Since π is a special way of writing the number (slightly greater than 3) that is the ratio of the circumference of a circle to its diameter, it is the ratio of one distance to another. Thus, radians really have no units, and *radian measure amounts to measuring angles in terms of real numbers.* It is this property of radians that makes them useful in many situations. Therefore, when radians are being used, it is customary that no units are indicated for the angle.

CAUTION ▶

When no units are indicated, the radian is understood to be the unit of angle measurement.

3.80 = 218°

Fig. 8-27

EXAMPLE 3 (a) $60° = \left(\dfrac{\pi}{180°}\right)(60.0°) = \dfrac{\pi}{3.00} = 1.05$

no units indicates radian measure

(b) $3.80 = \left(\dfrac{180°}{\pi}\right)(3.80) = 218°$

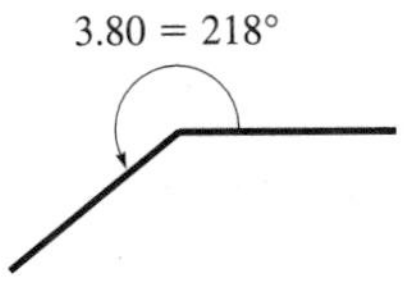

Since no units are indicated for 1.05 and 3.80 in this example, they are known to be in radian measure. Here, we must know that 3.80 is an angle measure. See Fig. 8-27.

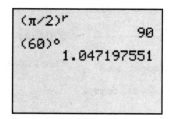

Fig. 8-28

Using the *angle* feature, a calculator can be used directly to change an angle expressed in degrees to an angle expressed in radians, or from an angle expressed in radians to an angle expressed in degrees (as we pointed out in Chapter 4 on page 106). In Fig. 8-28, we show the calculator display for changing $\pi/2$ rad to degrees (calculator in degree mode), and for changing 60° to radians (calculator in radian mode).

We can use a calculator to find the value of a function of an angle in radians. If the calculator is in radian mode, it then uses values in radians directly and will *consider any angle entered to be in radians*. The mode can be changed as needed, but

CAUTION ▶   *always be careful to have your calculator in the proper mode.*

Check the setting in the *mode* feature. If you are working in degrees, use the degree mode, but if you are working in radians, use the radian mode.

■ EXAMPLE 4   **(a)** To find the value of sin 0.7538, put the calculator in radian mode (note that no units are shown with 0.7538), and the value is found as shown in the first two lines of the calculator display in Fig. 8-29. Therefore,

$$\sin 0.7538 = 0.6844$$

no units indicates radian measure

(b) From the third and fourth lines of the display in Fig. 8-29, we see that

$$\tan 0.9977 = 1.550$$

(c) From the last two lines of the display in Fig. 8-29, we see that

$$\cos 2.074 = -0.4822$$

Fig. 8-29

In each case the calculator was in radian mode.   ------------■

In the following application, the resulting angle is a unitless number, and it is therefore in radian measure.

■ EXAMPLE 5   The velocity v of an object undergoing simple harmonic motion at the end of a spring is given by

$$v = A\sqrt{\frac{k}{m}}\cos\sqrt{\frac{k}{m}}\,t \qquad \text{the angle is } \left(\sqrt{\frac{k}{m}}\right)(t)$$

Here, m is the mass of the object (in g), k is a constant depending on the spring, A is the maximum distance the object moves, and t is the time (in s). Find the velocity (in cm/s) after 0.100 s of a 36.0-g object at the end of a spring for which $k = 400$ g/s², if $A = 5.00$ cm.

Substituting, we have

$$v = 5.00\sqrt{\frac{400}{36.0}}\cos\sqrt{\frac{400}{36.0}}\,(0.100)$$

Using calculator memory for $\sqrt{\frac{400}{36.0}}$, and with the calculator in radian mode, we have

$$v = 15.7 \text{ cm/s} \qquad \text{------------}■$$

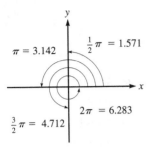

Fig. 8-30

For certain special situations, we may need to know a reference angle in radians. In order to determine the proper quadrant, we should remember that $\frac{1}{2}\pi = 90°$, $\pi = 180°$, $\frac{3}{2}\pi = 270°$, and $2\pi = 360°$. These are shown in Table 8-1 along with the approximate decimal values for angles in radians. See Fig. 8-30.

Table 8-1 Quadrantal Angles

Degrees	Radians	Radians (decimal)
90°	$\frac{1}{2}\pi$	1.571
180°	π	3.142
270°	$\frac{3}{2}\pi$	4.712
360°	2π	6.283

■EXAMPLE 6   An angle of 3.402 is greater than 3.142 but less than 4.712. Thus, it is a third-quadrant angle, and the reference angle is $3.402 - \pi = 0.260$. The π key can be used. See Fig. 8-31.

An angle of 5.210 is between 4.712 and 6.283. Therefore, it is in the fourth quadrant and the reference angle is $2\pi - 5.210 = 1.073$.

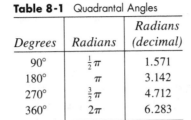

Fig. 8-31

■EXAMPLE 7   Express θ in radians, such that $\cos \theta = 0.8829$ and $0 \le \theta < 2\pi$.

We are to find θ in radians for the given value of the $\cos \theta$. Also, since θ is restricted to values between 0 and 2π, we must find a first-quadrant angle and a fourth-quadrant angle ($\cos \theta$ is positive in the first and fourth quadrants). With the calculator in radian mode, we find that

$$\cos 0.4888 = 0.8829$$

Therefore, for the fourth-quadrant angle,

$$\cos(2\pi - 0.4888) = \cos 5.794$$

This means

$$\theta = 0.4888 \quad \text{or} \quad \theta = 5.794$$

See Fig. 8-32.

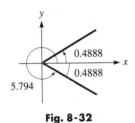

Fig. 8-32

When one first encounters radian measure,

CAUTION▶   *expressions such as* $\sin 1$ *and* $\sin \theta = 1$ *are often confused.*

The first is equivalent to $\sin 57.30°$, since $57.30° = 1$ (radian). The second means that θ is the angle for which the sine is 1. Since we know that $\sin 90° = 1$, we then can say that $\theta = 90°$ or $\theta = \pi/2$. The following example gives additional illustrations of evaluating expressions involving radians.

■EXAMPLE 8   (a) $\sin \dfrac{\pi}{3} = \dfrac{\sqrt{3}}{2}$ since $\dfrac{\pi}{3} = 60°$.

(b) $\sin 0.6050 = 0.5688$. (0.6050 rad = 34.66°.)

(c) $\tan \theta = 1.709$ means that $\theta = 59.67°$ (smallest positive θ).

(d) Since $59.67° = 1.041$, we can state that $\tan 1.041 = 1.708$.

--- EXERCISES *8-3* ---

In Exercises 1–8, express the given angle measurements in radian measure in terms of π.

1. 15°, 150°

2. 12°, 225°

3. 75°, 330°

4. 36°, 315°

5. 210°, 270°

6. 240°, 300°

7. 160°, 260°

8. 66°, 350°

In Exercises 9–16, the given numbers express angle measure. Express the measure of each angle in terms of degrees.

9. $\dfrac{2\pi}{5}, \dfrac{3\pi}{2}$

10. $\dfrac{3\pi}{10}, \dfrac{5\pi}{6}$

11. $\dfrac{\pi}{18}, \dfrac{7\pi}{4}$

12. $\dfrac{7\pi}{15}, \dfrac{4\pi}{3}$

13. $\dfrac{17\pi}{18}, \dfrac{5\pi}{3}$

14. $\dfrac{11\pi}{36}, \dfrac{5\pi}{4}$

15. $\dfrac{\pi}{12}, \dfrac{3\pi}{20}$

16. $\dfrac{7\pi}{30}, \dfrac{4\pi}{15}$

In Exercises 17–24, express the given angles in radian measure. Round off results to the number of significant digits in the given angle.

17. 23.0°

18. 54.3°

19. 252°

20. 104°

21. 333.5°

22. 168.7°

23. 178.5°

24. 86.1°

In Exercises 25–32, the given numbers express angle measure. Express the measure of each angle in terms of degrees, with the same accuracy as in the given value.

25. 0.750

26. 0.240

27. 3.407

28. 1.703

29. 2.45

30. 34.4

31. 16.42

32. 100.0

In Exercises 33–40, evaluate the given trigonometric functions by first changing the radian measure to degree measure. Round off results to four significant digits.

33. $\sin \dfrac{\pi}{4}$

34. $\cos \dfrac{\pi}{6}$

35. $\tan \dfrac{5\pi}{12}$

36. $\sin \dfrac{7\pi}{18}$

37. $\cos \dfrac{5\pi}{6}$

38. $\tan \dfrac{4\pi}{3}$

39. $\sec 4.5920$

40. $\cot 3.2732$

In Exercises 41–48, evaluate the given trigonometric functions directly, without first changing to degree measure.

41. $\tan 0.7359$

42. $\cos 0.9308$

43. $\sin 4.24$

44. $\tan 3.47$

45. $\sec 2.07$

46. $\sin 2.34$

47. $\cot 4.86$

48. $\csc 6.19$

In Exercises 49–56, find θ to four significant digits for $0 \le \theta < 2\pi$.

49. $\sin \theta = 0.3090$

50. $\cos \theta = -0.9135$

51. $\tan \theta = -0.2126$

52. $\sin \theta = -0.0436$

53. $\cos \theta = 0.6742$

54. $\cot \theta = 1.860$

55. $\sec \theta = -1.307$

56. $\csc \theta = 3.940$

In Exercises 57–60, evaluate the given expressions.

57. A flat plate of weight W oscillates as shown in Fig. 8-33. Its potential energy V is given by $V = \frac{1}{2}Wb\theta^2$, where θ is measured in radians. Find V if $W = 8.75$ lb, $b = 0.75$ ft, and $\theta = 5.5°$.

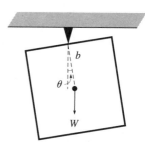

Fig. 8-33

W **58.** The charge q (in C) on a capacitor as a function of time is $q = A \sin \omega t$. If t is measured in seconds, in what units is ω measured? Explain.

59. The height h of a rocket launched 1200 m from an observer is found to be $h = 1200 \tan \dfrac{5t}{3t + 10}$ for $t < 10$ s, where t is the time after launch. Find h for $t = 8.0$ s.

60. The electric intensity I (in W/m^2) from the two radio antennas shown in Fig. 8-34 is a function of the angle θ given by $I = 0.023 \cos^2(\pi \sin \theta)$. Find I for $\theta = 40.0°$. ($\cos^2 \alpha = (\cos \alpha)^2$.)

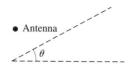

Fig. 8-34   • Antenna

Section 5.4

8-4 APPLICATIONS OF RADIAN MEASURE

Radian measure has numerous applications in mathematics and technology, some of which were indicated in the last four exercises of the previous section. In this section we illustrate a number of additional applications.

Arc Length

From geometry we know that *the length of an arc on a circle is proportional to the central angle* and that the length of arc of a complete circle is the circumference. Letting s stand for the length of arc, we may state that $s = 2\pi r$ for a complete circle. Since 2π is the central angle (in radians) of the complete circle, *we have for the length of arc*

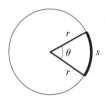

Fig. 8-35

$$\boxed{s = \theta r \quad (\theta \text{ in radians})} \qquad \textbf{(8-11)}$$

for any circular arc with central angle θ. If we know the central angle in radians and the radius of a circle, we can find the length of a circular arc directly by using Eq. (8-11). See Fig. 8-35.

EXAMPLE 1   In Fig. 8-36, $\theta = \pi/6$ and $r = 3.00$ in. Therefore,

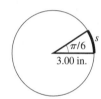

Fig. 8-36

$$\overset{\displaystyle \theta \text{ in radians}}{s = \left(\frac{\pi}{6}\right)(3.00) = \frac{\pi}{2.00} = 1.57 \text{ in.}} \qquad \blacksquare$$

Among the important applications of arc length are distances on the earth's surface. For most purposes the earth may be regarded as a sphere (the diameter at the equator is slightly greater than the distance between the poles). A *great circle* of the earth (or any sphere) is the circle of intersection of the surface of the sphere and a plane that passes through the center.

The equator is a great circle, and is designated as 0° *latitude*. Other *parallels of latitude* are parallel to the equator, with diameters decreasing to zero at the poles, which are 90° N and 90° S. See Fig. 8-37.

Meridians of longitude are half great circles between the poles. The *prime meridian* through Greenwich, England, is designated as 0°, with meridians to 180° measured east and west from Greenwich. Positions on the surface of the earth are designated by longitude and latitude.

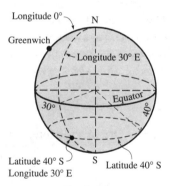

Fig. 8-37

See the chapter introduction.

EXAMPLE 2   The traditional definition of a *nautical mile* is the length of arc along a great circle of the earth for a central angle of 1′. The modern international definition is a distance of 1852 m. What measurement of the earth's radius does this definition use?

Here, $\theta = 1' = (1/60)°$ and $s = 1852$ m. Solving for r, we have

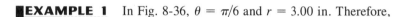

$$r = \frac{s}{\theta} = \frac{1852}{\left(\dfrac{1}{60}\right)°\left(\dfrac{\pi}{180°}\right)} = 6.367 \times 10^6 \text{ m} = 6367 \text{ km}$$

Historically, the fact that the earth is not a perfect sphere has led to many variations in the distance used for a nautical mile. 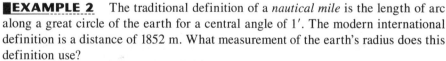 ▪

Area of a Sector of a Circle

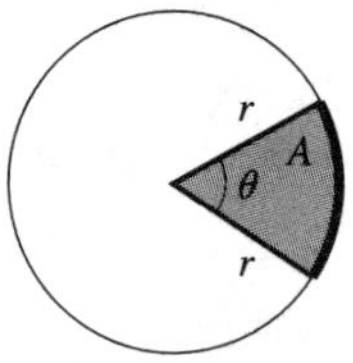

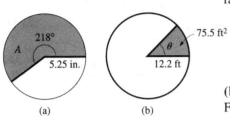

Fig. 8-38

Another application of radians is finding the area of a sector of a circle (see Fig. 8-38). We recall from geometry that areas of sectors of circles are proportional to their central angles. The area of a circle is $A = \pi r^2$, which can be written as $A = \frac{1}{2}(2\pi)r^2$. Since the angle for a complete circle is 2π, *the area of any sector of a circle in terms of the radius and central angle (in radians) is*

$$A = \frac{1}{2}\theta r^2 \quad (\theta \text{ in radians}) \qquad \textbf{(8-12)}$$

EXAMPLE 3   **(a)** The area of a sector of a circle with central angle 218° and a radius of 5.25 in. (see Fig. 8-39(a)) is

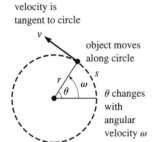

(a)   (b)

Fig. 8-39

$$A = \frac{1}{2}(218)\underbrace{\left(\frac{\pi}{180}\right)}_{\theta \text{ in radians}}(5.25)^2 = 52.4 \text{ in.}^2$$

(b) Given that the area of a sector is 75.5 ft² and the radius is 12.2 ft (see Fig. 8-39(b)), we find the central angle by solving for θ and then substituting.

$$\theta = \frac{2A}{r^2} = \frac{2(75.5)}{(12.2)^2} = 1.01 \quad \underset{\text{no units indicates radian measure}}{} $$

This means that the central angle is 1.01 rad, or 57.9°.   ∎

CAUTION ▶   We should note again that the equations in this section require that the angle θ *is expressed in radians.* A common error is to use θ in degrees.

Angular Velocity

velocity is
tangent to circle

Fig. 8-40

The average velocity of a moving object is defined by $v = s/t$, where v is the average velocity, s is the distance traveled, and t is the elapsed time. For an object moving in a circular path with constant speed, the distance traveled is the length of arc through which it moves. Therefore, if we divide both sides of Eq. (8-11) by t, we obtain

$$\frac{s}{t} = \frac{\theta r}{t} = \frac{\theta}{t}r$$

where θ/t is called the *angular velocity* and is designated by ω. Therefore,

$$v = \omega r \qquad \textbf{(8-13)}$$

Equation (8-13) expresses the relationship between the **linear velocity** *v and the* **angular velocity** *ω of an object moving around a circle of radius r.* See Fig. 8-40. In the figure, v is shown directed tangent to the circle, for that is its direction for the position shown. The direction of v changes constantly.

The units for ω are radians per unit of time. In this way the formula can be used directly. However, in practice, ω is often given in revolutions per minute or in some similar unit. In these cases it is necessary to convert the units of ω to radians per unit of time before substituting in Eq. (8-13).

EXAMPLE 4 A person on a hang glider is moving in a horizontal circular arc of radius 90.0 m with an angular velocity of 0.125 rad/s. The person's linear velocity is

$$v = (0.125)(90.0) = 11.3 \text{ m/s}$$

(Remember that radians are numbers and are not included in the final set of units.) This means that the person is moving along the circumference of the arc at 11.3 m/s (40.7 km/h). ▬

SOLVING A WORD PROBLEM

The first U.S. communications satellite was launched in July 1962.

EXAMPLE 5 A communications satellite remains at an altitude of 22,320 mi above a point on the equator. If the radius of the earth is 3960 mi, what is the velocity of the satellite?

In order for the satellite to remain over a point on the equator, it must rotate exactly once each day around the center of the earth (and it must remain at an altitude of 22,320 mi). Since there are 2π radians in each revolution, the angular velocity is

$$\omega = \frac{1 \text{ r}}{1 \text{ day}} = \frac{2\pi \text{ rad}}{24 \text{ h}} = 0.2618 \text{ rad/h}$$

The radius of the circle through which the satellite moves is its altitude plus the radius of the earth, or $22,320 + 3960 = 26,280$ mi. Thus, the velocity is

$$v = 0.2618(26,280) = 6880 \text{ mi/h} \qquad \text{▬}$$

SOLVING A WORD PROBLEM

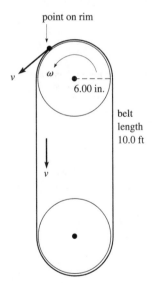

point on rim

v ω

6.00 in.

belt length 10.0 ft

v

Fig. 8-41

EXAMPLE 6 A pulley belt 10.0 ft long takes 2.00 s to make one complete revolution. The radius of the pulley is 6.00 in. What is the angular velocity (in revolutions per minute) of a point on the rim of the pulley? See Fig. 8-41.

Since the linear velocity of a point on the rim of the pulley is the same as the velocity of the belt, $v = 10.0/2.00 = 5.00$ ft/s. The radius of the pulley is $r = 6.00$ in. $= 0.500$ ft, and we can find ω by substituting into Eq. (8-13). This gives us

$$v = \omega r$$
$$5.00 = \omega(0.500)$$
$$\omega = 10.0 \text{ rad/s} \qquad \text{multiply by 60 s/1 min}$$
$$= 600 \text{ rad/min} \qquad \text{multiply by 1 r/}2\pi \text{ rad}$$
$$= 95.5 \text{ r/min} \qquad \text{r is the symbol for revolution}$$

As shown in Appendix B, the change of units can be handled algebraically as

$$10.0\frac{\text{rad}}{\text{s}} \times 60\frac{\text{s}}{\text{min}} = 600\frac{\text{rad}}{\text{min}}$$

$$\frac{600 \text{ rad/min}}{2\pi \text{ rad/r}} = 600\frac{\text{rad}}{\text{min}} \times \frac{1}{2\pi}\frac{\text{r}}{\text{rad}} = 95.5 \text{ r/min} \qquad \text{▬}$$

EXAMPLE 7 The current at any time in a certain alternating-current electric circuit is given by $i = I \sin 120\pi t$, where I is the maximum current and t is the time in seconds. Given that $I = 0.0685$ A, find i for $t = 0.00500$ s.

Substituting, with the calculator in radian mode, we get

$$i = 0.0685 \sin(120\pi)(0.00500)$$
$$= 0.0651 \text{ A} \qquad \text{▬}$$

EXERCISES *8-4*

In Exercises 1–12, for an arc length s, area of sector A, and central angle θ of a circle of radius r, find the indicated quantity for the given values.

1. $r = 3.30$ in., $\theta = \pi/3$, $s = ?$
2. $r = 21.2$ cm, $\theta = 2.65$, $s = ?$
3. $s = 1010$ mm, $\theta = 136.0°$, $r = ?$
4. $s = 0.3456$ ft, $\theta = 73.61°$, $r = ?$
5. $s = 0.3913$ mi, $r = 0.9449$ mi, $\theta = ?$
6. $s = 3.19$ m, $r = 2.29$ m, $\theta = ?$
7. $r = 4.9$ cm, $\theta = 3.6$, $A = ?$
8. $r = 46.3$ in., $\theta = 2\pi/5$, $A = ?$
9. $A = 0.0119$ ft^2, $\theta = 326.0°$, $r = ?$
10. $A = 1200$ mm^2, $\theta = 17°$, $r = ?$
11. $A = 16.5$ m^2, $r = 4.02$ m, $\theta = ?$
12. $A = 67.8$ mi^2, $r = 67.8$ mi, $\theta = ?$

In Exercises 13–48, solve the given problems.

13. While playing, the left spool of a VCR turns through 820°. For this part of the tape, it is 3.30 cm from the center of the spool to the tape. What length of tape is played?

14. The latitude of Miami is 26° N, and the latitude of the north end of the Panama Canal is 9° N. Both are at a longitude of 80° W. What is the distance between Miami and the Canal? Explain how the angle used in the solution is found. The radius of the earth is 3960 mi.

15. Of the estimated natural gas reserves in North America, 4.59×10^9 m^3 are in the United States, 2.66×10^9 m^3 are in Canada, and 1.99×10^9 m^3 are in Mexico. In making a *circle graph* (circular sectors represent percentages of the whole—a *pie chart*) with a radius of 4.00 cm for these data, what are the central angle and area of the sector that represents Canada's reserves?

16. A section of sidewalk is a circular sector of radius 3.00 ft and central angle 50.6°. What is the area of this section of sidewalk?

17. When between 12:00 noon and 1:00 P.M. are the minute and hour hands of a clock 180° apart?

18. A cam is in the shape of a circular sector, as shown in Fig. 8-42. What is the perimeter of the cam?

165.58°

Fig. 8-42   1.875 in.

19. A lawn sprinkler can water up to a distance of 65.0 ft. It turns through an angle of 115.0°. What area can it water?

20. A spotlight beam sweeps through a horizontal angle of 75.0°. If the range of the spotlight is 250 ft, what area can it cover?

21. If a car makes a U-turn in 6.0 s, what is its average angular velocity in the turn?

22. The roller on a computer printer makes 2200 r/min. What is its angular velocity?

23. What is the floor area of the hallway shown in Fig. 8-43? The outside and inside of the hallway are circular arcs.

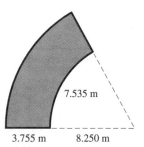

7.535 m

Fig. 8-43   3.755 m   8.250 m

24. The arm of a car windshield wiper is 12.75 in. long and is attached at the middle of a 15.00 in. blade. (Assume that the arm and blade are in line.) What area of the windshield is cleaned by the wiper if it swings through 110.0° arcs?

25. Part of a railroad track follows a circular arc with a central angle of 28.0°. If the radius of the arc of the inner rail is 93.67 ft and the rails are 4.71 ft apart, how much longer is the outer rail than the inner rail?

26. A wrecking ball is dropped as shown in Fig. 8-44. Its velocity at the bottom of its swing is $v = \sqrt{2gh}$, where g is the acceleration due to gravity. What is its angular velocity at the bottom if $g = 9.80$ m/s^2 and $h = 4.80$ m?

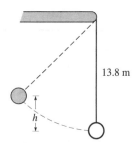

13.8 m

h

Fig. 8-44

27. Part of a security fence is built 2.50 m from a cylindrical storage tank 11.2 m in diameter. What is the area between the tank and this part of the fence if the central angle of the fence is 75.5°? See Fig. 8-45.

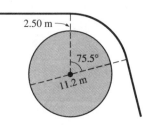

2.50 m

75.5°

11.2 m

Fig. 8-45

28. Through what angle does the drum in Fig. 8-46 turn in order to lower the crate 18.5 ft?

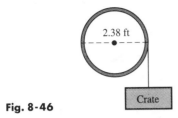

2.38 ft

Crate

Fig. 8-46

29. A section of road follows a circular arc with a central angle of 15.6°. The radius of the inside of the curve is 285.0 m, and the road is 15.2 m wide. What is the volume of the concrete in the road if it is 0.305 m thick?

30. The propeller of the motor on a motorboat is rotating at 130 rad/s. What is the linear velocity of a point on the tip of a blade if it is 22.5 cm long?

31. A storm causes a pilot to follow a circular-arc route, with a central angle of 12.8°, from city A to city B rather than the straight-line route of 185.0 km. How much farther does the plane fly due to the storm?

32. An interstate route exit is a circular arc 330 m long with a central angle of 79.4°. What is the radius of curvature of the exit?

33. A special vehicle for traveling on glacial ice has tires that are 12.0 ft in diameter. If the vehicle travels at 3.5 mi/h, what is the angular velocity of the tire in revolutions per minute?

34. The sweep second hand of a watch is 15.0 mm long. What is the linear velocity of the tip?

35. A computer diskette has a diameter of 3.50 in. and rotates at 360.0 r/min. What is the linear velocity of a point on the outer edge?

36. A rotating circular restaurant at the top of a hotel has a diameter of 25.0 m. If it completes one revolution in 30.0 min, what is the velocity of its outer surface?

37. Two streets meet at an angle of 82.0°. What is the length of the piece of curved curbing at the intersection if it is constructed along the arc of a circle 15.0 ft in radius? See Fig. 8-47.

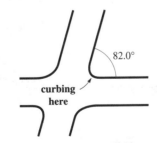

82.0°

curbing
here

Fig. 8-47

38. An ammeter needle is deflected 52.00° by a current of 0.2500 A. The needle is 3.750 in. long, and a circular scale is used. How long is the scale for a maximum current of 1.500 A?

39. A drill bit $\frac{3}{8}$ in. in diameter rotates at 1200 r/min. What is the linear velocity of a point on its circumference?

40. A helicopter blade is 2.75 m long and is rotating at 420 r/min. What is the linear velocity of the tip of the blade?

41. A waterwheel used to generate electricity has paddles 3.75 m long. The speed of the end of a paddle is one-fourth that of the water. If the water is flowing at the rate of 6.50 m/s, what is the angular velocity of the waterwheel?

42. A jet is traveling westward with the sun directly overhead (the jet is on a line between the sun and the center of the earth). How fast must the jet fly in order to keep the sun directly overhead? (Assume that the earth's radius is 3960 mi, the altitude of the jet is low, and the earth rotates about its axis once in 24.0 h.)

43. A 1500-kW wind turbine (windmill) rotates at 40.0 r/min. What is the linear velocity of a point on the end of a blade, if the blade is 35 ft long (from the center of rotation)?

44. What is the linear velocity of a point in Charleston, South Carolina, which is at a latitude of 32°46′ N? The radius of the earth is 3960 mi.

45. Through what total angle does the drive shaft of a car rotate in one second when the tachometer reads 2400 r/min?

46. A patio is in the shape of a circular sector with a central angle of 160.0°. It is enclosed by a railing of which the circular part is 11.6 m long. What is the area of the patio?

47. An oil storage tank 4.25 m long has a flat bottom as shown in Fig. 8-48. The radius of the circular part is 1.10 m. What volume of oil does the tank hold?

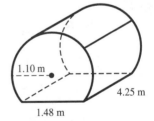

1.10 m

4.25 m

Fig. 8-48   1.48 m

48. Two equal beams of light illuminate the area shown in Fig. 8-49. What area is lit by both beams?

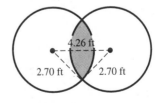

4.26 ft

2.70 ft   2.70 ft

Fig. 8-49

In Exercises 49–52, another use of radians is illustrated.

W **49.** Use a calculator (in radian mode) to evaluate the ratios $(\sin \theta)/\theta$ and $(\tan \theta)/\theta$ for $\theta = 0.1, 0.01, 0.001$, and 0.0001. From these values explain why it is possible to say that

$$\sin \theta = \tan \theta = \theta \qquad (8\text{-}14)$$

approximately for very small angles.

50. Using Eq. (8-14), evaluate $\tan 0.001°$. Compare with a calculator value.

51. An astronomer observes that a star 12.5 light-years away moves through an angle of $0.2''$ in one year. Assuming it moved in a straight line perpendicular to the initial line of observation, how many miles did the star move? (1 light-year $= 5.88 \times 10^{12}$ mi.) Use Eq. (8-14).

52. In calculating a back line of a lot, a surveyor discovers an error of $0.05°$ in an angle measurement. If the lot is 136.0 m deep, by how much is the back line calculation in error? See Fig. 8-50. Use Eq. (8-14).

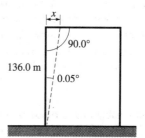

Fig. 8-50

Section 5.5

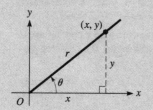

α is
reference angle

$$\sin \theta = \frac{y}{r} \qquad \cos \theta = \frac{x}{r} \qquad \tan \theta = \frac{y}{x}$$

$$\cot \theta = \frac{x}{y} \qquad \sec \theta = \frac{r}{x} \qquad \csc \theta = \frac{r}{y} \qquad (8\text{-}1)$$

$$F(\theta_2) = \pm F(180° - \theta_2) = \pm F(\alpha) \qquad (8\text{-}3)$$

$$F(\theta_3) = \pm F(\theta_3 - 180°) = \pm F(\alpha) \qquad (8\text{-}4)$$

$$F(\theta_4) = \pm F(360° - \theta_4) = \pm F(\alpha) \qquad (8\text{-}5)$$

$$\theta = \alpha \qquad \text{(first quadrant)}$$

$$\theta = 180° - \alpha \qquad \text{(second quadrant)}$$

$$\theta = 180° + \alpha \qquad \text{(third quadrant)}$$

$$\theta = 360° - \alpha \qquad \text{(fourth quadrant)} \qquad (8\text{-}6)$$

$$\pi \text{ rad} = 180° \qquad (8\text{-}8)$$

Radian-degree conversions

$$1° = \frac{\pi}{180} \text{ rad} = 0.01745 \text{ rad} \qquad (8\text{-}9)$$

$$1 \text{ rad} = \frac{180°}{\pi} = 57.30° \qquad (8\text{-}10)$$

Circular arc length

$$s = \theta r \qquad (\theta \text{ in radians}) \qquad (8\text{-}11)$$

Circular sector area

$$A = \frac{1}{2} \theta r^2 \qquad (\theta \text{ in radians}) \qquad (8\text{-}12)$$

Linear and angular velocity

$$v = \omega r \qquad (8\text{-}13)$$

REVIEW EXERCISES

In Exercises 1–4, find the trigonometric functions of θ. The terminal side of θ passes through the given point.

1. (6, 8)
2. (−12, 5)
3. (7, −2)
4. (−2, −3)

In Exercises 5–8, express the given trigonometric functions in terms of the same function of a positive acute angle.

5. cos 132°, tan 194°
6. sin 243°, cot 318°
7. sin 289°, sec (−15°)
8. cos 103°, csc (−100°)

In Exercises 9–12, express the given angle measurements in terms of π.

9. 40°, 153°
10. 22.5°, 324°
11. 48°, 202.5°
12. 27°, −162°

In Exercises 13–20, the given numbers represent angle measure. Express the measure of each angle in degrees.

13. $\dfrac{7\pi}{5}, \dfrac{13\pi}{18}$
14. $\dfrac{3\pi}{8}, \dfrac{7\pi}{20}$

15. $\dfrac{\pi}{15}, \dfrac{11\pi}{6}$
16. $\dfrac{17\pi}{10}, \dfrac{5\pi}{4}$

17. 0.560
18. 1.354
19. 3.607
20. 14.5

In Exercises 21–28, express the given angles in radians (not in terms of π).

21. 102°
22. 305°
23. 20.25°
24. 148.38°
25. 262.05°
26. 18.72°
27. 136.2°
28. 385.4°

In Exercises 29–48, determine the values of the given trigonometric functions directly on a calculator. The angles are approximate. Express answers to Exercises 41–44 to four significant digits.

29. cos 245.5°
30. sin 141.3°
31. cot 295°
32. tan 184°
33. csc 247.82°
34. sec 96.17°
35. sin 205.24°
36. cos 326.72°
37. tan 301.4°
38. sin 103.9°
39. tan 256.42°
40. cos 162.32°
41. $\sin \dfrac{9\pi}{5}$
42. $\sec \dfrac{5\pi}{8}$
43. $\cos \dfrac{7\pi}{6}$
44. $\tan \dfrac{23\pi}{12}$
45. sin 0.5906
46. tan 0.8035
47. csc 2.153
48. cot 5.190

In Exercises 49–52, find θ in degrees for 0° ≤ θ < 360°.

49. tan θ = 0.1817
50. sin θ = −0.9323
51. cos θ = −0.4730
52. cot θ = 1.196

In Exercises 53–56, find θ in radians for 0 ≤ θ < 2π.

53. cos θ = 0.8387
54. sin θ = 0.1045
55. sin θ = −0.8650
56. tan θ = 2.840

In Exercises 57–60, find θ in degrees for 0° ≤ θ < 360°.

57. cos θ = −0.7222, sin θ < 0
58. tan θ = −1.683, cos θ < 0
59. cot θ = 0.4291, cos θ < 0
60. sin θ = 0.2626, tan θ < 0

In Exercises 61–64, for an arc of length s, area of sector A, and central angle θ of circle of radius r, find the indicated quantity for the given values.

61. s = 20.3 in., θ = 107.5°, r = ?
62. s = 584 ft, r = 106 ft, θ = ?
63. A = 265 mm², r = 12.8 mm, θ = ?
64. A = 0.908 km², θ = 234.5°, r = ?

In Exercises 65–80, solve the given problems.

65. The instantaneous power p (in W) input to a resistor in an alternating-current circuit is $p = p_m \sin^2 377t$, where p_m is the maximum power input and t is the time (in s). Find p for $p_m = 0.120$ W and t = 2.00 ms. ($\sin^2 \theta = (\sin \theta)^2$.)

66. The horizontal distance x through which a pendulum moves is given by $x = a(\theta + \sin \theta)$, where a is a constant and θ is the angle between the vertical and the pendulum. Find x for a = 45.0 cm and θ = 0.175.

67. A sector gear with a pitch radius of 8.25 in. and a 6.60-in. arc of contact is shown in Fig. 8-51. What is the sector angle θ?

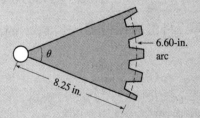

Fig. 8-51

68. Two pulleys have radii of 10.0 in. and 6.00 in., and their centers are 40.0 in. apart. If the pulley belt is uncrossed, what must be the length of the belt?

(W) **69.** The longitude of Anchorage, Alaska, is 150° W, and the longitude of St. Petersburg, Russia, is 30° E. Both cities are at a latitude of 60° N. (a) Find the great circle distance (see page 235) from Anchorage to St. Petersburg over the north pole. (b) Find the distance between them along the 60° N latitude arc. The radius of the earth is 3960 mi. What do the results show?

70. A piece of circular filter paper 15.0 cm in diameter is folded such that its effective filtering area is the same as that of a sector with central angle of 220°. What is the filtering area?

71. To produce an electric current, a circular loop of wire of diameter 25.0 cm is rotating about its diameter at 60.0 r/s in a magnetic field. What is the greatest linear velocity of any point on the loop?

72. Find the area of the decorative glass panel shown in Fig. 8-52. The panel is made of two equal circular sectors and an isosceles triangle.

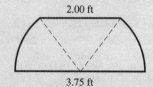

Fig. 8-52

2.00 ft

3.75 ft

73. A circular hood is to be used over a piece of machinery. It is to be made from a circular piece of sheet metal 3.25 ft in radius. A hole 0.75 ft in radius and a sector of central angle 80.0° are to be removed to make the hood. What is the area of the top of the hood?

74. The chain on a chain saw is driven by a sprocket 7.50 cm in diameter. If the chain is 108 cm long and makes one revolution in 0.250 s, what is the angular velocity (in r/s) of the sprocket?

75. An *ultracentrifuge,* used to observe the sedimentation of particles such as proteins, may rotate as fast as 80,000 r/min. If it rotates at this rate and is 7.20 cm in diameter, what is the linear velocity of a particle at the outer edge?

76. A computer is programmed to shade in a sector of a pie chart 2.44 cm in radius. If the perimeter of the shaded sector is 7.32 cm, what is the central angle (in degrees) of the sector? See Fig. 8-53.

2.44 cm

Fig. 8-53

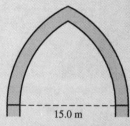

15.0 m

Fig. 8-54

77. A Gothic arch, commonly used in medieval European structures, is formed by two circular arcs. In one type, each arc is one-sixth of a circle, with the center of each at the base on the end of the other arc. See Fig. 8-54. Therefore, the width of the arch equals the radius of each arc. For such an arch, find the area of the opening if the width is 15.0 m.

78. The Trans-Alaska Pipeline was assembled in sections 40.0 ft long and 4.00 ft in diameter. If the depth of the oil in one horizontal section is 1.00 ft, what is the volume of oil in this section?

79. A laser beam is transmitted with a "width" of 0.0008° and makes a circular spot of radius 2.50 km on a distant object. How far is the object from the source of the laser beam? Use Eq. (8-14).

80. The planet Venus subtends an angle of 15″ to an observer on earth. If the distance between Venus and earth is 1.04×10^8 mi, what is the diameter of Venus? Use Eq. (8-14).

Writing Exercise

81. Write a paragraph explaining how you determine the units for the result of the following problem: An astronaut in a spacecraft circles the moon once each 1.95 h. If the altitude of the spacecraft is constant at 70.0 mi, what is its velocity? The radius of the moon is 1080 mi. (What is the answer?)

PRACTICE TEST

1. Change 150° to radians in terms of π.

2. Express sin 205° in terms of the sine of a positive acute angle. Do not evaluate.

3. Find sin θ and sec θ if θ is in standard position and the terminal side passes through $(-9, 12)$.

4. An airplane propeller blade is 2.80 ft long and rotates at 2200 r/min. What is the linear velocity of a point on the tip of the blade?

5. Given that 3.572 is the measure of an angle, express the angle in degrees.

6. If tan $\theta = 0.2396$, find θ, in degrees, for $0° \leq \theta < 360°$.

7. If cos $\theta = -0.8244$ and csc $\theta < 0$, find θ in radians for $0 \leq \theta < 2\pi$.

8. The floor of a sunroom is in the shape of a circular sector of arc length 32.0 ft and radius 8.50 ft. What is the area of the floor?

Section 5.2
Exercises 8-2, page 229

1. $\sin 20°$; $-\cos 40°$ **3.** $-\tan 75°$; $-\csc 58°$

5. $\cos 40°$; $-\tan 40°$ **7.** $-\sin 15° = -0.26$

9. $-\cos 73.7° = -0.281$ **11.** $\sec 31.67° = 1.175$

13. -0.523 **15.** -0.7620 **17.** -3.910

19. $237.99°$, $302.01°$ **21.** $66.40°$, $293.60°$

23. $102.0°$, $282.0°$ **25.** $119.5°$ **27.** $263°$ **29.** $306.21°$

31. $299.24°$ **33.** -0.7003 **35.** -0.777 **37.** $<$

39. $=$ **41.** 0.0183 A   **43.** 12.6 in.

45. The y-coordinate has the opposite sign for $\sin(-\theta)$ than it has for $\sin \theta$. $\cos(-\theta) = \dfrac{x}{r}$, $\tan(-\theta) = \dfrac{-y}{x}$, $\cot(-\theta) = \dfrac{x}{-y}$, $\sec(-\theta) = \dfrac{r}{x}$, $\csc(-\theta) = \dfrac{r}{-y}$

47. (a) 5.7 (b) -1.4

Section 5.3
Exercises 8-3, page 234

1. $\dfrac{\pi}{12}, \dfrac{5\pi}{6}$ **3.** $\dfrac{5\pi}{12}, \dfrac{11\pi}{6}$ **5.** $\dfrac{7\pi}{6}, \dfrac{3\pi}{2}$ **7.** $\dfrac{8\pi}{9}, \dfrac{13\pi}{9}$

9. $72°$, $270°$ **11.** $10°$, $315°$ **13.** $170°$, $300°$

15. $15°$, $27°$ **17.** 0.401 **19.** 4.40 **21.** 5.821

23. 3.115 **25.** $43.0°$ **27.** $195.2°$ **29.** $140°$

31. $940.8°$ **33.** 0.7071 **35.** 3.732 **37.** -0.8660

39. -8.327 **41.** 0.9056 **43.** -0.89 **45.** -2.1

47. -0.15 **49.** 0.3141, 2.827 **51.** 2.932, 6.074

53. 0.8309, 5.452 **55.** 2.442, 3.841

57. 0.030 ft·lb   **59.** 2900 m

Section 5.4
Exercises 8-4, page 238

1. 3.46 in.   **3.** 426 mm   **5.** $0.4141 = 23.73°$

7. 43 cm²   **9.** 0.0647 ft   **11.** $2.04 = 117.0°$

13. 42.7 cm   **15.** 1.81, 14.5 cm²   **17.** 32.73 min past noon

19. 4240 ft²   **21.** 0.52 rad/s   **23.** 34.73 m²

25. 2.30 ft   **27.** 22.6 m²   **29.** 369 m³   **31.** 0.4 km

33. 8.2 r/min   **35.** 3960 in./min   **37.** 25.7 ft

39. 1400 in./min   **41.** 0.433 rad/s   **43.** 8800 ft/min

45. 250 rad   **47.** 14.9 m³   **49.** ratios become very close to 1

51. 7.13×10^7 mi

Section 5.5
Review Exercises for Chapter 8, page 241

1. $\sin \theta = \dfrac{4}{5}$, $\cos \theta = \dfrac{3}{5}$, $\tan \theta = \dfrac{4}{3}$, $\cot \theta = \dfrac{3}{4}$, $\sec \theta = \dfrac{5}{3}$, $\csc \theta = \dfrac{5}{4}$

3. $\sin \theta = -\dfrac{2}{\sqrt{53}}$, $\cos \theta = \dfrac{7}{\sqrt{53}}$, $\tan \theta = -\dfrac{2}{7}$, $\cot \theta = -\dfrac{7}{2}$, $\sec \theta = \dfrac{\sqrt{53}}{7}$, $\csc \theta = -\dfrac{\sqrt{53}}{2}$

Section 5.1
Exercises 8-1, page 223

1. $+, -$ **3.** $+, +$ **5.** $-, +$ **7.** $+, -$

9. $-, -$ **11.** $-, +$

13. $\sin \theta = \dfrac{1}{\sqrt{5}}$, $\cos \theta = \dfrac{2}{\sqrt{5}}$, $\tan \theta = \dfrac{1}{2}$, $\cot \theta = 2$, $\sec \theta = \dfrac{1}{2}\sqrt{5}$, $\csc \theta = \sqrt{5}$

15. $\sin \theta = -\dfrac{3}{\sqrt{13}}$, $\cos \theta = -\dfrac{2}{\sqrt{13}}$, $\tan \theta = \dfrac{3}{2}$, $\cot \theta = \dfrac{2}{3}$, $\sec \theta = -\dfrac{1}{2}\sqrt{13}$, $\csc \theta = -\dfrac{1}{3}\sqrt{13}$

17. $\sin \theta = \dfrac{12}{13}$, $\cos \theta = -\dfrac{5}{13}$, $\tan \theta = -\dfrac{12}{5}$, $\cot \theta = -\dfrac{5}{12}$, $\sec \theta = -\dfrac{13}{5}$, $\csc \theta = \dfrac{13}{12}$

19. $\sin \theta = -\dfrac{2}{\sqrt{29}}$, $\cos \theta = \dfrac{5}{\sqrt{29}}$, $\tan \theta = -\dfrac{2}{5}$, $\cot \theta = -\dfrac{5}{2}$, $\sec \theta = \dfrac{1}{5}\sqrt{29}$, $\csc \theta = -\dfrac{1}{2}\sqrt{29}$

21. II   **23.** II   **25.** IV   **27.** III   **29.** IV   **31.** II

5. $-\cos 48°$, $\tan 14°$ **7.** $-\sin 71°$, $\sec 15°$ **9.** $\dfrac{2\pi}{9}$, $\dfrac{17\pi}{20}$

11. $\dfrac{4\pi}{15}$, $\dfrac{9\pi}{8}$ **13.** $252°$, $130°$ **15.** $12°$, $330°$ **17.** $32.1°$

19. $206.7°$ **21.** 1.78 **23.** 0.3534 **25.** 4.5736

27. 2.377 **29.** -0.415 **31.** -0.47 **33.** -1.080

35. -0.4264 **37.** -1.64 **39.** 4.140 **41.** -0.5878

43. -0.8660 **45.** 0.5569 **47.** 1.197

49. $10.30°$, $190.30°$ **51.** $118.23°$, $241.77°$

53. 0.5759, 5.707 **55.** 4.187, 5.238 **57.** $223.76°$

59. $246.78°$ **61.** 10.8 in.   **63.** $3.23 = 185.3°$

65. 0.0562 W   **67.** $0.800 = 45.8°$

69. (a) 4150 mi (b) 6220 mi; great circle route shortest of all routes

71. 4710 cm/s   **73.** 24.4 ft^2 **75.** 1.81×10^6 cm/s

77. 138 m^2 **79.** 3.58×10^5 km

TRIGONOMETRIC FUNCTIONS OF ANY ANGLE

8.1   Signs of the Trigonometric Functions   Section 5.1

1. sin 36° is positive since 36° is in QI where sine is positive.
cos 120° is negative since 120° is in QII where cosine is negative.

5. sec 150° is negative since 150° is in QII where secant is negative.
tan 220° is positive since 220° is in QIII where tangent is positive.

9. tan 460° is negative since 460° is QII where tangent is negative.
sin(−110°) is negative since −110° is in QIII where sine is negative.

13. $r = \sqrt{2^2 + 1^2} = \sqrt{4+1} = \sqrt{5}$ for $(2, 1)$.

$$\sin\theta = \frac{y}{r} = \frac{1}{\sqrt{5}} \qquad \csc\theta = \frac{r}{y} = \sqrt{5}$$

$$\cos\theta = \frac{x}{r} = \frac{2}{\sqrt{5}} \qquad \sec\theta = \frac{r}{x} = \frac{\sqrt{5}}{2}$$

$$\tan\theta = \frac{y}{x} = \frac{1}{2} \qquad \cot\theta = \frac{x}{y} = 2$$

17. $r = \sqrt{(-5)^2 + 12^2} = 13$ for $(-5, 12)$

$$\sin\theta = \frac{y}{r} = \frac{12}{13} \qquad \csc\theta = \frac{r}{y} = \frac{13}{12}$$

$$\cos\theta = \frac{x}{r} = \frac{-5}{13} \qquad \sec\theta = \frac{r}{x} = \frac{13}{-5}$$

$$\tan\theta = \frac{y}{x} = \frac{12}{-5} \qquad \cot\theta = \frac{x}{y} = \frac{-5}{12}$$

21. $\sin\theta$ is positive and $\cos\theta$ is negative
$\sin\theta$ positive in QI and QII
$\cos\theta$ negative in QII and QIII. The
terminal side of θ is in QII.

25. $\csc\theta$ is negative and $\tan\theta$ is negative
$\csc\theta$ negative in QIII and QIV
$\tan\theta$ negative in QII and QIV. The
terminal side of θ is in QIV.

29. $\tan\theta$ is negative, $\cos\theta$ is positive
$\tan\theta$ is negative in QII and QIV
$\cos\theta$ is positive in QI and QIV. The
terminal side of θ is in QIV.

Section 5.2

8.2   Trigonometric Functions of Any Angle

1. $\sin 160° = \sin(180° - 160°)$
$\qquad = \sin 20°$

$\cos 220° = \cos(180° + 40°)$
$\qquad = -\cos 40°$

5.

$$\cos 400° = \cos(360° + 40°)$$
$$= \cos 40°$$

$$\tan(-400°) = \tan(-360° - 40°)$$
$$= \tan(-40°)$$
$$= -\tan 40°$$

9. $\cos 106.3° = -\cos 73.7°$
$$= -0.281$$

13. $\tan 152.4° = -0.5228$

17. $\csc 194.82° = -3.9096$

21. $\cos \theta = 0.4003$

$\theta_{\text{ref}} = \cos^{-1}(0.4003)$
$$= 66.4°.$$

Since $\cos \theta$ is positive, θ is in QI or QIV. Therefore,

$\theta = 66.4°$ or
$\theta = 293.6°$
$0^0 \leq \theta < 360°$

25. $\sin \theta = 0.870,$

$\theta_{\text{ref}} = \sin^{-1}(0.870)$
$$= 60.4°$$

Since $0^0 \leq \theta < 360°$, $\cos \theta < 0$,

θ is in QII and $\theta = 119.5°$

29. $\tan \theta = -1.366,$

$\theta_{\text{ref}} = \tan^{-1}(-1.366)$
$$= -53.8°$$

Since $0^0 \leq \theta < 360°$, $\cos \theta > 0$,
θ is in QIV and $\theta = 306.2°$

33. $\sin \theta = -0.5736,$

$\theta_{\text{ref}} = \sin^{-1}(-0.5736)$
$$= -35°.$$

Since $\cos \theta > 0, \theta$ is in QIV.

where $k = 0, \pm 1, \pm 2, \cdots$
$\tan \theta = -0.7003$

37. $\sin 90° = 1, 2 \sin 45° = 2 \cdot \dfrac{\sqrt{2}}{2} = \sqrt{2}$

$$1 < \sqrt{2}$$
$$\sin 90° < 2 \sin 45°$$

41. $i = i_m \sin \theta$
$i = 0.0259 \cdot \sin 495.2°$
$i = 0.0183$ A

45.

$$\left.\begin{array}{l} \sin(-\theta) = \dfrac{-y}{r} \\[2mm] -\sin\theta = -\dfrac{y}{r} \end{array}\right\} \Rightarrow \sin(-\theta) = -\sin\theta \qquad \left.\begin{array}{l} \cot(-\theta) = \dfrac{x}{-y} \\[2mm] \cot\theta = \dfrac{x}{y} \end{array}\right\} \Rightarrow \cot(-\theta) = -\cot\theta$$

$$\left.\begin{array}{l} \cos(-\theta) = \dfrac{x}{r} \\[2mm] \cos\theta = \dfrac{x}{r} \end{array}\right\} \Rightarrow \cos(-\theta) = \cos\theta \qquad \left.\begin{array}{l} \sec(-\theta) = \dfrac{r}{x} \\[2mm] \sec\theta = \dfrac{r}{x} \end{array}\right\} \Rightarrow \sec(-\theta) = \sec\theta$$

$$\left.\begin{array}{l} \tan(-\theta) = \dfrac{-y}{x} \\[2mm] \tan\theta = \dfrac{y}{x} \end{array}\right\} \Rightarrow \tan(-\theta) = \tan\theta \qquad \left.\begin{array}{l} \csc(-\theta) = \dfrac{r}{-y} \\[2mm] \csc\theta = \dfrac{r}{y} \end{array}\right\} \Rightarrow \csc(-\theta) = -\csc\theta$$

Section 5.3

8.3   Radians

1. $15° = \dfrac{\pi}{180°}(15) = \dfrac{\pi}{12}$

$150° = \dfrac{\pi}{180°}(150) = \dfrac{5\pi}{6}$

5. $210° = \dfrac{\pi}{180°}(210) = \dfrac{7\pi}{6}$

$270° = \dfrac{\pi}{180°}(270) = \dfrac{3\pi}{2}$

9. $\dfrac{2\pi}{5} = \dfrac{180°}{\pi}\left(\dfrac{2\pi}{5}\right) = 72°$

$\dfrac{3\pi}{2} = \dfrac{180°}{\pi}\left(\dfrac{3\pi}{2}\right) = 270°$

13. $\dfrac{17\pi}{18} = \dfrac{180°}{\pi}\left(\dfrac{17\pi}{18}\right) = 170°$

$\dfrac{5\pi}{3} = \dfrac{180°}{\pi}\left(\dfrac{5\pi}{3}\right) = 300°$

17. $23° = \dfrac{\pi}{180°}(23) = 0.401$

21. $333.5° = \dfrac{\pi}{180°}(333.5) = 5.821$

25. $0.750 = \dfrac{180°}{\pi}(0.750) = 43.0°$

29. $2.45 = \dfrac{180°}{\pi}(2.45) = 140°$

33. $\sin\dfrac{\pi}{4} = \sin\left[\left(\dfrac{\pi}{4}\right)\left(\dfrac{180}{\pi}\right)\right]$

$ = \sin 45° = 0.7071$

37. $\cos\dfrac{5\pi}{6} = \cos\left[\left(\dfrac{5\pi}{6}\right)\left(\dfrac{180}{\pi}\right)\right]$

$ = \cos 150° = -0.8660$

41. $\tan 0.7359 = 0.9056$

45. $\sec 2.07 = \dfrac{1}{\cos 2.07} = -2.1$

49. $\sin\theta = 0.3090,\ \theta = 0.3141$
$\sin\theta$ is positive, θ is in QI and QII
In QI, $\theta = 0.3141$
In QII, $\theta = \pi - 0.3141 = 2.827$

53. $\cos\theta = 0.6742,\ \theta = 0.8309$
$\cos\theta$ is positive, θ is in QI and QIV.
In QI, $\theta = 0.8309$
In QIV, $\theta = 2\pi - 0.8309 = 5.452$

57. $V = \dfrac{1}{2}Wb\theta^2$

$V = \dfrac{1}{2}(8.75)(0.75)\left(5.5°\,\dfrac{\pi}{180°}\right)^2$

$V = 0.030\ \text{ft}\ \cdot\ \text{lb}$

Part 5   5.6 continued (a)   **275**

Section 5.4

8.4   Applications of Radian Measure

1. $s = r\theta = (3.30)\left(\dfrac{\pi}{3}\right) = 3.46$ in

5. $\theta = \dfrac{s}{r} = \dfrac{0.3913}{0.9449} = 0.4141 = 23.73°$

9. $A = \dfrac{1}{2}r^2\theta \Rightarrow r = \sqrt{\dfrac{2A}{\theta}} = \sqrt{\dfrac{2(0.0119)}{326°\,\dfrac{\pi}{180}}}$

$r = 0.0647$ ft

13. $s = r\theta = 3.30 \cdot \left(820° \cdot \dfrac{\pi}{180°}\right) = 47.2$

47.2 cm of tape is played.

17. From $\theta = w \cdot t$,

hour hand: $\theta = \dfrac{2\pi}{12} \cdot t$

minute hand: $\theta + \pi = \dfrac{2\pi}{1} \cdot t$, t in hours

$$\dfrac{\pi}{6} \cdot t + \pi = 2\pi \cdot t \Rightarrow t = \dfrac{6}{11} \text{ hour} = 32.73 \text{ minutes}$$

$$t = 32 \text{ minutes } 44 \text{ seconds}$$

at 32 minutes and 44 seconds after noon the hour and minute hands will be at $180°$.

21. $w = \dfrac{\theta}{t} = \dfrac{\pi}{6.0}$ rad/s $= 0.52$ rad/s

25.

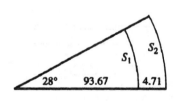

From $s = r\theta$

$s_1 = 93.67 \cdot 28.0° \cdot \dfrac{\pi}{180°}$

$s_1 = 45.78$

$s_2 = (93.67 + 4.71) \cdot 28.0° \cdot \dfrac{\pi}{180°}$

$s_2 = 48.08$

$s_2 - s_1 = 2.30$ ft. Outer rail is 2.30 ft longer.

29. $V = A \cdot t = \left[\dfrac{1}{2}r_1^2\theta - \dfrac{1}{2}r_2^2\theta\right] \cdot t = \dfrac{1}{2}\theta\left(r_1^2 - r_2^2\right) \cdot t$

$V = \dfrac{1}{2} \cdot 15.6° \cdot \dfrac{\pi}{180°}((285 + 15.2)^2 - 285^2) \cdot (0.305)$

$V = 369$ m^3

33. $v = r \cdot w \Rightarrow w = \dfrac{v}{r} = \dfrac{3.5 \frac{\text{mi}}{\text{h}}}{\frac{12.0 \text{ ft}}{2}} \cdot \dfrac{5280 \text{ ft}}{\text{mi}} \cdot \dfrac{\text{h}}{60 \text{ min}} \cdot \dfrac{1 \text{ r}}{2\pi \text{ rad}}$

$w = 8.2$ r/min

37.

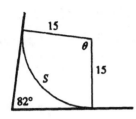

$$82.0° + 2 \cdot 90° + \theta = 360°$$
$$\theta = 98.0°$$

$$s = r\theta$$

$$s = 15.0 \cdot 98.0° \cdot \frac{\pi}{180°}$$

$$s = 25.7 \text{ ft}$$

Section 5.5

Chapter 8 Review Exercises

41. $w = \dfrac{v}{r} = \dfrac{\frac{1}{4} \cdot 6.5}{3.75} = 0.433 \text{ rad/s}$

45. $\theta = w \cdot t = 2400\dfrac{\text{r}}{\text{min}} \cdot \dfrac{2\pi \text{ rad}}{\text{r}} \cdot \dfrac{\text{min}}{60 \text{ s}} \cdot 1 \text{ s}$

$\theta = 80\pi \text{ rad} = 250 \text{ rad}$

49.

θ	$\dfrac{\sin\theta}{\theta}$	$\dfrac{\tan\theta}{\theta}$
0.0001	0.9999999983	1.000000003
0.001	0.9999998333	1.000000333
0.01	0.9999833334	1.000033335
0.1	0.9983341665	1.003346721

For small θ, in rad, $\theta \approx \sin\theta \approx \tan\theta$

1. $r = \sqrt{6^2 + 8^2} = 10$ for $(6, 8)$

$$\sin\theta = \frac{y}{r} = \frac{8}{10} = \frac{4}{5}$$

$$\cos\theta = \frac{x}{r} = \frac{6}{10} = \frac{3}{5}$$

$$\tan\theta = \frac{y}{x} = \frac{8}{6} = \frac{4}{3}$$

$$\csc\theta = \frac{r}{y} = \frac{5}{4}$$

$$\sec\theta = \frac{r}{x} = \frac{5}{3}$$

$$\cot\theta = \frac{x}{y} = \frac{3}{4}$$

9. $40° \cdot \dfrac{\pi}{180°} = \dfrac{2\pi}{9}$

$153° \cdot \dfrac{\pi}{180°} = \dfrac{17\pi}{20}$

17. $0.560 \cdot \dfrac{180°}{\pi} = 32.1°$

29. $\cos 245.5° = -0.415$

37. $\tan 301.4° = -1.64$

45. $\sin 0.5906 = 0.5569$

5. $\cos 132° = -\cos(180° - 132) = -\cos 48°$

$\tan 194° = \tan(194° - 180°) = \tan 14°$

13. $\dfrac{7\pi}{5} \cdot \dfrac{180°}{\pi} = 252°$; $\dfrac{13\pi}{18} \cdot \dfrac{180°}{\pi} = 130°$

21. $102° \cdot \dfrac{\pi}{180°} = 1.78$ **25.** $262.05° \cdot \dfrac{\pi}{180°} = 4.5736$

33. $\csc 247.82° = -1.080$

41. $\sin \dfrac{9\pi}{4} = -0.5878$

49. $\tan \theta = 0.1817, \; 0 \le \theta < 360°$
$\theta = \tan^{-1}(0.1817) = 10.3°$ in QI
$\theta = 180° + 10.3° = 190.3°$ in QIII

53. $\cos \theta = 0.8387, \; 0 \le \theta < 2\pi$
$\theta = \cos^{-1}(0.8387) = 0.5759$ in QI
$\theta = 2\pi - 0.5759 = 5.707$ in QIV

57. $\cos \theta = -0.7222, \; \sin \theta < 0$ for $0° \le \theta < 360° \Rightarrow \theta$ in QIII
$\theta = \cos^{-1}(-0.7222) = 136.2364165$ from calculator
reference angle $= 180° - \theta = 43.76°$
QIII angle $= 180° +$ reference angle $= 223.76°$.

61. $r = \dfrac{s}{\theta} = \dfrac{20.3 \text{ in}}{107.5° \cdot \dfrac{\pi}{180°}} = 10.8 \text{ in}$

65. $p = P_m \, \sin^2 377 \cdot t = .120 \, \sin^2(377 \cdot 2 \cdot 10^{-3})$
$p = 0.0562 \, W$

69. **(a)** $3960 \cdot 60° \cdot \dfrac{\pi}{180°} = 3960 \cdot \dfrac{\pi}{3}$ over with pole, 4150 mi

     (b) $3960 \cdot \sin 30° \cdot \pi = 3960 \cdot \dfrac{\pi}{2}$ along 60°N latitude arc, 6220 mi

The distance over the north pole is shorter.

73.

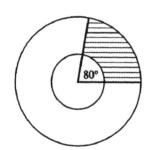

$A_{\text{circle}} \;\;= \pi \cdot 3.25^2 = A_1$
$A_{\text{hole}} \;\;\; = \pi \cdot 0.75^2 = A_2$
$A_{\text{hatched}} = \dfrac{1}{2} \cdot 80° \cdot \dfrac{\pi}{180°}(3.25^2 - 0.75^2) = A_3$
$A_{\text{hood}} \;\;= A - A_2 - A_3 = 24.4 \text{ ft}^2$

77. $A = \underbrace{\dfrac{1}{2} \cdot 15^2 \cdot 60° \cdot \dfrac{\pi}{180°}}_{\substack{\text{area of sector} \\ \text{formed by one arc}}} + (\dfrac{1}{2} \cdot 15^2 \cdot 60° \cdot \dfrac{\pi}{180°} - \underbrace{\dfrac{1}{2} \cdot 15 \cdot 15 \; \sin 60°}_{\substack{\text{area of equilateral} \\ \text{triangle inside} \\ \text{one sector}}})$

     $A = 138 \text{ m}^2$

81. $v = r \cdot w = (1080 \text{ mi} + 70.0 \text{ mi}) \cdot \dfrac{1 \text{ r}}{1.95 \text{ h}} \cdot \dfrac{2\pi \text{ rad}}{r}$
$v = 3705.5 \text{ mi/h}$

Part 5
Chapter 8

1. $150° = (\frac{\pi}{180})(150) = \frac{5\pi}{6}$

2. $\sin 205° = -\sin(205° - 180°) = -\sin 25°$

3. $x = -9, \quad y = 12$
   $r = \sqrt{(-9)^2 + 12^2} = 15$
   $\sin \theta = \frac{12}{15} = \frac{4}{5}$
   $\sec \theta = \frac{15}{-9} = -\frac{5}{3}$

4. $r = 2.80$ ft
   $\omega = 2200$ r/min $= (2200 \text{ r/min})(2\pi \text{ rad/r})$
   $\quad = 4400\pi$ rad/min
   $v = \omega r = (4400\pi)(2.80) = 39{,}000$ ft/min

5. $3.572 = 3.572(\frac{180°}{\pi}) = 204.7°$

6. $\tan \theta = 0.2396$
   $\theta_{\text{ref}} = 13.47°$
   $\theta = 13.47°$ or
   $\theta = 180° + 13.47° = 193.47°$

7. $\cos \theta = -0.8244$, $\csc \theta < 0$;
   $\cos \theta$ negative, $\csc \theta$ negative,
   θ in third quadrant
   $\theta_{\text{ref}} = 0.6017, \qquad \theta = 3.7432$

8. $s = r\theta$, $32.0 = 8.50\theta$ $s = 32.0$ ft
   $\theta = \frac{32.0}{8.50} = 3.76$ rad
   $A = \frac{1}{2}\theta r^2 = \frac{1}{2}(3.76)(8.50)^2$
   $\quad = 136$ ft^2

$r = 8.50$ ft

PART 6 – VECTORS AND OBLIQUE TRIANGLES

Part 6

CHAPTER 9

VECTORS AND OBLIQUE TRIANGLES

In the applications considered to this point we have dealt with only the magnitudes of the various quantities used. In this chapter we shall study *vectors,* for which we must indicate the *direction* of a given quantity as well as its magnitude. In order to specify the direction we use the trigonometric functions of any required angle, as developed in Chapter 8. Vectors are of great importance in many fields of science and technology, including physics, engineering, structural design, and navigation.

After developing the basic concepts associated with vectors, we then study methods of solving triangles that are not right triangles (*oblique* triangles). In using such triangles we must be able to use the trigonometric functions of oblique angles. As with right triangles, the applications of oblique triangles are found in many fields of science and technology.

The wind must be considered to find the proper heading for an aircraft. In Section 9-5 we use vectors and an oblique triangle to show how this may be done.

Section 6.1

9-1 INTRODUCTION TO VECTORS

A great many quantities with which we deal may be described by specifying their magnitudes. Generally, one can describe lengths of objects, areas, time intervals, monetary amounts, temperatures, and numerous other quantities by specifying a number: the magnitude of the quantity. *Such quantities are known as* **scalar** *quantities.*

SCALARS

Many other quantities are fully described only when both their magnitude and direction are specified. Such quantities are known as **vectors.** Examples of vectors are velocity and force. The following example illustrates a vector quantity and the difference between scalars and vectors.

VECTORS

■EXAMPLE 1   A jet is traveling at 600 mi/h. From this statement alone we know only the *speed* of the jet. *Speed is a scalar quantity,* and it tells us only the *magnitude* of the rate. Knowing only the speed of the jet, we know the rate at which it is moving, but we do not know where it is headed.

If we add the phrase "in a direction 10° south of west" to the sentence above about the jet, we specify the direction of travel as well as the speed. We then know the *velocity* of the jet; that is, we know the *direction* of travel as well as the *magnitude* of the rate at which it is traveling. *Velocity is a vector quantity.* Knowing the velocity of the jet, we know where it is headed and the rate at which it is moving. ━━━━━━━■

Let us analyze an example of the action of two vectors. Consider a boat moving in a river. For purposes of this example, we shall assume that the boat is driven by a motor that can move it at 8 mi/h in still water. We shall assume the current is moving downstream at 6 mi/h. We immediately see that the movement of the boat depends on the direction in which it is headed. If the boat heads downstream, it can travel at 14 mi/h, for the current is going 6 mi/h and the boat moves at 8 mi/h with respect to the water. If the boat heads upstream, however, it moves at the rate of only 2 mi/h, since the action of the boat and that of the river are counter to each other. If the boat heads directly across the river, the point it reaches on the other side will not be directly opposite the point from which it started. We can see that this is so because we know that as the boat heads across the river, the river is moving the boat downstream *at the same time.*

This last case should be investigated further. Assume that the river is 0.4 mi wide where the boat is crossing. It then takes 0.05 h (0.4 mi ÷ 8 mi/h = 0.05 h) to cross. In 0.05 h the river will carry the boat 0.3 mi (0.05 h × 6 mi/h = 0.3 mi) downstream. Therefore, when the boat reaches the other side it will be 0.3 mi downstream. From the Pythagorean theorem, we find that the boat traveled 0.5 mi from its starting point to its finishing point.

$$d^2 = 0.4^2 + 0.3^2 = 0.25$$
$$d = 0.5 \text{ mi}$$

Since this 0.5 mi was traveled in 0.05 h, the magnitude of the velocity of the boat was actually

$$v = \frac{d}{t} = \frac{0.5 \text{ mi}}{0.05 \text{ h}} = 10 \text{ mi/h}$$

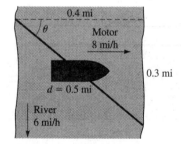

Fig. 9-1

Also, we see that the direction of this velocity can be represented along a line that makes an angle θ with the line directed directly across the river as shown in Fig. 9-1. We can find this angle by noting that

$$\tan \theta = \frac{0.3 \text{ mi}}{0.4 \text{ mi}} = 0.75$$
$$\theta = \tan^{-1} 0.75 = 37°$$

Therefore, when headed directly across the stream, the velocity of the boat is 10 mi/h at an angle of 37° downstream from a line directed directly across the stream.

Addition of Vectors

We have just seen two velocity vectors being *added*. Note that these vectors are not added the way numbers are added. We must take into account their directions as well as their magnitudes. Reasoning along these lines, let us now define the sum of two vectors.

We will represent a vector quantity by a letter printed in **boldface** type. The same letter in *italic* (lightface) type represents the magnitude only. Thus, **A** is a vector of magnitude *A*. In handwriting, one usually places an arrow over the letter to represent a vector, such as $\vec{A}$.

Let **A** and **B** represent vectors directed from *O* to *P* and *P* to *Q*, respectively (see Fig. 9-2). *The vector sum* **A** + **B** *is the vector* **R**, *from the* **initial point** *O to the* **terminal point** *Q. Here, vector* **R** *is called the* **resultant.** *In general, a resultant is a single vector that is the vector sum of any number of other vectors.*

There are two common methods of adding vectors by means of a diagram. The first is illustrated in Fig. 9-3. To add **B** to **A**, we shift **B** parallel to itself until its tail touches the head of **A**. *The vector sum* **A** + **B** *is the resultant vector* **R**, *which is drawn from the tail of* **A** *to the head of* **B**. In using this method, we can move a vector for addition as long as *we keep its magnitude and direction unchanged.* (Since the magnitude and direction specify a vector, two vectors in different *locations* are considered the same if they have the same magnitude and direction.) When using a diagram to add vectors, it must be drawn with reasonable accuracy.

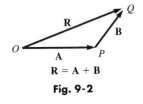

Fig. 9-2

CAUTION ▶

POLYGON METHOD

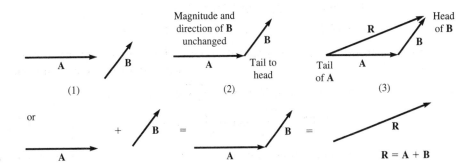

Fig. 9-3

Three or more vectors are added in the same general manner. We place the initial point of the second vector at the terminal point of the first vector, the initial point of the third vector at the terminal point of the second vector, and so on. The resultant is the vector from the initial point of the first vector to the terminal point of the last vector. The order in which they are added does not matter.

■EXAMPLE 2   The addition of vectors **A**, **B**, and **C** is shown in Fig. 9-4.

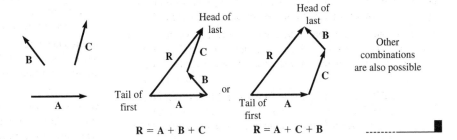

Fig. 9-4

PARALLELOGRAM METHOD Another method that is convenient when two vectors are being added is to *let the two vectors being added be the sides of a parallelogram. The resultant is then the diagonal of the parallelogram.* The initial point of the resultant is the *common initial point of the two vectors being added.* In using this method the vectors are first placed tail to tail. This method is illustrated in the following example.

EXAMPLE 3 The addition of vectors **A** and **B** is shown in Fig. 9-5.

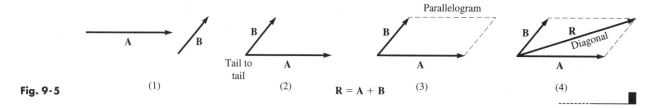

Fig. 9-5 (1)   (2)   R = A + B (3)   (4)

SCALAR MULTIPLE OF VECTOR If vector **C** is in the same direction as vector **A**, and **C** has a magnitude *n* times that of **A**, then **C** = *n***A**, where *the vector n***A** *is called the* **scalar multiple** *of vector* **A**. This means that 2**A** is a vector that is twice as long as **A** but is *in the same direction*. Note carefully that only the magnitudes of **A** and 2**A** are different, and their directions are the same. The addition of scalar multiples of vectors is illustrated in the following example.

EXAMPLE 4 For vectors **A** and **B** in Fig. 9-6, find vector 3**A** + 2**B**.

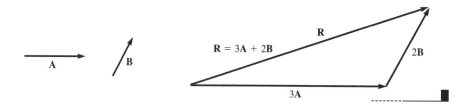

Fig. 9-6

SUBTRACTION OF VECTORS

NOTE ▶ Vector **B** may be subtracted from vector **A** by reversing the direction of **B** and proceeding as in vector addition. Thus, **A** − **B** = **A** + (−**B**), where *the minus sign indicates that vector* −**B** *has the opposite direction of vector* **B**. Vector subtraction is illustrated in the following example.

EXAMPLE 5 For vectors **A** and **B** in Fig. 9-7, find vector 2**A** − **B**.

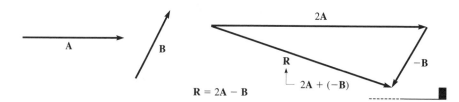

Fig. 9-7   R = 2A − B

Among the most important applications of vectors is that of the forces acting on a structure or on an object. The next example shows the addition of forces by using the parallelogram method.

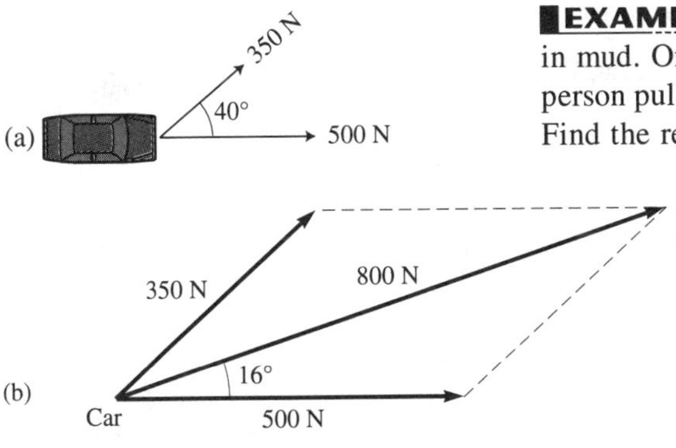

(a)

350 N

40°

500 N

(b)

350 N

800 N

16°

Car   500 N

Fig. 9-8

EXAMPLE 6 Two persons pull horizontally on ropes attached to a car mired in mud. One person pulls with a force of 500 N directly to the right, and the other person pulls with a force of 350 N at 40° from the first force, as shown in Fig. 9-8(a). Find the resultant force on the car.

We make a scale drawing of the forces as shown in Fig. 9-8(b), measuring the magnitudes of the forces with a ruler and the angles with a protractor. (The scale drawing of the forces is made larger and with a different scale than that in Fig. 9-8(a) in order to get better accuracy.) We then complete the parallelogram and draw in the diagonal that represents the resultant force. Finally, we find that the resultant force is about 800 N, and that it acts at an angle of about 16° from the first force. ■

Two other important vector quantities are *velocity* and *displacement*. Velocity as a vector is illustrated in Example 1. *The* **displacement** *of an object is the change in its position. Displacement is given by the distance from a reference point and the angle from a reference direction.* The following example illustrates the difference between *distance* and *displacement*.

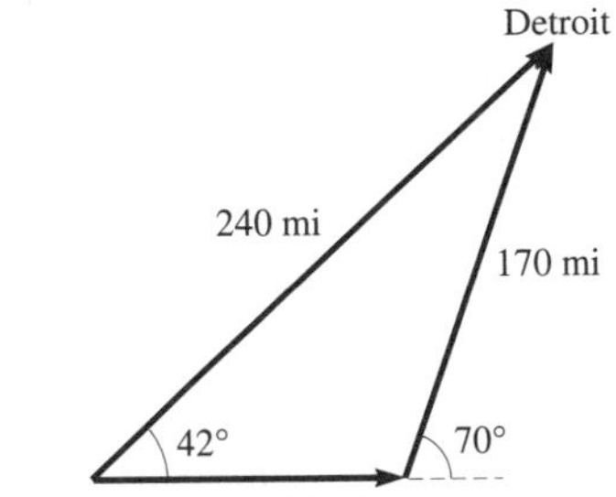

Detroit

240 mi

170 mi

42°   70°

Indianapolis   120 mi

Fig. 9-9

EXAMPLE 7 A jet travels due east from Indianapolis for 120 mi and then turns 70° north of east and travels another 170 mi to Detroit. Find the displacement of Detroit from Indianapolis.

We make a scale drawing in Fig. 9-9 to show the route taken by the jet. Measuring distances with a ruler and angles with a protractor, we find that Detroit is about 240 mi from Indianapolis, at an angle of about 42° north of east. By giving both the magnitude and *the direction*, we have given the displacement.

If the jet returned directly from Detroit to Indianapolis, its *displacement* from Indianapolis would be *zero*, although it traveled a *distance* of 530 mi. ■

EXERCISES *9-1*

Ⓦ *In Exercises 1–4, determine whether a scalar or a vector is described in (a) and (b). Explain your answers.*

1. (a) A person traveled 300 km to the southwest.
   (b) A person traveled 300 km.

2. (a) A small-craft warning reports winds of 25 mi/h.
   (b) A small-craft warning reports winds out of the north at 25 mi/h.

3. (a) An arm of an industrial robot pushes with a 10-lb force downward on a part.
   (b) A part is being pushed with a 10-lb force by an arm of an industrial robot.

4. (a) A ballistics test shows that a bullet hit a wall at a speed of 400 ft/s.
   (b) A ballistics test shows that a bullet hit a wall at a speed of 400 ft/s perpendicular to the wall.

In Exercises 5–8, add the given vectors by drawing the appropriate resultant. Use the parallelogram method in Exercises 7 and 8.

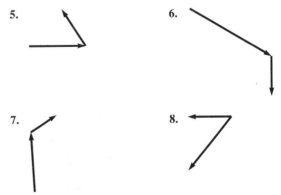

5.

6.

7.

8.

In Exercises 9–28, find the indicated vector sums and differences with the given vectors by means of diagrams. (You might find graph paper to be helpful.)

A   B   C   D   E

9. A + B   10. B + C   11. C + D   12. D + E

13. A + C + E   14. B + D + A   15. A + D + E

16. B + E + C   17. B + 3E   18. A + 2C

19. 3C + E   20. 2C + D   21. A − B

22. C − D   23. E − B   24. D − A

25. 3B − 2D   26. 2A − 3E

27. B + 2C − E   28. A + 4E − 3B

In Exercises 29–36, solve the given problems. Use a ruler and protractor as in Examples 6 and 7.

29. Two forces that act on an airplane wing are called the *lift* and the *drag*. Find the resultant of these forces acting on the airplane wing in Fig. 9-10.

Fig. 9-10

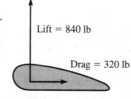

Lift = 840 lb

Drag = 320 lb

30. Two electric charges create an electric field intensity, a vector quantity, at a given point. The field intensity is 30 kN/C to the right and 60 kN/C at an angle of 45° above the horizontal to the right. Find the resultant electric field intensity at this point.

31. A rocket takes off, moving at 2000 ft/s horizontally and 1500 ft/s vertically. Find its resultant velocity.

32. A small plane travels at 120 mi/h in still air. It is headed due south in a wind of 30 mi/h from the northeast. What is the resultant velocity of the plane?

33. A driver takes the wrong road at an intersection and travels 4 mi north, then 6 mi east, and finally 10 mi to the southeast to reach the home of a friend. What is the displacement of the friend's home from the intersection?

34. A ship travels 20 km in a direction of 30° south of east and then turns due south for another 40 km. What is the ship's displacement from its initial position?

35. Three ropes hold a helium-filled balloon in place, but two of the ropes break. The remaining rope holds the balloon with a tension of 510 N at an angle of 80° with the ground due to a wind. The weight (a vertical force) of the balloon and contents is 400 N, and the upward buoyant force is 900 N. The wind creates a horizontal force of 90 N on the balloon. What is the resultant force on the balloon?

36. A crate weighing 100 N is suspended by two ropes. The force in one rope is 70 N and is directed to the left at an angle of 60° above the horizontal. What must be the other force in order that the resultant force (including the weight) on the crate is zero?

Section 6.2

9-2 COMPONENTS OF VECTORS

Adding vectors by means of diagrams is very useful in developing an understanding of vector quantities. However, unless the diagrams are drawn with great care and accuracy, the results we can obtain are quite approximate. Therefore, it is necessary to develop other methods to obtain results of sufficient accuracy.

In this section we show how a given vector can be considered to be the sum of two other vectors, with any required degree of accuracy. In the following section we show how this will allow us to add vectors in order to obtain the sum of vectors with the required accuracy in the result.

Two vectors which, when added together, have a resultant equal to the original vector are called **components** *of the original vector.* In the illustration of the boat in Section 9-1, the velocities of 8 mi/h across the river and 6 mi/h downstream are components of the 10 mi/h vector directed at the angle θ.

RESOLVING A VECTOR INTO COMPONENTS

In practice, there are certain components of a vector that are of particular importance. If a vector is placed with its initial point at the origin of a rectangular coordinate system and its direction is indicated by an angle in standard position, we may find its *x*- and *y*-**components.** *These components are vectors directed along the coordinate axes and that, when added together, have a resultant equal to the given vector.* The initial points of these components are at the origin, and the terminal points are located at the points where perpendicular lines from the terminal point of the given vector cross the axes. *Finding these component vectors is called* **resolving** *the vector into its components.*

EXAMPLE 1   Find the *x*- and *y*-components of the vector **A** shown in Fig. 9-11. The magnitude of **A** is 7.25.

From the figure we see that A_x, the magnitude of the *x*-component $\mathbf{A}_x$, is related to **A** by

$$\frac{A_x}{A} = \cos 62.0°$$

$$A_x = A \cos 62.0°$$

In the same way, A_y, the magnitude of the *y*-component $\mathbf{A}_y$, is related to **A** ($\mathbf{A}_y$ could be placed along the vertical dashed line) by

$$\frac{A_y}{A} = \sin 62.0°$$

$$A_y = A \sin 62.0°$$

From these relations, knowing that $A = 7.25$, we have

$$A_x = 7.25 \cos 62.0° = 3.40$$
$$A_y = 7.25 \sin 62.0° = 6.40$$

This means that the *x*-component is directed along the *x*-axis to the right and has a magnitude of 3.40. Also, the *y*-component is directed along the *y*-axis upward and its magnitude is 6.40. These two component vectors can replace vector **A,** since the effect they have is the same as **A.**

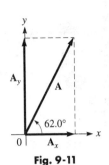

Fig. 9-11

EXAMPLE 2   Resolve a vector 14.4 units long and directed at an angle of 126.0° into its *x*- and *y*-components. See Fig. 9-12.

Placing the initial point of the vector at the origin and putting the angle in standard position, we see that the vector directed along the *x*-axis, $\mathbf{V}_x$, is related to the vector **V** of magnitude V by

$$V_x = V \cos 126.0°$$

(magnitude of vector / standard position angle)

or in terms of the reference angle by

$$V_x = -V \cos 54.0° \longleftarrow \text{reference angle}$$

(directed along negative x-axis)

since $\cos 126.0° = -\cos 54.0°$. We see that the minus sign shows that the *x*-component is directed in the negative direction, that is, to the left.

Since the vector directed along the *y*-axis, $\mathbf{V}_y$, could also be placed along the vertical dashed line, it is related to the vector **V** by

$$V_y = V \sin 126.0° = V \sin 54.0°$$

Thus, the vectors $\mathbf{V}_x$ and $\mathbf{V}_y$ have the magnitudes

$$V_x = 14.4 \cos 126.0° = -8.46 \qquad V_y = 14.4 \sin 126.0° = 11.6$$

Therefore, we have resolved the given vector into two components: one, directed along the negative *x*-axis, of magnitude 8.46, and the other, directed along the positive *y*-axis, of magnitude 11.6.

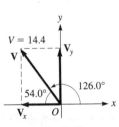

Fig. 9-12

From Examples 1 and 2, we can see that the steps used in finding the *x*- and *y*-components of a vector are as follows:

> **Steps Used in Finding the x- AND y-COMPONENTS OF A VECTOR**
>
> **1.** *Place vector* **A** *such that θ is in standard position.*
> **2.** *Calculate* A_x *and* A_y *from* $A_x = A \cos \theta$ *and* $A_y = A \sin \theta$. *We may use the reference angle if we note the direction of the component.*
> **3.** *Check the components to see if each is in the correct direction and has a magnitude that is proper for the reference angle.*

■EXAMPLE 3   Resolve vector **A,** of magnitude 375.4 and direction $\theta = 205.32°$, into its *x*- and *y*-components. See Fig. 9-13.

By placing **A** such that θ is in standard position, we see that

$$A_x = A \cos 205.32° = 375.4 \cos 205.32° = -339.3$$

and

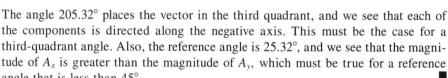

$$A_y = A \sin 205.32° = 375.4 \sin 205.32° = -160.5$$

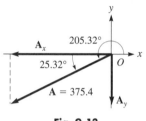

Fig. 9-13

The angle 205.32° places the vector in the third quadrant, and we see that each of the components is directed along the negative axis. This must be the case for a third-quadrant angle. Also, the reference angle is 25.32°, and we see that the magnitude of A_x is greater than the magnitude of A_y, which must be true for a reference angle that is less than 45°.   ■

■EXAMPLE 4   The tension **T** in a cable supporting the sign shown in Fig. 9-14(a) is 85.0 lb. If the cable makes an angle of 53.5° with the horizontal, find the horizontal and vertical components of the tension.

The tension in the cable is the force that the cable exerts on the sign. Showing the tension in Fig. 9-14(b), we see that

$$T_y = T \sin 53.5° = 85.0 \sin 53.5°$$
$$= 68.3 \text{ lb}$$
$$T_x = T \cos 53.5° = 85.0 \cos 53.5°$$
$$= 50.6 \text{ lb}$$

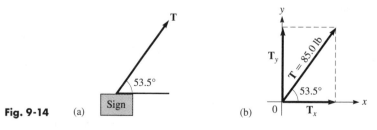

Fig. 9-14   (a)   (b)

The angle 53.5° is the reference angle, and $T_y > T_x$. This must be true for a reference angle greater than 45°.   ■

EXERCISES *9-2*

In Exercises 1–4, find the horizontal and vertical components of the vectors shown in the given figures. In each the magnitude of the vector is 750.

1.
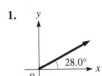

2.

3.

4.

In Exercises 5–16, find the x- and y- components of the given vectors by use of the trigonometric functions.

5. Magnitude 8.60, $\theta = 68.0°$
6. Magnitude 9750, $\theta = 243.0°$
7. Magnitude 76.8, $\theta = 145.0°$
8. Magnitude 0.0998, $\theta = 296.0°$
9. Magnitude 9.04, $\theta = 283.3°$
10. Magnitude 16,400, $\theta = 156.5°$
11. Magnitude 2.65, $\theta = 197.3°$
12. Magnitude 67.8, $\theta = 22.5°$
13. Magnitude 0.8734, $\theta = 157.83°$
14. Magnitude 509.4, $\theta = 221.87°$
15. Magnitude 89,760, $\theta = 7.84°$
16. Magnitude 1.806, $\theta = 301.83°$

In Exercises 17–24, find the required horizontal and vertical components of the given vectors.

17. A nuclear submarine approaches the surface of the ocean at 25.0 km/h and at an angle of 17.3° with the surface. What are the components of its velocity? See Fig. 9-15.

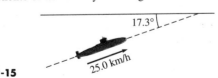

Fig. 9-15

18. Water is flowing downhill at 18.0 ft/s through a pipe that is at an angle of 66.4° with the horizontal. What are the components of its velocity?

19. The tension in a rope attached to a boat is 55.0 lb. The rope is attached to the boat 12.0 ft below the level at which it is being drawn in. At the point where there are 36.0 ft of rope out, what force tends to bring the boat toward the wharf, and what force tends to raise the boat? See Fig. 9-16.

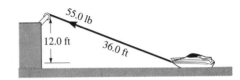

Fig. 9-16

20. A car is being unloaded from a ship. It is supported by a cable from a crane and guided into position by a horizontal rope. If the tension in the cable is 2790 lb and the cable makes an angle of 3.5° with the vertical, what are the weight W of the car and the tension T in the rope? (The weight of the cable is negligible to that of the car.) See Fig. 9-17.

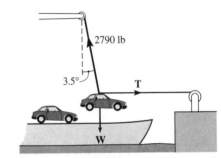

Fig. 9-17

21. A jet is 145 km at a position 37.5° north of east of Tahiti. What are the components of the jet's displacement from Tahiti?

22. The end of a robot arm is 3.50 ft on a line 78.6° above the horizontal from the point where it does a weld. What are the components of the displacement from the end of the robot arm to the welding point?

23. At one point the *Pioneer* space probe was entering the gravitational field of Jupiter at an angle of 2.55° below the horizontal with a velocity of 18,550 mi/h. What were the components of its velocity?

24. Two upward forces are acting on a bolt. One force of 60.5 lb acts at an angle of 82.4° above the horizontal, and the other force of 37.2 lb acts at an angle of 50.5° below the first force. What is the total upward force on the bolt? See Fig. 9-18.

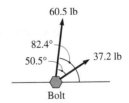

Fig. 9-18

Section 6.3 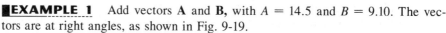 *9-3* VECTOR ADDITION BY COMPONENTS

Now that we have developed the meaning of the components of a vector, we are able to add vectors to any degree of required accuracy. To do this we use the components of the vector, the Pythagorean theorem, and the tangent of the standard position angle of the resultant. In the following example, two vectors at right angles are added.

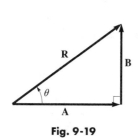

Fig. 9-19

■**EXAMPLE 1**   Add vectors **A** and **B,** with $A = 14.5$ and $B = 9.10$. The vectors are at right angles, as shown in Fig. 9-19.

We can find the magnitude R of the resultant vector **R** by use of the Pythagorean theorem. This leads to

$$R = \sqrt{A^2 + B^2} = \sqrt{(14.5)^2 + (9.10)^2}$$
$$= 17.1$$

We shall now determine the direction of the resultant vector **R** by specifying its direction as the angle θ in Fig. 9-19, that is, the angle that **R** makes with vector **A.** Therefore, we have

$$\tan \theta = \frac{B}{A} = \frac{9.10}{14.5}$$
$$\theta = 32.1°$$

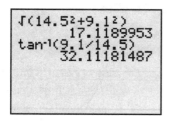

Fig. 9-20

Calculation of the values of R and θ are shown in the calculator window in Fig. 9-20. As we showed in Chapter 4, it is not necessary to record or store the value of the quotient $9.10/14.5$, as we can calculate the value of θ directly on the calculator as $\tan^{-1}(9.10/14.5)$.

Therefore, we see that **R** is a vector of magnitude $R = 17.1$ and in a direction $32.1°$ from vector **A.**

We note that Fig. 9-19 shows vectors **A** and **B** as horizontal and vertical, respectively. This means they are the horizontal and vertical components of the resultant vector **R.** However, we would find the resultant of any two vectors *at right angles* in the same way. --------■

If vectors are to be added and they are not at right angles, we first place each vector with its tail at the origin. Next, we resolve each vector into its *x*- and *y*-components. We then add all the *x*-components and add all the *y*-components to determine the *x*- and *y*-components of the resultant. Then, by using the Pythagorean theorem we find the magnitude of the resultant, and by use of the tangent we find the angle that gives us the direction of the resultant.

CAUTION▶   *Remember, a vector is not completely specified unless both its magnitude and its direction are specified.* A common error is to determine the magnitude, but not to find the angle θ that is used to define its direction.

The following examples illustrate the addition of vectors by first finding the components of the given vectors.

EXAMPLE 2 Find the resultant of two vectors **A** and **B** such that $A = 1200$, $\theta_A = 270.0°$, $B = 1750$, and $\theta_B = 115.0°$.

We first place the vectors on a coordinate system with the tail of each at the origin as shown in Fig. 9-21(a). We then resolve each vector into its x- and y-components, as shown in Fig. 9-21(b) and as calculated below. (Note that **A** is vertical and has no horizontal component.) Next, the components are combined, as in Fig. 9-21(c) and as calculated. Finally, the magnitude of the resultant and the angle θ (to determine the direction), as shown in Fig. 9-21(d), are calculated.

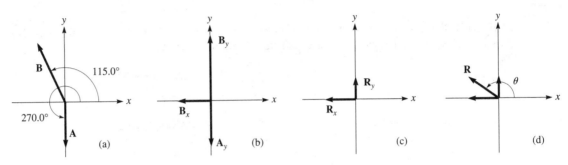

Fig. 9-21

$$A_x = A \cos 270.0° = 1200 \cos 270.0° = 0$$
$$B_x = B \cos 115.0° = 1750 \cos 115.0° = -739.6$$
$$A_y = A \sin 270.0° = 1200 \sin 270.0° = -1200$$
$$B_y = B \sin 115.0° = 1750 \sin 115.0° = 1586$$

— Fig. 9-21(b)

$$R_x = A_x + B_x = 0 - 739.6 = -739.6$$
$$R_y = A_y + B_y = -1200 + 1586 = 386$$

— Fig. 9-21(c)

$$R = \sqrt{R_x^2 + R_y^2} = \sqrt{(-739.6)^2 + 386^2} = 834$$
$$\tan \theta = \frac{R_y}{R_x} = \frac{386}{-739.6} \qquad \theta = 152.4° \longleftarrow 180° - 27.6°$$

— Fig. 9-21(d)

Thus, the resultant has a magnitude of 834 and is directed at a standard-position angle of 152.4°. In finding θ from a calculator,

CAUTION ▶

*the calculator display shows an angle of $-27.6°$. However, we know θ is a second-quadrant angle, since **R**$_x$ is negative and **R**$_y$ is positive.*

Therefore, we must use 27.6° as a reference angle. For this reason, it is usually advisable to *find the reference angle first* by disregarding the signs of R_x and R_y when finding θ. Thus,

$$\tan \theta_{\text{ref}} = \left| \frac{R_y}{R_x} \right| = \frac{386}{739.6} \qquad \theta_{\text{ref}} = 27.6°$$

The values shown in this example have been rounded off. In using the calculator, R_x and R_y are each calculated in one step and stored for the calculation of R and θ, and we will show these steps in the next example. However, here we wished to show the individual steps and results to more clearly show the method.

When we found R_y we saw that we were able to do a vector addition as a scalar addition. Also, since the magnitude of the components and the resultant are much smaller than either of the original vectors, this vector addition would have been difficult to do accurately by means of a diagram.

EXAMPLE 3   Find the resultant **R** of the two vectors shown in Fig. 9-22(a), **A** of magnitude 8.075 and standard position angle of 57.26° and **B** of magnitude 5.437 and standard-position angle of 322.15°.

In Fig. 9-22(b) we show the components of vectors **A** and **B,** and then in Fig. 9-22(c) we show the resultant and its components.

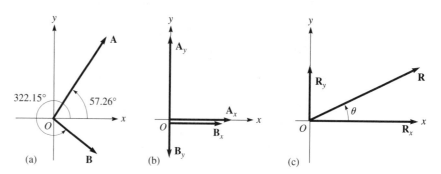

Fig. 9-22   (a)   (b)   (c)

Vector	Magnitude	Angle	x-component	y-component
A	8.075	57.26°	$A_x = 8.075 \cos 57.26° = 4.367$	$A_y = 8.075 \sin 57.26° = 6.792$
B	5.437	322.15°	$B_x = 5.437 \cos 322.15° = 4.293$	$B_y = 5.437 \sin 322.15° = -3.336$
R			$R_x = A_x + B_x = 8.660$	$R_y = A_y + B_y = 3.456$

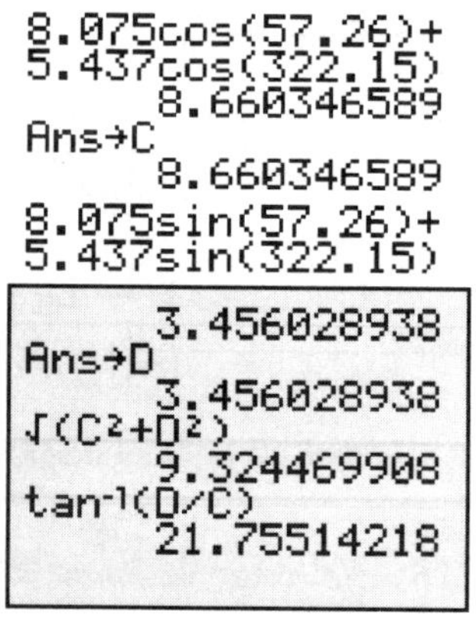

```
8.075cos(57.26)+
5.437cos(322.15)
        8.660346589
Ans→C
        8.660346589
8.075sin(57.26)+
5.437sin(322.15)
┌─────────────────┐
│       3.456028938│
│Ans→D             │
│       3.456028938│
│√(C²+D²)          │
│       9.324469908│
│tan⁻¹(D/C)        │
│       21.75514218│
└─────────────────┘
```

Fig. 9-23

$$R = \sqrt{R_x^2 + R_y^2} = \sqrt{(8.660)^2 + (3.456)^2} = 9.324$$

$$\theta = \tan^{-1}\frac{R_y}{R_x} = \tan^{-1}\left(\frac{3.456}{8.660}\right) = 21.76° \quad \longleftarrow \quad \text{don't forget the direction}$$

The resultant vector is 9.324 units long and is directed at a standard-position angle of 21.76°, as shown in Fig. 9-22(c). We know that the resultant is in the first quadrant since both R_x and R_y are positive.

In the table above, we have shown rounded-off values for each result. However, when using a calculator it is necessary only to calculate R_x and R_y in one step each, store these values, and use them to calculate R and θ. This is shown in the calculator window in Fig. 9-23. The lines shown above the window are those that are displaced in proceeding with the solution.

In the calculator solution C = R_x and D = R_y. In finding this solution we see that both R_x and R_y are positive, which means that θ is a first-quadrant angle. ■

Some general formulas can be derived from the previous examples. For a given vector **A,** directed at an angle θ, of magnitude A, and with components A_x and A_y, we have the following relations:

$$A_x = A \cos \theta \quad A_y = A \sin \theta \tag{9-1}$$

$$A = \sqrt{A_x^2 + A_y^2} \tag{9-2}$$

$$\theta_{\text{ref}} = \tan^{-1}\frac{|A_y|}{|A_x|} \tag{9-3}$$

The value of θ is found by using the reference angle from Eq. (9-3) and the quadrant in which the resultant lies.

From the previous examples we see that the following procedure is used for adding vectors.

> **Procedure for Adding Vectors By Components**
> 1. *Add the x-components of the given vectors to obtain R_x.*
> 2. *Add the y-components of the given vectors to obtain R_y.*
> 3. *Find the magnitude of the resultant* **R**. Use Eq. (9-2) in the form
> $$R = \sqrt{R_x^2 + R_y^2}$$
> 4. *Find the standard-position angle θ for the resultant* **R**. First find the reference angle θ_{ref} for the resultant **R** by using Eq. (9-3) in the form
> $$\theta_{ref} = \tan^{-1} \frac{|R_y|}{|R_x|}$$

Some calculators have a specific feature for adding vectors.

See Appendix C for a graphing calculator program ADDVCTR. It can be used to add vectors.

EXAMPLE 4 Find the resultant of the three given vectors in Fig. 9-24. The magnitudes of these vectors are $T = 422$, $U = 405$, and $V = 210$.

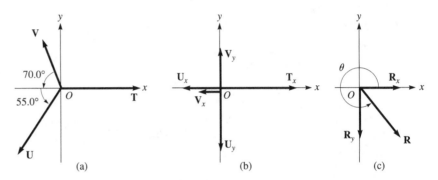

Fig. 9-24

We could change the given angles to standard-position angles. However, we will use the given angles, *being careful to give the proper sign to each component*. In the following table we show the x- and y-components of the given vectors, and the sums of these components give us the components of **R**.

```
422cos(0)-405cos
(55)-210cos(70)
       117.8773132
Ans→A
       117.8773132
422sin(0)-405sin
(55)+210sin(70)

   -134.4211276
Ans→B
   -134.4211276
√(A²+B²)
       178.7850679
tan⁻¹(abs(B)/A)
       48.75165091
```

Fig. 9-25

Vector	Magnitude	Ref. Angle	x-component	y-component
T	422	0°	$422 \cos 0° =$ 422.0	$422 \sin 0° =$ 0.0
U	405	55.0°	$-405 \cos 55.0° = -232.3$	$-405 \sin 55.0° = -331.8$
V	210	70.0°	$-210 \cos 70.0° = -71.8$	$+210 \sin 70.0° =$ 197.3
R			117.9	Note the variation -134.5 due to rounding off

In the calculator solution shown in Fig. 9-25, $A = R_x$, $B = R_y$, and abs means absolute value. From this display we have

$$R = 179 \quad \text{and} \quad \theta_{ref} = 48.8°$$

Since R_x is positive and R_y is negative, we know that θ **is a fourth-quadrant angle.** Therefore, to find θ we subtracted θ_{ref} from 360°. This means

$$\theta = 180° - 48.8° = 311.2°$$

EXERCISES *9-3*

*In Exercises 1–4, vectors **A** and **B** are at right angles. Find the magnitude and direction (the angle from vector **A**) of the resultant.*

1. $A = 14.7$
$B = 19.2$

2. $A = 592$
$B = 195$

3. $A = 3.086$
$B = 7.143$

4. $A = 1734$
$B = 3297$

In Exercises 5–12, with the given sets of components, find R and θ.

5. $R_x = 5.18$, $R_y = 8.56$

6. $R_x = 89.6$, $R_y = -52.0$

7. $R_x = -0.982$, $R_y = 2.56$

8. $R_x = -729$, $R_y = -209$

9. $R_x = -646$, $R_y = 2030$

10. $R_x = -31.2$, $R_y = -41.2$

11. $R_x = 0.6941$, $R_y = -1.246$

12. $R_x = 7.627$, $R_y = -6.353$

In Exercises 13–28, add the given vectors by using the trigonometric functions and the Pythagorean theorem.

13. $A = 18.0$, $\theta_A = 0.0°$
$B = 12.0$, $\theta_B = 27.0°$

14. $A = 154$, $\theta_A = 90.0°$
$B = 128$, $\theta_B = 43.0°$

15. $C = 56.0$, $\theta_C = 76.0°$
$D = 12.0$, $\theta_D = 160.0°$

16. $A = 6.89$, $\theta_A = 123.0°$
$B = 29.0$, $\theta_B = 260.0°$

17. $A = 9.821$, $\theta_A = 34.27°$
$B = 17.45$, $\theta_B = 752.50°$

18. $E = 1.653$, $\theta_E = 36.37°$
$F = 0.9807$, $\theta_F = 253.06°$

19. $A = 12.653$, $\theta_A = 98.472°$
$B = 15.147$, $\theta_B = 332.092°$

20. $L = 121.36$, $\theta_L = 292.362°$
$M = 112.98$, $\theta_M = 197.892°$

21. $A = 21.9$, $\theta_A = 236.2°$
$B = 96.7$, $\theta_B = 11.5°$
$C = 62.9$, $\theta_C = 143.4°$

22. $A = 6300$, $\theta_A = 189.6°$
$B = 1760$, $\theta_B = 320.1°$
$C = 3240$, $\theta_C = 75.4°$

23. $U = 0.364$, $\theta_U = 175.7°$
$V = 0.596$, $\theta_V = 319.5°$
$W = 0.129$, $\theta_W = 100.6°$

24. $A = 6.4$, $\theta_A = 126°$
$B = 5.9$, $\theta_B = 238°$
$C = 3.2$, $\theta_C = 72°$

25. The vectors shown in Fig. 9-26

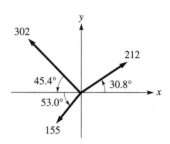

Fig. 9-26

26. The vectors shown in Fig. 9-27

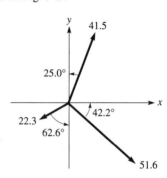

Fig. 9-27

27. Three forces of 3200 lb, 1300 lb, and 2100 lb act on a bolt as shown in Fig. 9-28. Find the resultant force.

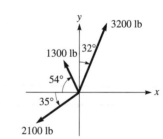

Fig. 9-28

28. A naval crusier on maneuvers travels 54.0 km at 18.7° west of north, then turns and travels 64.5 km at 15.6° south of east, and finally turns to travel 72.4 km at 38.1° east of south. Find its displacement from its original position. See Fig. 9-29.

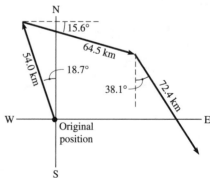

Fig. 9-29

Section 6.4

9-4 APPLICATIONS OF VECTORS

In Section 9-1 we introduced the important vector quantities of force, velocity, and displacement, and we found vector sums by use of diagrams. Now we can use the method of Section 9-3 to find sums of these kinds of vectors and others and to use them in various types of applications.

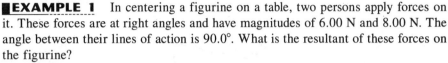

(Top view)

8.00 N

θ

Figurine   6.00 N

Fig. 9-30

EXAMPLE 1   In centering a figurine on a table, two persons apply forces on it. These forces are at right angles and have magnitudes of 6.00 N and 8.00 N. The angle between their lines of action is 90.0°. What is the resultant of these forces on the figurine?

By means of an appropriate diagram (Fig. 9-30), we may better visualize the actual situation. We note that a good choice of axes (unless specified, it is often convenient to choose the *x*- and *y*-axes to fit the problem) is to have the *x*-axis in the direction of the 6.00-N force and the *y*-axis in the direction of the 8.00-N force. (This is possible since the angle between them is 90°.) With this choice we note that the two given forces will be the *x*- and *y*-components of the resultant. Therefore, we arrive at the following results:

$$F_x = 6.00 \text{ N}, \quad F_y = 8.00 \text{ N}$$
$$F = \sqrt{(6.00)^2 + (8.00)^2} = 10.0 \text{ N}$$
$$\theta = \tan^{-1}\frac{F_y}{F_x} = \tan^{-1}\frac{8.00}{6.00}$$
$$= 53.1°$$

We would state that the resultant has a magnitude of 10.0 N and acts at an angle of 53.1° from the 6.00-N force. ------------∎

> The metric unit of force, the newton (N), is named for the great English mathematician and physicist Sir Isaac Newton (1642–1727). His name will appear on other pages of this text, as some of his many accomplishments are noted.

SOLVING A WORD PROBLEM

EXAMPLE 2   A ship sails 32.50 mi due east and then turns 41.25° north of east. After sailing another 16.18 mi, where is it with reference to the starting point?

In this problem we are to find the resultant displacement of the ship from the two given displacements. The problem is diagramed in Fig. 9-31, where the first displacement is labeled vector **A** and the second as vector **B.**

Since east corresponds to the positive *x*-direction, we see that the *x*-component of the resultant is $\mathbf{A} + \mathbf{B}_x$ and the *y*-component of the resultant is $\mathbf{B}_y$. Therefore, we have the following results:

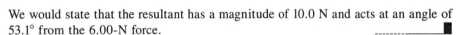

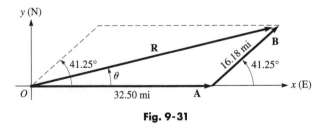

y (N)

41.25°

R

B

16.18 mi

41.25°

θ

O   32.50 mi   A   → x (E)

Fig. 9-31

$$R_x = A + B_x = 32.50 + 16.18 \cos 41.25°$$
$$= 32.50 + 12.16$$
$$= 44.66 \text{ mi}$$
$$R_y = 16.18 \sin 41.25° = 10.67 \text{ mi}$$
$$R = \sqrt{(44.66)^2 + (10.67)^2} = 45.92 \text{ mi}$$
$$\theta = \tan^{-1}\frac{10.67}{44.66} = 13.44°$$

Therefore, the ship is 45.92 mi from the starting point, in a direction 13.44° north of east. ------------∎

SOLVING A WORD PROBLEM

An aircraft's *heading* is the direction in which it is pointed. Its *air speed* is the speed at which it travels through the air surrounding it. Due to the wind, the heading and air speed, and its actual direction and speed relative to the ground, will differ.

■**EXAMPLE 3**   An airplane headed due east is in a wind blowing from the southeast. What is the resultant velocity of the plane with respect to the surface of the earth if the velocity of the plane with respect to the air is 600 km/h and that of the wind is 100 km/h? See Fig. 9-32.

Let $\mathbf{v}_{px}$ be the velocity of the plane in the *x*-direction (east), $\mathbf{v}_{py}$ the velocity of the plane in the *y*-direction, $\mathbf{v}_{wx}$ the *x*-component of the velocity of the wind, $\mathbf{v}_{wy}$ the *y*-component of the velocity of the wind, and $\mathbf{v}_{pa}$ the velocity of the plane with respect to the air. Therefore,

$$v_{px} = v_{pa} - v_{wx} = 600 - 100(\cos 45.0°) = 529 \text{ km/h}$$

$$v_{py} = v_{wy} = 100(\sin 45.0°) = 70.7 \text{ km/h}$$

$$v = \sqrt{(529)^2 + (70.7)^2} = 534 \text{ km/h}$$

$$\tan \theta = \tan^{-1}\frac{v_{py}}{v_{px}} = \tan^{-1}\frac{70.7}{529} = 7.6°$$

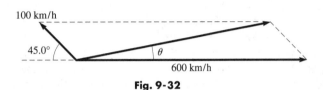

100 km/h

45.0° θ

600 km/h

Fig. 9-32

We have determined that the plane is traveling 534 km/h and is flying in a direction 7.6° north of east. From this we observe that a plane does not necessarily head in the direction of its destination.

EQUILIBRIUM OF FORCES

NOTE▶

As we have seen, an important vector quantity is the force acting on an object. One of the most important applications of vectors involves forces that are in **equilibrium.** *For an object to be in equilibrium, the net force acting on it in any direction must be zero.* This condition is satisfied if the sum of the *x*-components of the force is zero and the sum of the *y*-components of the force is also zero. The following two examples illustrate forces in equilibrium.

SOLVING A WORD PROBLEM

■**EXAMPLE 4**   A cement block is resting on a straight inclined plank that makes an angle of 30.0° with the horizontal. If the block weighs 80.0 lb, what is the force of friction between the block and the plank?

The weight of the cement block is the force exerted on the block due to gravity. Therefore, the weight is directed vertically downward. The frictional force tends to oppose the motion of the block and is directed upward along the plank. The frictional force must be sufficient to counterbalance that component of the weight of the block that is directed down the plank for the block to be at rest (not moving). The plank itself "holds up" that component of the weight that is perpendicular to the plank. A convenient set of coordinates (see Fig. 9-33) is one with the origin at the center of the block, and with the *x*-axis directed up the plank and the *y*-axis perpendicular to the plank. The magnitude of the frictional force $\mathbf{F}_f$ is given by

$$F_f = 80.0 \cos 60.0° = 40.0 \text{ lb}$$ component of weight down plank equals frictional force

We have used the 60.0° angle since it is the reference angle. We could have expressed the frictional force as $F_f = 80.0 \sin 30.0°$.

Here, we have assumed that the block is small enough that we may calculate all forces as though they act at the center of the block (although we know that the frictional force acts at the surface between the block and the plank).

y   *x*

$\mathbf{F}_f$

80.0 cos 60.0°   60.0°

30.0°

30.0°   80.0 lb

Fig. 9-33

Newton's *third law of motion* states that when an object exerts a force on another object, the second object exerts on the first object a force of the same magnitude but in the opposite direction. The force exerted by the plank on the block is an illustration of this law. (Sir Isaac Newton, again. See page 257).

SOLVING A WORD PROBLEM

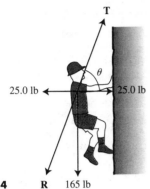

Fig. 9-34

■EXAMPLE 5 A 165-lb mountain climber suspended by a rope pushes on the side of a cliff with a horizontal force of 25.0 lb. What is the tension **T** in the rope if the climber is in equilibrium? See Fig. 9-34.

For the climber to be in equilibrium, the tension in the rope must be equal and opposite to the resultant of the climber's weight and the force against the cliff. This means that the magnitude of the x-component of the tension is 25.0 lb (the reaction force of the cliff—another illustration of Newton's third law—see Example 4) and the magnitude of the y-component is 165 lb (see Fig. 9-34). Therefore,

$$T = \sqrt{25.0^2 + 165^2} = 167 \text{ lb}$$

$$\theta = \tan^{-1}\frac{165}{25.0} = 81.4°$$

SOLVING A WORD PROBLEM

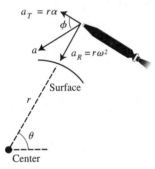

Fig. 9-35

■EXAMPLE 6 For a spacecraft moving in a circular path around the earth, the tangential component $\mathbf{a}_T$ and the centripetal component $\mathbf{a}_R$ of its acceleration are given by the expressions shown in Fig. 9-35. The radius of the circle through which it is moving (from the center of the earth to the spacecraft) is r, its angular velocity is ω, and its angular acceleration is α (the rate at which ω is changing).

While going into orbit, at one point a spacecraft is moving in a circular path 230 km above the surface of the earth. At this point $r = 6.60 \times 10^6$ m, $\omega = 1.10 \times 10^{-3}$ rad/s, and $\alpha = 0.420 \times 10^{-6}$ rad/s². Calculate the magnitude of the resultant acceleration and the angle it makes with the tangential component.

$$a_R = r\omega^2 = 6.60 \times 10^6(1.10 \times 10^{-3})^2 = 7.99 \text{ m/s}^2$$
$$a_T = r\alpha = 6.60 \times 10^6(0.420 \times 10^{-6}) = 2.77 \text{ m/s}^2$$

Since a tangent line to a circle is perpendicular to the radius at the point of tangency, $\mathbf{a}_T$ is perpendicular to $\mathbf{a}_R$. Thus,

$$a = \sqrt{a_T^2 + a_R^2} = 8.45 \text{ m/s}^2$$
$$\phi = \tan^{-1}\frac{a_R}{a_T} = \tan^{-1}\frac{7.99}{2.77} = 70.9°$$

The value of $a = 8.45$ m/s² is found directly on a calculator, without first rounding off the values of a_R and a_T. If we use the rounded-off values of 7.99 m/s² and 2.77 m/s² we would get 8.46 m/s².

EXERCISES *9-4*

In Exercises 1–24, solve the given problems.

1. Two hockey players strike the puck at the same time, hitting it with horizontal forces of 5.75 lb and 3.25 lb that are perpendicular to each other. Find the resultant of these forces.

2. To straighten a small tree, two horizontal ropes perpendicular to each other are attached to the tree. If the tensions in the ropes are 18.5 lb and 23.0 lb, what is the resultant force on the tree?

3. In lifting a heavy piece of equipment from the mud, a cable from a crane exerts a vertical force of 6500 N, and a cable from a truck exerts a force of 8300 N at 10.0° above the horizontal. Find the resultant of these forces.

4. At a point in the plane, two electric charges create an electric field (a vector quantity) of 25.9 kN/C at 10.8° above the horizontal to the right and 12.6 kN/C at 83.4° below the horizontal to the right. Find the resultant electric field.

5. A motorboat leaves a dock and travels 1580 ft due west, then turns 35.0° to the south and travels another 1640 ft to a second dock. What is the displacement of the second dock from the first dock?

6. Toronto is 650 km at 19.0° north of east from Chicago. Cincinnati is 390 km at 48.0° south of east from Chicago. What is the displacement of Cincinnati from Toronto?

7. From a fixed point, a surveyor locates a pole at 215.6 ft due east and a building corner at 358.2 ft at 37.72° north of east. What is the displacement of the building from the pole?

8. A rocket is launched with a vertical component of velocity of 2840 km/h and a horizontal component of velocity of 1520 km/h. What is its resultant velocity?

9. A storm front is moving east at 22.0 km/h and south at 12.5 km/h. Find the resultant velocity of the front.

10. In an accident, a truck with momentum (a vector quantity) of 22,100 kg·m/s strikes a car with momentum of 17,800 kg·m/s from the rear. The angle between their directions of motion is 25.0°. What is the resultant momentum?

11. In an automobile safety test, a shoulder and seat belt exerts a force of 95.0 lb directly backward and a force of 83.0 lb backward at an angle of 20.0° below the horizontal on a dummy. If the belt holds the dummy from moving farther forward, what force did the dummy exert on the belt? See Fig. 9-36.

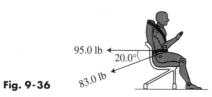

Fig. 9-36

95.0 lb
20.0°
83.0 lb

12. Two perpendicular forces act on a ring at the end of a chain that passes over a pulley and holds an automobile engine. If the forces have the values shown in Fig. 9-37, what is the weight of the engine?

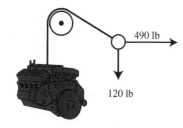

490 lb

120 lb

Fig. 9-37

13. A plane flies at 550 km/h into a head wind of 60 km/h at 78° with the direction of the plane. Find the resultant velocity of the plane with respect to the ground. See Fig. 9-38.

Wind
60 km/h

78°

550 km/h

Fig. 9-38

14. A ship's navigator determines that the ship is moving through the water at 17.5 mi/h with a heading of 26.3° north of east, but that the ship is actually moving at 19.3 mi/h in a direction of 33.7° north of east. What is the velocity of the current?

15. A space shuttle is moving in orbit at 18,250 mi/h. A satellite is launched to the rear at 120 mi/h at an angle of 5.20° from the direction of the shuttle. Find the velocity of the shuttle.

16. A block of ice slides down a (frictionless) ramp with an acceleration of 5.3 m/s². If the ramp makes an angle of 32.7° with the horizontal, find g, the acceleration due to gravity. See Fig. 9-39.

5.3 m/s²
g
32.7°

Fig. 9-39

17. While starting up, a circular saw blade 8.20 in. in diameter is rotating at 212 rad/min and has an angular acceleration of 318 rad/min². What is the acceleration of the tip of one of the teeth? (See Example 6.)

18. A boat travels across a river, reaching the opposite bank at a point directly opposite that from which it left. If the boat travels 6.00 km/h in still water and the current of the river flows at 3.00 km/h, what was the velocity of the boat in the water?

19. In searching for a boat lost at sea, a Coast Guard cutter leaves a port and travels 75.0 mi due east. It then turns north of east and travels another 75.0 mi, and finally turns another 65.0° toward the west and travels another 75.0 mi. What is its displacement from the port?

20. A car is held stationary on a ramp by two forces. One is the force of 480 lb by the brakes, which hold it from rolling down the ramp. The other is a reaction force by the ramp of 2250 lb, perpendicular to the ramp. This force keeps the car from going through the ramp. See Fig. 9-40. What is the weight of the car, and at what angle with the horizontal is the ramp inclined?

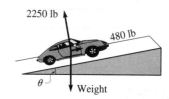

2250 lb
480 lb
θ
Weight

Fig. 9-40

21. A plane is moving at 75.0 m/s, and a package with weather instruments is ejected horizontally from the plane at 15.0 m/s, perpendicular to the direction of the plane. If the vertical velocity v_v (in m/s), as a function of time t (in s) of fall, is given by $v_v = 9.80t$, what is the velocity of the package after 2.00 s (before its parachute opens)?

22. A flat rectangular barge, 48.0 m long and 20.0 m wide, is headed directly across a stream at 4.5 km/h. The stream flows at 3.8 km/h. What is the velocity, relative to the riverbed, of a person walking diagonally across the barge at 5.0 km/h while facing the opposite upstream bank?

23. In Fig. 9-41, a long, straight conductor perpendicular to the plane of the paper carries an electric current i. A bar magnet having poles of strength m lies in the plane of the paper. The vectors $\mathbf{H}_i$, $\mathbf{H}_N$, and $\mathbf{H}_S$ represent the components of the magnetic intensity $\mathbf{H}$ due to the current and to the N and S poles of the magnet, respectively. The magnitudes of the components of $\mathbf{H}$ are given by

$$H_i = \frac{1}{2\pi}\frac{i}{a} \qquad H_N = \frac{1}{4\pi}\frac{m}{b^2} \qquad H_S = \frac{1}{4\pi}\frac{m}{c^2}$$

Given that $a = 0.300$ m, $b = 0.400$ m, $c = 0.300$ m, the length of the magnet is 0.500 m, $i = 4.00$ A, and $m = 2.00$ A·m, calculate the resultant magnetic intensity $\mathbf{H}$. The component $\mathbf{H}_i$ is parallel to the magnet.

24. Solve the problem of Exercise 23 if $\mathbf{H}_i$ is directed away from the magnet, making an angle of 10.0° with the direction of the magnet.

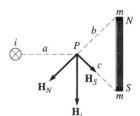

Fig. 9-41

Section 6.5

9-5 OBLIQUE TRIANGLES, THE LAW OF SINES

To this point we have limited our study of triangle solution to right triangles. However, *many triangles that require solution do not contain a right angle. Such triangles are called* **oblique triangles.** We now discuss solutions of oblique triangles.

In Section 4-4 we stated that we need to know three parts, at least one of them a side, to solve a triangle. There are four possible such combinations of parts, and these combinations are as follows:

Case 1. Two angles and one side
Case 2. Two sides and the angle opposite one of them
Case 3. Two sides and the included angle
Case 4. Three sides

There are several ways in which oblique triangles may be solved, but we shall restrict our attention to the two most useful methods, the **law of sines** and the **law of cosines.** In this section we shall discuss the law of sines and show that it may be used to solve Case 1 and Case 2.

Let ABC be an oblique triangle with sides a, b, and c opposite angles A, B, and C, respectively. By drawing a perpendicular h from B to side b, or its extension, we see from Fig. 9-42(a) that

$$h = c \sin A \quad \text{or} \quad h = a \sin C \tag{9-4}$$

and from Fig. 9-42(b)

$$h = c \sin A \quad \text{or} \quad h = a \sin (180° - C) = a \sin C \tag{9-5}$$

We see that the results are precisely the same in Eqs. (9-4) and (9-5). Setting the results for h equal to each other, we have

$$c \sin A = a \sin C \quad \text{or} \quad \frac{a}{\sin A} = \frac{c}{\sin C} \tag{9-6}$$

By dropping a perpendicular from A to a, we also derive the result

$$c \sin B = b \sin C \quad \text{or} \quad \frac{b}{\sin B} = \frac{c}{\sin C} \tag{9-7}$$

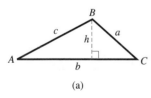

(a)

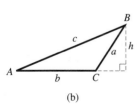

(b)

Fig. 9-42

Combining Eqs. (9-6) and (9-7), *for any triangle with sides a, b, and c, opposite angles A, B, and C, respectively,* such as the one shown in Fig. 9-43, *we have the* **law of sines:**

LAW OF SINES

$$\frac{a}{\sin A} = \frac{b}{\sin B} = \frac{c}{\sin C}$$

(9-8)

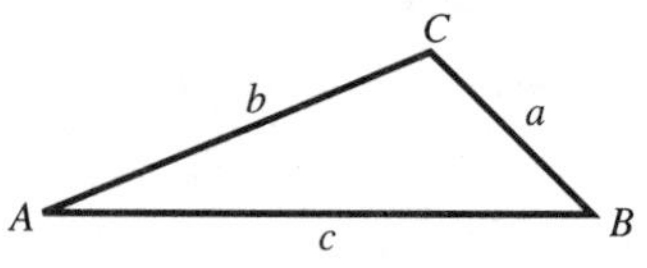

Another form of the law of sines can be obtained by equating the reciprocals of each of the fractions in Eq. (9-8). The law of sines is a statement of proportionality between the sides of a triangle and the sines of the angles opposite them. We should note that there are actually three equations combined in Eq. (9-8). Of these, we use the one with three known parts of the triangle and we find the fourth part. In finding the complete solution of a triangle, it may be necessary to use two of the three equations.

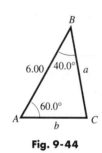

Fig. 9-43

Case 1: Two Angles and One Side

Now we see how the law of sines is used in the solution of a triangle in which two angles and one side are known. If two angles are known, the third may be found from the fact that the sum of the angles in a triangle is 180°. At this point we must be able to find the ratio between the given side and the sine of the angle opposite it. Then, by use of the law of sines, we may find the other two sides.

■**EXAMPLE 1**   Given $c = 6.00$, $A = 60.0°$, and $B = 40.0°$, find a, b, and C.
First, we can see that

$$C = 180.0° - (60.0° + 40.0°) = 80.0°$$

We now know side c and angle C, which allows us to use Eq. (9-8). Therefore, using the equation relating a, A, c, and C, we have

$$\frac{a}{\sin 60.0°} = \frac{6.00}{\sin 80.0°} \quad \text{or} \quad a = \frac{6.00 \sin 60.0°}{\sin 80.0°} = 5.28$$

Now, using the equation relating b, B, c, and C, we have

$$\frac{b}{\sin 40.0°} = \frac{6.00}{\sin 80.0°} \quad \text{or} \quad b = \frac{6.00 \sin 40.0°}{\sin 80.0°} = 3.92$$

Thus, $a = 5.28$, $b = 3.92$, and $C = 80.0°$. See Fig. 9-44. We could also have used the form of Eq. (9-8) relating a, A, b, and B in order to find b, but any error in calculating a would make b in error as well. Of course, any error in calculating C would make both a and b in error.
The calculator solution is shown in Fig. 9-45.   ----------■

Fig. 9-44

```
180-(60+40)
            80
6sin(60)/sin(80)
     5.276311449
6sin(40)/sin(80)
     3.916221868
```

Fig. 9-45

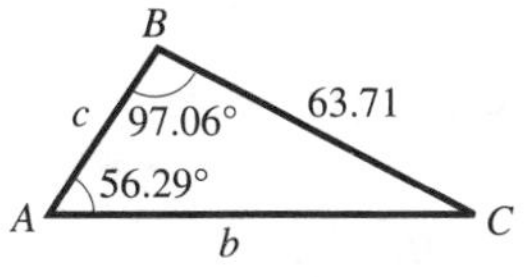

EXAMPLE 2   Solve the triangle with the following given parts: $a = 63.71$, $A = 56.29°$, and $B = 97.06°$. See Fig. 9-46.

From the figure, we see that we are to find angle C and sides b and c. We first determine angle C.

$$C = 180° - (A + B) = 180° - (56.29° + 97.06°)$$
$$= 26.65°$$

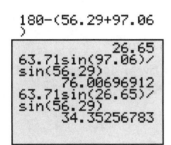

Fig. 9-46

We will now use the ratio $a/\sin A$ to find sides b and c, using Eq. (9-8) (the law of sines).

$$\frac{b}{\sin 97.06°} = \frac{63.71}{\sin 56.29°} \quad \text{or} \quad b = \frac{63.71 \sin 97.06°}{\sin 56.29°} = 76.01$$

and

$$\frac{c}{\sin 26.65°} = \frac{63.71}{\sin 56.29°} \quad \text{or} \quad c = \frac{63.71 \sin 26.65°}{\sin 56.29°} = 34.35$$

Thus, $b = 76.01$, $c = 34.35$, and $C = 26.65°$. See Fig. 9-46.
The calculator solution is shown in Fig. 9-47.

```
180-(56.29+97.06
)
             26.65
63.71sin(97.06)/
sin(56.29)
        76.00696912
63.71sin(26.65)/
sin(56.29)
        34.35256783
```

Fig. 9-47

If the given information is appropriate, the law of sines may be used to solve applied problems. The following example illustrates the use of the law of sines in such a problem.

SOLVING A WORD PROBLEM

EXAMPLE 3   Two observers A and B sight a helicopter due east. The observers are 3540 ft apart, and the angles of elevation they each measure to the helicopter are 32.0° and 44.0°, respectively. How far is observer A from the helicopter? See Fig. 9-48.

Letting H represent the position of the helicopter, we see that angle B within the triangle ABH is $180° - 44.0° = 136.0°$. This means that the angle at H within the triangle is

$$H = 180° - (32.0° + 136.0°) = 12.0°$$

Now, using the law of sines to find required side AH, we have

$$\text{required side opposite known angle} \longrightarrow \frac{AH}{\sin 136.0°} = \frac{3540}{\sin 12.0°} \longleftarrow \text{known side opposite known angle}$$

or

$$AH = \frac{3540 \sin 136.0°}{\sin 12.0°} = 11,800 \text{ ft}$$

Thus, observer A is about 11,800 ft from the helicopter.

The first successful helicopter was made in the United States by Igor Sikorsky in 1939.

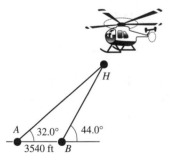

Fig. 9-48

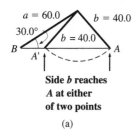

Case 2: Two Sides and the Angle Opposite One of Them

For a triangle in which we know two sides and the angle opposite one of the given sides, the solution will be either *one triangle,* or *two triangles,* or even possibly *no triangle.* In the following examples we illustrate how each of these results is possible.

$a = 60.0$
$b = 40.0$
$30.0°$
$b = 40.0$
B
A
A'
Side *b* reaches *A* at either of two points
(a)
C
$a = 60.0$
$b = 40.0$
$30.0°$
B
A
c
(b)
C'
$a = 60.0$
$30.0°$
$b = 40.0$
B
c'
A'
(c)

Fig. 9-49

EXAMPLE 4 Solve the triangle with the following given parts: $a = 60.0$, $b = 40.0$, and $B = 30.0°$.

By making a good scale drawing, Fig. 9-49(a), we see that the angle opposite a may be at either position A or A'. Both positions of this angle satisfy the given parts. Therefore, there are two triangles that result. Using the law of sines, we solve the case in which A, opposite side a, is an acute angle.

$$\frac{60.0}{\sin A} = \frac{40.0}{\sin 30.0°} \quad \text{or} \quad \sin A = \frac{60.0 \sin 30.0°}{40.0}$$

$$A = \sin^{-1}\left(\frac{60.0 \sin 30.0°}{40.0}\right) = 48.6°$$

$$C = 180° - (30.0° + 48.6°) = 101.4°$$

Therefore, $A = 48.6°$ and $C = 101.4°$. Using the law of sines again to find c, we have

$$\frac{c}{\sin 101.4°} = \frac{40.0}{\sin 30.0°}$$

$$c = \frac{40.0 \sin 101.4°}{\sin 30.0°} = 78.4$$

Thus we have $A = 48.6°$, $C = 101.4°$, and $c = 78.4$. See Fig. 9-49(b).

The other solution is the case in which A', opposite side a, is an obtuse angle. Here we have

$$A' = 180° - A = 180° - 48.6°$$

$$= 131.4°$$

$$C' = 180° - (30.0° + 131.4°)$$

$$= 18.6°$$

Using the law of sines to find c', we have

$$\frac{c'}{\sin 18.6°} = \frac{40.0}{\sin 30.0°}$$

$$c' = \frac{40.0 \sin 18.6°}{\sin 30.0°} = 25.5$$

This means that the second solution is $A' = 131.4°$, $C' = 18.6°$, and $c' = 25.5$. See Fig. 9-49(c).

The complete sequence for the calculator solution is shown in Fig. 9-50. The upper window shows the completion of the solution for A, C, and c. The lower window shows the solution for A', C', and c'. ∎

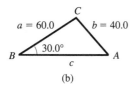

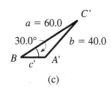

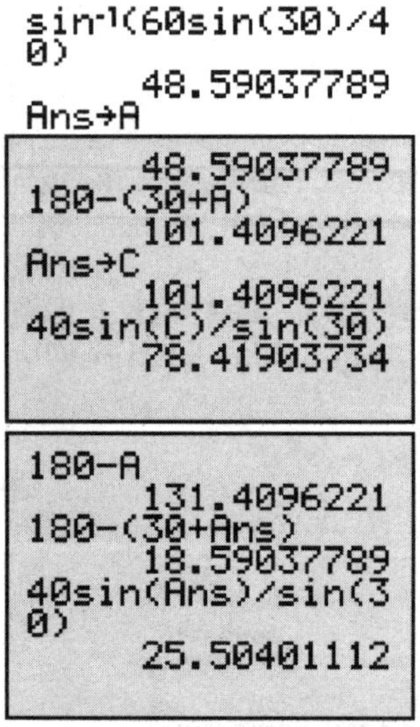

sin⁻¹(60sin(30)/40)
48.59037789
Ans→A
48.59037789
180-(30+A)
101.4096221
Ans→C
101.4096221
40sin(C)/sin(30)
78.41903734
180-A
131.4096221
180-(30+Ans)
18.59037789
40sin(Ans)/sin(30)
25.50401112

Fig. 9-50

EXAMPLE 5 In Example 4, if $b > 60.0$, only one solution would result. In this case, side b would intercept side c at A. It also intercepts the extension of side c, but this would require that angle B not be included in the triangle (see Fig. 9-51). Thus, only one solution may result if $b > a$.

In Example 4, there would be *no solution* if side b were not at least 30.0. If this were the case, side b would not be long enough to even touch side c. It can be seen that b must at least equal $a \sin B$. If it is just equal to $a \sin B$, there is *one solution*, a right triangle. See Fig. 9-52.

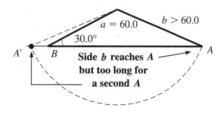

Fig. 9-51

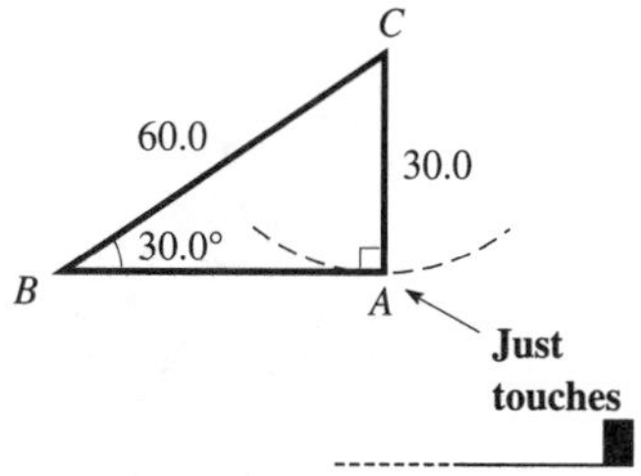

Fig. 9-52

Just touches

AMBIGUOUS CASE

Summarizing the results for Case 2 as illustrated in Examples 4 and 5, we make the following conclusions. Given sides a and b and angle A (assuming here that a and A ($A < 90°$) are corresponding parts), we have the following summary of solutions for Case 2.

> **Summary of Solutions:**
> **Two Sides and the Angle Opposite One of Them**
> 1. **No solution** *if $a < b \sin A$.* See Fig. 9-53(a).
> 2. **A right triangle solution** *if $a = b \sin A$.* See Fig. 9-53(b).
> 3. **Two solutions** *if $b \sin A < a < b$.* See Fig. 9-53(c).
> 4. **One solution** *if $a > b$.* See Fig. 9-53(d).

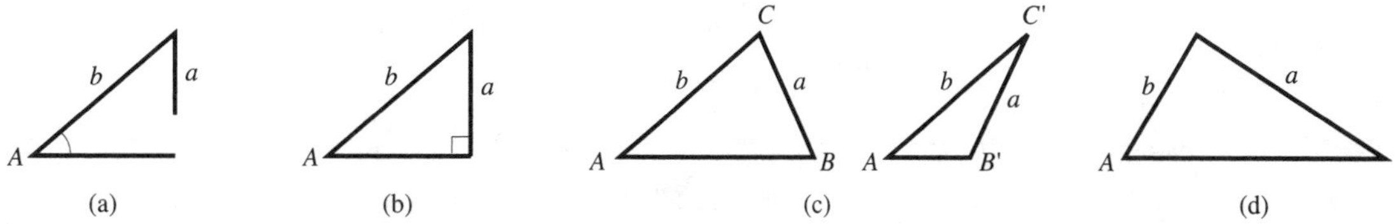

CAUTION

(a)

(b)

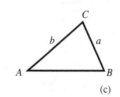

(c)

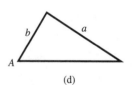

(d)

Fig. 9-53

NOTE

We note that *in order to have two solutions, we must know two sides and the angle opposite one of the sides, and the shorter side must be opposite the known angle.*

If there is *no solution*, the calculator will indicate an *error*. If the solution is a *right triangle*, the calculator will show an angle of *exactly 90°* (no extra decimal digits will be displayed.)

For the reason that two solutions may result from it, Case 2 is called the **ambiguous case**. The following example illustrates Case 2 in an applied problem.

SOLVING A WORD PROBLEM

See the chapter introduction.

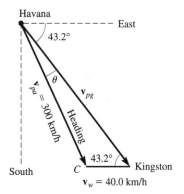

Fig. 9-54

EXAMPLE 6   Kingston, Jamaica is 43.2° south of east of Havana, Cuba. What should be the heading of a plane from Havana to Kingston if the wind is from the west at 40.0 km/h and the plane's speed with respect to the air is 300 km/h?

The heading should be set so that the resultant of the plane's velocity with respect to the air $\mathbf{v}_{pa}$ and the velocity of the wind $\mathbf{v}_w$ will be in the direction from Havana to Kingston. This means that the resultant velocity $\mathbf{v}_{pg}$ of the plane with respect to the ground must be at an angle of 43.2° south of east from Havana.

Using the given information we draw the vector triangle shown in Fig. 9-54. In the triangle, we know that the angle at Kingston is 43.2° by noting the alternate interior angles (see page 50). By finding θ, the required heading can be found. There can be only one solution, since $v_{pa} > v_w$. Using the law of sines, we have

$$\underset{\substack{\text{known side}\\ \text{opposite}\\ \text{required angle}}}{\longrightarrow}\ \frac{40.0}{\sin \theta} = \frac{300}{\sin 43.2°}\ \underset{\substack{\text{known side}\\ \text{opposite}\\ \text{known angle}}}{\longleftarrow}$$

$$\sin \theta = \frac{40.0 \sin 43.2°}{300}, \qquad \theta = 5.2°$$

Therefore, the heading should be 43.2° + 5.2° = 48.4° south of east. Compare this example with Example 3 on page 258.

If we attempt to use the law of sines for the solution of Case 3 or Case 4, we find that we do not have sufficient information to complete one of the ratios. These cases can, however, be solved by the law of cosines, which we shall consider in the next section.

EXAMPLE 7   Given the three sides of a triangle $a = 5$, $b = 6$, $c = 7$, we would set up the ratios

$$\frac{5}{\sin A} = \frac{6}{\sin B} = \frac{7}{\sin C}$$

However, since there is no way to determine a complete ratio from these equations, we cannot find the solution of the triangle in this manner.

EXERCISES 9-5

In Exercises 1–20, solve the triangles with the given parts.

1. $a = 45.7$, $A = 65.0°$, $B = 49.0°$

2. $b = 3.07$, $A = 26.0°$, $C = 120.0°$

3. $c = 4380$, $A = 37.4°$, $B = 34.6°$

4. $a = 93.2$, $B = 17.9°$, $C = 82.6°$

5. $a = 4.601$, $b = 3.107$, $A = 18.23°$

6. $b = 3.625$, $c = 2.946$, $B = 69.37°$

7. $b = 77.51$, $c = 36.42$, $B = 20.73°$

8. $a = 150.4$, $c = 250.9$, $C = 76.43°$

9. $b = 0.0742$, $B = 51.0°$, $C = 3.4°$

10. $c = 729$, $B = 121.0°$, $C = 44.2°$

11. $a = 63.8$, $B = 58.4°$, $C = 22.2°$

12. $a = 13.0$, $A = 55.2°$, $B = 67.5°$

13. $b = 4384$, $B = 47.43°$, $C = 64.56°$

14. $b = 283.2$, $B = 13.79°$, $C = 76.38°$

15. $a = 5.240$, $b = 4.446$, $B = 48.13°$

16. $a = 89.45$, $c = 37.36$, $C = 15.62°$

17. $b = 2880$, $c = 3650$, $B = 31.4°$

18. $a = 0.841$, $b = 0.965$, $A = 57.1°$

19. $a = 45.0$, $b = 126$, $A = 64.8°$

20. $a = 20$, $c = 10$, $C = 30°$

In Exercises 21–32, use the law of sines to solve the given problems.

21. The Pentagon (headquarters of the U.S. Department of Defense) is one of the world's largest office buildings in the world. It is a regular pentagon (five sides), 921 ft on a side. Find the greatest straight-line distance from one point on the outside of the building to another outside point (the length of a diagonal).

22. Two ropes hold a 175-lb crate as shown in Fig. 9-55. Find the tensions T_1 and T_2 in the ropes. (*Hint:* Move vectors so that they are tail to head to form a triangle. The vector sum $T_1 + T_2$ must equal 175 lb for equilibrium. See page 258.)

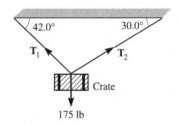

Fig. 9-55

23. Find the tension **T** in the left guy wire attached to the top of the tower shown in Fig. 9-56. (*Hint:* The horizontal components of the tensions must be equal and opposite for equilibrium. See page 258. Thus, move the tension vectors tail to head to form a triangle with a vertical resultant. This resultant equals the upward force at the top of the tower for equilibrium. This last force is not shown and does not have to be calculated.)

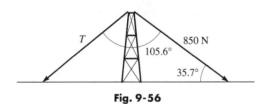

Fig. 9-56

24. Find the distance from Atlanta to Raleigh, North Carolina, from Fig. 9-57.

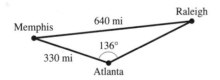

Fig. 9-57

25. Find the distance between Gravois Ave. and Jefferson Ave. along Arsenal St. in St. Louis, from Fig. 9-58.

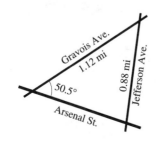

Fig. 9-58

26. When an airplane is landing at an 8250-ft runway, the angles of depression to the ends of the runway are 10.0° and 13.5°. How far is the plane from the near end of the runway?

27. Find the total length of the path of the laser beam that is shown in Fig. 9-59.

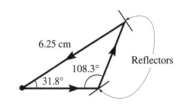

Fig. 9-59

28. In widening a highway, it is necessary for a construction crew to cut into the bank along the highway. The present angle of elevation of the straight slope of the bank is 23.0°, and the new angle is to be 38.5°, leaving the top of the slope at its present position. If the slope of the present bank is 220 ft long, how far horizontally into the bank at its base must they dig?

29. A communications satellite is directly above the extension of a line between receiving towers A and B. It is determined from radio signals that the angle of elevation of the satellite from tower A is 89.2°, and the angle of elevation from tower B is 86.5°. See Fig. 9-60. If A and B are 1290 km apart, how far is the satellite from A? (Neglect the curvature of the Earth.)

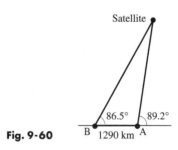

Fig. 9-60

30. Point *P* on the mechanism shown in Fig. 9-61 is driven back and forth horizontally. If the minimum value of angle θ is 32.0°, what is the distance between extreme positions of *P?* What is the maximum possible value of angle θ?

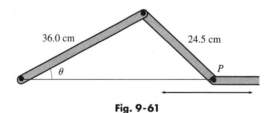

Fig. 9-61

31. A boat owner wishes to cross a river 2.60 km wide and go directly to a point on the opposite side 1.75 km downstream. The boat goes 8.00 km/h in still water, and the stream flows at 3.50 km/h. What should the boat's heading be?

32. A triangular support was measured to have a side of 25.3 in., a second side of 14.0 in., and an angle of 36.5° opposite the second side. Find the length of the third side.

Section 6.6
9-6 THE LAW OF COSINES

As we noted at the end of the preceding section, the law of sines cannot be used to solve a triangle if the only information given is that of Case 3 (two sides and the included angle) or Case 4 (three sides). Therefore, it is necessary to develop another method of finding at least one more part of the triangle. Therefore, in this section we develop the *law of cosines,* by which we can solve a triangle for Case 3 and Case 4. After obtaining another part of the triangle by the law of cosines, we can then use the law of sines to complete the solution. We do this because the law of sines generally provides a simpler method of solution than does the law of cosines.

Consider any oblique triangle, for example, either of the triangles shown in Fig. 9-62. For each of these triangles we see that $h/b = \sin A$, or $h = b \sin A$. Also, by using the Pythagorean theorem, we obtain $a^2 = h^2 + x^2$ for each triangle. Thus (with $(\sin A)^2 = \sin^2 A$), we have

$$a^2 = b^2 \sin^2 A + x^2 \tag{9-9}$$

In Fig. 9-62(a), we see that $(c - x)/b = \cos A$, or $c - x = b \cos A$. Solving for x, we have $x = c - b \cos A$. In Fig. 9-62(b), we have $c + x = b \cos A$, and solving for x, we have $x = b \cos A - c$. Substituting these relations into Eq. (9-9), we obtain

$$a^2 = b^2 \sin^2 A + (c - b \cos A)^2$$

and

$$\tag{9-10}$$

$$a^2 = b^2 \sin^2 A + (b \cos A - c)^2$$

respectively. When expanded, these give

$$a^2 = b^2 \sin^2 A + b^2 \cos^2 A + c^2 - 2bc \cos A$$
$$= b^2(\sin^2 A + \cos^2 A) + c^2 - 2bc \cos A \tag{9-11}$$

Recalling the definitions of the trigonometric functions, we know that $\sin \theta = y/r$ and $\cos \theta = x/r$. Thus, $\sin^2 \theta + \cos^2 \theta = (y^2 + x^2)/r^2$. However, $x^2 + y^2 = r^2$, which means that

$$\sin^2 \theta + \cos^2 \theta = 1 \tag{9-12}$$

This equation is valid for any angle θ, since we have made no assumptions as to any of the properties of θ. Therefore, by substituting Eq. (9-12) into Eq. (9-11), we arrive at the **law of cosines.**

LAW OF COSINES

$$a^2 = b^2 + c^2 - 2bc \cos A \tag{9-13}$$

Using the method above, we may also show that

and

$$b^2 = a^2 + c^2 - 2ac \cos B$$

$$c^2 = a^2 + b^2 - 2ab \cos C$$

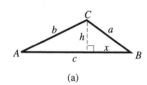
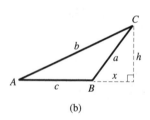

(a)

(b)

Fig. 9-62

Case 3: Two Sides and the Included Angle

If we know two sides and the included angle of a triangle, we see by the forms of the law of cosines that we may directly solve for the side opposite the given angle. Thus, as we noted at the beginning of this section, we may complete the solution by using the law of sines.

EXAMPLE 1 Solve the triangle with $a = 45.0$, $b = 67.0$, and $C = 35.0°$. See Fig. 9-63.

Since angle C is known, we first solve for side c, using the law of cosines in the form

$$c^2 = a^2 + b^2 - 2ab \cos C$$

Substituting, we have

unknown side opposite known angle

$$c^2 = 45.0^2 + 67.0^2 - 2(45.0)(67.0)\cos 35.0°$$

known sides

$$c = \sqrt{45.0^2 + 67.0^2 - 2(45.0)(67.0)\cos 35.0°} = 39.7$$

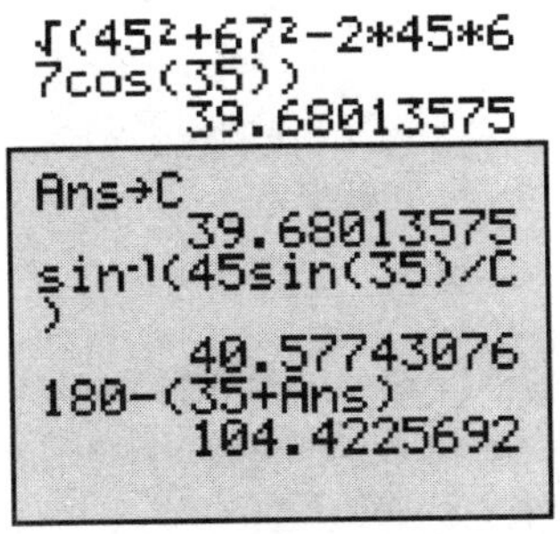

From the law of sines, we now have

$$\frac{45.0}{\sin A} = \frac{67.0}{\sin B} = \frac{39.7}{\sin 35.0°} \longleftarrow \text{ sides}$$
$$\longleftarrow \text{ opposite angles}$$

$$\sin A = \frac{45.0 \sin 35.0°}{39.7}, \qquad A = 40.6°$$

The calculator solution is shown in Fig. 9-64. As shown, we found that $B = 104.4°$ using the fact that the sum of the angles is 180°, rather than using the relation from the law of sines.

Therefore, we have found that $c = 39.7$, $A = 40.6°$, and $B = 104.4°$. ∎

EXAMPLE 2 Solve the triangle with $a = 0.1762$, $c = 0.5034$, and $B = 129.20°$. See Fig. 9-65.

Again, the given parts are two sides and the included angle, or Case 3. Since B is the known angle, we use the form of the law of cosines that includes angle B. This means that we find b first.

$$b^2 = a^2 + c^2 - 2ac \cos B$$
$$= 0.1762^2 + 0.5034^2 - 2(0.1762)(0.5034)\cos 129.20°$$
$$b = 0.6297$$

From the law of sines, we have

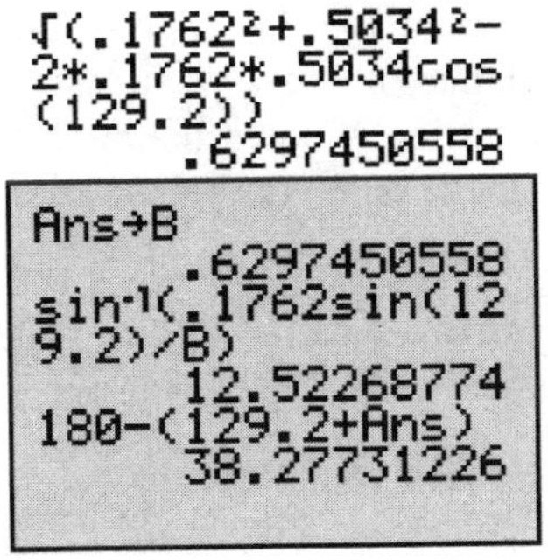

$$\frac{0.1762}{\sin A} = \frac{0.6297}{\sin 129.20°} = \frac{0.5034}{\sin C}$$

$$\sin A = \frac{0.1762 \sin 129.20°}{0.6297}, \qquad A = 12.52°$$

As shown in Fig. 9-66, we complete the solution by using the fact that the sum of the angles is 180° to find $C = 38.28°$.

Thus, $b = 0.6297$, $A = 12.52°$, and $C = 38.28°$. ∎

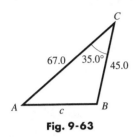

Fig. 9-63

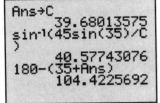

Fig. 9-64

Fig. 9-65

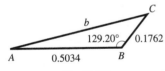

Fig. 9-66

Case 4: Three Sides

Given the three sides of a triangle, we may solve for the angle opposite any of the sides using the law of cosines. In solving for an angle, *the best procedure is to find the largest angle first.* This avoids the ambiguous case if we switch to the law of sines and the triangle has an obtuse angle. *The largest angle is always opposite the longest side.* Another procedure is to use the law of cosines to find two angles.

CAUTION ▶

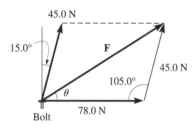

Fig. 9-68

■EXAMPLE 3 Solve the triangle given the three sides $a = 49.33$, $b = 21.61$, and $c = 42.57$. See Fig. 9-67.

Since the longest side is $a = 49.33$, we first solve for angle A.

$$a^2 = b^2 + c^2 - 2bc \cos A$$

$$\cos A = \frac{b^2 + c^2 - a^2}{2bc} = \frac{21.61^2 + 42.57^2 - 49.33^2}{2(21.61)(42.57)}$$

$$A = 94.81°$$

From the law of sines, we now have

$$\frac{49.33}{\sin A} = \frac{21.61}{\sin B} = \frac{42.57}{\sin C}$$

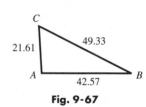

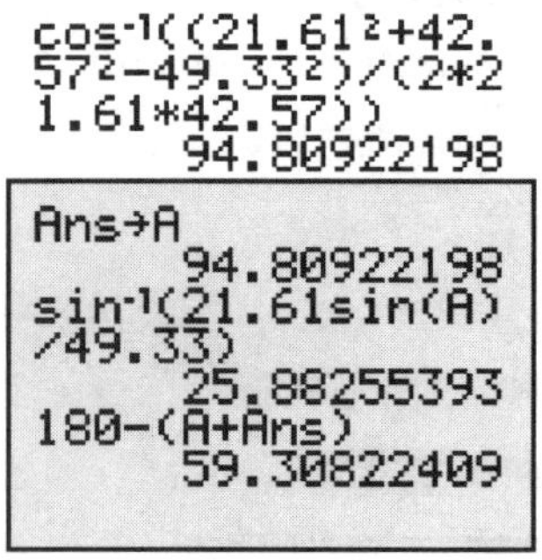

Fig. 9-67

The complete calculator solution is shown in Fig. 9-68. Therefore,

$$B = 25.88° \quad \text{and} \quad C = 59.31° \qquad \text{------------■}$$

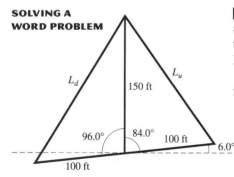

Fig. 9-69

■EXAMPLE 4 Two forces are acting on a bolt. One is a 78.0-N force acting horizontally to the right, and the other is a force of 45.0 N acting upward to the right, 15.0° from the vertical. Find the resultant force **F**. See Fig. 9-69.

Moving the 45.0-N vector to the right, and using the lower triangle with the 105.0° angle, we find the magnitude of **F** as

$$F = \sqrt{78.0^2 + 45.0^2 - 2(78.0)(45.0)\cos 105.0°}$$
$$= 99.6 \text{ N}$$

To find θ, we use the law of sines:

$$\frac{45.0}{\sin \theta} = \frac{99.6}{\sin 105.0°}, \quad \sin \theta = \frac{45.0 \sin 105.0°}{99.6}$$

This gives us $\theta = 25.9°$.

We can also solve this problem using vector components.   ------------■

SOLVING A WORD PROBLEM

Fig. 9-70

■EXAMPLE 5 A vertical radio antenna is to be built on a hill that makes an angle of 6.0° with the horizontal. Guy wires are to be attached at a point 150 ft up the antenna and at points 100 ft from the base of the antenna. What will be the lengths of the guy wires positioned directly up and directly down the hill?

Making an appropriate figure, as in Fig. 9-70, we can set up the equations needed for the solution.

$$L_u^2 = 100^2 + 150^2 - 2(100)(150)\cos 84.0°$$
$$L_u = 171 \text{ ft}$$
$$L_d^2 = 100^2 + 150^2 - 2(100)(150)\cos 96.0°$$
$$L_d = 189 \text{ ft} \qquad \text{------------■}$$

Following is a summary of solving an oblique triangle by use of the law of sines or the law of cosines.

> **Solving Oblique Triangles**
> **Case 1: Two Angles and One Side**
> Find the unknown angle by subtracting the sum of the known angles from 180°. Use the **law of sines** to find the unknown sides.
> **Case 2: Two Sides and the Angle Opposite One of Them**
> Use the known side and the known angle opposite it to find the angle opposite the other known side. Find the third angle from the fact that the sum of the angles is 180°. Use the **law of sines** to find the third side. **CAUTION:** There may be two solutions. See page 265 for a summary of Case 2 and the *ambiguous case.*
> **Case 3: Two Sides and the Included Angle**
> Find the third side by using the **law of cosines.** Find a second angle by using the **law of sines.** Complete the solution using the fact that the sum of the angles is 180°.
> **Case 4: Three Sides**
> Find the *largest angle* (opposite the longest side) by using the **law of cosines.** Find a second angle by using the **law of sines.** Complete the solution by using the fact that the sum of the angles is 180°.

Other variations in finding the solutions can be used. For example, after finding the third side in Case 3 or finding the largest angle in Case 4, the solution can be completed by using the law of sines. All angles in Case 4 can be found by using the law of cosines. The methods shown above are those which are normally used.

EXERCISES 9-6

In Exercises 1–20, solve the triangles with the given parts.

1. $a = 6.00$, $b = 7.56$, $C = 54.0°$
2. $b = 87.3$, $c = 34.0$, $A = 130.0°$
3. $a = 4530$, $b = 924$, $C = 98.0°$
4. $a = 0.0845$, $c = 0.116$, $B = 85.0°$
5. $a = 39.53$, $b = 45.22$, $c = 67.15$
6. $a = 23.31$, $b = 27.26$, $c = 29.17$
7. $a = 385.4$, $b = 467.7$, $c = 800.9$
8. $a = 0.2433$, $b = 0.2635$, $c = 0.1538$
9. $a = 320$, $b = 847$, $C = 158.0°$
10. $b = 18.3$, $c = 27.1$, $A = 58.7°$
11. $a = 21.4$, $c = 4.28$, $B = 86.3°$
12. $a = 11.3$, $b = 5.10$, $C = 77.6°$
13. $b = 103.7$, $c = 159.1$, $C = 104.67°$
14. $a = 49.32$, $b = 54.55$, $B = 114.36°$
15. $a = 0.4937$, $b = 0.5956$, $c = 0.6398$
16. $a = 69.72$, $b = 49.30$, $c = 56.29$

17. $a = 723$, $b = 598$, $c = 158$
18. $a = 1.78$, $b = 6.04$, $c = 4.80$
19. $a = 15$, $A = 15°$, $B = 140°$
20. $a = 17$, $b = 24$, $c = 37$

In Exercises 21–32, use the law of cosines to solve the given problems.

21. A nuclear submarine leaves its base and travels at 23.5 mi/h. For 2.00 h it travels along a course 32.1° north of west. It then turns an additional 21.5° north of west and travels for another 1.00 h. How far from its base is it?

22. The robot arm shown in Fig. 9-71 places packages on a conveyor belt. What is the distance *x?*

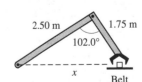

Fig. 9-71

23. In order to get around an obstruction, an oil pipeline is constructed in two straight sections, one 3.756 km long and the other 4.675 km long, with an angle of 168.85° between the sections where they are joined. How much more pipeline was necessary due to the obstruction?

24. In a baseball field the four bases are at the vertices of a square 90.0 ft on a side. The pitching rubber is 60.5 ft from home plate. See Fig. 9-72. How far is it from the pitching rubber to first base?

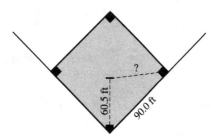

Fig. 9-72

25. A plane leaves an airport and travels 624 km due east. It then turns toward the north and travels another 326 km. It then turns again less than 180° and travels another 846 km directly back to the airport. Through what angles did it turn?

26. The apparent depth of an object submerged in water is less than its actual depth. A coin is actually 5.00 in. from an observer's eye just above the surface, but it appears to be only 4.25 in. The real light ray from the coin makes an angle with the surface that is 8.1° greater than the angle the apparent ray makes. How much deeper is the coin than it appears to be? See Fig. 9-73.

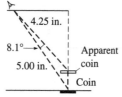

Fig. 9-73

27. A nut is in the shape of a regular hexagon (six sides). If each side is 9.53 mm, what opening on a wrench is necessary to tighten the nut? See Fig. 9-74.

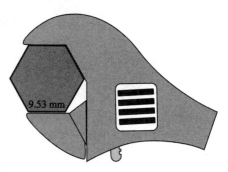

Fig. 9-74

28. Two ropes support a 78.3-lb crate from above. The tensions in the ropes are 50.6 lb and 37.5 lb. What is the angle between the ropes? (See Exercise 22 of Section 9-5.)

29. A ferryboat travels at 11.5 km/h with respect to the water. Because of the river current, it is traveling at 12.7 km/h with respect to the land in the direction of its destination. If the ferryboat's heading is 23.6° from the direction of its destination, what is the velocity of the current?

30. The airline distance from Denver to Dallas is 660 mi. It is 800 mi from Denver to St. Louis and 550 mi from Dallas to St. Louis. Find the angle between the routes from Dallas.

31. An air traffic controller sights two planes that are due east from the control tower and headed toward each other. One is 15.8 mi from the tower at an angle of elevation of 26.4°, and the other is 32.7 mi from the tower at an angle of elevation of 12.4°. How far apart are the planes?

(W) 32. A triangular machine part has sides of 5 cm and 8 cm. Explain why the law of sines, or the law of cosines, is used to start the solution of the triangle if the third known part is (a) the third side, (b) the angle opposite the 5-cm side, or (c) the angle between the 5-cm and 8-cm sides.

Section 6.7

CHAPTER EQUATIONS

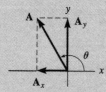

Vector components	$A_x = A \cos \theta \quad A_y = A \sin \theta$	**(9-1)**
	$A = \sqrt{A_x^2 + A_y^2}$	**(9-2)**
	$\theta_{ref} = \tan^{-1} \dfrac{|A_y|}{|A_x|}$	**(9-3)**
Law of sines	$\dfrac{a}{\sin A} = \dfrac{b}{\sin B} = \dfrac{c}{\sin C}$	**(9-8)**

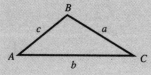

Law of cosines	$a^2 = b^2 + c^2 - 2bc \cos A$	**(9-13)**
	$b^2 = a^2 + c^2 - 2ac \cos B$	
	$c^2 = a^2 + b^2 - 2ab \cos C$	

REVIEW EXERCISES

In Exercises 1–4, find the x- and y-components of the given vectors by use of the trigonometric functions.

1. $A = 65.0$, $\theta_A = 28.0°$

2. $A = 8.05$, $\theta_A = 149.0°$

3. $A = 0.9204$, $\theta_A = 215.59°$

4. $A = 657.1$, $\theta_A = 343.74°$

*In Exercises 5–8, vectors **A** and **B** are at right angles. Find the magnitude and direction of the resultant.*

5. $A = 327$
   $B = 505$

6. $A = 68$
   $B = 29$

7. $A = 4964$
   $B = 3298$

8. $A = 26.52$
   $B = 89.86$

In Exercises 9–16, add the given vectors by use of the trigonometric functions and the Pythagorean theorem.

9. $A = 780$, $\theta_A = 28.0°$
   $B = 346$, $\theta_B = 320.0°$

10. $J = 0.0120$, $\theta_J = 370.5°$
   $K = 0.00781$, $\theta_K = 260.0°$

11. $A = 22.51$, $\theta_A = 130.16°$
   $B = 7.604$, $\theta_B = 200.09°$

12. $A = 18,760$, $\theta_A = 110.43°$
   $B = 4835$, $\theta_B = 350.20°$

13. $Y = 51.33$, $\theta_Y = 12.25°$
   $Z = 42.61$, $\theta_Z = 291.77°$

14. $A = 70.31$, $\theta_A = 122.54°$
   $B = 30.29$, $\theta_B = 214.82°$

15. $A = 75.0$, $\theta_A = 15.0°$
   $B = 26.5$, $\theta_B = 192.4°$
   $C = 54.8$, $\theta_C = 344.7°$

16. $S = 8120$, $\theta_S = 141.9°$
   $T = 1540$, $\theta_T = 165.2°$
   $U = 3470$, $\theta_U = 296.0°$

In Exercises 17–36, solve the triangles with the given parts.

17. $A = 48.0°$, $B = 68.0°$, $a = 14.5$

18. $A = 132.0°$, $b = 7.50$, $C = 32.0°$

19. $a = 22.8$, $B = 33.5°$, $C = 125.3°$

20. $A = 71.0°$, $B = 48.5°$, $c = 8.42$

21. $A = 17.85°$, $B = 154.16°$, $c = 7863$

22. $a = 1.985$, $b = 4.189$, $c = 3.652$

23. $b = 76.07$, $c = 40.53$, $B = 110.09°$

24. $A = 77.06°$, $a = 12.07$, $c = 5.104$

25. $b = 14.5$, $c = 13.0$, $C = 56.6°$

26. $B = 40.6°$, $b = 7.00$, $c = 18.0$

27. $a = 186$, $B = 130.0°$, $c = 106$

28. $b = 750$, $c = 1100$, $A = 56°$

29. $a = 7.86$, $b = 2.45$, $C = 22.0°$

30. $a = 0.208$, $c = 0.697$, $B = 105.4°$

31. $A = 67.16°$, $B = 96.84°$, $c = 532.9$

32. $A = 43.12°$, $a = 7.893$, $b = 4.113$

33. $a = 17$, $b = 12$, $c = 25$

34. $a = 9064$, $b = 9953$, $c = 1106$

35. $a = 5.30$, $b = 8.75$, $c = 12.5$

36. $a = 47.4$, $b = 40.0$, $c = 45.5$

In Exercises 37–60, solve the given problems.

37. For any triangle ABC show that

$$\frac{a^2 + b^2 + c^2}{2abc} = \frac{\cos A}{a} + \frac{\cos B}{b} + \frac{\cos C}{c}$$

Ⓦ 38. In solving a triangle for Case 3 (two sides and the included angle), explain what type of solution is obtained if the included angle is a right angle.

39. An architect determines the two acute angles and one of the legs of a right triangular wall panel. Show that the area A_t is

$$A_t = \frac{a^2 \sin B}{2 \sin A}$$

40. A surveyor determines the three angles and one side of a triangular tract of land. (a) Show that the area A_t can be found from $A_t = \dfrac{a^2 \sin B \sin C}{2 \sin A}$. (b) For a right triangle, show that this agrees with the formula in Exercise 39.

41. Find the horizontal and vertical components of the force shown in Fig. 9-75.

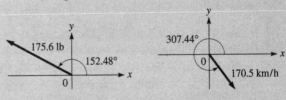

Fig. 9-75   **Fig. 9-76**

42. Find the horizontal and vertical components of the velocity shown in Fig. 9-76.

43. In a ballistics test, a bullet was fired into a block of wood with a velocity of 2200 ft/s and at an angle of 71.3° with the surface of the block. What was the component of the velocity perpendicular to the surface?

44. A storm cloud is moving at 15 mi/h from the northwest. A television tower is 60° south of east of the cloud. What is the component of the cloud's velocity toward the tower?

45. During a 3.00-minute period after taking off, the supersonic jet Concorde traveled at 480 km/h at an angle of 24.0° above the horizontal. What was its gain in altitude during this period?

46. In Fig. 9-77 force **F** represents the total surface tension force around the circumference on the liquid in the capillary tube. The vertical component of **F** holds up the liquid in the tube above the liquid surface outside the tube. What is the vertical component of **F**?

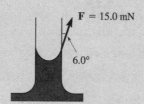

F = 15.0 mN

6.0°

Fig. 9-77

47. A helium-filled balloon rises vertically at 3.5 m/s as the wind carries it horizontally at 5.0 m/s. What is the resultant velocity of the balloon?

48. A crater on the moon is 150 mi in diameter. If the distance to the moon (to each side of the crater) from the earth is 240,000 mi, what angle is subtended by the crater at an observer's position on the earth?

49. In Fig. 9-78 a damper mechanism in an air-conditioning system is shown. If $\theta = 27.5°$ when the spring is at its shortest and longest lengths, what are these lengths?

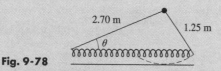

2.70 m

1.25 m

θ

Fig. 9-78

50. A bullet is fired from the ground of a level field at an angle of 39.0° above the horizontal. It travels in a straight line at 2200 ft/s for 0.20 s when it strikes a target. The sound of the strike is recorded 0.32 s later on the ground. If sound travels at 1130 ft/s, where is the recording device located?

51. Two satellites are being observed at the same observing station. One is 22,500 mi from the station, and the other is 18,700 mi away. The angle between their lines of observation is 105.4°. How far apart are the satellites?

52. Find the side x in the truss in Fig. 9-79.

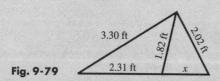

3.30 ft

1.82 ft

2.02 ft

2.31 ft

x

Fig. 9-79

53. The angle of depression of a fire noticed west of a fire tower is 6.2°. The angle of depression of a pond, also west of the tower, is 13.5°. If it is known that the tower is 2.25 km from the pond on a direct line to the pond, how far is the fire from the pond?

54. A surveyor wishes to find the distance between two points between which there is a security-restricted area. The surveyor measures the distance from each of these points to a third point and finds them to be 226.73 m and 185.12 m. If the angle between the lines of sight from the third point to the other points is 126.724°, how far apart are the two points?

55. Atlanta is 290 mi and 51.0° south of east from Nashville. The pilot of an airplane due north of Atlanta radios Nashville and finds the plane is on a line 10.5° south of east from Nashville. How far is the plane from Nashville?

56. In going around a storm, a plane flies 125 mi south, then 140 mi at 30.0° south of west, and finally 225 mi at 15.0° north of west. What is the displacement of the plane from its original position?

57. A sailboat is headed due north, and its sail is set perpendicular to the wind, which is from the south of west. The component of the force of the wind in the direction of the heading is 480 N, and the component perpendicular to the heading (the *drift* component) is 650 N. What is the force exerted by the wind, and what is the direction of the wind? See Fig. 9-80.

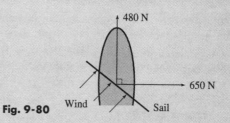

480 N

650 N

Wind   Sail

Fig. 9-80

58. Boston is 650 km and 21.0° south of west from Halifax, Nova Scotia. Radio signals locate a ship 10.5° east of south from Halifax and 5.6° north of east from Boston. How far is the ship from each city?

59. One end of a 1450-ft bridge is sighted from a distance of 3250 ft. The angle between the lines of sight of the ends of the bridge is 25.2°. From these data, how far is the observer from the other end of the bridge?

60. A plane is traveling horizontally at 1250 ft/s. A missile is fired horizontally from it 30.0° from the direction in which the plane is traveling. If the missile leaves the plane at 2040 ft/s, what is its velocity 10.0 s later if the vertical component is given by $v_V = -32.0t$ (in ft/s)?

Writing Exercise

61. A laser experiment uses a prism with a triangular base that has sides of 2.00 cm, 3.00 cm, and 4.50 cm. Write two or three paragraphs explaining how to find the angles of the triangle.

PRACTICE TEST

In all triangle solutions, sides a, b, c, are opposite angles A, B, C, respectively.

1. By use of a diagram, find the vector sum $2\mathbf{A} + \mathbf{B}$ for the given vectors.

2. For the triangle in which $a = 22.5$, $B = 78.6°$, and $c = 30.9$, find b.

3. A surveyor locates a tree 36.50 m to the northeast of a set position. The tree is 21.38 m north of a utility pole. What is the displacement of the utility pole from the set position?

4. For the triangle in which $A = 18.9°$, $B = 104.2°$, and $a = 426$, find c.

5. Solve the triangle in which $a = 9.84$, $b = 3.29$, and $c = 8.44$.

6. Find the horizontal and vertical components of a vector of magnitude 871 that is directed at a standard-position angle of 284.3°.

7. A ship leaves a port and travels due west. At a certain point it turns 31.5° north of west and travels an additional 42.0 mi to a point 63.0 mi on a direct line from the port. How far from the port is the point where the ship turned?

8. Find the sum of the vectors for which $A = 449$, $\theta_A = 74.2°$, $B = 285$, and $\theta_B = 208.9°$. Use the trigonometric functions and the Pythagorean theorem.

9. Solve the triangle for which $a = 22.3$, $b = 29.6$, and $A = 36.5°$.

35.

Section 6.2
Exercises 9-2, page 251

1. 662, 352   **3.** -349, -664 **5.** 3.22, 7.97

7. -62.9, 44.1   **9.** 2.08, -8.80 **11.** -2.53, -0.788

13. -0.8088, 0.3296   **15.** 88,920, 12,240

17. 23.9 km/h, 7.43 km/h   **19.** 51.9 lb, 18.3 lb

21. 115 km, 88.3 km   **23.** 18,530 mi/h, -825.3 mi/h

Section 6.3
Exercises 9-3, page 256

1. $R = 24.2$, $\theta = 52.6°$ with A

3. $R = 7.781$, $\theta = 66.63°$ with A

5. $R = 10.0$, $\theta = 58.8°$ **7.** $R = 2.74$, $\theta = 111.0°$

9. $R = 2130$, $\theta = 107.7°$ **11.** $R = 1.426$, $\theta = 299.12°$

13. $R = 29.2$, $\theta = 10.8°$ **15.** $R = 58.5$, $\theta = 87.8°$

17. $R = 27.27$, $\theta = 33.14°$ **19.** $R = 12.735$, $\theta = 25.216°$

21. $R = 50.2$, $\theta = 50.3°$ **23.** $R = 0.242$, $\theta = 285.9°$

25. $R = 235$, $\theta = 121.7°$ **27.** 2700 lb, $\theta = 107°$

Section 6.4
Exercises 9-4, page 259

1. 6.60 lb, 29.5° from the 5.75-lb force

3. 11,000 N, 44° above horizontal

5. 3070 ft, 17.8° S of W   **7.** 229.4 ft, 72.82° N of E

9. 25.3 km/h, 29.6° S of E   **11.** 175 lb, 9.3° above horizontal

13. 540 km/h, 6° from direction of plane

15. 18,130 mi/h, 0.03° from direction of shuttle

17. 184,000 in./min², $\phi = 89.6°$ **19.** 138 mi, 65.0° N of E

21. 79.0 m/s, 11.3° from direction of plane, 75.6° from vertical

23. 4.05 A/m, 11.5° with magnet

Section 6.5
Exercises 9-5, page 266

1. $b = 38.1$, $C = 66.0°$, $c = 46.1$

3. $a = 2800$, $b = 2620$, $C = 108.0°$

5. $B = 12.20°$, $C = 149.57°$, $c = 7.448$

7. $a = 110.5$, $A = 149.70°$, $C = 9.57°$

9. $A = 125.6°$, $a = 0.0776$, $c = 0.00566$

11. $A = 99.4°$, $b = 55.1$, $c = 24.4$

13. $A = 68.01°$, $a = 5520$, $c = 5376$

15. $A_1 = 61.36°$, $C_1 = 70.51°$, $c_1 = 5.628$; $A_2 = 118.64°$, $C_2 = 13.23°$, $c_2 = 1.366$

Section 6.1
Exercises 9-1, page 247

1. (a) vector: magnitude and direction are specified; (b) scalar: only magnitude is specified

3. (a) vector: magnitude and direction are specified; (b) scalar: only magnitude is specified

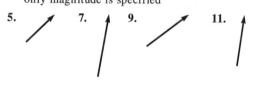

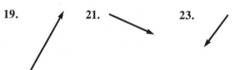

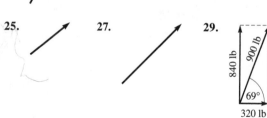

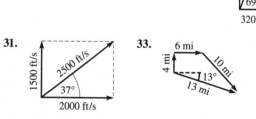

17. $A_1 = 107.3°$, $a_1 = 5280$, $C_1 = 41.3°$; $A_2 = 9.9°$,
$a_2 = 952$, $C_2 = 138.7°$

19. no solution   **21.** 1490 ft   **23.** 880 N   **25.** 0.88 mi

27. 13.94 cm   **29.** 27,300 km

31. 77.3° with bank downstream

Section 6.6
Exercises 9-6, page 271

1. $A = 50.3°$, $B = 75.7°$, $c = 6.31$

3. $A = 70.9°$, $B = 11.1°$, $c = 4750$

5. $A = 34.72°$, $B = 40.67°$, $C = 104.61°$

7. $A = 18.21°$, $B = 22.28°$, $C = 139.51°$

9. $A = 6.0°$, $B = 16.0°$, $c = 1150$

11. $A = 82.3°$, $b = 21.6$, $C = 11.4°$

13. $A = 36.24°$, $B = 39.09°$, $a = 97.22$

15. $A = 46.94°$, $B = 61.82°$, $C = 71.24°$

17. $A = 137.9°$, $B = 33.7°$, $C = 8.4°$

19. $b = 37$, $C = 25°$, $c = 24$

21. 69.4 mi   **23.** 0.039 km   **25.** 57.3°, 141.7°

27. 16.5 mm   **29.** 5.09 km/h   **31.** 17.8 mi

Section 6.7
Review Exercises for Chapter 9, page 273

1. $A_x = 57.4$, $A_y = 30.5$ **3.** $A_x = -0.7485$, $A_y = -0.5357$

5. $R = 602$, $\theta = 57.1°$ with A

7. $R = 5960$, $\theta = 33.60°$ with A **9.** $R = 965$, $\theta = 8.6°$

11. $R = 26.12$, $\theta = 146.03°$ **13.** $R = 71.93$, $\theta = 336.50°$

15. $R = 99.42$, $\theta = 359.57°$

17. $b = 18.1$, $C = 64.0°$, $c = 17.5$

19. $A = 21.2°$, $b = 34.8$, $c = 51.5$

21. $a = 17,340$, $b = 24,660$, $C = 7.99°$

23. $A = 39.88°$, $a = 51.94$, $C = 30.03°$

25. $A_1 = 54.8°$, $a_1 = 12.7$, $B_1 = 68.6°$; $A_2 = 12.0°$,
$a_2 = 3.24$, $B_2 = 111.4°$

27. $A = 32.3°$, $b = 267$, $C = 17.7°$

29. $A = 148.7°$, $B = 9.3°$, $c = 5.66$

31. $a = 1782$, $b = 1920$, $C = 16.00°$

33. $A = 37°$, $B = 25°$, $C = 118°$

35. $A = 20.6°$, $B = 35.6°$, $C = 123.8°$

37. Add the 3 forms of law of cosines together; simplify; divide
by $2abc$.

39. $A_t = \frac{1}{2}ab$; $b = \dfrac{a \sin B}{\sin A}$; substitute

41. -155.7 lb, 81.14 lb   **43.** 2100 ft/s   **45.** 9.8 km

47. 6.1 m/s, 35° with horizontal   **49.** 2.30 m, 2.49 m

51. 32,900 mi   **53.** 2.65 km   **55.** 190 mi

57. 810 N, 36° N of E   **59.** 2510 ft or 3370 ft (ambiguous)

VECTORS AND OBLIQUE TRIANGLES

9.1   Introduction to Vectors
Section 6.1

1. **(a)** 300 km sw is a vector; it has magnitude and direction

   (b) 300 km is a scalar; it has only magnitude

5.

$\vec{R} = \vec{V} + \vec{U}$

9.

13.

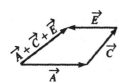

17.

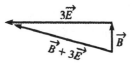

21.

25.

29.

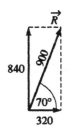

from drawing
$\vec{R}$ is approximately
900 lb at 70°

33.

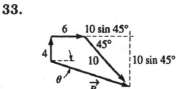

From drawing,

$R = 13$ mi

$\theta = 13°$

Section 6.2

9.2 Components of Vectors

1. horizontal component $= 750 \cos 28° = 662$
vertical component $= 750 \sin 28° = 352$

5.

$V_x = 8.6 \cos 68° = 3.22$
$V_y = 8.6 \sin 68° = 7.97$

9.

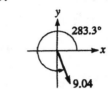

$V_x = 9.04 \cos 283.3° = 2.08$
$V_y = 9.04 \sin 283.3° = -8.80$

13.

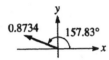

$V_x = 0.8734 \cos 157.83° = -0.8088$
$V_y = 0.8734 \sin 157.83° = 0.3296$

17.

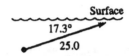

$V_x = 25.0 \cos 17.3° = 23.9 \text{ km/h}$
$V_y = 25.0 \sin 17.3° = 7.43 \text{ km/h}$

21.

$V_x = 145 \cos 37.5° = 115 \text{ km to the east}$
$V_y = 145 \sin 37.5° = 88.3 \text{ km to the north}$

Section 6.3

9.3 Vector Addition by Components

1.

$R = \sqrt{14.7^2 + 19.2^2} = 24.2$

$\theta = \tan^{-1} \dfrac{19.2}{14.7} = 52.6°$

5.

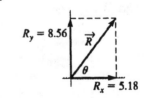

$R = \sqrt{5.18^2 + 8.56^2} = 10.0$

$\theta = \tan^{-1} \dfrac{8.56}{5.18} = 58.8°$

9.

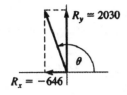

$$R = \sqrt{(-646)^2 + 2030^2} = 2130$$

$$\tan^{-1}\frac{2030}{-646} = -72.3° \text{ from calculator}$$

$$\theta = 180° - 72.3° = 107.7°$$

13.

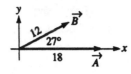

$$R_x = 18 + 12\cos 27°$$
$$R_y = 0 + 12\sin 27°$$
$$R = \sqrt{R_x^2 + R_y^2} = 29.2$$

$$\theta = \tan^{-1}\frac{R_y}{R_x} = 10.8°$$

17.

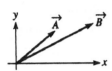

$$R_x = A_x + B_x = 9.821\cos 34.27° + 17.45\cos 752.5°$$
$$R_y = 9.821\sin 34.27° + 17.45\sin 752.5°$$
$$R = \sqrt{R_x^2 + R_y^2} = 27.27$$

$$\theta = \tan^{-1}\frac{R_y}{R_x} = 33.14°$$

21. $R_x = A_x + B_x + C_x$
$R_x = 21.9\cos 236.2° + 96.7\cos 11.5° + 62.9\cos 143.4°$
$R_y = A_y + B_y + C_y$
$R_y = 21.9\sin 236.2° + 96.7\sin 11.5° + 62.9\sin 143.4°$
$R = \sqrt{R_x^2 + R_y^2} = 50.2$

$$\theta = \tan^{-1}\frac{R_y}{R_x} = 50.3°$$

25. $R_x = 302\cos(180° - 45.4°) + 155\cos(180° + 53.0°) + 212\cos 30.8° = -123$
$R_y = 302\sin(180° - 45.4°) + 155\sin(180° + 53°) + 212\sin 30.8° = 200$
$R = \sqrt{R_x^2 + R_y^2} = 235$

$$\theta = \tan^{-1}\frac{R_y}{R_x} = -58.4° \text{ from calculator}$$

$$\theta_R = 180° - 58.4 = 121.6° \text{ since } \theta_R \text{ is in QII}$$

Section 6.4

9.4   Applications of Vectors

1.

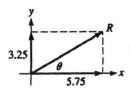

$$R = \sqrt{5.75^2 + 3.25^2} = 6.60 \text{ lb}$$

$$\theta = \tan^{-1} \frac{3.25}{5.75} = 29.5°$$

5.

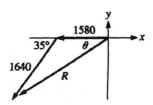

$$R_x = -1580 - 1640 \cos 35.0°$$
$$R_y = -1640 \sin 35.0°$$
$$R = \sqrt{R_x^2 + R_y^2} = 3070 \text{ ft}$$

$$\theta = \tan^{-1} \frac{R_y}{R_x} = 17.8° \text{ S of W}$$

9.

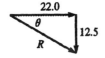

$$R = \sqrt{22.0^2 + 12.5^2} = 25.3 \text{ km/h}$$
$$\theta = \tan^{-1} \frac{12.5}{22.0} = 29.6°$$

13.

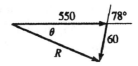

$$R = \sqrt{R_x^2 + R_y^2}$$
$$R = \sqrt{(550 - 60 \cos 78°)^2 + (60 \sin 78°)^2}$$
$$R = 540 \text{ km/h}$$

$$\theta = \tan^{-1} \frac{60 \sin 78°}{550 - 60 \cos 78°}$$

$$\theta = 6°$$

17. $r = \dfrac{d}{2} = \dfrac{8.20}{2} = 4.10$

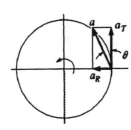

$$a = \sqrt{a_T^2 + a_R^2} = \sqrt{(\alpha r)^2 + (w^2 r)^2}$$
$$a = \sqrt{(318(4.10))^2 + (212^2 \cdot 4.10)^2}$$
$$a = 184,000 \text{ in/min}^2$$

$$\theta = \tan^{-1} \frac{a_R}{a_T} = \tan^{-1} \frac{w_r^2 r}{\alpha r} = \tan^{-1} \frac{212^2}{318}$$

$$\theta = 89.6°$$

21. top view of plane

$$V_H = \sqrt{75.0^2 + 15.0^2} = 76.5$$

$$\theta = \tan^{-1}\frac{15.0}{75.0} = 11.3°$$

$$V_v = 9.80(2.00) = 19.6$$

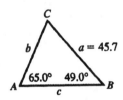

$$V = \sqrt{76.5^2 + 19.6^2}$$
$$V = 79.0 \text{ m/s}$$

$$\alpha = \tan^{-1}\frac{19.6}{76.5}$$

$$\alpha = 14.4°, \ 75.6° \text{ from vertical}$$

Section 6.5

9.5   Oblique Triangles, the Law of Sines

1.

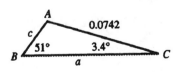

$$C = 180° - 65.0° - 49.0° = 66.0°$$

$$\frac{a}{\sin A} = \frac{b}{\sin B} = \frac{c}{\sin C}$$

$$\frac{45.7}{\sin 65.0°} = \frac{b}{\sin 49.0°} \Rightarrow b = 38.1$$

$$\frac{45.7}{\sin 65.0°} = \frac{c}{\sin 66.0°} \Rightarrow c = 46.1$$

5.

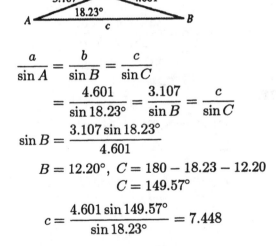

$$\frac{a}{\sin A} = \frac{b}{\sin B} = \frac{c}{\sin C}$$

$$= \frac{4.601}{\sin 18.23°} = \frac{3.107}{\sin B} = \frac{c}{\sin C}$$

$$\sin B = \frac{3.107 \sin 18.23°}{4.601}$$

$$B = 12.20°, \ C = 180 - 18.23 - 12.20$$
$$C = 149.57°$$

$$c = \frac{4.601 \sin 149.57°}{\sin 18.23°} = 7.448$$

9.

$$A = 180° - 51.0° - 3.4° = 125.6°$$

$$\frac{a}{\sin A} = \frac{b}{\sin B} = \frac{c}{\sin C}$$

$$\frac{a}{\sin 125.6°} = \frac{0.0742}{\sin 51.0°} = \frac{c}{\sin 3.4°}$$

$$a = \frac{0.0742 \sin 125.6°}{\sin 51.0°} = 0.0776$$

$$c = \frac{0.0742 \sin 3.4°}{\sin 51.0°} = 0.00566$$

13.

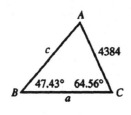

$$A = 180° - 47.73° - 64.56°$$
$$= 68.01°$$

$$\frac{a}{\sin A} = \frac{b}{\sin B}$$
$$= \frac{c}{\sin C}$$

$$\frac{a}{\sin 68.01°} = \frac{4384}{\sin 47.43°}$$
$$= \frac{c}{\sin 64.56°}$$

$$a = \frac{4384 \sin 68.01°}{\sin 47.43°}$$
$$= 5520$$

$$c = \frac{4384 \sin 64.56°}{\sin 47.43°}$$
$$= 5376$$

17.

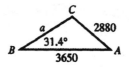

$$\frac{a}{\sin A} = \frac{b}{\sin B} = \frac{c}{\sin C}$$
$$\frac{a}{\sin A} = \frac{2880}{\sin 31.4°} = \frac{3650}{\sin C}$$
$$\sin C = \frac{3650 \sin 31.4°}{2880} \Rightarrow C = 41.3° \text{ or } 138.7°$$

Case I. $C = 41.3°$,
$$A = 180° - 31.4° - 41.3°$$
$$= 107.3°$$

$$\frac{a}{\sin 107.3°} = \frac{2880}{\sin 31.4°}$$
$$a = 5280$$

Case II. $C = 138.7°$,
$$A = 180° - 31.4° - 138.7°$$
$$= 9.9°$$

$$\frac{a}{\sin 9.9°} = \frac{2880}{\sin 31.4°}$$
$$a = 950$$

21.

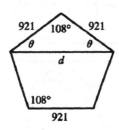

$$2\theta + 108° = 180°$$
$$\theta = 36°$$

$$\frac{921}{\sin \theta} = \frac{d}{\sin 108°}$$
$$d = \frac{921 \sin 108°}{\sin 36°}$$
$$d = 1490 \text{ ft}$$

25. $d =$ distance along Arsenal from Gravois to Jefferson

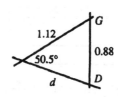

$$\frac{1.12}{\sin D} = \frac{0.88}{\sin 50.5}$$
$$D = 79.1° \quad \text{or} \quad 100.9°$$

from drawing $\angle$ is acute.

$$C = 180° - 50.5° - 79.1° = 50.4°$$
$$\frac{d}{\sin C} = \frac{0.88}{\sin 50.5°}$$
$$d = \frac{0.88 \sin 50.4°}{\sin 50.5°}$$
$$d = 0.88 \text{ mi}$$

29. $C = 180° - 86.5 - 90.8° = 2.7°$

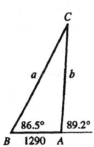

$$\frac{b}{\sin 86.5°} = \frac{1290}{\sin 2.7°}$$

$$b = 27,300 \text{ km}$$

$A = 180° - 89.2° = 90.8°$

Section 6.6

9.6   The Law of Cosines

1.

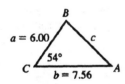

$c^2 = a^2 + b^2 - 2ab \cos C$
$c^2 = 6.00^2 + 7.56^2 - 2(6.00)(7.56) \cos 54.0°$
$c = 6.31$
$b^2 + c^2 - 2bc \cos A = a^2$

$7.56^2 + 6.31^2 - 2(7.56)(6.31) \cos A = 6^2$
$$\cos A = 0.639$$
$$A = 50.3°$$

$B = 180° - 54.0° - 50.3°$
$B = 75.7°$

5.

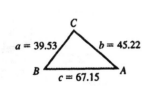

$$b^2 = a^2 + c^2 - 2ac \cos B$$
$$45.22^2 = 39.53^2 + 67.15^2 - 2(39.53)(67.15) \cos B$$
$$\cos B = 0.7585$$
$$B = 40.67°$$

$b^2 + c^2 - 2bc \cos A = a^2$

$45.22^2 + 67.15^2 - 2(45.22)(67.15) \cos A = 39.53^2$
$$\cos A = 0.8219$$
$$A = 34.73°$$
$C = 180 - 40.67° - 34.73° = 104.6°$

9.

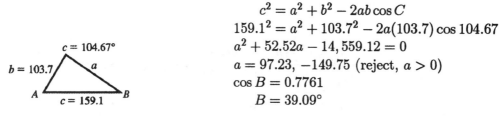

$$c^2 = a^2 + b^2 - 2ab\cos C = 320^2 + 847^2 - 2(320)(847)\cos 158.0$$
$$c = 1150$$
$$b^2 + c^2 - 2bc\cos A = a^2$$
$$847^2 + 1150^2 - 2(847)(1150)\cos A = 320^2$$
$$\cos A = 0.9946$$
$$A = 6.0°$$
$$a^2 + c^2 - 2ac\cos B = b^2$$
$$320^2 + 1150^2 - 2(320)(1150)\cos B = 847^2$$
$$\cos B = 0.9612$$
$$B = 16.0°$$

13.

$$c^2 = a^2 + b^2 - 2ab\cos C$$
$$159.1^2 = a^2 + 103.7^2 - 2a(103.7)\cos 104.67$$
$$a^2 + 52.52a - 14,559.12 = 0$$
$$a = 97.23, \ -149.75 \ (\text{reject, } a > 0)$$
$$\cos B = 0.7761$$
$$B = 39.09°$$

$c = 104.67°$
$b = 103.7$
a
A
$c = 159.1$
B

$$a^2 + c^2 - 2ac\cos B = b^2$$
$$97.23^2 + 159.1^2 - 2(97.23)(159.1)\cos B = 103.7^2$$
$$A = 180° - C - B = 180° - 104.67 - 39.09° = 36.24°$$

17.

A
$c = 158$
$b = 598$
B
$a = 723$
C

$$a^2 = b^2 + c^2 - 2bc\cos A$$
$$723^2 = 598^2 + 158^2 - 2(598)(158)\cos A$$
$$\cos A = -0.7417$$
$$A = 137.9°$$
$$b^2 = a^2 + c^2 - 2ac\cos B$$
$$598^2 = 723^2 + 158^2 - 2(723)(158)\cos B$$
$$\cos B = 0.8320$$
$$B = 33.7°$$
$$C = 180° - A - B = 180° - 137.9° - 33.7° = 8.4°$$

21.

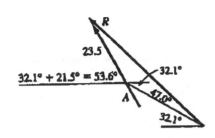

from $d = rt$, $23.5(2.00) = 47.0$ and
$$23.5(1.00) = 23.5$$
$$\measuredangle = 32.1° + 90° + (90° - 53.6°)$$
$$\measuredangle = 158.5°$$

$$R^2 = 23.5^2 + 47^2 - 2(23.5)(47)\cos 158.5°$$
$$R = 69.4 \text{ miles from base}$$

25.

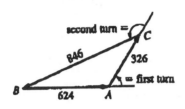

$$846^2 = 624^2 + 326^2 - 2(624)(326)\cos A$$
$$\cos A = -0.5409$$
$$A = 122.7°$$
$$\text{first turn} = 180° - 122.7° = 57.3°$$
$$624^2 = 846^2 + 326^2 - 2(846)(326)\cos C$$
$$\cos C = 0.7843$$
$$C = 38.3°$$
$$\text{second turn} = 180° - 38.3° = 141.7°$$

29.

$$c^2 = 12.7^2 + 11.5^2 - 2(12.7)(11.5)\cos 23.6°$$
$$c = 5.09 \text{ km/h}$$

Section 6.7

Chapter 9 Review Exercises

1.

y-component $= 65.0\cos 28.0° = 57.4$
x-component $= 65.0\sin 28.0° = 30.5$

5.

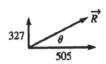

$$R = \sqrt{327^2 + 505^2} = 602$$

$$\theta = \tan^{-1}\frac{327}{505} = 32.9°$$

9.

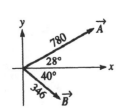

$$R_x = 780\cos 28.0° + 346\cos 40.0° = 954$$
$$R_y = 780\sin 28.0° - 346\sin 40.0° = 144$$

$$R = \sqrt{R_x^2 + R_y^2} = \sqrt{954^2 + 144^2} = 965$$

$$\theta_R = \tan^{-1}\frac{144}{954} = 8.6°$$

13.

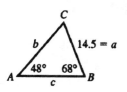

$$Y_x = 51.33 \cos 12.25° = 5016$$
$$Y_y = 51.33 \sin 12.25° = 10.89$$
$$Z_x = 42.61 \cos 68.23° = 15.80$$
$$Z_y = -42.61 \sin 68.23° = -39.57$$
$$R_x = 50.16 + 15.80 = 65.98$$
$$R_y = 10.89 - 39.57 = -28.68$$
$$R = \sqrt{R_x^2 + R_y^2} = \sqrt{65.98^2 + (-28.68)^2} = 71.94$$

$$\tan\theta = \frac{R_y}{R_x} = \frac{-28.68}{65.98}$$

$$\theta = 336.50°, \ \theta_{\text{ref}} = 23.50°$$

17.

$$C = 180° - 48.0° - 68.0° = 64.0°$$

$$\frac{14.5}{\sin 48.0°} = \frac{b}{\sin 68.0°} = \frac{c}{\sin 64.0°}$$

$$b = \frac{14.5 \sin 68.0°}{\sin 48.0°} = 18.1,$$

$$c = \frac{14.5 \sin 64.0°}{\sin 48.0°} = 17.5$$

21.

$$C = 180° - 17.85° - 154.16° = 7.99°$$

$$\frac{a}{\sin 17.85°} = \frac{b}{\sin 154.16} = \frac{7863}{\sin 7.99°}$$

$$b = \frac{7863 \sin 154.16°}{\sin 7.99°} = 24{,}660$$

$$a = \frac{7863 \sin 17.85°}{\sin 7.99°} = 17{,}340$$

25.

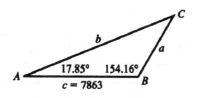

$$\frac{a}{\sin A} = \frac{14.5}{\sin B} = \frac{13.0}{\sin 56.6}$$

$$\sin B = \frac{14.5 \sin 56.6}{13.0}$$

$$B = 68.6° \quad \text{or} \quad 111.4°$$

<u>Case I:</u> $B = 68.6°$, $A = 180° - 68.6° - 56.6° = 54.8°$

$$\frac{a}{\sin 54.8°} = \frac{13.0}{\sin 56.6°} \Rightarrow a = 12.7$$

<u>Case II:</u> $B = 111.4°$, $A = 180° - 111.4° - 56.6° = 12.0°$

$$\frac{a}{\sin 12.0°} = \frac{13.0}{\sin 56.6°} \Rightarrow a = 3.24$$

29.

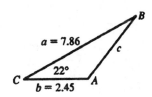

$$c^2 = a^2 + b^2 - 2ab \cos C$$
$$c^2 = 7.86^2 + 2.45^2 - 2(7.86)(2.45) \cos 22.0°$$
$$c = 5.66$$
$$a^2 = b^2 + c^2 - 2bc \cos A$$
$$7.86^2 = 2.45^2 + 5.66^2 - 2(2.45)(5.66) \cos A$$
$$\cos A = -0.8560$$
$$A = 148.9°$$
$$B = 180° = C - A = 180° - 22° - 148.9°$$
$$B = 9.1°$$

33.

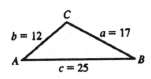

$$a^2 = b^2 + c^2 - 2bc \cos A$$
$$17^2 = 12^2 + 25^2 - 2(12)(25) \cos A$$
$$\cos A = 0.8$$
$$A = 37°$$
$$b^2 = a^2 + c^2 - 2ac \cos B$$
$$12^2 = 17^2 + 25^2 - 2(17)(25) \cos B$$
$$\cos B = 0.9059$$
$$B = 25°$$
$$C = 180° - 37° - 25° = 118°$$

37.

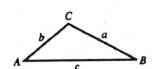

$$a^2 = b^2 + c^2 - 2bc \cos A$$
$$b^2 = a^2 + c^2 - 2ac \cos B$$
$$\underline{c^2 = a^2 + b^2 - 2ab \cos C \quad add}$$

$$a^2 + b^2 + c^2 = 2a^2 + 2b^2 + 2c^2 - 2bc \cos A - 2ac \cos B - 2ab \cos C$$
$$a^2 + b^2 + c^2 = 2bc \cos A + 2ac \cos B + 2ab \cos G$$

$$\frac{a^2 + b^2 + c^2}{2abc} = \frac{\cos A}{a} + \frac{\cos}{b} + \frac{\cos C}{c}$$

41. horizontal component $= 175.6 \cos 152.48° = -155.7$ lb
vertical component $= 175.6 \sin 152.48° = 81.14$ lb

45.

$$d = 480 \text{ km/h} \cdot 3 \text{ min} \cdot \frac{\text{h}}{60 \text{ min}}$$

$$d = 24 \text{ km}$$
$$h = d \sin 24° = 24 \sin 24°$$
$$h = 9.8 \text{ km}$$

49. $x^2 + 2.7^2 - 2 \cdot x \cdot 2.7 \cos 27.5° = 1.25^2$
$x^2 - 5.4 \cdot \cos 27.5 \cdot x + 5.7275 = 0$

$$x = \frac{5.4 \cos 27.5 \pm \sqrt{(-5.4 \cos 27.5)^2 - 4(1)(5.7275)}}{2(1)}$$

$x = 2.30,\ 2.49$ m

53.

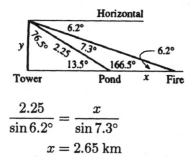

$$\frac{2.25}{\sin 6.2°} = \frac{x}{\sin 7.3°}$$

$$x = 2.65 \text{ km}$$

57.

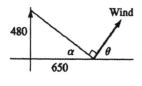

$$\tan \alpha = \frac{480}{650}$$

$\alpha = 36.4°$ N of E
$F = \sqrt{F_x^2 + F_y^2}$
$\quad = \sqrt{650^2 + 480^2}$
$\quad = 810$ N

61.

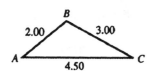

Use law of cosines three times.

$2.00^2 + 4.50^2 - 2(2.00)(4.50) \cos A = 3.00^2$
$A = 32.1°$
$2.00^2 + 3.00^2 - 2(2.00)(3.00) \cos B = 4.50^2$
$B = 127.2°$
$3.00^2 + 4.50^2 - 2(3.00)(4.50) \cos C = 2.00^2$
$C = 20.7°$

Part 6
Chapter 9

1.
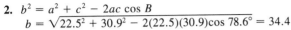

2. $b^2 = a^2 + c^2 - 2ac \cos B$
$b = \sqrt{22.5^2 + 30.9^2 - 2(22.5)(30.9)\cos 78.6°} = 34.4$

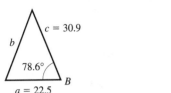

3. $x^2 = 36.50^2 + 21.38^2 - 2(36.50)(21.38)\cos 45.00°$

$x = 26.19 \text{ m}$ $\dfrac{21.38}{\sin \alpha} = \dfrac{26.19}{\sin 45.00°}$

$\sin \alpha = \dfrac{21.38 \sin 45.00°}{26.19}$, $\alpha = 35.26°$

$\theta = 45.00° - 35.26° = 9.74°$
Displacement is 26.19 m,
9.74° N of E.

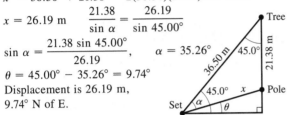

4. $C = 180° - (18.9° + 104.2°) = 56.9°$

$\dfrac{c}{\sin C} = \dfrac{a}{\sin A}$ $c = \dfrac{426 \sin 56.9°}{\sin 18.9°} = 1100$

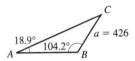

5. Since a is longest side, find A first.
$a^2 = b^2 + c^2 - 2bc \cos A$
$\cos A = \dfrac{b^2 + c^2 - a^2}{2bc} = \dfrac{3.29^2 + 8.44^2 - 9.84^2}{2(3.29)(8.44)}$

$A = 105.4°$
$\dfrac{b}{\sin B} = \dfrac{a}{\sin A}$
$\sin B = \dfrac{b \sin A}{a} = \dfrac{3.29 \sin 105.4°}{9.84}$
$B = 18.8°$
$C = 180° - (105.4° + 18.8°) = 55.8°$

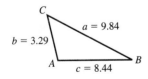

6. $A_x = 871 \cos 284.3° = 215$
$A_y = 871 \sin 284.3° = -844$

7. $\dfrac{63.0}{\sin 148.5°} = \dfrac{42.0}{\sin A}$ $\dfrac{x}{\sin 11.1°} = \dfrac{63.0}{\sin 148.5°}$

$\sin A = \dfrac{42.0 \sin 148.5°}{63.0}$ $x = \dfrac{63.0 \sin 11.1°}{\sin 148.5°}$

$A = 20.4°$ $= 23.2 \text{ mi}$
$C = 180° - (148.5° + 20.4°) = 11.1°$

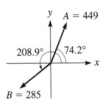

8. $A_x = 449 \cos 74.2°$ $B_x = 285 \cos 208.9°$
$A_y = 449 \sin 74.2°$ $B_y = 285 \sin 208.9°$
$R_x = A_x + B_x = 449 \cos 74.2° + 285 \cos 208.9°$
$\quad = -127.3$
$R_y = A_y + B_y = 449 \sin 74.2° + 285 \sin 208.9°$
$\quad = 294.3$
$R = \sqrt{(-127.3)^2 + 294.3^2} = 321$
$\tan \theta_{ref} = \dfrac{294.3}{127.3}$, $\theta_{ref} = 66.6°$, $\theta = 113.4°$

θ is in second quadrant, since R_x
is negative and R_y is positive.

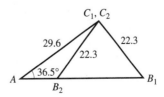

9. $29.6 \sin 36.5° = 17.6$
$17.6 < 22.3 < 29.6$ means two solutions.
$\dfrac{29.6}{\sin B} = \dfrac{22.3}{\sin 36.5°}$, $\sin B = \dfrac{29.6 \sin 36.5°}{22.3}$
$B_1 = 52.1°$ $C_1 = 180° - 36.5° - 52.1° = 91.4°$
$B_2 = 180° - 52.1° = 127.9°$,
$C_2 = 180° - 36.5° - 127.9° = 15.6°$
$\dfrac{c_1}{\sin 91.4°} = \dfrac{22.3}{\sin 36.5°}$, $c_1 = \dfrac{22.3 \sin 91.4°}{\sin 36.5°} = 37.5$
$\dfrac{c_2}{\sin 15.6°} = \dfrac{22.3}{\sin 36.5°}$, $c_2 = \dfrac{22.3 \sin 15.6°}{\sin 36.5°} = 10.1$

PART 7 – GRAPHS OF THE TRIGONOMETRIC FUNCTIONS

CHAPTER  GRAPHS OF THE TRIGONOMETRIC FUNCTIONS

One of the clearest ways of showing the properties of the trigonometric functions is by means of their graphs. In addition, their graphs are very valuable in numerous areas of application that do not involve solving triangles. These important applications are found in electronics, communications, optics, acoustics, mechanical vibrations, and in many areas of physics.

These graphs are particularly useful in applications that involve any type of wave motion and periodic values, which repeat on a regular basis. Filtering electronic signals in communications, mixing musical sounds on a tape in a recording studio, studying the seasonal temperatures of an area, and analyzing ocean waves and tides illustrate some of the many applications of this type of periodic motion.

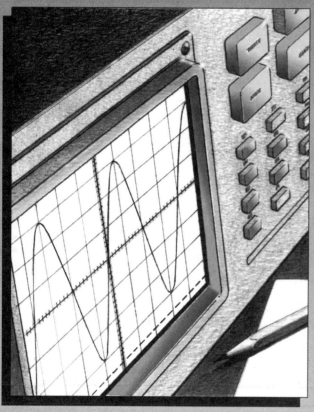

In Section 10-6 we show the resulting curve when an oscilloscope is used to combine and display electric signals.

Section 7.1

10-1 GRAPHS OF $y = a \sin x$ AND $y = a \cos x$

The graphs of the trigonometric functions are constructed on the rectangular coordinate system. In plotting and sketching the trigonometric functions, *it is normal to express the angle in radians.* By using radians, *x and the trigonometric function of x are expressed as real numbers.*

Therefore, in order that we can plot and sketch the graphs of the trigonometric functions,

NOTE▶   *it is necessary to be able to readily use angles expressed in radians.*

If necessary, review Section 8-3 on radian measure of angles for this purpose.

In this section, the graphs of the sine and cosine functions are shown. We begin by making a table of values of x and y for the function $y = \sin x$, where we are using x and y in the standard way as the *independent variable* and *dependent variable*. We plot the points to obtain the graph in Fig. 10-1.

x	0	$\frac{\pi}{6}$	$\frac{\pi}{3}$	$\frac{\pi}{2}$	$\frac{2\pi}{3}$	$\frac{5\pi}{6}$	π	$\frac{7\pi}{6}$	$\frac{4\pi}{3}$	$\frac{3\pi}{2}$	$\frac{5\pi}{3}$	$\frac{11\pi}{6}$	2π
y	0	0.5	0.87	1	0.87	0.5	0	−0.5	−0.87	−1	−0.87	−0.5	0

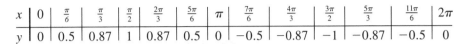

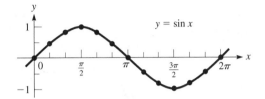

Fig. 10-1

The graph of $y = \cos x$ may be drawn in the same way. The next table gives values for plotting the graph of $y = \cos x$, and the graph is shown in Fig. 10-2.

x	0	$\frac{\pi}{6}$	$\frac{\pi}{3}$	$\frac{\pi}{2}$	$\frac{2\pi}{3}$	$\frac{5\pi}{6}$	π	$\frac{7\pi}{6}$	$\frac{4\pi}{3}$	$\frac{3\pi}{2}$	$\frac{5\pi}{3}$	$\frac{11\pi}{6}$	2π
y	1	0.87	0.5	0	−0.5	−0.87	−1	−0.87	−0.5	0	0.5	0.87	1

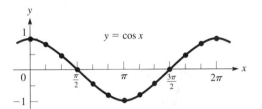

Fig. 10-2

The graphs are continued beyond the values shown in the tables to indicate that *they continue indefinitely in each direction.* To show this more clearly, in Figs. 10-3 and 10-4, we show the graphs of $y = \sin x$ and $y = \cos x$ from $x = -10$ to $x = 10$. (Note that $2\pi \approx 6.3$ for the graphs in Figs. 10-1 and 10-2.)

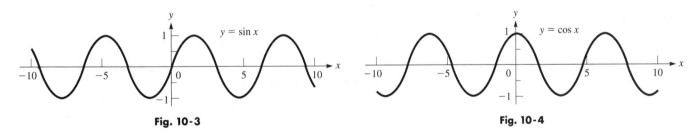

Fig. 10-3   **Fig. 10-4**

From these tables and graphs, it can be seen that *the graphs of y = sin x and y = cos x are of exactly the same shape (called* **sinusoidal**), *with the cosine curve displaced π/2 units to the left of the sine curve.* The shape of these curves should be recognized readily, with special note as to the points at which they cross the axes. This information will be especially valuable in *sketching* similar curves, since the basic sinusoidal shape remains the same. It will not be necessary to plot numerous points every time we wish to sketch such a curve.

AMPLITUDE

To obtain the graph of $y = a \sin x$, we note that all the y-values obtained for the graph of $y = \sin x$ are to be multiplied by the number a. In this case the greatest value of the sine function is $|a|$. *The number $|a|$ is called the* **amplitude** *of the curve and represents the greatest y-value of the curve*. Also, the curve will have no value less than $-|a|$. This is true for $y = a \cos x$ as well as for $y = a \sin x$.

■EXAMPLE 1 Plot the graph of $y = 2 \sin x$.

Since $a = 2$, the amplitude of this curve is $|2| = 2$. This means that the maximum value of y is 2 and the minimum value is $y = -2$. The table of values follows, and the curve is shown in Fig. 10-5.

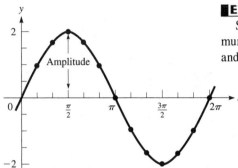

Fig. 10-5

x	0	$\frac{\pi}{6}$	$\frac{\pi}{3}$	$\frac{\pi}{2}$	$\frac{2\pi}{3}$	$\frac{5\pi}{6}$	π
y	0	1	1.73	2	1.73	1	0

x	$\frac{7\pi}{6}$	$\frac{4\pi}{3}$	$\frac{3\pi}{2}$	$\frac{5\pi}{3}$	$\frac{11\pi}{6}$	2π
y	-1	-1.73	-2	-1.73	-1	0

■EXAMPLE 2 Plot the graph of $y = -3 \cos x$.

In this case $a = -3$, and this means that the amplitude is $|-3| = 3$. Therefore, the maximum value of y is 3, and the minimum value of y is -3. The table of values follows, and the curve is shown in Fig. 10-6.

x	0	$\frac{\pi}{6}$	$\frac{\pi}{3}$	$\frac{\pi}{2}$	$\frac{2\pi}{3}$	$\frac{5\pi}{6}$	π
y	-3	-2.6	-1.5	0	1.5	2.6	3

x	$\frac{7\pi}{6}$	$\frac{4\pi}{3}$	$\frac{3\pi}{2}$	$\frac{5\pi}{3}$	$\frac{11\pi}{6}$	2π
y	2.6	1.5	0	-1.5	-2.6	-3

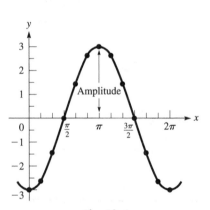

Fig. 10-6

TABLE 10-1

	$x = 0, \pi, 2\pi$	$\frac{\pi}{2}, \frac{3\pi}{2}$
$y = a \sin x$	zeros	max. or min.
$y = a \cos x$	max. or min.	zeros

Note from Example 2 that *the effect of the negative sign before the number a is to* **invert** *the curve about the x-axis*. The effect of the number a can also be seen readily from these examples.

From the previous examples we see that the function $y = a \sin x$ has zeros for $x = 0, \pi, 2\pi$ and that it has its maximum or minimum values for $x = \pi/2, 3\pi/2$. The function $y = a \cos x$ has its zeros for $x = \pi/2, 3\pi/2$ and its maximum or minimum values for $x = 0, \pi, 2\pi$. This is summarized in Table 10-1. Therefore, by knowing the general shape of the sine curve, where it has its zeros, and what its amplitude is, *we can rapidly* **sketch** *curves of the form $y = a \sin x$ and $y = a \cos x$*.

Since the graphs of $y = a \sin x$ and $y = a \cos x$ can extend indefinitely to the right and to the left, we see that the domain of each is all real numbers. We should note that the key values of $x = 0, \pi/2, \pi, 3\pi/2$, and 2π are those only for x from 0 to 2π. Corresponding values ($x = 5\pi/2, 3\pi$, and their negatives) could also be used. Also from the graphs we can readily see that the range of these functions is $-|a| \le f(x) \le |a|$.

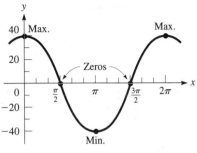

Fig. 10-7

EXAMPLE 3   Sketch the graph of $y = 40 \cos x$.

First, we set up a table of values for the points where the curve has its zeros, maximum points, and minimum points.

x	0	$\frac{\pi}{2}$	π	$\frac{3\pi}{2}$	2π
y	40	0	-40	0	40
	max.		min.		max.

Now, we plot these points and join them, knowing the basic sinusoidal shape of the curve. See Fig. 10-7.

The graphs of $y = a \sin x$ and $y = a \cos x$ can be displayed easily on a graphing calculator. In the next example we will see that the calculator displays the features of the curve we should expect from our previous discussion.

EXAMPLE 4   Display the graph of $y = -2 \sin x$ on a graphing calculator.

Using *radian* mode on the calculator, Fig. 10-8(a) shows the calculator view for the key values in the following table.

x	0	$\frac{\pi}{2}$	π	$\frac{3\pi}{2}$	2π
y	0	-2	0	2	0
		min.		max.	

We see the amplitude of 2 and the effect of the negative sign in inverting the curve, as expected. Fig. 10-8(b) shows the calculator graph for $x = -10$ to $x = 10$.

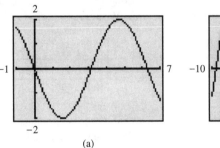
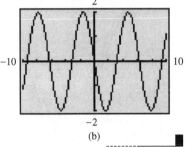

Fig. 10-8   (a)   (b)

═══════════════ **EXERCISES** *10-1* ═══════════════

In Exercises 1–4, complete the following table for the given functions and then plot the resulting graphs.

x	$-\pi$	$-\frac{3\pi}{4}$	$-\frac{\pi}{2}$	$-\frac{\pi}{4}$	0	$\frac{\pi}{4}$	$\frac{\pi}{2}$	$\frac{3\pi}{4}$	π
y									

x	$\frac{5\pi}{4}$	$\frac{3\pi}{2}$	$\frac{7\pi}{4}$	2π	$\frac{9\pi}{4}$	$\frac{5\pi}{2}$	$\frac{11\pi}{4}$	3π
y								

1. $y = \sin x$ **2.** $y = \cos x$

3. $y = 3 \cos x$ **4.** $y = -4 \sin x$

In Exercises 5–20, sketch the graphs of the given functions. Check each using a graphing calculator.

5. $y = 3 \sin x$ **6.** $y = 5 \sin x$

7. $y = \frac{5}{2} \sin x$ **8.** $y = 35 \sin x$

9. $y = 2 \cos x$ **10.** $y = 3 \cos x$

11. $y = 0.8 \cos x$ **12.** $y = \frac{3}{2} \cos x$

13. $y = -\sin x$ **14.** $y = -3 \sin x$

15. $y = -1.5 \sin x$ **16.** $y = -0.2 \sin x$

17. $y = -\cos x$ **18.** $y = -8 \cos x$

19. $y = -50 \cos x$ **20.** $y = -0.4 \cos x$

Although units of π are convenient, we must remember that π is only a number. Numbers that are not multiples of π may be used. In Exercises 21–24, plot the indicated graphs by finding the values of y that correspond to values of x of 0, 1, 2, 3, 4, 5, 6, and 7 on a calculator. (Remember, the numbers 0, 1, 2, and so on represent radian measure.)

21. $y = \sin x$

22. $y = -3 \sin x$

23. $y = \cos x$

24. $y = 2 \cos x$

In Exercises 25–28, the graph of a function of the form $y = a \sin x$ or $y = a \cos x$ is shown. Determine the specific function for each.

25.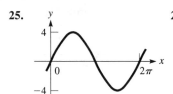

26.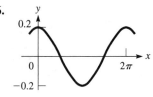

27.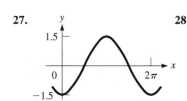

28.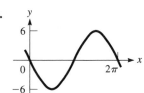

Section 7.2

10-2 GRAPHS OF $y = a \sin bx$ AND $y = a \cos bx$

In graphing the function $y = \sin x$, we see that the values of y repeat every 2π units of x. This is because $\sin x = \sin(x + 2\pi) = \sin(x + 4\pi)$, and so forth. For any function F, we say that it has a *period P* if $F(x) = F(x + P)$. For functions that are periodic, such as the sine and the cosine, *the* **period** *is the x-distance between a point and the next corresponding point for which the value of y repeats.*

Let us now plot the curve $y = \sin 2x$. This means that we choose a value for x, multiply this value by 2, and find the sine of the result. This leads to the following table of values for this function.

PERIOD OF A FUNCTION

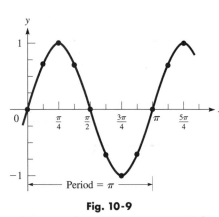

Fig. 10-9

NOTE ▶

x	0	$\frac{\pi}{8}$	$\frac{\pi}{4}$	$\frac{3\pi}{8}$	$\frac{\pi}{2}$	$\frac{5\pi}{8}$	$\frac{3\pi}{4}$	$\frac{7\pi}{8}$	π	$\frac{9\pi}{8}$	$\frac{5\pi}{4}$
$2x$	0	$\frac{\pi}{4}$	$\frac{\pi}{2}$	$\frac{3\pi}{4}$	π	$\frac{5\pi}{4}$	$\frac{3\pi}{2}$	$\frac{7\pi}{4}$	2π	$\frac{9\pi}{4}$	$\frac{5\pi}{2}$
y	0	0.7	1	0.7	0	-0.7	-1	-0.7	0	0.7	1

Plotting these points, we have the curve shown in Fig. 10-9.

From the table and Fig. 10-9, we see that $y = \sin 2x$ repeats after π units of x. The effect of the 2 is that the period of $y = \sin 2x$ is half the period of the curve of $y = \sin x$. We then conclude that if the period of a function $F(x)$ is P, then the period of $F(bx)$ is P/b. Since each of the functions $\sin x$ and $\cos x$ has a period of 2π, *each of the functions* $\sin bx$ *and* $\cos bx$ *has a period of* $2\pi/b$.

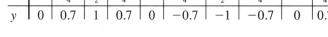

EXAMPLE 1   **(a)** The period of $\sin 3x$ is $\dfrac{2\pi}{3}$, which means that the curve of the function $y = \sin 3x$ will repeat every $\frac{2\pi}{3}$ (approximately 2.09) units of x.

(b) The period of $\cos 4x$ is $\dfrac{2\pi}{4} = \dfrac{\pi}{2}$.

(c) The period of $\sin \frac{1}{2}x$ is $\dfrac{2\pi}{\frac{1}{2}} = 4\pi$. In this case we see that the period is longer than that of the basic sine curve.   ■

■**EXAMPLE 2** (a) The period of $\sin \pi x$ is $2\pi/\pi = 2$. That is, the curve of the function $\sin \pi x$ repeats every 2 units.

   (b) The period of $\cos 3\pi x$ is $\dfrac{2\pi}{3\pi} = \dfrac{2}{3}$.

   (c) The period of $\sin \dfrac{\pi}{4} x$ is $\dfrac{2\pi}{\frac{\pi}{4}} = 8$.

   (d) The period of $\sin 3x$ is $\dfrac{2\pi}{3} = 2.09$, and the period of $\sin \pi x$ is $\frac{2\pi}{\pi} = 2$.

We can see that these two periods differ only slightly since π is only slightly larger than 3. ------------■

Combining the value of the period with the value of the amplitude from Section 10-1, we conclude that *the functions $y = a \sin bx$ and $y = a \cos bx$ each has an amplitude of $|a|$ and a period of $2\pi/b$.* These properties are very useful in sketching these functions.

■**EXAMPLE 3** Sketch the graph of $y = 3 \sin 4x$ for $0 \le x \le \pi$.
   Since $a = 3$, we can immediately see that the amplitude is 3. Also, from the $4x$ we see that the period is $2\pi/4 = \pi/2$. Therefore, we know that $y = 0$ for $x = 0$ and also for $x = \pi/2$. Since we know that this sine function is zero halfway between $x = 0$ and $x = \pi/2$, we find that $y = 0$ for $x = \pi/4$. The graph of the sine function reaches its maximum or minimum values halfway between the zeros. This tells us that $y = 3$ for $x = \pi/8$, and $y = -3$ for $x = 3\pi/8$. A table for these important values follows. We should also note that the values of x that are listed are those for which $4x = 0, \pi/2, \pi, 3\pi/2, 2\pi$, and so on.

x	0	$\frac{\pi}{8}$	$\frac{\pi}{4}$	$\frac{3\pi}{8}$	$\frac{\pi}{2}$	$\frac{5\pi}{8}$	$\frac{3\pi}{4}$	$\frac{7\pi}{8}$	π
y	0	3	0	-3	0	3	0	-3	0

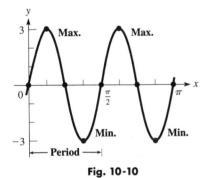

Fig. 10-10

Using the values from the table and the fact that we know the curve is sinusoidal in form, we sketch the graph of this function in Fig. 10-10. We see again that knowing the key values and the basic shape of the curve allows us to *sketch* the graph of the curve quickly and easily. ------------■

We see from Example 3 that *an important distance in sketching a sine curve or a cosine curve is one-fourth of the period.* For $y = a \sin bx$, it is one-fourth of the period from the origin to the first value of x where y is at its maximum (or minimum) value. Then we proceed another one-fourth period to a zero, another one-fourth period to the next minimum (or maximum) value, another to the next zero (this is where the period is completed), and so on. Thus,

NOTE ▶

by finding one-fourth of the period, we can easily find the important values for sketching the curve.

Similarly, one-fourth of the period is used in sketching the graph of $y = a \cos bx$. For this function, its maximum (or minimum) occurs for $y = 0$. At the following one-fourth period values, there is a zero, a minimum (or maximum), a zero, and a maximum (or minimum) at the start of the next period.

On the next page we summarize the important values for sketching the graphs of $y = a \sin bx$ and $y = a \cos bx$.

> ### Important Values for Sketching $y = a \sin bx$ and $y = a \cos bx$
> 1. *The amplitude:* $|a|$
> 2. *The period:* $2\pi/b$
> 3. *Values of the function for each one-fourth period*

■EXAMPLE 4   Sketch the graph of $y = -2 \cos 3x$ for $0 \le x \le 2\pi$.

We note that the amplitude is 2 and the period is $\frac{2\pi}{3}$. This means that one-fourth of the period is $\frac{1}{4} \times \frac{2\pi}{3} = \frac{\pi}{6}$. Since the cosine curve is at a maximum or minimum for $x = 0$, we find that $y = -2$ for $x = 0$ (the negative value is due to the minus sign before the function), which means it is a minimum point. The curve then has a zero at $x = \frac{\pi}{6}$, a maximum value of 2 at $x = 2(\frac{\pi}{6}) = \frac{\pi}{3}$, a zero at $x = 3(\frac{\pi}{6}) = \frac{\pi}{2}$, and its next value of -2 at $x = 4(\frac{\pi}{6}) = \frac{2\pi}{3}$, and so on. Therefore, we have the following table.

x	0	$\frac{\pi}{6}$	$\frac{\pi}{3}$	$\frac{\pi}{2}$	$\frac{2\pi}{3}$	$\frac{5\pi}{6}$	π	$\frac{7\pi}{6}$	$\frac{4\pi}{3}$	$\frac{3\pi}{2}$	$\frac{5\pi}{3}$	$\frac{11\pi}{6}$	2π
y	-2	0	2	0	-2	0	2	0	-2	0	2	0	-2

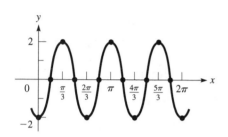

Fig. 10-11

Using this table and the sinusoidal shape of the cosine curve, we sketch the function of Fig. 10-11.   ■

■EXAMPLE 5   A generator produces a voltage $V = 200 \cos 50\pi t$, where t is the time in seconds (50π has units of rad/s; thus, $50\pi t$ is an angle in radians). Use a graphing calculator to display the graph of V as a function of t for $0 \le t \le 0.06$ s.

The amplitude is 200 V and the period is $2\pi/(50\pi) = 0.04$ s. Since the period is not in terms of π, it is more convenient to use decimal units for t rather than to use units in terms of π as in the previous graphs. Thus, we have the following table of values:

t (seconds)	0	0.01	0.02	0.03	0.04	0.05	0.06
V (volts)	200	0	-200	0	200	0	-200

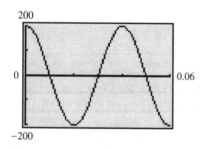

Fig. 10-12

For the graphing calculator, we use x for t and y for V. This means we graph the function $y_1 = 200 \cos 50\pi x$, as shown in Fig. 10-12. From the amplitude of 200 V and the above table, we choose the *window* values shown in Fig. 10-12. We do not consider negative values of t, for they have no real meaning in this problem.   ■

EXERCISES 10-2

In Exercises 1–20, find the period of each function.

1. $y = 2 \sin 6x$
2. $y = 4 \sin 2x$
3. $y = 3 \cos 8x$
4. $y = 28 \cos 10x$
5. $y = -2 \sin 12x$
6. $y = -\sin 5x$
7. $y = -\cos 16x$
8. $y = -4 \cos 2x$
9. $y = 520 \sin 2\pi x$
10. $y = 2 \sin 3\pi x$

11. $y = 3 \cos 4\pi x$
12. $y = 4 \cos 10\pi x$
13. $y = 3 \sin \frac{1}{3}x$
14. $y = -2 \sin \frac{2}{5}x$
15. $y = -\frac{1}{2} \cos \frac{2}{3}x$
16. $y = \frac{1}{3} \cos \frac{1}{4}x$
17. $y = 0.4 \sin \dfrac{2\pi x}{3}$
18. $y = 1.5 \cos \dfrac{\pi x}{10}$
19. $y = 3.3 \cos \pi^2 x$
20. $y = 2.5 \sin \dfrac{2x}{\pi}$

In Exercises 21–40, sketch the graphs of the given functions. Check each using a graphing calculator. (These are the same functions as in Exercises 1–20.)

21. $y = 2 \sin 6x$ **22.** $y = 4 \sin 2x$

23. $y = 3 \cos 8x$ **24.** $y = 28 \cos 10x$

25. $y = -2 \sin 12x$ **26.** $y = -\sin 5x$

27. $y = -\cos 16x$ **28.** $y = -4 \cos 2x$

29. $y = 520 \sin 2\pi x$ **30.** $y = 2 \sin 3\pi x$

31. $y = 3 \cos 4\pi x$ **32.** $y = 4 \cos 10\pi x$

33. $y = 3 \sin \frac{1}{3} x$ **34.** $y = -2 \sin \frac{2}{5} x$

35. $y = -\frac{1}{2} \cos \frac{2}{3} x$ **36.** $y = \frac{1}{3} \cos \frac{1}{4} x$

37. $y = 0.4 \sin \dfrac{2\pi x}{3}$ **38.** $y = 1.5 \cos \dfrac{\pi x}{10}$

39. $y = 3.3 \cos \pi^2 x$ **40.** $y = 2.5 \sin \dfrac{2x}{\pi}$

In Exercises 41–44, the period is given for a function of the form $y = \sin bx$. Write the function corresponding to the given period.

41. $\dfrac{\pi}{3}$ **42.** $\dfrac{2\pi}{5}$ **43.** 2   **44.** 6

In Exercises 45–48, sketch the indicated graphs.

45. The standard electric voltage in a 60-Hz alternating-current circuit is given by $V = 170 \sin 120\pi t$, where t is the time in seconds. Sketch the graph of V as a function of t for $0 \le t \le 0.05$ s.

46. To tune the instruments of an orchestra before a concert, an A note is struck on a piano. The piano wire vibrates with a displacement y (in mm) given by $y = 3.20 \cos 880\pi t$, where t is in seconds. Sketch the graph of y vs. t for $0 \le t \le 0.01$ s.

47. The velocity v (in in./s) of a piston is $v = 450 \cos 3600t$, where t is in seconds. Sketch the graph of v vs. t for $0 \le t \le 0.006$ s.

48. The displacement y (in m) of the end of a robot arm for welding is $y = 12.75 \sin 0.419t$, where t is in seconds. Sketch the graph of y as a function of t for $0 \le t \le 15$ s.

In Exercises 49–52, the graph of a function of the form $y = a \sin bx$ or $y = a \cos bx$ is shown. Determine the specific function for each.

49.
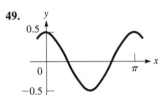

50.
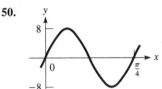

51.
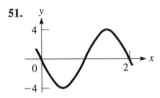

52.
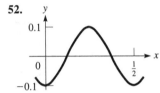

Section 7.3

$10\text{-}3$ GRAPHS OF $y = a \sin(bx + c)$ AND $y = a \cos(bx + c)$

Another important quantity in graphing the sine and cosine functions is the *phase angle*. In the function $y = a \sin(bx + c)$, *c* represents the **phase angle**. Its meaning is illustrated in the following example.

■**EXAMPLE 1**   Sketch the graph of $y = \sin(2x + \frac{\pi}{4})$.

Note that $c = \pi/4$. Therefore, in order to obtain values for the table, we assume a value for *x*, multiply it by 2, add $\pi/4$ to this value, and then find the sine of the result. The values that are shown are those for which $2x + \pi/4 = 0, \pi/4, \pi/2, 3\pi/4, \pi$, and so on, which are the important values for $y = \sin 2x$.

x	$-\frac{\pi}{8}$	0	$\frac{\pi}{8}$	$\frac{\pi}{4}$	$\frac{3\pi}{8}$	$\frac{\pi}{2}$	$\frac{5\pi}{8}$	$\frac{3\pi}{4}$	$\frac{7\pi}{8}$	π
y	0	0.7	1	0.7	0	-0.7	-1	-0.7	0	0.7

When we solve $2x + \pi/4 = 0$, we get $x = -\pi/8$, and this gives $y = \sin 0 = 0$. The other values for y are found in the same way. The graph is shown in Fig. 10-13. ---------- ■

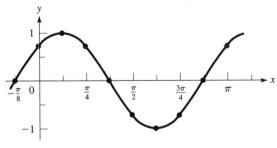

Fig. 10-13

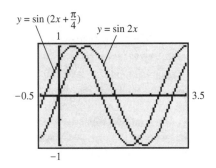

Fig. 10-14

See Appendix C for a graphing calculator program SINECURV. It displays the graphs of $y = \sin x$, $y = 2 \sin x$, $y = \sin 2x$, and $y = 2 \sin(2x - \pi/3)$.

Carefully note the difference between $y = \sin(bx + c)$ and $y = \sin bx + c$. Writing $\sin(bx + c)$ means to find the sine of the quantity of $bx + c$, whereas $\sin bx + c$ means to find the sine of bx and then add the value c.

We see from Example 1 that *the graph of $y = \sin(2x + \frac{\pi}{4})$ is precisely the same as the graph of $y = \sin 2x$, except that it is **shifted** $\pi/8$ units to the left.* In Fig. 10-14 a graphing calculator view shows the graphs of $y = \sin 2x$ and $y = \sin(2x + \frac{\pi}{4})$. We see that the shapes are the same and that the graph of $y = \sin(2x + \frac{\pi}{4})$ is about 0.4 unit ($\pi/8 \approx 0.39$) to the left of the graph of $y = \sin 2x$.

In general, the effect of c in the equation $y = a \sin(bx + c)$ is to shift the curve of $y = a \sin bx$ to the left if $c > 0$, or shift the curve to the right if $c < 0$. The amount of this shift is given by $-c/b$. Due to its importance in sketching curves, *the quantity $-c/b$ is called the **displacement** (or **phase shift**).*

We can see the reason that the displacement is $-c/b$ by noting corresponding points on the graphs of $y = \sin bx$ and $y = \sin(bx + c)$. For $y = \sin bx$, when $x = 0$, then $y = 0$. For $y = \sin(bx + c)$, when $x = -c/b$, then $y = 0$. The point $(-c/b, 0)$ on the graph of $y = \sin(bx + c)$ is $-c/b$ units to the left of the point $(0, 0)$ on the graph of $y = \sin x$. In Fig. 10-14, $-c/b = -\pi/8$.

Therefore, we use the displacement combined with the amplitude and the period along with the other information from the previous sections to sketch curves of the functions $y = a \sin(bx + c)$ and $y = a \cos(bx + c)$, where $b > 0$.

Important Quantities to Determine for Sketching Graphs of $y = a \sin(bx + c)$ and $y = a \cos(bx + c)$

$$\text{Amplitude} = |a|$$
$$\text{Period} = \frac{2\pi}{b}$$
$$\text{Displacement} = -\frac{c}{b}$$

(10-1)

By use of these quantities and the one-fourth period distance, the graphs of the sine and cosine functions can be readily sketched. A general illustration of the graph of $y = a \sin(bx + c)$ is shown in Fig. 10-15. Note that

CAUTION▶ *the displacement is **negative** (to the left) for $c > 0$* (Fig. 10-15(a))
*the displacement is **positive** (to the right) for $c < 0$* (Fig. 10-15(b))

Note that we can find the displacement for the graphs of $y = a \sin(bx + c)$ by solving $bx + c = 0$ for x. We see that $x = -c/b$.

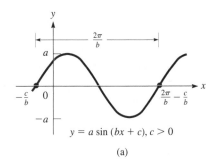

(a)

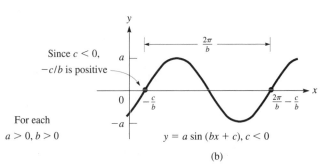

(b)

Fig. 10-15

EXAMPLE 2   Sketch the graph of $y = 2 \sin(3x - \pi)$.

First, we note that $a = 2$, $b = 3$, and $c = -\pi$. Therefore, the amplitude is 2, the period is $2\pi/3$, and the displacement is $-(-\pi/3) = \pi/3$. (We can also get the displacement from $3x - \pi = 0$, $x = \pi/3$.)

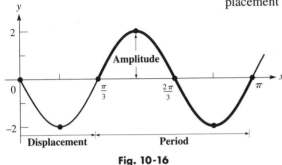

Fig. 10-16

We see that the curve "starts" at $x = \pi/3$ and starts repeating $2\pi/3$ units to the right of this point. Be sure to grasp this point well. *The period tells us the number of units along the x-axis between such corresponding points.* One-fourth of the period is $\frac{1}{4}(\frac{2\pi}{3}) = \frac{\pi}{6}$.

Important values are at $\frac{\pi}{3}$, $\frac{\pi}{3} + \frac{\pi}{6} = \frac{\pi}{2}$, $\frac{\pi}{3} + 2(\frac{\pi}{6}) = \frac{2\pi}{3}$, and so on. We now make the table of important values and sketch the graph shown in Fig. 10-16.

x	0	$\frac{\pi}{6}$	$\frac{\pi}{3}$	$\frac{\pi}{2}$	$\frac{2\pi}{3}$	$\frac{5\pi}{6}$	π
y	0	-2	0	2	0	-2	0

We note that since the period is $2\pi/3$, the curve passes through the origin. ∎

EXAMPLE 3   Sketch the graph of the function $y = -\cos(2x + \frac{\pi}{6})$.

First we determine that

(1) the amplitude is 1

(2) the period is $\frac{2\pi}{2} = \pi$

(3) the displacement is $-\frac{\pi}{6} \div 2 = -\frac{\pi}{12}$

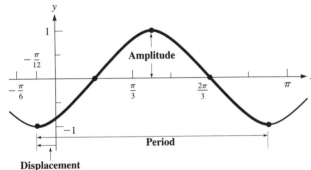

Fig. 10-17

We now make a table of important values, noting that the curve starts repeating π units to the right of $-\frac{\pi}{12}$.

x	$-\frac{\pi}{12}$	$\frac{\pi}{6}$	$\frac{5\pi}{12}$	$\frac{2\pi}{3}$	$\frac{11\pi}{12}$
y	-1	0	1	0	-1

From this table we sketch the graph in Fig. 10-17. ∎

Each of the heavy portions of the graphs in Figs. 10-16 and 10-17 is called a *cycle* of the curve. A **cycle** *is any section of the graph that includes exactly one period.*

EXAMPLE 4   View the graph of $y = 2\cos(\frac{1}{2}x - \frac{\pi}{6})$ on a graphing calculator.

From the values $a = 2$, $b = 1/2$, and $c = -\pi/6$, we determine that

(1) the amplitude is 2

(2) the period is $2\pi \div \frac{1}{2} = 4\pi$

(3) the displacement is $-(-\frac{\pi}{6}) \div \frac{1}{2} = \frac{\pi}{3}$

We now make a table of important values.

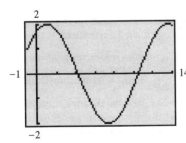

Fig. 10-18

x	$\frac{\pi}{3}$	$\frac{4\pi}{3}$	$\frac{7\pi}{3}$	$\frac{10\pi}{3}$	$\frac{13\pi}{3}$
y	2	0	-2	0	2

This table helps us choose the values for the *window* settings in Fig. 10-18. We choose Xmin $= -1$ in order to start to the left of the y-axis and Xmax $= 14$ since $13\pi/3 \approx 13.6$. Also, we choose Ymin $= -2$ and Ymax $= 2$ since the amplitude is 2. We see that the graph in Fig. 10-18 is a little more than one cycle. ∎

The following example illustrates the use of the graph of a trigonometric function in an applied problem.

■EXAMPLE 5   The cross section of a certain water wave is $y = 0.7 \sin(\frac{\pi}{2}x + \frac{\pi}{4})$, where x and y are measured in feet. Display two cycles of y vs. x on a graphing calculator.

From the values $a = 0.7$ ft, $b = \pi/2$ ft^{-1} (this means 1/ft, or per foot), and $c = \pi/4$, we can find the amplitude, period, and displacement:

(1) amplitude = 0.7 ft

(2) period = $\dfrac{2\pi}{\frac{\pi}{2}} = 4$ ft

(3) displacement = $-\dfrac{\frac{\pi}{4}}{\frac{\pi}{2}} = -0.5$ ft

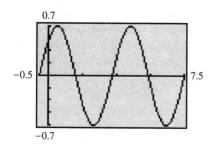

Fig. 10-19

Using these values, we choose the following values for the *window* settings.

(1) Xmin = -0.5 (the displacement is -0.5 ft)

(2) Xmax = 7.5 (the period is 4 ft, and we want two periods, starting at $x = -0.5$)($-0.5 + 8 = 7.5$)

(3) Ymin = -0.7, Ymax = 0.7 (the amplitude is 0.7 ft)

The graphing calculator view is shown in Fig. 10-19. The negative values of x have the significance of giving points to the wave to the left of the origin. (When *time* is used, no actual physical meaning is generally given to negative values of t.) ■

EXERCISES *10-3*

In Exercises 1–24, determine the amplitude, period, and displacement for each function. Then sketch the graphs of the functions. Check each using a graphing calculator.

1. $y = \sin\left(x - \dfrac{\pi}{6}\right)$

2. $y = 3 \sin\left(x + \dfrac{\pi}{4}\right)$

3. $y = \cos\left(x + \dfrac{\pi}{6}\right)$

4. $y = 2 \cos\left(x - \dfrac{\pi}{8}\right)$

5. $y = 2 \sin\left(2x + \dfrac{\pi}{2}\right)$

6. $y = -\sin\left(3x - \dfrac{\pi}{2}\right)$

7. $y = -\cos(2x - \pi)$

8. $y = 4 \cos\left(3x + \dfrac{\pi}{3}\right)$

9. $y = \dfrac{1}{2} \sin\left(\dfrac{1}{2}x - \dfrac{\pi}{4}\right)$

10. $y = 2 \sin\left(\dfrac{1}{4}x + \dfrac{\pi}{2}\right)$

11. $y = 3 \cos\left(\dfrac{1}{3}x + \dfrac{\pi}{3}\right)$

12. $y = \dfrac{1}{3} \cos\left(\dfrac{1}{2}x - \dfrac{\pi}{8}\right)$

13. $y = \sin\left(\pi x + \dfrac{\pi}{8}\right)$

14. $y = -2 \sin(2\pi x - \pi)$

15. $y = \dfrac{3}{4} \cos\left(4\pi x - \dfrac{\pi}{5}\right)$

16. $y = 25 \cos\left(3\pi x + \dfrac{\pi}{2}\right)$

17. $y = -0.6 \sin(2\pi x - 1)$

18. $y = 1.8 \sin\left(\pi x + \dfrac{1}{3}\right)$

19. $y = 40 \cos(3\pi x + 2)$

20. $y = 3 \cos(6\pi x - 1)$

21. $y = \sin(\pi^2 x - \pi)$

22. $y = -\dfrac{1}{2} \sin\left(2x - \dfrac{1}{\pi}\right)$

23. $y = -\dfrac{3}{2} \cos\left(\pi x + \dfrac{\pi^2}{6}\right)$

24. $y = \pi \cos\left(\dfrac{1}{\pi}x + \dfrac{1}{3}\right)$

In Exercises 25 and 26, sketch the indicated curves. In Exercises 27 and 28, use a graphing calculator to view the indicated curves.

25. A wave traveling in a string may be represented by the equation $y = A \sin 2\pi\left(\dfrac{t}{T} - \dfrac{x}{\lambda}\right)$. Here, A is the amplitude, t is the time the wave has traveled, x is the distance from the origin, T is the time required for the wave to travel one *wavelength* λ (the Greek letter lambda). Sketch three cycles of the wave for which $A = 2.00$ cm, $T = 0.100$ s, $\lambda = 20.0$ cm, and $x = 5.00$ cm.

26. The electric current i (in μA) in a certain circuit is given by $i = 3.8 \cos 2\pi(t + 0.20)$, where t is the time in seconds. Sketch three cycles of this function.

27. A certain satellite circles the earth such that its distance y, in miles north or south (altitude is not considered) from the equator, is $y = 4500 \cos(0.025t - 0.25)$, where t is the time (in min) after launch. View two cycles of the graph.

28. In performing a test on a patient, a medical technician used an ultrasonic signal given by the equation $I = A \sin(\omega t + \theta)$. View two cycles of the graph of I vs. t if $A = 5$ nW/m², $\omega = 2 \times 10^5$ rad/s, and $\theta = 0.4$.

W *In Exercises 29–32, give the specific form of the equation by evaluating a, b, and c through an inspection of the given curve. Explain how a, b, and c are found.*

29. $y = a \sin(bx + c)$
Fig. 10-20

30. $y = a \cos(bx + c)$
Fig. 10-20

31. $y = a \cos(bx + c)$
Fig. 10-21

32. $y = a \sin(bx + c)$
Fig. 10-21

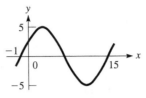

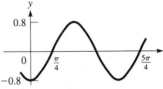

Fig. 10-20   **Fig. 10-21**

Section 7.4

$10\text{-}4$ GRAPHS OF $y = \tan x$, $y = \cot x$, $y = \sec x$, $y = \csc x$

In this section we briefly consider the graphs of the other trigonometric functions. We show the basic form of each curve, and then from these we are able to sketch other curves for these functions.

Considering the values of the trigonometric functions we found in Chapter 8, we set up the following table for $y = \tan x$. The graph is shown in Fig. 10-22.

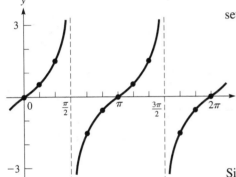

Fig. 10-22

x	0	$\frac{\pi}{6}$	$\frac{\pi}{3}$	$\frac{\pi}{2}$	$\frac{2\pi}{3}$	$\frac{5\pi}{6}$	π
y	0	0.6	1.7	*	−1.7	−0.6	0

x	$\frac{7\pi}{6}$	$\frac{4\pi}{3}$	$\frac{3\pi}{2}$	$\frac{5\pi}{3}$	$\frac{11\pi}{6}$	2π
y	0.6	1.7	*	−1.7	−0.6	0

*Undefined.

Since the curve is not defined for $x = \pi/2$, $x = 3\pi/2$, and so forth, we use a calculator and find that the value of $\tan x$ becomes very large as x gets closer to $\pi/2$, although *there is no point on the curve for $x = \pi/2$*. For example, if $x = 1.55$,

NOTE ▶

$\tan x = 48.08$ ($\pi/2 \approx 1.57$). We note that *the period of the tangent curve is π*. This differs from the period of the sine and cosine functions.

By knowing the values of $\sin x$, $\cos x$, and $\tan x$, we can find the necessary values of $\csc x$, $\sec x$, and $\cot x$. This is due to the reciprocal relationships among the functions that we showed in Section 4-3. We show these relationships by

$$\csc x = \frac{1}{\sin x} \qquad \sec x = \frac{1}{\cos x} \qquad \cot x = \frac{1}{\tan x} \qquad \textbf{(10-2)}$$

Therefore, to graph $y = \cot x$, $y = \sec x$, and $y = \csc x$, we can obtain the necessary values from the corresponding reciprocal function. On the following page we show the graphs of these functions, as well as a more extensive graph of $y = \tan x$.

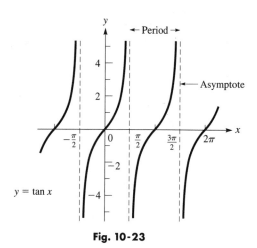

Fig. 10-23

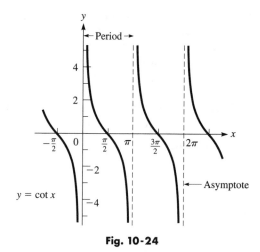

Fig. 10-24

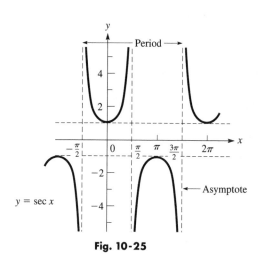

Fig. 10-25

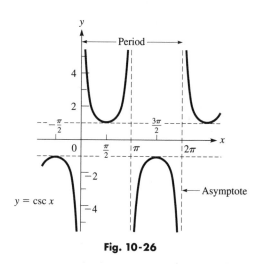

Fig. 10-26

We see from these graphs that the period of $y = \tan x$ and $y = \cot x$ is π and that the period of $y = \sec x$ and $y = \csc x$ is 2π. *The vertical dashed lines in these figures are* **asymptotes** (see Sections 3-4 and 21-6). The curves *approach* these lines, but they never actually touch them.

The functions are not defined for the values of x for which the curve has asymptotes. This means that the domains do not include these values of x. Thus, we see that the domains of $y = \tan x$ and $y = \sec x$ include all real numbers, except the values $x = -\pi/2$, $\pi/2$, $3\pi/2$, and so on. The domain of $y = \cot x$ and $y = \csc x$ include all real numbers except $x = -\pi$, 0, π, 2π, and so on.

From the graphs we see that the ranges of $y = \tan x$ and $y = \cot x$ are all real numbers, but that the ranges of $y = \sec x$ and $y = \csc x$ do not include the real numbers between -1 and 1.

To sketch functions such as $y = a \sec x$, we may first sketch $y = \sec x$ and then multiply the y-values by a. *Here a is not an amplitude,* since the ranges of these functions are not limited in the same way they are for the sine and cosine functions.

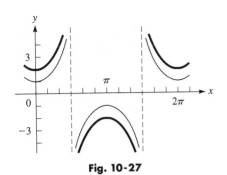

Fig. 10-27

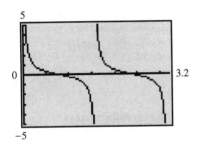

Fig. 10-28

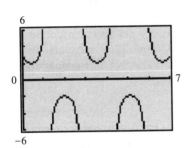

Fig. 10-29

■**EXAMPLE 1** Sketch the graph of $y = 2 \sec x$.

First, we sketch in $y = \sec x$, shown as the light curve in Fig. 10-27. Then we multiply the y-values of this secant function by 2. Although we can only estimate these values and do this approximately, a reasonable graph can be sketched this way. The desired curve is shown in color in Fig. 10-27. ----------■

Using a graphing calculator we can display the graphs of these functions more easily and more accurately than by sketching them. By knowing the general shape and period of the function, the values for the *window* settings can be determined without having to reset them too often.

■**EXAMPLE 2** View at least two cycles of the graph of $y = 0.5 \cot 2x$ on a graphing calculator.

Since the period of $y = \cot x$ is π, the period of $y = \cot 2x$ is $\pi/2$. Therefore, we choose the *window* settings as follows:

Xmin = 0   ($x = 0$ is one asymptote of the curve)

Xmax = 3.2   ($\pi \approx 3.14$; the period is $\pi/2$; two periods is π)

Ymin = −5, Ymax = 5   (the range is all x; this shows enough of the curve)

We must remember to enter the function as $y_1 = 0.5 (\tan 2x)^{-1}$, since $\cot x = (\tan x)^{-1}$. The graphing calculator view is shown in Fig. 10-28. We can view many more cycles of the curve with appropriate *window* settings. ----------■

■**EXAMPLE 3** View at least two periods of the graph of $y = 2 \sec (2x - \frac{\pi}{4})$ on a graphing calculator.

Since the period of $\sec x$ is 2π, the period of $\sec (2x - \frac{\pi}{4})$ is $2\pi/2 = \pi$. Recalling that $\sec x = (\cos x)^{-1}$, the curve will have the same displacement as $y = \cos (2x - \frac{\pi}{4})$. This displacement is $-\frac{-\pi/4}{2} = \frac{\pi}{8}$. Therefore, we choose the following *window* settings.

Xmin = 0   (the displacement is positive)

Xmax = 7   (displacement = $\pi/8$; period = π; $\pi/8 + 2\pi = 17\pi/8 \approx 6.7$)

Ymin = −6, Ymax = 6   (there is no curve between $y = -2$ and $y = 2$)

With $y_1 = 2(\cos (2x - \pi/4))^{-1}$, Fig. 10-29 shows the calculator view. ----------■

━━━━━━━━━ **EXERCISES** *10-4* ━━━━━━━━━

In Exercises 1–4, fill in the following table for each function and plot the graph from these points.

x	$-\frac{\pi}{2}$	$-\frac{\pi}{3}$	$-\frac{\pi}{4}$	$-\frac{\pi}{6}$	0	$\frac{\pi}{6}$	$\frac{\pi}{4}$	$\frac{\pi}{3}$	$\frac{\pi}{2}$	$\frac{2\pi}{3}$	$\frac{3\pi}{4}$	$\frac{5\pi}{6}$	π
y													

1. $y = \tan x$ **2.** $y = \cot x$ **3.** $y = \sec x$ **4.** $y = \csc x$

In Exercises 5–12, sketch the graphs of the given functions by use of the basic curve forms (Figs. 10-23, 10-24, 10-25, and 10-26). See Example 1.

5. $y = 2 \tan x$ **6.** $y = 3 \cot x$

7. $y = \frac{1}{2} \sec x$ **8.** $y = \frac{3}{2} \csc x$

9. $y = -2 \cot x$ **10.** $y = -0.1 \tan x$

11. $y = -3 \csc x$ **12.** $y = -\frac{1}{2} \sec x$

In Exercises 13–20, view at least two cycles of the graphs of the given functions on a graphing calculator.

13. $y = \tan 2x$ **14.** $y = 2 \cot 3x$

15. $y = \frac{1}{2} \sec 3x$ **16.** $y = 4 \csc 2x$

17. $y = 2 \cot \left(2x + \frac{\pi}{6}\right)$ **18.** $y = \tan \left(3x - \frac{\pi}{2}\right)$

19. $y = 18 \csc \left(3x - \frac{\pi}{3}\right)$ **20.** $y = 3 \sec \left(2x + \frac{\pi}{4}\right)$

In Exercises 21–24, sketch the appropriate graphs. Check each on a graphing calculator.

21. A drafting student draws a circle through the three vertices of a right triangle. The hypotenuse of the triangle is the diameter d of the circle, and from Fig. 10-30, we see that $d = a \sec \theta$. Sketch the graph of d as a function of θ for $a = 3.00$ in.

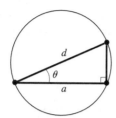

Fig. 10-30

22. Near Antarctica, an iceberg with a vertical face 200 m high is seen from a small boat. At a distance x from the iceberg, the angle of elevation θ of the top of the iceberg can be found from the equation $x = 200 \cot \theta$. Sketch x as a function of θ.

23. A mechanism with two springs is shown in Fig. 10-31, where point A is restricted to move horizontally. From the law of sines we see that $b = (a \sin B) \csc A$. Sketch the graph of b as a function of A for $a = 4.00$ cm and $B = \pi/4$.

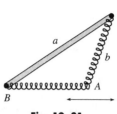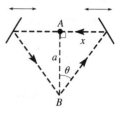

Fig. 10-31　　　　**Fig. 10-32**

24. In a laser experiment, two mirrors move horizontally in equal and opposite distances from point A. The laser path from and to point B is shown in Fig. 10-32. From the figure we see that $x = a \tan \theta$. Sketch the graph of $x = f(\theta)$ for $a = 5.00$ cm.

Section 7.5　*10-5* APPLICATIONS OF THE TRIGONOMETRIC GRAPHS

In this section we introduce an important physical concept and indicate some of the technical applications.

In Section 8-4 we discussed the velocity of an object moving in a circular path. When this object moves with constant velocity, its *projection* on a diameter moves with what is known as **simple harmonic motion.** For example, consider an object moving around a circle in a plane parallel to rays of light. The movement of the object's shadow on a wall (perpendicular to the light) is simple harmonic motion. The object could be the end of a spoke of a rotating wheel.

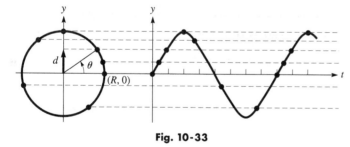

Fig. 10-33

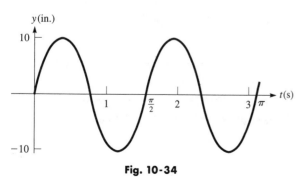

Fig. 10-34

EXAMPLE 1　In Fig. 10-33, assume a particle starts at the end of the radius at $(R, 0)$, and moves counterclockwise around the circle with constant angular velocity ω. *The displacement of the projection on the y-axis is d and is given by $d = R \sin \theta$.* The displacement is shown for a few different positions of the end of the radius.

Since $\theta/t = \omega$, or $\theta = \omega t$, we have

$$\boxed{d = R \sin \omega t} \qquad \text{(10-3)}$$

as the equation for the displacement of this projection, with time t as the independent variable.

For the case where $R = 10.0$ in. and $\omega = 4.00$ rad/s, we have

$$d = 10.0 \sin 4.00t$$

By sketching or viewing the graph of this function, we can find the displacement d of the projection for a given time t. The graph is shown in Fig. 10-34. ■

In Example 1, note that *time is the independent variable*. This is motion for which the object (the end of the projection) remains at the same horizontal position ($x = 0$) and moves only vertically according to a sinusoidal function. In the previous sections, we dealt with functions in which y is a sinusoidal function of the horizontal displacement x. Think of a water wave. At *one point* of the wave, the motion is only vertical and sinusoidal with time. At *one given time,* a picture would indicate a sinusoidal movement from one horizontal position to the next.

EXAMPLE 2 A windmill is used to pump water. The radius of the blade is 2.5 m, and it is moving with constant angular velocity. If the vertical displacement of the end of the blade is timed from the point it is at an angle of 45° ($\pi/4$ rad) from the horizontal [see Fig. 10-35(a)], the displacement d is given by

$$d = 2.5 \sin\left(\omega t + \frac{\pi}{4}\right)$$

If the blade makes an angle of 90° ($\pi/2$ rad) when $t = 0$ (see Fig. 10-35(b)), the displacement d is given by

$$d = 2.5 \sin\left(\omega t + \frac{\pi}{2}\right)$$

or $d = 2.5 \cos \omega t$

If timing started at the first maximum for the displacement, the resulting curve for the displacement would be that of the cosine function.   ▬

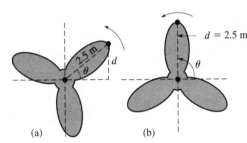

Fig. 10-35

Other examples of simple harmonic motion are (1) the movement of a pendulum bob through its arc (a very close approximation to simple harmonic motion), (2) the motion of an object "bobbing" in water, (3) the movement of the end of a vibrating rod (which we hear as sound), and (4) the displacement of a weight moving up and down on a spring. Other phenomena that give rise to equations like those for simple harmonic motion are found in the fields of optics, sound, and electricity. The equations for such phenomena have the same mathematical form because they result from vibratory movement or motion in a circle.

EXAMPLE 3 A very important use of the trigonometric curves arises in the study of alternating current, which is caused by the motion of a wire passing through a magnetic field. If the wire is moving in a circular path, with angular velocity ω, the current i in the wire at time t is given by an equation of the form

$$i = I_m \sin(\omega t + \alpha)$$

where I_m is the maximum current attainable and α is the phase angle.

The current may be represented by a sinusoidal wave. Given that $I_m = 6.00$ A, $\omega = 120\pi$ rad/s, and $\alpha = \pi/6$, we have the equation

$$i = 6.00 \sin(120\pi t + \tfrac{\pi}{6})$$

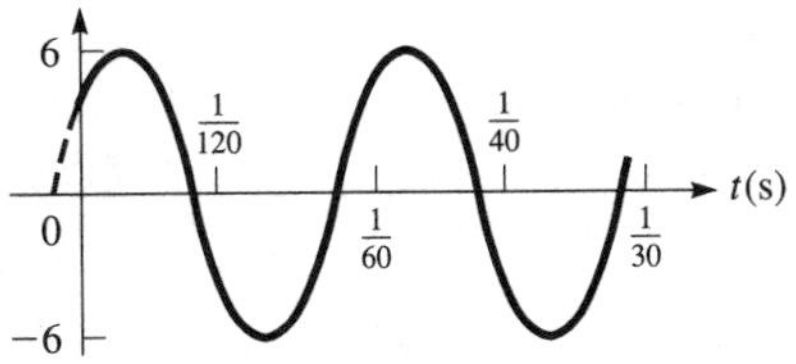

From this equation we see that the amplitude is 6.00 A, the period is $\frac{1}{60}$ s, and the displacement is $-\frac{1}{720}$ s. From these values we draw the graph as shown in Fig. 10-36. Since the current takes on both positive and negative values, we conclude that it moves alternately in one direction and then the other.   ▬

Fig. 10-36

Named for the German physicist Heinrich Hertz (1857–1894).

It is a common practice to express the rate of rotation in terms of *the* **frequency** *f, the number of cycles per second,* rather than directly in terms of the angular velocity ω, the number of radians per second. *The unit for frequency is the* **hertz** (Hz), *and* 1 Hz = 1 cycle/s. Since there are 2π rad in one cycle, we have

$$\omega = 2\pi f \qquad\qquad \textbf{(10-4)}$$

It is the frequency *f* that is referred to in electric current, on radio stations, for musical tones, and so on.

EXAMPLE 4 For the electric current in Example 3, $\omega = 120\pi$ rad/s. The corresponding frequency *f* is

$$f = \frac{120\pi}{2\pi} = 60 \text{ Hz}$$

This means that 120π rad/s corresponds to 60 cycles/s. This is the standard frequency used for alternating current.

EXERCISES 10-5

A graphing calculator may be used in the following exercises.

In Exercises 1 and 2, sketch two cycles of the curve of the projection of Example 1 as a function of time for the given values.

1. $R = 2.40$ cm, $\omega = 2.00$ rad/s
2. $R = 1.80$ ft, $f = 0.250$ Hz

In Exercises 3 and 4, a point on a cam is 8.30 cm from the center of rotation. The cam is rotating with a constant angular velocity, and the vertical displacement $d = 8.30$ cm for $t = 0$ s. See Fig. 10-37. Sketch two cycles of d as a function of t for the given values.

3. $f = 3.20$ Hz
4. $\omega = 3.20$ rad/s

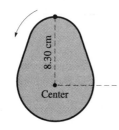

Fig. 10-37

In Exercises 5 and 6, a satellite is orbiting the earth such that its displacement D north of the equator (or south if $D < 0$) is given by $D = A \sin(\omega t + \alpha)$. Sketch two cycles of D as a function of t for the given values.

5. $A = 500$ mi, $\omega = 3.60$ rad/h, $\alpha = 0$
6. $A = 850$ km, $f = 1.6 \times 10^{-4}$ Hz, $\alpha = \pi/3$

In Exercises 7 and 8, for an alternating-current circuit in which the voltage e is given by $e = E \sin(\omega t + \alpha)$, sketch two cycles of the voltage as a function of time for the given values.

7. $E = 170$ V, $f = 60.0$ Hz, $\alpha = -\pi/3$
8. $E = 80$ V, $\omega = 377$ rad/s, $\alpha = \pi/2$

In Exercises 9 and 10, refer to the wave in the string described in Exercise 25 of Section 10-3. For a point on the string, the displacement y is given by $y = A \sin 2\pi\left(\dfrac{t}{T} - \dfrac{x}{\lambda}\right)$. We see that each point on the string moves with simple harmonic motion. Sketch two cycles of y as a function of t for the given values.

9. $A = 3.20$ cm, $T = 0.050$ s, $\lambda = 40.0$ cm, $x = 5.00$ cm
10. $A = 1.45$ in., $T = 0.250$ s, $\lambda = 24.0$ in., $x = 20.0$ in.

In Exercises 11 and 12, the air pressure within a plastic container changes above and below the external atmospheric pressure by $p = p_0 \sin 2\pi ft$. Sketch two cycles of $p = f(t)$ for the given values.

11. $p_0 = 2.80$ lb/in.^{2}, $f = 2.30$ Hz
12. $p_0 = 45.0$ kPa, $f = 0.450$ Hz

In Exercises 13–16, sketch the required curves.

13. The vertical displacement *y* of a point at the end of a propeller blade of a small boat is $y = 14.0 \sin 40.0\pi t$. Sketch two cycles of *y* (in cm) as a function of *t* (in s).
14. The rotating beacon of a parked police car is 12 m from a straight wall. (a) Sketch the graph of the length *L* of the light beam, where $L = 12 \sec \pi t$, for $0 \le t \le 2.0$ s. (b) Which part(s) of the graph show meaningful values? Explain.
15. Sketch two cycles of the radio signal $e = 0.014 \cos(2\pi ft + \pi/4)$ (*e* in volts, *f* in hertz, and *t* in seconds) for a station broadcasting with $f = 950$ kHz ("95" on the AM radio dial).
16. Sketch two cycles of the acoustical intensity *I* of the sound wave for which $I = A \cos(2\pi ft - \alpha)$, given that *t* is in seconds, $A = 0.027$ W/cm^2, $f = 240$ Hz, and $\alpha = 0.80$.

Section 7.6

10-6 COMPOSITE TRIGONOMETRIC CURVES

Many applications involve functions that in themselves are a combination of two or more simpler functions. In this section we discuss methods by which the curve of such a function can be found by combining values from the simpler functions.

■EXAMPLE 1   Sketch the graph of $y = 2 + \sin 2x$.

This function is the sum of the simpler functions $y_1 = 2$ and $y_2 = \sin 2x$. We may find values for y by adding 2 to each important value of $y_2 = \sin 2x$.

For $y_2 = \sin 2x$, the amplitude is 1 and the period is $2\pi/2 = \pi$. Therefore, we obtain the values in the following table and sketch the graph in Fig. 10-38.

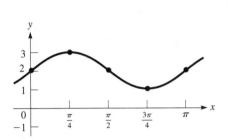

3
2
1

0        $\frac{\pi}{4}$ $\frac{\pi}{2}$ $\frac{3\pi}{4}$ π
−1

Fig. 10-38

x	0	$\frac{\pi}{4}$	$\frac{\pi}{2}$	$\frac{3\pi}{4}$	π
$\sin 2x$	0	1	0	−1	0
$2 + \sin 2x$	2	3	2	1	2

Addition of Ordinates

Another way to sketch the resulting graph is to *first sketch the two simpler curves and then add the y-values graphically. This method is called* **addition of ordinates** and is illustrated in the following example.

■EXAMPLE 2   Sketch the graph of $y = 2 \cos x + \sin 2x$.

On the same set of coordinate axes, we sketch the curves $y = 2 \cos x$ and $y = \sin 2x$. These are shown as dashed and solid light curves in Fig. 10-39. For various values of x, we determine the distance above or below the x-axis of each curve and add these distances, noting that those above the axis are positive and those below the axis are negative. We thereby graphically **add** *the y-values* of these two curves for these values of x to obtain the points on the resulting curve, shown in color in Fig. 10-39.

For example, for the x-value at A we add the two lengths shown (side-by-side for clarity) to get the length for y. At B we see that both lengths are negative, and the value for y is the sum of these two negative values. At C one length is positive and one is negative, and we must subtract the lower length from the upper one to get the length for y.

We add (or subtract) these lengths for enough x-values to get a proper curve. Some points are easily found. Where one curve crosses the x-axis, its value is zero, and the resulting curve has its point on the other curve for this value of x. Here, $\sin 2x$ is zero at $x = \pi/2$, π, and so forth. For these values, the points on the resulting curve lie on the curve of $2 \cos x$.

We should also add the values where each curve is at its maximum or its minimum. In this case, $\sin 2x = 1$ at $x = \pi/4$, and the two values should be added here to get a point on the resulting curve.

At $x = 5\pi/4$, *we must take extra care in combining values, since*

$\sin 2x$ is **positive** and $2 \cos x$ is **negative.**

Reasonable care and accuracy are needed to sketch a proper resulting curve. The graph is shown in Fig. 10-39.

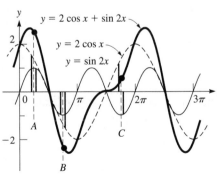

$y = 2 \cos x + \sin 2x$
$y = 2 \cos x$
$y = \sin 2x$

Fig. 10-39

We have shown how a fairly complex curve can be sketched graphically. However, it is expected that a graphing calculator (or a computer *grapher*) will be used to view most graphs, particularly ones that are difficult to sketch. The graphing calculator can display such curves much more easily and with much greater accuracy. We can use information about the amplitude, period, and displacement in choosing values for the *window* feature on the calculator.

■EXAMPLE 3   Use a graphing calculator to display the graph of $y = \frac{x}{2} - \cos x$.

Here, we note that the curve is a combination of the straight line $y = x/2$ and the trigonometric curve $y = \cos x$. There are several good choices for the *window* settings, depending on how much of the curve is to be viewed. To see a little more than one period of $\cos x$, we can make the following choices:

Xmin $= -1$ (to start to the left of the *y*-axis)

Xmax $= 7$ (the period of $\cos x$ is $2\pi \approx 6.3$)

Ymin $= -2$ (the line passes through $(0,0)$; the amplitude of $y = \cos x$ is 1)

Ymax $= 4$ (the slope of the line is $1/2$)

The graphing calculator view of the curve is shown in Fig. 10-40(a). The graph of $y = \frac{x}{2} - \cos x$, $y = \frac{x}{2}$, and $y = -\cos x$ is shown in Fig. 10-40(b).

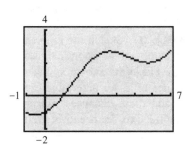
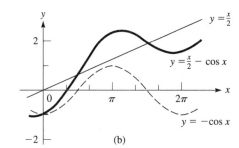

Fig. 10-40   (a)   (b)

NOTE ▶   The reason for showing $y = -\cos x$, and not $y = \cos x$, is that if *addition of ordinates* were being used, *it is much easier to add graphic values than to subtract them.* In using the method of addition of ordinates, we could *add* the ordinates of $y = x/2$ and $y = -\cos x$ to get the resulting curve of $y = \frac{x}{2} - \cos x$.   ■

■EXAMPLE 4   View the graph of $y = \cos \pi x - 2 \sin 2x$ on a graphing calculator.

The combination of $y = \cos \pi x$ and $y = 2 \sin 2x$ leads to the following choices for the *window* settings:

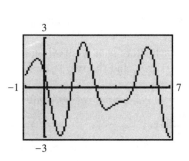

Fig. 10-41

Xmin $= -1$ (to start to the left of the *y*-axis)

Xmax $= 7$ (the periods are 2 and π; this shows at least two periods of each)

Ymin $= -3$, Ymax $= 3$ (the sum of the amplitudes is 3)

There are many possible choices for Xmin and Xmax to get a good view of the graph on a calculator. However, since the sum of the amplitudes is 3, we know that the curve cannot be below $y = -3$ or above $y = 3$.

The graphing calculator view is shown in Fig. 10-41.

This graph can be constructed by using addition of ordinates, although it is difficult to do very accurately.   ■

Lissajous Figures

An important application of trigonometric curves is made when they are added at *right angles*. The methods for doing this are shown in the following examples.

■EXAMPLE 5 Plot the graph for which the values of x and y are given by the equations $y = \sin 2\pi t$ and $x = 2 \cos \pi t$. *Equations given in this form, x and y in terms of a third variable, are called* **parametric equations.**

Since both x and y are in terms of t, by assuming values of t we find corresponding values of x and y and use these values to plot the graph. Since the periods of $\sin 2\pi t$ and $2 \cos \pi t$ are $t = 1$ and $t = 2$, respectively, we will use values of $t = 0$, 1/4, 1/2, 3/4, 1, and so on. These give us convenient values of 0, $\pi/4$, $\pi/2$, $3\pi/4$, π, and so on to use in the table. We plot the points in Fig. 10-42.

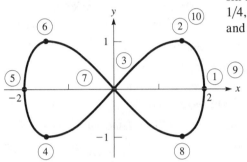

Fig. 10-42

t	0	$\frac{1}{4}$	$\frac{1}{2}$	$\frac{3}{4}$	1	$\frac{5}{4}$	$\frac{3}{2}$	$\frac{7}{4}$	2	$\frac{9}{4}$
x	2	1.4	0	−1.4	−2	−1.4	0	1.4	2	1.4
y	0	1	0	−1	0	1	0	−1	0	1
Point number	1	2	3	4	5	6	7	8	9	10

Since x and y are trigonometric functions of a third variable t and since the x- and y-axes are at right angles, values of x and y obtained in this manner result in a combination of two trigonometric curves at right angles. *Figures obtained in this manner are called* **Lissajous figures.** Note that the Lissajous figure in Fig. 10-42 *is not a function* since there are *two* values of y for each value of x (except $x = -2$, 0, 2) in the domain.

In practice, Lissajous figures can be shown by applying different voltages to an *oscilloscope* and displaying the electric signals on a screen similar to that on a television set.

Named for the French physicist Jules
Lissajous (1822–1880).

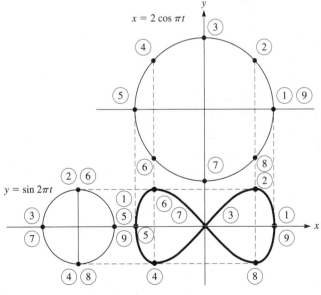

Fig. 10-43

■EXAMPLE 6 If we place a circle on the x-axis and another on the y-axis, we may represent the coordinates (x, y) for the curve of Example 5 by the lengths of the projections (see Example 1 of Section 10-5) of a point moving around each circle. A careful study of Fig. 10-43 will clarify this. We note that the radius of the circle giving the x-values is 2 and that the radius of the circle giving the y-values is 1. This is due to the way in which x and y are defined. Also, due to these definitions, the point revolves around the y-circle twice as fast as the corresponding point around the x-circle.

See the chapter introduction.

On an oscilloscope, the curve would result when
two electric signals are used. The first would have
twice the amplitude and one-half the frequency of
the other.

Most graphing calculators can be used to display a curve defined by parametric equations. To do this it is necessary to use the *mode* feature and make the selection for *parametric equations*. Use the manual for the calculator, as there are some differences in how this is done on the various calculators. In the example that follows, we display the graphs of parametric equations on a graphing calculator.

EXAMPLE 7 Use a graphing calculator to display the graph defined by the parametric equations $x = 2 \cos \pi t$ and $y = \sin 2\pi t$. These are the same equations as those used in Examples 5 and 6.

First we select the parametric equation option from the *mode* feature, and enter the parametric equations $x_{1T} = 2 \cos \pi t$ and $y_{1T} = \sin 2\pi t$. Then we make the following *window* settings:

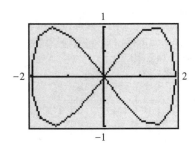

Fig. 10-44

Tmin = 0 (standard default settings, and the usual choice)

Tmax = 2 (the periods are 2 and 1; the longer period is 2)

Tstep = .1047 (standard default setting; curve is smoother with 0.01)

Xmin = −2, Xmax = 2 (smallest and largest possible values of x), Xscl = 1

Ymin = −1, Ymax = 1 (smallest and largest possible values of y), Yscl = 0.5

The calculator graph is shown in Fig. 10-44.

EXERCISES *10-6*

In Exercises 1–8, sketch the curves of the given functions by addition of ordinates.

1. $y = 1 + \sin x$

2. $y = 3 - 2 \cos x$

3. $y = \frac{1}{3}x + \sin 2x$

4. $y = x - \sin x$

5. $y = \frac{1}{10}x^2 - \sin \pi x$

6. $y = \frac{1}{4}x^2 + \cos 3x$

7. $y = \sin x + \cos x$

8. $y = \sin x + \sin 2x$

In Exercises 9–20, display the graphs of the given functions on a graphing calculator.

9. $y = x^3 + 10 \sin 2x$

10. $y = \frac{1}{x^2 + 1} - \cos \pi x$

11. $y = \sin x - \sin 2x$

12. $y = \cos 3x - \sin x$

13. $y = 20 \cos 2x + 30 \sin x$

14. $y = \frac{1}{2} \sin 4x + \cos 2x$

15. $y = 2 \sin x - \cos x$

16. $y = 8 \sin 0.5x - 12 \sin x$

17. $y = \sin \pi x - \cos 2x$

18. $y = 2 \cos 4x - \cos\left(x - \frac{\pi}{4}\right)$

19. $y = 2 \sin\left(2x - \frac{\pi}{6}\right) + \cos\left(2x + \frac{\pi}{3}\right)$

20. $y = 3 \cos 2\pi x + \sin \frac{\pi}{2}x$

In Exercises 21–24, plot the Lissajous figures.

21. $x = \sin t, y = \sin t$

22. $x = 2 \cos t, y = \cos(t + 4)$

23. $x = \cos \pi t, y = \sin \pi t$

24. $x = \cos\left(t + \frac{\pi}{4}\right), y = \sin 2t$

In Exercises 25–32, use a graphing calculator to display the Lissajous figures.

25. $x = \cos \pi\left(t + \frac{1}{6}\right), y = 2 \sin \pi t$

26. $x = \sin^2 \pi t, y = \cos \pi t$

27. $x = 2 \cos 3t, y = \cos 2t$

28. $x = 2 \sin \pi t, y = 3 \sin 3\pi t$

29. $x = \sin t, y = \sin 5t$

30. $x = 2 \cos t, y = \sin 5t$

31. $x = 2 \cos \pi t, y = 3 \sin(2\pi t - \frac{\pi}{4})$

32. $x = 2 \cos 3\pi t, y = \cos 5\pi t$

In Exercises 33–40, sketch the appropriate curves. A graphing calculator may be used.

33. An analysis of the temperature records for Louisville, Kentucky, indicate that the average daily temperature T (in °F) during the year is approximately $T = 56 - 22 \cos[\frac{\pi}{6}(x - 0.5)]$, where x is measured in months ($x = 0.5$ is Jan 15, etc.). Sketch the graph of T vs. x for one year.

34. An analysis of data shows that the mean density d (in mg/cm^3) of a calcium compound in the bones of women is given by $d = 139.3 + 48.6 \sin(0.0674x - 0.210)$, where x represents the ages of women ($20 \le x \le 80$ years). (A woman is considered to be osteoporotic if $d < 115$ mg/cm^3.) Sketch the graph.

35. The vertical displacement y (in ft) of a buoy floating in water is given by $y = 3.0 \cos 0.2t + 1.0 \sin 0.4t$, where t is in seconds. Sketch the graph of y as a function of t for the first 40 s.

36. The strain e (dimensionless) on a cable caused by vibration is $e = 0.0080 - 0.0020 \sin 30t + 0.0040 \cos 10t$, where t is measured in seconds. Sketch two cycles of e as a function of t.

37. The electric current i (in mA) in a certain circuit is given by $i = 0.32 + 0.50 \sin t - 0.20 \cos 2t$, where t is in milliseconds. Sketch two cycles of i as a function of t.

38. The available solar energy depends on the amount of sunlight, and the available time in a day for sunlight depends on the time of the year. An approximate correction factor (in min) to standard time is $C = 10 \sin \frac{1}{29}(n - 80) - 7.5 \cos \frac{1}{58}(n - 80)$, where n is the number of the day of the year. Sketch C as a function of n.

39. Two signals are seen on an oscilloscope as being at right angles. The equations for the displacements of these signals are $x = 4 \cos \pi t$ and $y = 2 \sin 3\pi t$. Sketch the figure that appears on the oscilloscope.

40. In the study of optics, light is said to be *elliptically polarized* if certain optic vibrations are out of phase. These may be represented by Lissajous figures. Determine the Lissajous figure for two light waves given by $w_1 = \sin \omega t$ and $w_2 = \sin(\omega t + \frac{\pi}{4})$.

Section 7.7

CHAPTER EQUATIONS

For the graphs of $y = a \sin(bx + c)$ and $y = a \cos(bx + c)$

$$\text{Amplitude} = |a|$$

$$\text{Period} = \frac{2\pi}{b}$$

$$\text{Displacement} = -\frac{c}{b}$$

(10-1)

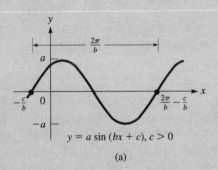

$$y = a \sin(bx + c), c > 0$$

(a)

For each
$a > 0, b > 0$

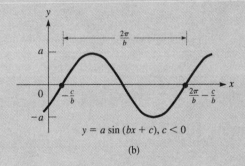

$$y = a \sin(bx + c), c < 0$$

(b)

Reciprocal relationships

$$\csc x = \frac{1}{\sin x} \qquad \sec x = \frac{1}{\cos x} \qquad \cot x = \frac{1}{\tan x}$$

(10-2)

Simple harmonic motion

$$d = R \sin \omega t$$

(10-3)

Angular velocity and frequency

$$\omega = 2\pi f$$

(10-4)

REVIEW EXERCISES

In Exercises 1–28, sketch the curves of the given trigonometric functions. Check each using a graphing calculator.

1. $y = \frac{2}{3} \sin x$
2. $y = -4 \sin x$
3. $y = -2 \cos x$
4. $y = 2.3 \cos x$
5. $y = 2 \sin 3x$
6. $y = 4.5 \sin 12x$
7. $y = 2 \cos 2x$
8. $y = 24 \cos 6x$
9. $y = 3 \cos \frac{1}{3}x$
10. $y = 3 \sin \frac{1}{2}x$
11. $y = \sin \pi x$
12. $y = 3 \sin 4\pi x$
13. $y = 5 \cos 2\pi x$
14. $y = -\cos 6\pi x$
15. $y = -0.5 \sin \frac{\pi}{6}x$
16. $y = 8 \sin \frac{\pi}{4}x$
17. $y = 2 \sin\left(3x - \frac{\pi}{2}\right)$
18. $y = 3 \sin\left(\frac{x}{2} + \frac{\pi}{2}\right)$
19. $y = -2 \cos(4x + \pi)$
20. $y = 0.8 \cos\left(\frac{x}{6} - \frac{\pi}{2}\right)$
21. $y = -\sin\left(\pi x + \frac{\pi}{6}\right)$
22. $y = 2 \sin(3\pi x - \pi)$
23. $y = 8 \cos\left(4\pi x - \frac{\pi}{2}\right)$
24. $y = 3 \cos(2\pi x + \pi)$
25. $y = 3 \tan x$
26. $y = \frac{1}{4} \sec x$
27. $y = -\frac{1}{3} \csc x$
28. $y = -5 \cot x$

In Exercises 29–32, sketch the curves of the given functions by addition of ordinates.

29. $y = 2 + \frac{1}{2} \sin 2x$
30. $y = \frac{1}{2}x - \cos \frac{1}{3}x$
31. $y = \sin 2x + 3 \cos x$
32. $y = \sin 3x + 2 \cos 2x$

In Exercises 33–40, display the curves of the given functions on a graphing calculator.

33. $y = 2 \sin x - \cos 2x$
34. $y = \sin 3x - 2 \cos x$
35. $y = \cos\left(x + \frac{\pi}{4}\right) - 2 \sin 2x$
36. $y = 2 \cos \pi x + \cos(2\pi x - \pi)$
37. $y = \frac{\sin x}{x}$
38. $y = \sqrt{x} \sin 0.5x$

(W) 39. $y = \sin^2 x + \cos^2 x$ $(\sin^2 x = (\sin x)^2)$
What conclusion can be drawn from the graph?

(W) 40. $y = \sin\left(x + \frac{\pi}{4}\right) - \cos\left(x - \frac{\pi}{4}\right) + 1$
What conclusion can be drawn from the graph?

In Exercises 41–44, give the specific form of the indicated equation by evaluating a, b, and c through an inspection of the given curve.

41. $y = a \sin(bx + c)$
(Figure 10-45)
42. $y = a \cos(bx + c)$
(Figure 10-45)

43. $y = a \cos(bx + c)$
(Figure 10-46)
44. $y = a \sin(bx + c)$
(Figure 10-46)

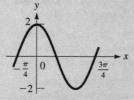

Fig. 10-45   **Fig. 10-46**

In Exercises 45–48, display the Lissajous figures on a graphing calculator.

45. $x = -\cos 2\pi t$, $y = 2 \sin \pi t$
46. $x = \sin\left(t + \frac{\pi}{6}\right)$, $y = \sin t$
47. $x = \cos\left(2\pi t + \frac{\pi}{4}\right)$, $y = \cos \pi t$
48. $x = \cos\left(t - \frac{\pi}{6}\right)$, $y = \cos\left(2t + \frac{\pi}{3}\right)$

In Exercises 49–64, sketch the appropriate curves. A graphing calculator may be used.

49. The range R of a rocket is given by $R = \dfrac{v_0^2 \sin 2\theta}{g}$. Sketch R as a function of θ for $v_0 = 1000$ m/s and $g = 9.8$ m/s^2. See Fig. 10-47.

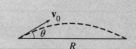

Fig. 10-47

50. The blade of a saber saw moves vertically up and down at 18 strokes per second. The vertical displacement y (in cm) is given by $y = 1.2 \sin 36\pi t$, where t is in seconds. Sketch at least two cycles of the graph of y vs. t.

51. The velocity v (in cm/s) of a piston in a certain engine is given by $v = \omega D \cos \omega t$, where ω is the angular velocity of the crankshaft in radians per second and t is the time in seconds. Sketch the graph of v vs. t if the engine is at 3000 r/min and $D = 3.6$ cm.

52. A light wave for the color yellow can be represented by the equation $y = A \sin 3.4 \times 10^{15} t$. With A as a constant, sketch two cycles of y as a function of t (in s).

53. The electric current i (in A) in a circuit in which there is a *full-wave rectifier* is $i = 10 |\sin 120\pi t|$. Sketch the graph of $i = f(t)$ for $0 \leq t \leq 0.05$ s. What is the period of the current?

54. A circular disk suspended by a thin wire attached to the center of one of its flat faces is twisted through an angle θ. Torsion in the wire tends to turn the disk back in the opposite direction (thus, the name *torsion pendulum* is given to this device). The angular displacement θ (in rad) as a function of time t (in s) is $\theta = \theta_0 \cos(\omega t + \alpha)$, where θ_0 is the maximum angular displacement, ω is a constant that depends on the properties of the disk and wire, and α is the phase angle. Sketch the graph of θ vs. t if $\theta_0 = 0.100$ rad, $\omega = 2.50$ rad/s, and $\alpha = \pi/4$. See Fig. 10-48.

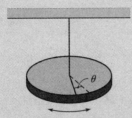

Fig. 10-48

55. At 40° N latitude the number of hours h of daylight each day during the year is approximately $h = 12.2 + 2.8 \sin[\frac{\pi}{6}(x - 2.7)]$, where x is measured in months ($x = 0.5$ is Jan. 15, etc.) Sketch the graph of h vs. x for one year. (Some of the cities near 40° N are Philadelphia, Madrid, Naples, Ankara, and Beijing.)

(W) 56. The equation in Exercise 55 can be used for the number of hours of daylight at 40° S latitude with the appropriate change. Explain what change is necessary and determine the proper equation. Sketch the graph. (This would be appropriate for southern Argentina and Wellington, New Zealand.)

57. If the upper end of a spring is not fixed and is being moved with a sinusoidal motion, the motion of the bob at the end of the spring is affected. Sketch the curve if the motion of the upper end of a spring is being moved by an external force and the bob moves according to the equation $y = 4 \sin 2t - 2 \cos 2t$.

58. The loudness L (in decibels) of a fire siren as a function of the time t (in s) is approximately $L = 40 - 35 \cos 2t + 60 \sin t$. Sketch this function for $0 \le t \le 10$ s.

59. The path of a roller mechanism used in an assembly line process is given by $x = \theta - \sin \theta$ and $y = 1 - \cos \theta$. Sketch the path for $0 \le \theta \le 2\pi$.

60. The equations for two voltage signals that give a resulting curve on an oscilloscope are $x = 6 \sin \pi t$ and $y = 4 \cos 4\pi t$. Sketch the graph of the curve displayed on the oscilloscope.

61. The impedance Z (in Ω) and resistance R (in Ω) for an alternating-current circuit are related by $Z = R \sec \theta$, where θ is called the *phase angle*. Sketch the graph for Z as a function of θ for $-\pi/2 < \theta < \pi/2$.

62. For an object sliding down an inclined plane at constant speed, the coefficient of friction μ between the object and the plane is given by $\mu = \tan \theta$, where θ is the angle between the plane and the horizontal. Sketch the graph of μ vs. θ.

63. The charge q (in C) on a certain capacitor as a function of the time t (in s) is given by $q = 0.0003(3 - 2 \sin 100t \cos 100t)$. Sketch two cycles of q vs. t.

64. The instantaneous power p (in W) in an electric circuit is defined as the product of the instantaneous voltage e and the instantaneous current i (in A). If we have $e = 100 \cos 200t$ and $i = 2 \cos(200t + \frac{\pi}{4})$, plot the graph e vs. t and the graph of i vs. t on the same coordinate system. Then sketch the graph of p vs. t by multiplying appropriate values of e and i.

Writing Exercise

65. A wave passing through a string can be described at any instant by the equation $y = a \sin(bx + c)$. Write one or two paragraphs explaining the change in the wave (a) if a is doubled, (b) if b is doubled, and (c) if c is doubled.

PRACTICE TEST

In Problems 1–4, sketch the graphs of the given functions.

1. $y = 0.5 \cos \frac{\pi}{2} x$

2. $y = 2 + 3 \sin x$

3. $y = 3 \sec x$

4. $y = 2 \sin(2x - \frac{\pi}{3})$

5. A wave is traveling in a string. The displacement y (in in.) as a function of the time t (in s) from its equilibrium position is given by $y = A \cos(2\pi/T)t$. T is the period (in s) of the motion. If $A = 0.200$ in. and $T = 0.100$ s, sketch two cycles of y vs t.

6. Sketch the graph of $y = 2 \sin x + \cos 2x$ by addition of ordinates.

7. Use a graphing calculator to display the Lissajous figure for which $x = \sin \pi t$ and $y = 2 \cos 2\pi t$.

8. Sketch two cycles of the curve of a projection on the end of a radius on the y-axis. The radius is of length R and it is rotating counterclockwise about the origin at 2.00 rad/s. It starts at an angle of $\pi/6$ with the positive x-axis.

Section 7.1
Exercises 10-1, page 279

1. 0, −0.7, −1, −0.7, 0, 0.7, 1, 0.7, 0, −0.7, −1, −0.7, 0, 0.7, 1, 0.7, 0

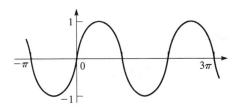

3. −3, −2.1, 0, 2.1, 3, 2.1, 0, −2.1, −3, −2.1, 0, 2.1, 3, 2.1, 0, −2.1, −3

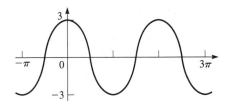

5. 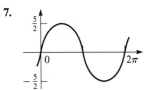 **7.**

9. 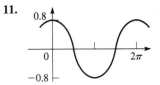 **11.**

13. 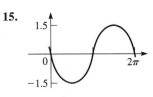 **15.**

17. 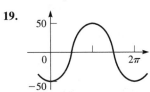 **19.**

21. 0, 0.84, 0.91, 0.14, −0.76, −0.96, −0.28, 0.66

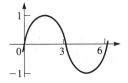

23. 1, 0.54, −0.42, −0.99, −0.65, 0.28, 0.96, 0.75

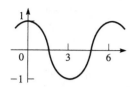

25. $y = 4 \sin x$ **27.** $y = -1.5 \cos x$

Section 7.2
Exercises 10-2, page 282

1. $\dfrac{\pi}{3}$ **3.** $\dfrac{\pi}{4}$ **5.** $\dfrac{\pi}{6}$ **7.** $\dfrac{\pi}{8}$ **9.** 1

11. $\dfrac{1}{2}$ **13.** 6π **15.** 3π **17.** 3   **19.** $\dfrac{2}{\pi}$

21. 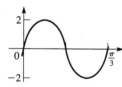   **23.**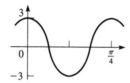

25. 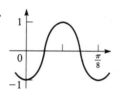   **27.**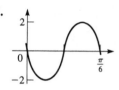

29. 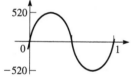   **31.**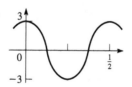

33. 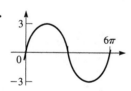   **35.**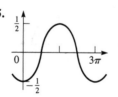

37. 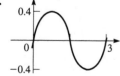   **39.**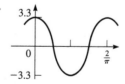

41. $y = \sin 6x$ **43.** $y = \sin \pi x$

45.

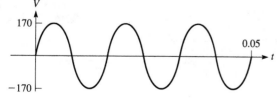

47.

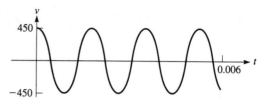

49. $y = \frac{1}{2} \cos 2x$ **51.** $y = -4 \sin \pi x$

Section 7.3
Exercises 10-3, page 286

1. $1, 2\pi, \dfrac{\pi}{6}$ **3.** $1, 2\pi, -\dfrac{\pi}{6}$

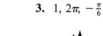 

5. $2, \pi, -\dfrac{\pi}{4}$ **7.** $1, \pi, \dfrac{\pi}{2}$

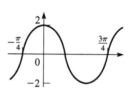 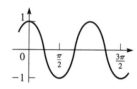

9. $\dfrac{1}{2}, 4\pi, \dfrac{\pi}{2}$ **11.** $3, 6\pi, -\pi$

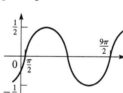 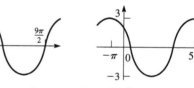

13. $1, 2, -\dfrac{1}{8}$ **15.** $\dfrac{3}{4}, \dfrac{1}{2}, \dfrac{1}{20}$

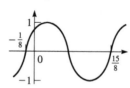 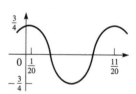

17. $0.6, 1, \dfrac{1}{2\pi}$ **19.** $40, \dfrac{2}{3}, -\dfrac{2}{3\pi}$

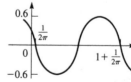 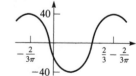

21. $1, \frac{2}{\pi}, \frac{1}{\pi}$

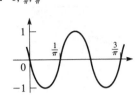

23. $\frac{3}{2}, 2, -\frac{\pi}{6}$

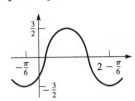

25.

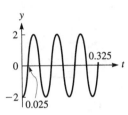

27.

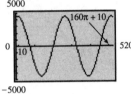

29. $y = 5 \sin(\frac{\pi}{8}x + \frac{\pi}{8})$. As shown: amplitude $= 5$;
period $= \frac{2\pi}{b} = 16$, $b = \frac{\pi}{8}$;
displacement $= -\frac{c}{b} = -1$, $c = \frac{\pi}{8}$

31. $y = -0.8 \cos 2x$. As shown:
amplitude $= |-0.8| = 0.8$; period $= \frac{2\pi}{b} = \pi$, $b = 2$;
displacement $= -\frac{c}{b} = 0$, $c = 0$

Section 7.4
Exercises 10-4, page 289

1. undef., -1.7, -1, -0.58, 0, 0.58, 1, 1.7, undef., -1.7, -1, -0.58, 0

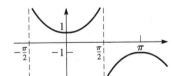

3. undef., 2, 1.4, 1.2, 1, 1.2, 1.4, 2, undef., -2, -1.4, -1.2, -1

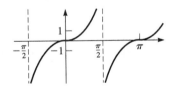

5.

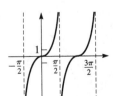

7.

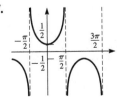

9.

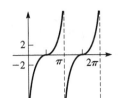

11.

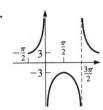

13.

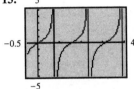

15.

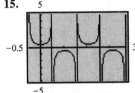

17.

19.

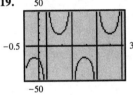

21.

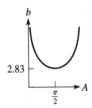

23.

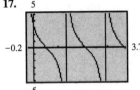

Section 7.5
Exercises 10-5, page 292

1.

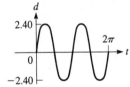

3.

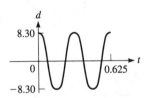

5.

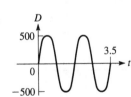

7.

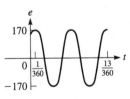

9.

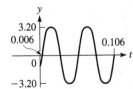

11.

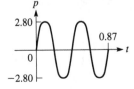

13.

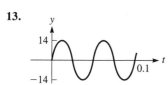

15.

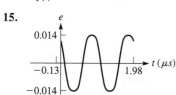

Section 7.6
Exercises 10-6, page 296

1.

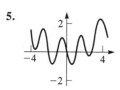

3.

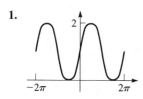

5.

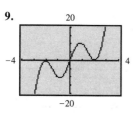

7.

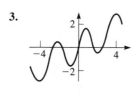

9.

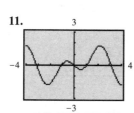

11.

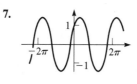

13.

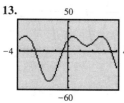

15.

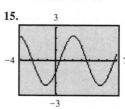

17.

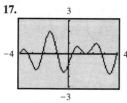

19.

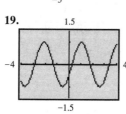

21.

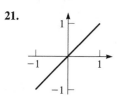

23.

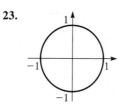

25.

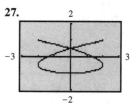

27.

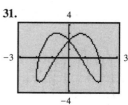

29.

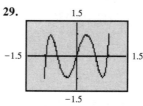

31.

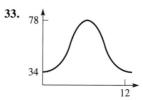

33.

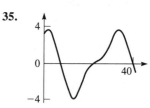

35.

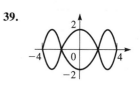

37.

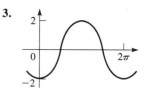

39.

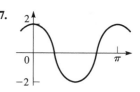

Section 7.7
Review Exercises for Chapter 10, page 298

1.

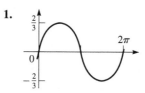

3.

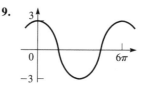

5.

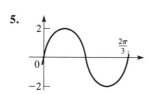

7.

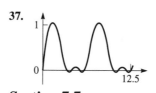

9.

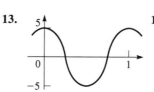

11.

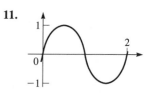

13.

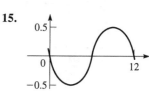

15.

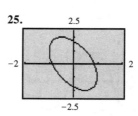

17.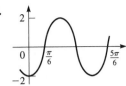

19.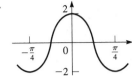

21.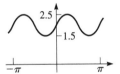

23.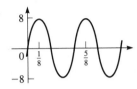

25.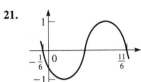

27.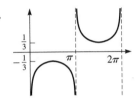

29.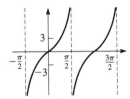

31.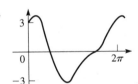

33.

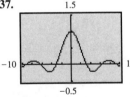

35.

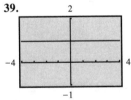

37.

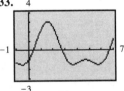

39.

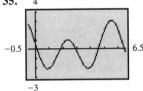

41. $y = 2\sin\left(2x + \frac{\pi}{2}\right)$ **43.** $y = \cos\left(\frac{\pi}{4}x - \frac{3\pi}{4}\right)$

45.

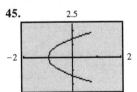

47.

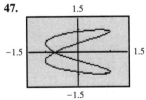

49.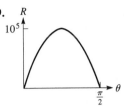

51.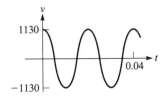

53.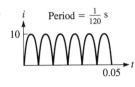

55.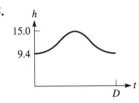

57.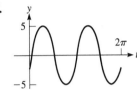

59.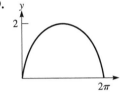

61.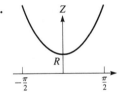

63.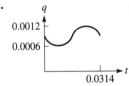

GRAPHS OF THE TRIGONOMETRIC FUNCTIONS

10.1 Graphs of $y = a \sin x$ and $y = a \cos x$

Section 7.1

1. $y = \sin x$

x	$-\pi$	$-\frac{3\pi}{4}$	$-\frac{\pi}{2}$	$-\frac{\pi}{4}$	0	$\frac{\pi}{4}$	$\frac{\pi}{2}$	$\frac{3\pi}{4}$	π
y	0	$-\frac{\sqrt{2}}{2}$	-1	$-\frac{\sqrt{2}}{2}$	0	$\frac{\sqrt{2}}{2}$	1	$\frac{\sqrt{2}}{2}$	0

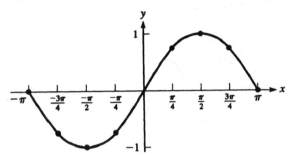

5. $y = 3 \sin x$ has amplitude 3 and x-intercepts $0, \pi, 2\pi$.

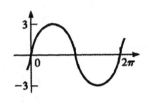

x	y
0	0
$\frac{\pi}{2}$	3
π	0
$\frac{3\pi}{2}$	-3
2π	0

9. $y = 2 \cos x$ has amplitude 2 and x-intercepts $\frac{\pi}{2}, \frac{3\pi}{2}$.

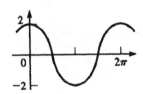

x	y
0	2
$\frac{\pi}{2}$	0
π	-2
$\frac{3\pi}{2}$	0
2π	2

13. $y = -\sin x$ has amplitude 1 and x-intercepts $0, \pi, 2\pi$. The negative sign inverts the graph.

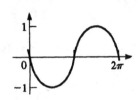

x	y
0	0
$\frac{\pi}{2}$	-1
π	0
$\frac{3\pi}{2}$	1
2π	0

17. $y = -\cos x$ has amplitude 1 and x-intercepts $\frac{\pi}{2}, \frac{3\pi}{2}$. The negative inverts the graph.

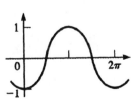

x	y
0	-1
$\frac{\pi}{2}$	0
π	1
$\frac{3\pi}{2}$	0
2π	-1

21. Sketch $y = \sin x$ for $x = 0, 1, 2, 3, 4, 5, 6, 7$.

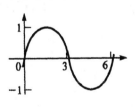

x	y
0	0
1	0.84
2	0.91
3	0.41
4	-0.76
5	-0.96
6	-0.28
7	0.66

25. The graph passes through $(0,0), (\pi, 0)$, and $(2\pi, 0)$ with amplitude 4. The graph is $y = 4 \sin x$.

Section 7.2

10.2   Graphs of $y = a \sin bx$ and $y = a \cos bx$

1. Since $\sin bx$ has period $\dfrac{2\pi}{b}$, $y = 2 \sin 6x$ has period of $\dfrac{2\pi}{6} = \dfrac{\pi}{3}$.

5. $y = -2 \sin 12x$ has period of $\dfrac{2\pi}{12} = \dfrac{\pi}{6}$.

9. $y = 520 \sin 2\pi x$ has period of $\dfrac{2\pi}{2\pi} = 1$.

13. $y = 3 \sin \dfrac{1}{3}x$ has period of $\dfrac{2\pi}{\dfrac{1}{3}} = 6\pi$.

17. $y = 0.4 \sin \dfrac{2\pi x}{3}$ has period of $\dfrac{2\pi}{\dfrac{2\pi}{3}} = 3$.

21. $y = 2 \sin 6x$ has amplitude 2 and period of $\frac{\pi}{3}$.

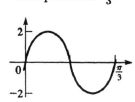

x	y
0	0
$\frac{\pi}{12}$	2
$\frac{\pi}{6}$	0
$\frac{\pi}{4}$	-2
$\frac{\pi}{3}$	0

25. $y = -2 \sin 12x$ has amplitude 2 and period of $\frac{\pi}{6}$.

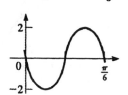

x	y
0	0
$\frac{\pi}{24}$	-2
$\frac{\pi}{12}$	0
$\frac{\pi}{8}$	2
$\frac{\pi}{6}$	0

29. $y = 520 \sin 2\pi x$ has amplitude 520 and period of 1.

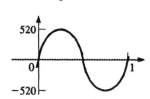

x	y
0	0
0.25	520
0.50	0
0.75	-520
1.0	0

33. $y = 3 \sin \dfrac{1}{3}x$ has amplitude 3 and period of 6π.

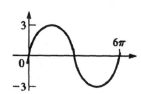

x	y
0	0
$\frac{3\pi}{2}$	3
3π	0
$\frac{9\pi}{2}$	-3
6π	0

37. $y = 0.4 \sin \dfrac{2\pi x}{3}$ has amplitude 0.4 and period of 3.

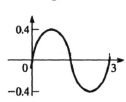

x	y
0	0
0.75	0.4
1.50	0
2.25	-0.4
3.0	0

41. $b = \dfrac{2\pi}{\dfrac{\pi}{3}} = 6$; $y = \sin 6x$

45. $V = 170 \sin 120\pi t$

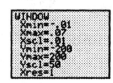

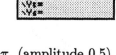

49. $y = \dfrac{1}{2} \cos 2x$ period of π, (amplitude 0.5)

Section 7.3

10.3   Graphs of $y = a\sin(bx + c)$ and $y = a\cos(bx + c)$

1. $y = \sin\left(x - \dfrac{\pi}{6}\right);\ a = 1,\ b = 1,\ c = -\dfrac{\pi}{6}$

Amplitude is $|a| = 1$; period is $\dfrac{2\pi}{b} = 2\pi$;

displacement is $-\dfrac{c}{b} = \dfrac{\pi}{6}$.

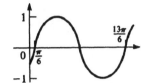

5. $y = 2\sin\left(2x + \dfrac{\pi}{2}\right);\ a = 2,\ ,b = 2, c = \dfrac{\pi}{2}$

Amplitude is $|a| = 2$; period $= \dfrac{2\pi}{b} = \pi$

and displacement $= \dfrac{c}{b} = -\dfrac{\pi}{4}$.

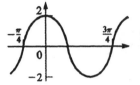

9. $y = \dfrac{1}{2}\sin\left(\dfrac{x}{2} - \dfrac{\pi}{4}\right);\ a = \dfrac{1}{2},\ b = \dfrac{1}{2},\ c = -\dfrac{\pi}{4}$

Amplitude $= |a| = \dfrac{1}{2}$; period $= \dfrac{2\pi}{b} = 4\pi$,

displacement $= -\dfrac{c}{b} = \dfrac{\pi}{2}$.

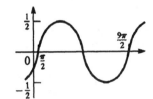

13. $y = \sin\left(\pi x + \dfrac{\pi}{8}\right);\ a = 1,\ b = \pi,\ c = \dfrac{\pi}{8}$

Amplitude $= |a| = 1$; period $= \dfrac{2\pi}{b} = 2$,

displacement $= -\dfrac{c}{b} = -\dfrac{1}{8}$.

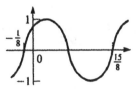

17. $y = -0.6\sin(2\pi x - 1);\ a = -0.6$
$b = 2\pi, c = -1$
Amplitude $= |a| = 0.6$

period $= \dfrac{2\pi}{b} = 1$,

displacement $= -\dfrac{c}{b} = \dfrac{1}{2\pi}$.

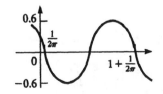

21. $y = \sin(\pi^2 x - \pi);\ a = 1,\ b = \pi^2, c = -\pi$

Amplitude $= |a| = 1$

period $= \dfrac{2\pi}{b} = \dfrac{2}{\pi}$,

displacement $= -\dfrac{c}{b} = \dfrac{1}{\pi}$.

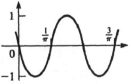

25. $y = 2.00 \sin 2 \left(\dfrac{t}{0.100} - \dfrac{5.00}{20.0} \right)$; $a = 200$,

$b = \dfrac{2\pi}{0.100}, \ c = \dfrac{-5.00(2\pi)}{20.0}$

Amplitude $= |a| = 2.00$,

period $= \dfrac{2\pi}{b} = 0.100$

displacement $= -\dfrac{c}{b} = 0.025$

29. $y = a \sin(bx + c)$

Amplitude is 5, period $= \dfrac{2\pi}{b} = 16$, $b = \dfrac{\pi}{8}$

displacement $= -\dfrac{c}{b} = -1, c = \dfrac{\pi}{8}$

$y = 5 \left(\dfrac{\pi}{8} x + \dfrac{\pi}{8} \right)$.

Section 7.4

10.4 Graphs of $y = \tan x$, $y = \cot x$, $y = \sec x$, $y = \csc x$

1.

x	$-\dfrac{\pi}{2}$	$-\dfrac{\pi}{3}$	$-\dfrac{\pi}{4}$	$-\dfrac{\pi}{6}$	0	$\dfrac{\pi}{6}$	$\dfrac{\pi}{4}$	$\dfrac{\pi}{3}$	$\dfrac{\pi}{2}$	$\dfrac{2\pi}{3}$	$\dfrac{3\pi}{4}$	$\dfrac{5\pi}{6}$	π
y	$*$	$-\sqrt{3}$	-1	$\dfrac{-1}{\sqrt{3}}$	0	$\dfrac{1}{\sqrt{3}}$	1	$\sqrt{3}$	$*$	$-\sqrt{3}$	-1	$\dfrac{1}{-\sqrt{3}}$	0

$y = \tan x$

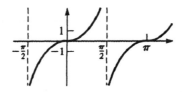

5. $y = 2 \tan x$ is the graph of $y = \tan x$ stretched by a factor of 2.

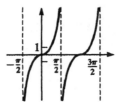

9. The graph of $y = -2 \cot x$ is the graph of $y = \tan x$ reflected in the x-axis and stretched by a factor of 2.

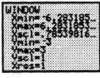 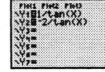 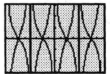

13. Since the period of $y = \tan x$ is π, the period of $y = \tan 2x$ is $\dfrac{\pi}{2}$. Graph $y_1 = \tan(2x)$ using

$x_{\min} = -\dfrac{\pi}{4}$, $x_{\max} = \dfrac{3\pi}{4}$, $y_{\min} = -3$, $y_{\max} = 3$.

 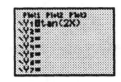 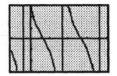

17. Since the period of $\cot x$ is π, the period of $y = 2\cot\left(2x + \dfrac{\pi}{6}\right)$ is $\dfrac{\pi}{2}$. The displacement is

$-\dfrac{\pi/6}{2} = -\dfrac{\pi}{12}$. Graph $y_1 = 2/\tan(2x + \pi/6)$ using $x_{\min} = -\dfrac{\pi}{4}$, $x_{\max} = \pi$, $y_{\min} = -3$, $y_{\max} = 3$.

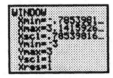  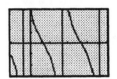

21. $d = 3.00\sec\theta$, $0 \le \theta \le \dfrac{\pi}{2}$

θ	0	$\dfrac{\pi}{2}$
$\sec\theta$	1	$*$
$3.00\sec\theta$	3.00	$*$

Section 7.5

10.5 Applications of the Trigonometric Graphs

1. $d = R\sin wt = 2.40\sin 2t$ has amplitude $a = 2.40$ cm, period $= \dfrac{2\pi}{2} = \pi$ s and displacement $= 0$ s.

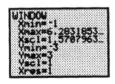  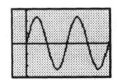

5. $D = A\sin(wt + \partial) = 500\sin(3.6t)$ has amplitude $a = 500$ mi, period $= \dfrac{2\pi}{3.6} = \dfrac{5\pi}{9}$ h, and displacement $= 0$ h.

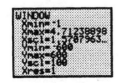  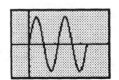

9. $y = A \sin 2\pi \left(\dfrac{t}{T} - \dfrac{x}{\lambda} \right)$

$y = 3.20 \sin 2\pi \left(\dfrac{t}{0.050} - \dfrac{5.00}{40.0} \right)$ has amplitude $a = 3.20$ cm, period $= \dfrac{2\pi}{\dfrac{2\pi}{0.050}} = 0.050$ s, and

displacement $= -\dfrac{\dfrac{-2\pi(5.00)}{40.0}}{\dfrac{2\pi}{0.050}} = 0.00625$ s

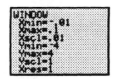  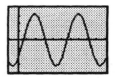

13. $y = 14.0 \sin 40.0\pi t$ has a $a = 14.0$ cm, period $= \dfrac{2\pi}{40\pi} = \dfrac{1}{20}$ s, and displacement $= 0$ s.

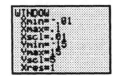  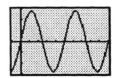

Section 7.6

10.6   Composite Trigonometric Curves

1. $y = 1 + \sin x$

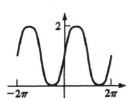

x	-2π	$-\frac{3\pi}{2}$	$-\pi$	$-\frac{\pi}{2}$	0	$\frac{\pi}{2}$	π	$\frac{3\pi}{2}$	2π
y	1	2	1	0	1	2	1	0	1

5. $y = \dfrac{1}{10}x^2 - \sin \pi x$

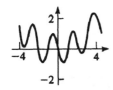

x	-4	-3.43	-2.55	-1.88	-1.47	-1.03	-0.51	0	0.49	0.97	1.53	2.15	2.45	2.73	4
y	1.60	0.20	1.64	0	-0.78	0	1.03	0	-0.98	0	1.23	0	-0.39	0	1.6

9. Graph $y_1 = x^3 + 10\sin 2x$ on graphing calculator with $x_{\min} = -5, x_{\max} = 5, y_{\min} = -50, y_{\max} = 50$.

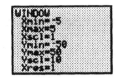  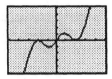

13. Graph $y_1 = 20\cos 2x + 30\sin x$ on a graphing calculator with $x_{\min} = -10, x_{\max} = 10,$ $y_{\min} = -50, y_{\max} = 50$.

  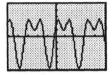

17. Graph $y_1 = \sin \pi x - \cos 2x$ on a graphing calculator with $x_{\min} = -8, x_{\max} = 8, y_{\min} = -3, y_{\max} = 3$.

 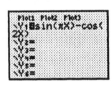 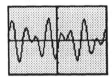

21. $x = \sin t, \ y = \sin t$

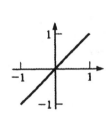

t	x	y
$-\frac{\pi}{2}$	-1	-1
$-\frac{\pi}{4}$	-0.71	-0.71
0	0	0
$\frac{\pi}{4}$	0.71	0.71
$\frac{\pi}{2}$	1	1

25. In parametric mode graph $x_{1T} = \cos \pi \left(t + \frac{1}{6} \right), \ y_{1T} = 2\sin \pi t$ with a graphing calculator.

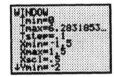   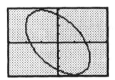

29. In parametric mode graph $x_{1T} = \sin t, \ y_{1T} = \sin 5t$ with a graphing calculator.

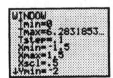 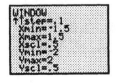  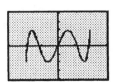

33. $T = 56 - 22\cos\left[\dfrac{\pi}{6}(x - 0.5)\right]$

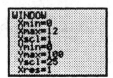 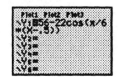 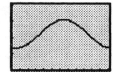

37. To graph $i = 0.32 + 0.50\sin t - 0.20\cos 2t$, let $y_1 = 0.32 + 0.50\sin t - 0.20\cos 2t$ on a graphing calculator with $x_{\min} = -1, x_{\max} = 12, y_{\min} = -0.1, y_{\max} = 1.1$

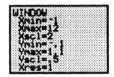 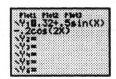 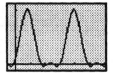

Section 7.7

Chapter 10 Review Exercises

1. $y = \dfrac{2}{3}\sin x$

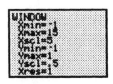 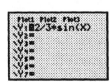 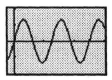

5. $y = 2\sin 3x$

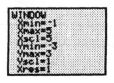  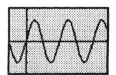

9. $y = 3\cos\dfrac{1}{3}x$

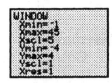 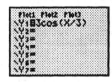 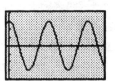

13. $y = 5\cos 2\pi x$

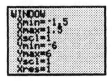 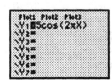 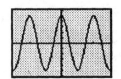

17. $y = 2\sin\left(3x - \dfrac{\pi}{2}\right)$

  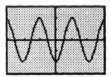

21. $y = -\sin\left(\pi x + \dfrac{\pi}{6}\right)$

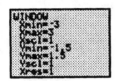 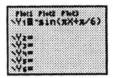 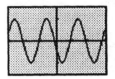

25. $y = 3\tan x$

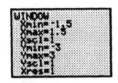 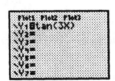 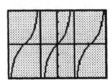

29. $y = 2 + \dfrac{1}{2}\sin 2x$

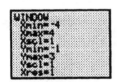 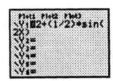 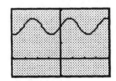

33. $y = 2\sin x - \cos 2x$

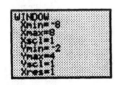 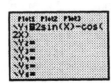 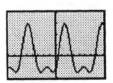

37. $y = \dfrac{\sin x}{x}$

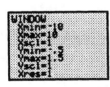 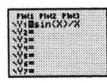 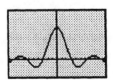

41. From the graph, $a = 2$, period $= \pi = \dfrac{2\pi}{b} \Rightarrow b = 2$, and displacement $= -\dfrac{c}{b} = -\dfrac{\pi}{4} \Rightarrow c = \dfrac{\pi}{2}$.

$y = a\sin(bx + c)$ is $y = 2\sin\left(2x + \dfrac{\pi}{2}\right)$.

45. $x = -\cos 2\pi t,\ y = 2\sin \pi t$

  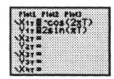 

49. $R = \dfrac{v_0^2 \sin 2\theta}{g} = \dfrac{(1000)^2 \sin 2\theta}{9.8}$

 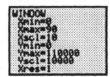  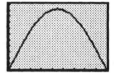

53. $i = 10\,|\sin 120\pi t|$, $0 \le t \le 0.05$, period $= \dfrac{.05}{6} \approx 0.00835$

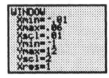  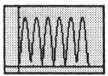

57. $y = 4\sin 2t - 2\cos 2t$

 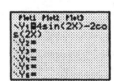 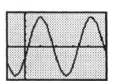

61. $Z = R\sec\theta,\ -\dfrac{\pi}{2} < \theta < \dfrac{\pi}{2}$. Graph shown is for an R value of 1. In general, the y-int would be R.

  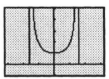

65. (a) If a is doubled in $y = a\sin(bx + c)$ the amplitude will be doubled.

    (b) If b is doubled in $y = a\sin(bx + c)$ the period will be reduced by one half.

    (c) If c is doubled in $y = a\sin(bx + c)$ the displacement will be doubled.

Part 7
Chapter 10

1. $y = 0.5 \cos \frac{\pi}{2} x$
Amp. $= 0.5$, disp. $= 0$,

per. $= \dfrac{2\pi}{\pi/2} = 4$

x	0	1	2	3	4
y	0.5	0	-0.5	0	0.5

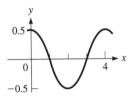

2. $y = 2 + 3 \sin x$
For $y_1 = 3 \sin x$,
amp. $= 3$, per. $= 2\pi$,
disp. $= 0$

x	0	$\frac{\pi}{2}$	π	$\frac{3\pi}{2}$	2π
$y_1 = 3 \sin x$	0	3	0	-3	0
$y = 2 + 3 \sin x$	2	5	2	-1	2

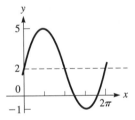

3. $y = 3 \sec x$

$\sec x = \dfrac{1}{\cos x}$

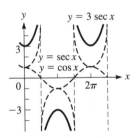

4. $y = 2 \sin(2x - \frac{\pi}{3})$
Amp. $= 2$, per. $= \frac{2\pi}{2} = \pi$

disp. $= -\dfrac{-\pi/3}{2} = \dfrac{\pi}{6}$

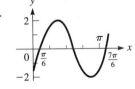

x	$\frac{\pi}{6}$	$\frac{5\pi}{12}$	$\frac{2\pi}{3}$	$\frac{11\pi}{12}$	$\frac{7\pi}{6}$
y	0	2	0	-2	0

$\frac{\pi}{6} + \frac{\pi}{4} = \frac{5\pi}{12}, \frac{\pi}{6} + \frac{\pi}{2} = \frac{2\pi}{3}, \frac{\pi}{6} + \frac{3\pi}{4} = \frac{11\pi}{12}$

5. $y = A \cos \frac{2\pi}{T} t$
$A = 0.200$ in., $T = 0.100$ s,
$y = 0.200 \cos 20\pi t$,
amp. $= 0.200$ in., per. $= 0.100$ s

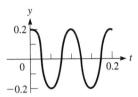

6. $y = 2 \sin x + \cos 2x$
For $y_1 = 2 \sin x$,
amp. $= 2$, per. $= 2\pi$, disp. $= 0$
For $y_2 = \cos 2x$,
amp. $= 1$, per. $= \frac{2\pi}{2} = \pi$, disp. $= 0$

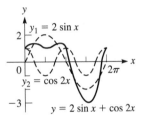

7. $x = \sin \pi t$, $y = 2 \cos 2\pi t$

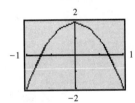

8. $d = R \sin(\omega t + \frac{\pi}{6})$
$\omega = 2.00$ rad/s
$d = R \sin(2.00t + \frac{\pi}{6})$

Amp. $= R$, per. $= \dfrac{2\pi}{2.00} = \pi$ s $= 3.14$ s,

disp. $= \dfrac{-\pi/6}{2.00} = -\dfrac{\pi}{12}$ s $= -0.26$ s

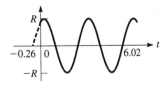

PART 8 – ADDITIONAL TOPICS IN TRIGONOMETRY

Section 8.1

Part 8

20-1 FUNDAMENTAL TRIGONOMETRIC IDENTITIES

From Chapters 4 and 8, we recall that the definition of the sine of an angle θ is $\sin \theta = y/r$ and that the definition of the cosecant of an angle θ is $\csc \theta = r/y$ (see Fig. 20-1). Since $y/r = 1/(r/y)$, we see that $\sin \theta = 1/\csc \theta$. The definitions hold true for *any* angle, which means this relation between $\sin \theta$ and $\csc \theta$ is true for *any* angle. *This type of relation, which is true for any value of the variable, is called an* **identity**. Of course, values where division by zero would be indicated are excluded.

In this section we develop several important identities among the trigonometric functions. We also show how the basic identities are used to verify other identities. From the definitions, we have

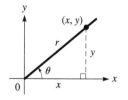

Fig. 20-1

$$\sin \theta \csc \theta = \frac{y}{r} \times \frac{r}{y} = 1 \quad \text{or} \quad \sin \theta = \frac{1}{\csc \theta} \quad \text{or} \quad \csc \theta = \frac{1}{\sin \theta}$$

$$\cos \theta \sec \theta = \frac{x}{r} \times \frac{r}{x} = 1 \quad \text{or} \quad \cos \theta = \frac{1}{\sec \theta} \quad \text{or} \quad \sec \theta = \frac{1}{\cos \theta}$$

$$\tan \theta \cot \theta = \frac{y}{x} \times \frac{x}{y} = 1 \quad \text{or} \quad \tan \theta = \frac{1}{\cot \theta} \quad \text{or} \quad \cot \theta = \frac{1}{\tan \theta}$$

$$\frac{\sin \theta}{\cos \theta} = \frac{y/r}{x/r} = \frac{y}{x} = \tan \theta; \qquad \frac{\cos \theta}{\sin \theta} = \frac{x/r}{y/r} = \frac{x}{y} = \cot \theta$$

Also, from the definitions and the Pythagorean theorem in the form of $x^2 + y^2 = r^2$, we arrive at the following identities.

By dividing the Pythagorean relation through by r^2, we have

$$\left(\frac{x}{r}\right)^2 + \left(\frac{y}{r}\right)^2 = 1 \quad \text{which leads us to} \quad \cos^2 \theta + \sin^2 \theta = 1$$

By dividing the Pythagorean relation by x^2, we have

$$1 + \left(\frac{y}{x}\right)^2 = \left(\frac{r}{x}\right)^2 \quad \text{which leads us to} \quad 1 + \tan^2 \theta = \sec^2 \theta$$

By dividing the Pythagorean relation by y^2, we have

$$\left(\frac{x}{y}\right)^2 + 1 = \left(\frac{r}{y}\right)^2 \quad \text{which leads us to} \quad \cot^2 \theta + 1 = \csc^2 \theta$$

BASIC IDENTITIES

The term $\cos^2 \theta$ is the common way of writing $(\cos \theta)^2$, and it means to square the value of the cosine of the angle. Obviously, the same holds true for the other functions.

Summarizing these results, we have the following important identities.

$\sin \theta = \dfrac{1}{\csc \theta}$	(20-1)	$\tan \theta = \dfrac{\sin \theta}{\cos \theta}$	(20-4)	$\sin^2 \theta + \cos^2 \theta = 1$	(20-6)
$\cos \theta = \dfrac{1}{\sec \theta}$	(20-2)	$\cot \theta = \dfrac{\cos \theta}{\sin \theta}$	(20-5)	$1 + \tan^2 \theta = \sec^2 \theta$	(20-7)
$\tan \theta = \dfrac{1}{\cot \theta}$	(20-3)			$1 + \cot^2 \theta = \csc^2 \theta$	(20-8)

In using these basic identities, θ may stand for any angle or number or expression representing an angle or a number.

EXAMPLE 1   (a) $\sin(x + 1) = \dfrac{1}{\csc(x + 1)}$ using Eq. (20-1)

(b) $\tan 157° = \dfrac{\sin 157°}{\cos 157°}$ using Eq. (20-4)

(c) $\sin^2\left(\dfrac{\pi}{4}\right) + \cos^2\left(\dfrac{\pi}{4}\right) = 1$ using Eq. (20-6) ∎

EXAMPLE 2   We shall check the last two illustrations of Example 1 for the particular values of θ that are used.

(a) Using a calculator, we find that

$$\sin 157° = 0.3907311285 \quad \text{and} \quad \cos 157° = -0.9205048535$$

Considering Eq. (20-4) and illustration (b) in Example 1, by dividing we find that

$$\frac{\sin 157°}{\cos 157°} = \frac{0.3907311285}{-0.9205048535} = -0.4244748162$$

We also find that $\tan 157° = -0.4244748162$, which shows that

$$\tan 157° = \frac{\sin 157°}{\cos 157°}$$

(b) To check illustration (c) of Example 1, we refer to the values found in Example 2 of Section 4-3, or to Fig. 20-2. These tell us that

$$\sin 45° = \frac{1}{\sqrt{2}} = \frac{\sqrt{2}}{2} \quad \text{and} \quad \cos 45° = \frac{\sqrt{2}}{2}$$

Since $\frac{\pi}{4} = 45°$, by adding the squares of $\sin 45°$ and $\cos 45°$, we have

$$\sin^2\left(\frac{\pi}{4}\right) + \cos^2\left(\frac{\pi}{4}\right) = \left(\frac{\sqrt{2}}{2}\right)^2 + \left(\frac{\sqrt{2}}{2}\right)^2 = \frac{1}{2} + \frac{1}{2} = 1$$

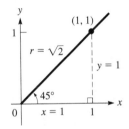

Fig. 20-2

We see that this checks with Eq. (20-6) for these values. ∎

Proving Trigonometric Identities

A great many identities exist among the trigonometric functions. We are going to use the basic identities that have been developed in Eqs. (20-1) through (20-8), along with a few additional ones developed in later sections to prove the validity of still other identities.

CAUTION ▶   *The ability to prove trigonometric identities depends to a large extent on being very familiar with the basic identities* so that you can *recognize them in somewhat **different forms.***

If you do not learn these basic identities and learn them well, you will have difficulty in following the examples and doing the exercises. The more readily you recognize these forms, the more easily you will be able to prove such identities.

In proving identities, we should look for combinations that appear in, or are very similar to, those in the basic identities. This is illustrated in the following examples.

EXAMPLE 3   In proving the identity

$$\sin x = \frac{\cos x}{\cot x}$$

we know that $\cot x = \dfrac{\cos x}{\sin x}$. Since $\sin x$ appears on the left, substituting for $\cot x$ on the right will eliminate $\cot x$ and introduce $\sin x$. This should help us proceed in proving the identity. Thus,

$$\sin x = \frac{\cos x}{\cot x} = \frac{\cos x}{\dfrac{\cos x}{\sin x}} = \frac{\cos x}{1} \times \frac{\sin x}{\cos x}$$

Eq. (20-5)   invert

$$= \sin x \qquad \text{cancel } \cos x \text{ factors}$$

By showing that the right side may be changed exactly to $\sin x$, the expression on the left side, we have proved the identity. ∎

Some important points should be made in relation to the proof of the identity of Example 3. We must recognize what basic identities may be useful. The proof of an identity requires the use of basic algebraic operations, and these must be done carefully and correctly. Although in Example 3 we changed the right side to the form on the left, we could have changed the left to the form on the right. From this and the fact that various substitutions are possible, we see that a variety of procedures can be used to prove any given identity.

As we point out here, performing the *algebraic operations* carefully and correctly is very important when working with trigonometric expressions. Operations such as substituting, factoring, and simplifying fractions are frequently used.

EXAMPLE 4   Prove that $\tan \theta \csc \theta = \sec \theta$.

In proving this identity, we know that $\tan \theta = \dfrac{\sin \theta}{\cos \theta}$ and also that $\dfrac{1}{\cos \theta} = \sec \theta$. Thus, by substituting for $\tan \theta$, we introduce $\cos \theta$ in the denominator, which is equivalent to introducing $\sec \theta$ in the numerator. Therefore, changing only the left side, we have

$$\tan \theta \csc \theta = \frac{\sin \theta}{\cos \theta} \csc \theta = \frac{\sin \theta}{\cos \theta} \frac{1}{\sin \theta}$$

Eq. (20-4)   Eq. (20-1)

$$= \frac{1}{\cos \theta} \qquad \text{cancel } \sin \theta \text{ factors}$$

$$= \sec \theta \qquad \text{using Eq. (20-2)}$$

Having changed the left side into the form on the right side, we have proven the identity.

NOTE ▶

Many variations of the preceding steps are possible. Also, we could have changed the right side to obtain the form on the left. For example,

$$\tan \theta \csc \theta = \sec \theta = \frac{1}{\cos \theta} \qquad \text{using Eq. (20-2)}$$

$$= \frac{\sin \theta}{\cos \theta \sin \theta} = \frac{\sin \theta}{\cos \theta} \frac{1}{\sin \theta} \qquad \begin{array}{l}\text{multiply numerator and} \\ \text{denominator by } \sin \theta \text{ and rewrite}\end{array}$$

$$= \tan \theta \csc \theta \qquad \text{using Eqs. (20-4) and (20-1)} \quad \blacksquare$$

In proving the identities of Examples 3 and 4, we have shown that the expression on one side of the equal sign can be changed into the expression on the other side. Although making the restriction that we change only one side is not entirely necessary, *we shall restrict the method of proof to changing only one side into the same form as the other side.* In this way we know the form we are to obtain, and by looking ahead we are better able to make the proper changes.

There is no set procedure for working with identities. The most important factors are to (1) *recognize the proper forms,* (2) *see what effect a change may have* before performing it, and (3) *perform it correctly.* Normally, *it is easier to change the form of the more complicated side to the same form as the less complicated side.* If the forms are about the same, a close look often suggests possible steps to use.

CAUTION ▶

EXAMPLE 5 Prove the identity $\dfrac{\cos x \csc x}{\cot^2 x} = \tan x$.

First, we note that the left-hand side has several factors and the right-hand side has only one. Therefore, let us transform the left-hand side. Next, we note that we want $\tan x$ as the final result. We know that $\cot x = 1/\tan x$. Thus,

$$\frac{\cos x \csc x}{\cot^2 x} = \frac{\cos x \csc x}{\dfrac{1}{\tan^2 x}} = \cos x \csc x \tan^2 x$$

At this point, we have two factors of $\tan x$ on the left. Since we want only one, let us factor out one. Therefore,

$$\cos x \csc x \tan^2 x = \tan x(\cos x \csc x \tan x)$$

Now, replacing $\tan x$ within the parentheses by $\sin x/\cos x$, we have

$$\tan x(\cos x \csc x \tan x) = \frac{\tan x(\cos x \csc x \sin x)}{\cos x}$$

Now we may cancel $\cos x$. Also, $\csc x \sin x = 1$ from Eq. (19-1). Finally,

$$\frac{\tan x (\cos x \csc x \sin x)}{\cos x} = \tan x\left(\frac{\cos x}{\cos x}\right)(\csc x \sin x)$$
$$= \tan x (1)(1) = \tan x$$

Since we have transformed the left-hand side into $\tan x$, we have proven the identity. Of course, it is not necessary to rewrite expressions as we did in this example. This was done here only to include the explanations. ------------ ∎

EXAMPLE 6 In finding the radiation rate of an accelerated electric charge, it is necessary to show that $\sin^3 \theta = \sin \theta - \sin \theta \cos^2 \theta$. Show this by changing the left side.

Since each term on the right has a factor of $\sin \theta$, we see that we can proceed by writing $\sin^3 \theta$ as $\sin \theta (\sin^2 \theta)$. Then the factor $\sin^2 \theta$ and the $\cos^2 \theta$ on the right suggest the use of Eq. (20-6). Thus we have

$$\sin^3 \theta = \sin \theta(\sin^2 \theta) = \sin \theta(1 - \cos^2 \theta)$$
$$= \sin \theta - \sin \theta \cos^2 \theta \qquad \text{multiplying}$$

Since we wanted to substitute for $\sin^2 \theta$, we used Eq. (20-6) in the form

$$\sin^2 \theta = 1 - \cos^2 \theta \qquad \text{------------} \ ∎$$

EXAMPLE 7   Prove the identity $\dfrac{\sec^2 y}{\cot y} - \tan^3 y = \tan y$.

Here we shall simplify the left side. We can remove cot y from the denominator, since cot $y = 1/\tan y$. Also, the presence of $\sec^2 y$ suggests the use of Eq. (20-7). Therefore, we have

$$\frac{\sec^2 y}{\cot y} - \tan^3 y = \frac{\sec^2 y}{\dfrac{1}{\tan y}} - \tan^3 y = \sec^2 y \tan y - \tan^3 y$$

$$= \tan y \,(\sec^2 y - \tan^2 y) = \tan y (1)$$

$$= \tan y$$

Here we have used Eq. (20-7) in the form $\sec^2 y - \tan^2 y = 1$.   ▪

EXAMPLE 8   Prove the identity $\dfrac{1 - \sin x}{\sin x \cot x} = \dfrac{\cos x}{1 + \sin x}$.

The combination $1 - \sin x$ also suggests $1 - \sin^2 x$, since multiplying $(1 - \sin x)$ by $(1 + \sin x)$ gives $1 - \sin^2 x$, which can then be replaced by $\cos^2 x$. Thus, changing only the left side, we have

$$\frac{1 - \sin x}{\sin x \cot x} = \frac{(1 - \sin x)(1 + \sin x)}{\sin x \cot x (1 + \sin x)} \qquad \text{multiply numerator and denominator by } 1 + \sin x$$

$$= \frac{1 - \sin^2 x}{\sin x \left(\dfrac{\cos x}{\sin x}\right)(1 + \sin x)} = \frac{\cos^2 x}{\cos x\,(1 + \sin x)} \longleftarrow \text{Eq. (20-6)}$$

$$\qquad\qquad\qquad\qquad\qquad\qquad\qquad\qquad \text{cancel sin } x$$

$$= \frac{\cos x}{1 + \sin x} \qquad\qquad\qquad \text{cancel cos } x \qquad\qquad ▪$$

EXAMPLE 9   Prove the identity $\sec^2 x + \csc^2 x = \sec^2 x \csc^2 x$.

Here we note the presence of $\sec^2 x$ and $\csc^2 x$ on each side. This suggests the possible use of the square relationships. By replacing the $\sec^2 x$ on the right-hand side by $1 + \tan^2 x$, we can create $\csc^2 x$ plus another term. The left-hand side is the $\csc^2 x$ plus another term, so this procedure should help. Thus, changing only the right side,

$$\sec^2 x + \csc^2 x = \sec^2 x \csc^2 x$$

$$= (1 + \tan^2 x)(\csc^2 x) \qquad \text{using Eq. (20-7)}$$

$$= \csc^2 x + \tan^2 x \csc^2 x \qquad \text{multiplying}$$

$$= \csc^2 x + \left(\frac{\sin^2 x}{\cos^2 x}\right)\left(\frac{1}{\sin^2 x}\right) \qquad \text{using Eqs. (20-4) and (20-1)}$$

$$= \csc^2 x + \frac{1}{\cos^2 x} \qquad \text{cancel sin}^2 x$$

$$= \csc^2 x + \sec^2 x \qquad \text{using Eq. (20-2)}$$

We could have used many other variations of this procedure, and they would have been perfectly valid.   ▪

EXAMPLE 10   Simplify the expression $\dfrac{\csc x}{\tan x + \cot x}$.

We proceed with a simplification such as this in a manner similar to proving an identity, although we do not know just what the result should be. One procedure for this simplification is shown as follows.

$$\frac{\csc x}{\tan x + \cot x} = \frac{\csc x}{\tan x + \dfrac{1}{\tan x}} = \frac{\csc x}{\dfrac{\tan^2 x + 1}{\tan x}}$$

$$= \frac{\csc x \tan x}{\tan^2 x + 1} = \frac{\csc x \tan x}{\sec^2 x} = \frac{\dfrac{1}{\sin x}\dfrac{\sin x}{\cos x}}{\dfrac{1}{\cos^2 x}}$$

$$= \frac{1}{\sin x \cos x}\frac{\sin x \cos^2 x}{1} = \cos x$$

A graphing calculator can be used to check an identity or a simplification. This is done by graphing the function on each side of an identity, or the initial expression and the final expression for a simplification. If the two graphs are the same, the identity or simplification is probably shown to be correct, although this is not strictly a proof.

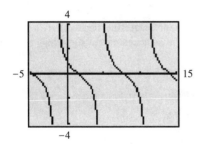

Fig. 20-3

EXAMPLE 11   (a) Use a graphing calculator to verify the identity of Example 8.

Noting this identity as $\dfrac{1 - \sin x}{\sin x \cot x} = \dfrac{\cos x}{1 + \sin x}$, on a graphing calculator, we let

$$y_1 = (1 - \sin x)/(\sin x/\tan x) \qquad \text{(noting that } \cot x = 1/\tan x)$$
$$y_2 = \cos x/(1 + \sin x)$$

We then graph these two functions as shown in Fig. 20-3. We choose a domain that obviously includes more than one period of each function. Also, after the first curve is plotted, we must watch the screen carefully to see if any new points are plotted for the second curve (use a heavier curve if possible). Since these curves are the same, the identity appears to be verified (although it has not been *proven*).

───── **EXERCISES** *20-1* ─────

In Exercises 1–4, use a calculator to check the indicated basic identities for the given angles.

1. Eq. (20-3) for $\theta = 56°$

2. Eq. (20-5) for $\theta = 280°$

3. Eq. (20-6) for $\theta = \dfrac{4\pi}{3}$

4. Eq. (20-7) for $\theta = \dfrac{5\pi}{6}$

In Exercises 5–40, prove the given identities.

5. $\dfrac{\cot \theta}{\cos \theta} = \csc \theta$

6. $\dfrac{\tan y}{\sin y} = \sec y$

7. $\dfrac{\sin x}{\tan x} = \cos x$

8. $\dfrac{\csc \theta}{\sec \theta} = \cot \theta$

9. $\sin y \cot y = \cos y$

10. $\cos x \tan x = \sin x$

11. $\sin x \sec x = \tan x$

12. $\cot \theta \sec \theta = \csc \theta$

13. $\csc^2 x (1 - \cos^2 x) = 1$

14. $\cos^2 x (1 + \tan^2 x) = 1$

15. $\sin x (1 + \cot^2 x) = \csc x$

16. $\sec \theta (1 - \sin^2 \theta) = \cos \theta$

17. $\tan y (\cot y + \tan y) = \sec^2 y$

18. $\csc x (\csc x - \sin x) = \cot^2 x$

19. $\sin x \tan x + \cos x = \sec x$

20. $\sec x \csc x - \cot x = \tan x$

21. $\cos \theta \cot \theta + \sin \theta = \csc \theta$

22. $\csc x \sec x - \tan x = \cot x$

23. $\cot \theta \sec^2 \theta - \cot \theta = \tan \theta$

24. $\sin y + \sin y \cot^2 y = \csc y$

25. $\tan x + \cot x = \sec x \csc x$

26. $\tan x + \cot x = \tan x \csc^2 x$

27. $\cos^2 x - \sin^2 x = 1 - 2 \sin^2 x$

28. $\tan^2 y \sec^2 y - \tan^4 y = \tan^2 y$

29. $\dfrac{\sin x}{1 - \cos x} = \csc x + \cot x$

30. $\dfrac{1 + \cos x}{\sin x} = \dfrac{\sin x}{1 - \cos x}$

31. $\tan^2 x \cos^2 x + \cot^2 x \sin^2 x = 1$

32. $\dfrac{\sin \theta}{\csc \theta} + \dfrac{\cos \theta}{\sec \theta} = 1$

33. $\dfrac{\sec \theta}{\cos \theta} - \dfrac{\tan \theta}{\cot \theta} = 1$

34. $\dfrac{\csc \theta}{\sin \theta} - \dfrac{\cot \theta}{\tan \theta} = 1$

35. $2 \sin^4 x - 3 \sin^2 x + 1 = \cos^2 x (1 - 2 \sin^2 x)$

36. $\dfrac{\sin^4 x - \cos^4 x}{1 - \cot^4 x} = \sin^4 x$

37. $\dfrac{1}{2} \sin \pi t \left(\dfrac{\sin \pi t}{1 - \cos \pi t} + \dfrac{1 - \cos \pi t}{\sin \pi t} \right) = 1$

38. $\dfrac{\cot \omega t}{\sec \omega t - \tan \omega t} - \dfrac{\cos \omega t}{\sec \omega t + \tan \omega t} = \sin \omega t + \csc \omega t$

39. $1 + \sin^2 x + \sin^4 x + \cdots = \sec^2 x$

40. $1 - \tan^2 x + \tan^4 x - \cdots = \cos^2 x \quad (-\frac{\pi}{4} < x < \frac{\pi}{4})$

In Exercises 41–48, simplify the given expressions. The result will be one of $\sin x$, $\cos x$, $\tan x$, $\cot x$, $\sec x$, *or* $\csc x$.

41. $\dfrac{\tan x \csc^2 x}{1 + \tan^2 x}$

42. $\dfrac{\cos x - \cos^3 x}{\sin x - \sin^3 x}$

43. $\cot x (\sec x - \cos x)$

44. $\sin x (\tan x + \cot x)$

45. $\dfrac{\tan x + \cot x}{\csc x}$

46. $\dfrac{1 + \tan x}{\sin x} - \sec x$

47. $\dfrac{\cos x + \sin x}{1 + \tan x}$

48. $\dfrac{\sec x - \cos x}{\tan x}$

In Exercises 49–56, use a graphing calculator to verify the given identities by comparing the graphs of each side.

49. $\sin x (\csc x - \sin x) = \cos^2 x$

50. $\cos y (\sec y - \cos y) = \sin^2 y$

51. $\sec \theta \tan \theta \csc \theta = \tan^2 \theta + 1$

52. $\sin x \cos x \tan x = 1 - \cos^2 x$

53. $\dfrac{\sec x + \csc x}{1 + \tan x} = \csc x$

54. $\dfrac{\cot x + 1}{\cot x} = 1 + \tan x$

55. $\dfrac{1 - 2 \cos^2 x}{\sin x \cos x} = \tan x - \cot x$

56. $\cos^3 x \csc^3 x \tan^3 x = \csc^2 x - \cot^2 x$

In Exercises 57–60, solve the given problems involving trigonometric identities.

57. When designing a solar energy collector, it is necessary to account for the latitude and longitude of the location, the angle of the sun, and the angle of the collector. In doing this, the equation

    $\cos \theta = \cos A \cos B \cos C + \sin A \sin B$

    is used. If $\theta = 90°$, show that $\cos C = -\tan A \tan B$.

58. In studying the gravitational force between two objects, the expression $(r - R \cos \theta)^2 + (R \sin \theta)^2$ occurs. Show that this expression can be written as $r^2 - 2rR \cos \theta + R^2$.

59. Show that the length l of the straight brace shown in Fig. 20-4 can be found from the equation

    $l = \dfrac{a(1 + \tan \theta)}{\sin \theta}$

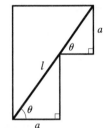

Fig. 20-4

60. In determining the path of least time between two points under certain conditions, it is necessary to show that

    $\sqrt{\dfrac{1 + \cos \theta}{1 - \cos \theta}} \sin \theta = 1 + \cos \theta$

    Show this by transforming the left-hand side.

In Exercises 61–64, solve the given problems.

61. Show that $\sin^2 x (1 - \sec^2 x) + \cos^2 x (1 + \sec^4 x)$ has a constant value.

62. Show that $\cot y \csc y \sec y - \csc y \cos y \cot y$ has a constant value.

63. Prove that $\sec^2 \theta + \csc^2 \theta = \sec^2 \theta \csc^2 \theta$ by expressing each function in terms of its x, y, and r definition. See Example 9.

64. Prove that $\dfrac{\csc \theta}{\tan \theta + \cot \theta} = \cos \theta$ by expressing each function in terms of its x, y, and r definition. See Example 10.

In Exercises 65–68, use the given substitutions to show that the given equations are valid. In each, $0 < \theta < \pi/2$.

65. If $x = \cos \theta$, show that $\sqrt{1 - x^2} = \sin \theta$.

66. If $x = 3 \sin \theta$, show that $\sqrt{9 - x^2} = 3 \cos \theta$.

67. If $x = 2 \tan \theta$, show that $\sqrt{4 + x^2} = 2 \sec \theta$.

68. If $x = 4 \sec \theta$, show that $\sqrt{x^2 - 16} = 4 \tan \theta$.

Section 8.2

21-9 POLAR COORDINATES

The Swiss mathematician Jakob Bernoulli (1654–1705) was among the first to make significant use of polar coordinates.

Thus far we have graphed all curves in one coordinate system. This system, the rectangular coordinate system, is probably the most useful and widely applicable system. However, for certain types of curves, other coordinate systems prove to be better adapted. These coordinate systems are widely used, especially when certain applications of higher mathematics are involved. We shall discuss one of these systems here.

Instead of designating a point by its x- and y-coordinates, we can specify its location by its radius vector and the angle the radius vector makes with the x-axis. Thus, the r and θ that are used in the definitions of the trigonometric functions can also be used as the coordinates of points in the plane. The important aspect of choosing coordinates is that, for each set of values, there must be only one point which corresponds to this set. We can see that this condition is satisfied by the use of r and θ as coordinates. *In* **polar coordinates,** *the origin is called the* **pole,** *and the half-line for which the angle is zero (equivalent to the positive x-axis) is called the* **polar axis.** The coordinates of a point are designated as (r, θ). We shall use radians when measuring the value of θ. See Fig. 21-91.

Fig. 21-91

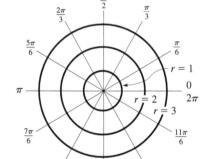

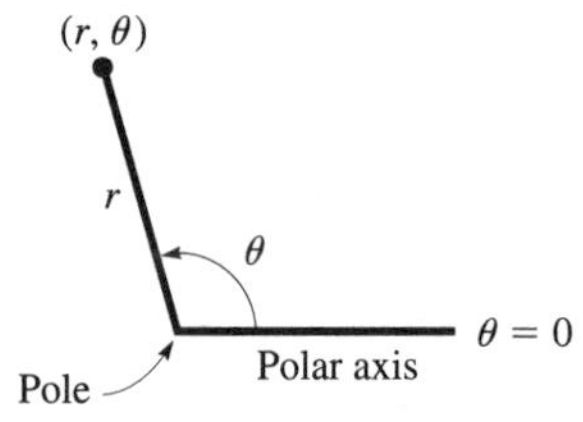

When using polar coordinates, we generally label the lines for some of the values of θ; namely, those for $\theta = 0$ (the polar axis), $\theta = \pi/2$ (equivalent to the positive y-axis), $\theta = \pi$ (equivalent to the negative x-axis), $\theta = 3\pi/2$ (equivalent to the negative y-axis), and possibly others. In Fig. 21-92, these lines and those for multiples of $\pi/6$ are shown. Also, the circles for $r = 1$, $r = 2$, and $r = 3$ are shown in this figure.

Fig. 21-92

EXAMPLE 1 **(a)** If $r = 2$ and $\theta = \pi/6$, we have the point as shown in Fig. 21-93. The coordinates (r, θ) of this point are written as $(2, \pi/6)$ when polar coordinates are used. This point corresponds to $(\sqrt{3}, 1)$ in rectangular coordinates.

(b) In Fig. 21-93, the polar coordinate point $(1, 3\pi/4)$ is also shown. It is equivalent to the point $(-\sqrt{2}/2, \sqrt{2}/2)$ in rectangular coordinates.

(c) In Fig. 21-93, the polar coordinate point $(2, 5)$ is also shown. It is equivalent approximately to the point $(0.6, -1.9)$ in rectangular coordinates. Remember, the 5 is an angle in radian measure.

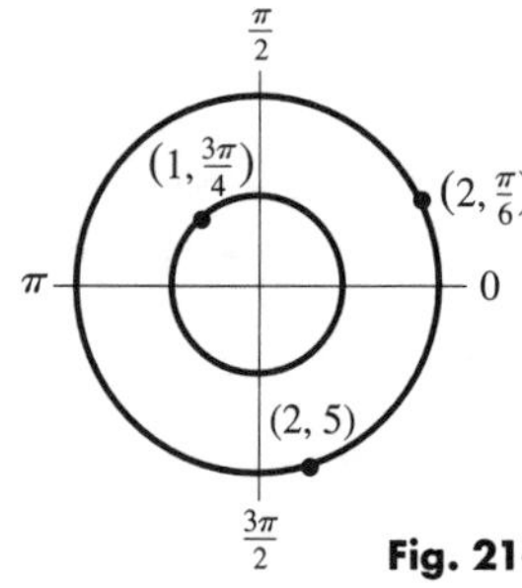

Fig. 21-93

One difference between rectangular coordinates and polar coordinates is that, for each point in the plane, there are limitless possibilities for the polar coordinates of that point. For example, the point $(2, \frac{\pi}{6})$ can also be represented by $(2, \frac{13\pi}{6})$ since the angles $\frac{\pi}{6}$ and $\frac{13\pi}{6}$ are coterminal. We also remove one restriction on r that we imposed in the definition of the trigonometric functions. That is, r is allowed to take on positive and negative values. If r is negative, θ is located as before, but **the point is found r units from the pole but on the opposite side** from that on which it is positive.

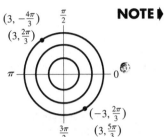

Fig. 21-94

NOTE ▶

EXAMPLE 2 The coordinates $(3, 2\pi/3)$ and $(3, -4\pi/3)$ represent the same point. However, the point $(-3, 2\pi/3)$ is on the opposite side of the pole, three units from the pole. Another possible set of coordinates for the point $(-3, 2\pi/3)$ is $(3, 5\pi/3)$. See Fig. 21-94.

When plotting a point in polar coordinates, it is generally easier to *first locate the terminal side of θ and then measure r along this terminal side.* This is illustrated in the following example.

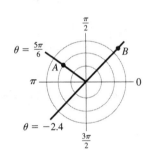

Fig. 21-95

EXAMPLE 3 Plot the points $A(2, 5\pi/6)$ and $B(-3.2, -2.4)$ in the polar coordinate system.

To locate A we determine the terminal side of $\theta = 5\pi/6$ and then determine $r = 2$. See Fig. 21-95.

To locate B we find the terminal side of $\theta = -2.4$, measuring clockwise from the polar axis (and recalling that $\pi = 3.14 = 180°$). Then we locate $r = -3.2$ on the opposite side of the pole. See Fig. 21-95.

We will find that points with negative values of r occur frequently when plotting curves in polar coordinates.

Polar and Rectangular Coordinates

The relationships between the polar coordinates of a point and the rectangular coordinates of the same point come from the definitions of the trigonometric functions. Those most commonly used are (see Fig. 21-96):

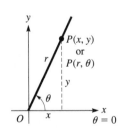

Fig. 21-96

$$x = r \cos \theta \qquad y = r \sin \theta \qquad \text{(21-35)}$$

$$\tan \theta = \frac{y}{x} \qquad r = \sqrt{x^2 + y^2} \qquad \text{(21-36)}$$

The following examples show the use of Eqs. (21-35) and (21-36) in changing coordinates in one system to coordinates in the other system. Also, these equations are used to transform equations from one system to the other.

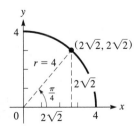

Fig. 21-97

EXAMPLE 4 Using Eqs. (21-35), we can transform the polar coordinates of $(4, \pi/4)$ into the rectangular coordinates $(2\sqrt{2}, 2\sqrt{2})$, since

$$x = 4 \cos \frac{\pi}{4} = 4\left(\frac{\sqrt{2}}{2}\right) = 2\sqrt{2} \quad \text{and} \quad y = 4 \sin \frac{\pi}{4} = 4\left(\frac{\sqrt{2}}{2}\right) = 2\sqrt{2}$$

See Fig. 21-97.

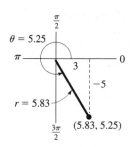

Fig. 21-98

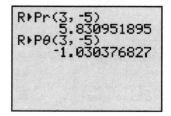

Fig. 21-99

The cyclotron was invented in 1931 at the University of California. It was the first accelerator to deflect particles into circular paths.

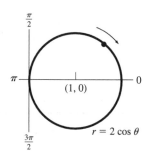

Fig. 21-100

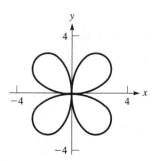

Fig. 21-101

■EXAMPLE 5 Using Eqs. (21-36), we can transform the rectangular coordinates $(3, -5)$ into polar coordinates.

$$\tan \theta = -\frac{5}{3}, \qquad \theta = 5.25 \qquad (\text{or } -1.03)$$
$$r = \sqrt{3^2 + (-5)^2} = 5.83$$

We know that θ is a fourth-quadrant angle since x is positive and y is negative. Therefore, the point $(3, -5)$ in rectangular coordinates can be expressed as the point $(5.83, 5.25)$ in polar coordinates (see Fig. 21-98). Other polar coordinates for the point are also possible. ─────■

Calculators are programmed to make conversions between rectangular coordinates and polar coordinates. The manual for any model should be consulted to determine how any particular model is used for these conversions. For a calculator that uses the *angle* feature, the display for the conversions of Example 5 is shown in Fig. 21-99.

■EXAMPLE 6 If an electrically charged particle enters a magnetic field at right angles to the field, the particle follows a circular path. This fact is used in the design of nuclear particle accelerators.

A proton (positively charged) enters a magnetic field such that its path may be described by the rectangular equation $x^2 + y^2 = 2x$, where measurements are in meters. Find the polar equation of this circle.

We change this equation expressed in the rectangular coordinates x and y into an equation expressed in the polar coordinates r and θ by using the relations $r^2 = x^2 + y^2$ and $x = r \cos \theta$ as follows:

$$x^2 + y^2 = 2x \qquad \text{rectangular equation}$$
$$r^2 = 2r \cos \theta \qquad \text{substitute}$$
$$r = 2 \cos \theta \qquad \text{divide by } r$$

This is the polar equation of the circle, which is shown in Fig. 21-100. ─────■

■EXAMPLE 7 Find the rectangular equation of the *rose* $r = 4 \sin 2\theta$.

Using the trigonometric identity $\sin 2\theta = 2 \sin \theta \cos \theta$ and Eqs. (21-35) and (21-36) leads to the solution.

$$
\begin{aligned}
r &= 4 \sin 2\theta && \text{polar equation}\\
&= 4(2 \sin \theta \cos \theta) = 8 \sin \theta \cos \theta && \text{using identity}\\
\sqrt{x^2 + y^2} &= 8 \left(\frac{y}{r}\right)\left(\frac{x}{r}\right) = \frac{8xy}{r^2} = \frac{8xy}{x^2 + y^2} && \text{using Eqs. (21-35) and (21-36)}\\
x^2 + y^2 &= \frac{64x^2 y^2}{(x^2 + y^2)^2} && \text{squaring both sides}\\
(x^2 + y^2)^3 &= 64x^2 y^2 && \text{simplifying}
\end{aligned}
$$

Plotting the graph of this equation from the rectangular equation would be complicated. However, as we will see in the next section, plotting this graph in polar coordinates is quite simple. The curve is shown in Fig. 21-101. ─────■

EXERCISES *21-9*

In Exercises 1–12, plot the given polar coordinate points on polar coordinate paper.

1. $\left(3, \dfrac{\pi}{6}\right)$ **2.** $(2, \pi)$ **3.** $\left(\dfrac{5}{2}, -\dfrac{2\pi}{5}\right)$

4. $\left(5, -\dfrac{\pi}{3}\right)$ **5.** $\left(-2, \dfrac{7\pi}{6}\right)$ **6.** $\left(-5, \dfrac{\pi}{4}\right)$

7. $\left(-3, -\dfrac{5\pi}{4}\right)$ **8.** $\left(-4, -\dfrac{5\pi}{3}\right)$ **9.** $\left(0.5, -\dfrac{8\pi}{3}\right)$

10. $(2.2, -6\pi)$ **11.** $(2, 2)$ **12.** $(-1, -1)$

In Exercises 13–16, find a set of polar coordinates for each of the points for which the rectangular coordinates are given.

13. $(\sqrt{3}, 1)$ **14.** $(-1, -1)$

15. $\left(-\dfrac{\sqrt{3}}{2}, -\dfrac{1}{2}\right)$ **16.** $(-5, 4)$

In Exercises 17–20, find the rectangular coordinates for each of the points for which the polar coordinates are given.

17. $\left(8, \dfrac{4\pi}{3}\right)$ **18.** $(-4, -\pi)$

19. $(3.0, -0.40)$ **20.** $(-1.0, 1.0)$

In Exercises 21–28, find the polar equation of each of the given rectangular equations.

21. $x = 3$ **22.** $y = x$

23. $x + 2y = 3$ **24.** $x^2 + y^2 = 0.81$

25. $x^2 + (y - 2)^2 = 4$ **26.** $x^2 - y^2 = 0.01$

27. $x^2 + 4y^2 = 4$ **28.** $y^2 = 4x$

In Exercises 29–40, find the rectangular equation of each of the given polar equations. In Exercises 29–36, identify the curve that is represented by the equation.

29. $r = \sin \theta$ **30.** $r = 4 \cos \theta$

31. $r \cos \theta = 4$ **32.** $r \sin \theta = -2$

33. $r = \dfrac{2}{\cos \theta - 3 \sin \theta}$ **34.** $r = e^{r \cos \theta} \csc \theta$

35. $r = 4 \cos \theta + 2 \sin \theta$ **36.** $r \sin(\theta + \pi/6) = 3$

37. $r = 2(1 + \cos \theta)$ **38.** $r = 1 - \sin \theta$

39. $r^2 = \sin 2\theta$ **40.** $r^2 = 16 \cos 2\theta$

In Exercises 41–44, find the required equations.

41. Under certain conditions, the *x*- and *y*-components of a magnetic field *B* are given by the equations

$$B_x = \frac{-ky}{x^2 + y^2} \quad \text{and} \quad B_y = \frac{kx}{x^2 + y^2}$$

Write these equations in terms of polar coordinates.

42. In designing a domed roof for a building, an architect uses the equation $x^2 + \dfrac{y^2}{k^2} = 1$, where *k* is a constant. Write this equation in polar form.

43. The shape of a cam can be described by the polar equation $r = 3 - \sin \theta$. Find the rectangular equation for the shape of the cam.

44. The polar equation of the path of a weather satellite of the earth is $r = \dfrac{4800}{1 + 0.14 \cos \theta}$, where *r* is measured in miles. Find the rectangular equation of the path of this satellite. The path is an ellipse, with the earth at one of the foci.

Section 8.1
Exercises 20-1, page 515

(*Note:* "Answers" to trigonometric identities are intermediate steps of suggested reductions of the left member.)

1. $1.483 = \dfrac{1}{0.6745}$

3. $\left(-\dfrac{1}{2}\sqrt{3}\right)^2 + \left(-\dfrac{1}{2}\right)^2 = \dfrac{3}{4} + \dfrac{1}{4} = 1$

5. $\dfrac{\cos\theta}{\sin\theta}\left(\dfrac{1}{\cos\theta}\right) = \dfrac{1}{\sin\theta}$

7. $\dfrac{\sin x}{\dfrac{\sin x}{\cos x}} = \dfrac{\sin x}{1}\left(\dfrac{\cos x}{\sin x}\right)$ **9.** $\sin y\left(\dfrac{\cos y}{\sin y}\right)$

11. $\sin x\left(\dfrac{1}{\cos x}\right)$ **13.** $\csc^2 x\,(\sin^2 x)$

15. $\sin x\,(\csc^2 x) = (\sin x)(\csc x)(\csc x)$
$= \sin x\left(\dfrac{1}{\sin x}\right)\csc x$

17. $\tan y \cot y + \tan^2 y = 1 + \tan^2 y$

19. $\sin x\left(\dfrac{\sin x}{\cos x}\right) + \cos x = \dfrac{\sin^2 x + \cos^2 x}{\cos x} = \dfrac{1}{\cos x}$

21. $\cos\theta\left(\dfrac{\cos\theta}{\sin\theta}\right) + \sin\theta = \dfrac{\cos^2\theta + \sin^2\theta}{\sin\theta} = \dfrac{1}{\sin\theta}$

23. $\cot\theta\,(\sec^2\theta - 1) = \cot\theta\,\tan^2\theta = (\cot\theta\,\tan\theta)\tan\theta$

25. $\dfrac{\sin x}{\cos x} + \dfrac{\cos x}{\sin x} = \dfrac{\sin^2 x + \cos^2 x}{\cos x \sin x} = \dfrac{1}{\cos x \sin x}$

27. $(1 - \sin^2 x) - \sin^2 x$

29. $\dfrac{\sin x\,(1 + \cos x)}{1 - \cos^2 x} = \dfrac{1 + \cos x}{\sin x}$

31. $\dfrac{\sin^2 x}{\cos^2 x}\cos^2 x + \dfrac{\cos^2 x}{\sin^2 x}\sin^2 x = \sin^2 x + \cos^2 x$

33. $\dfrac{\dfrac{\sec\theta}{1} - \dfrac{\tan\theta}{1}}{\sec\theta \qquad \tan\theta} = \sec^2\theta - \tan^2\theta$

35. $(2\sin^2 x - 1)(\sin^2 x - 1)$

37. $\dfrac{\sin\pi t}{2}\left(\dfrac{\sin^2\pi t + (1 - \cos\pi t)^2}{(1 - \cos\pi t)\sin\pi t}\right)$

$\qquad = \dfrac{\sin^2\pi t + 1 - 2\cos\pi t + \cos^2\pi t}{2(1 - \cos\pi t)} = \dfrac{2(1 - \cos\pi t)}{2(1 - \cos\pi t)}$

39. Infinite series: $\dfrac{1}{1 - \sin^2 x} = \dfrac{1}{\cos^2 x}$ **41.** $\cot x$

43. $\sin x$ **45.** $\sec x$ **47.** $\cos x$

49.   **51.**

53.   **55.**

57. $0 = \cos A \cos B \cos C + \sin A \sin B,$

$\qquad \cos C = -\dfrac{\sin A \sin B}{\cos A \cos B}$

59. $l = a\csc\theta + a\sec\theta = a\left(\dfrac{1}{\sin\theta} + \dfrac{\tan\theta}{\sin\theta}\right)$

61. $\sin^2 x - \sin^2 x\sec^2 x + \cos^2 x + \cos^2 x\sec^4 x$
$\qquad = \sin^2 x - \tan^2 x + \cos^2 x + \sec^2 x = 2$

63. $\left(\dfrac{r}{x}\right)^2 + \left(\dfrac{r}{y}\right)^2 = \dfrac{r^2(x^2 + y^2)}{x^2 y^2}$

65. $\sqrt{1 - \cos^2\theta} = \sqrt{\sin^2\theta}$

67. $\sqrt{4 + 4\tan^2\theta} = 2\sqrt{1 + \tan^2\theta}$

ADDITIONAL TOPICS IN TRIGONOMETRY

20.1 Fundamental Trigonometric Identities

Section 8.1

1. Verify $\tan\theta = \dfrac{1}{\cot\theta}$ for $\theta = 56°$

$\tan 56° = 1.483$; $\cot 56° = 0.6745$

$\dfrac{1}{0.6745} = 1.483 = \tan 56°$

5. $\dfrac{\cot\theta}{\cos\theta} = \cot\theta \times \dfrac{1}{\cos\theta}$

$\qquad = \dfrac{\cos\theta}{\sin\theta} \times \dfrac{1}{\cos\theta}$

$\qquad = \dfrac{1}{\sin\theta} = \csc\theta$

9. $\sin y \cot y = \dfrac{\sin y}{1} \times \dfrac{\cos y}{\sin y}$

$\qquad\qquad = \cos y$

13. $\csc^2 x(1 - \cos^2 x) = \dfrac{1}{\sin^2 x} \times \dfrac{\sin^2 x}{1}$

$\qquad\qquad\qquad = \dfrac{\sin^2 x}{\sin^2 x} = 1$

17. $\tan y(\cot y + \tan y) = \tan y \cot y + \tan^2 y = \tan y \times \left(\dfrac{1}{\tan y}\right) + \tan^2 y = 1 + \tan^2 y = \sec^2 y$

21. $\cos\theta \cot\theta + \sin\theta = \cos\theta \times \dfrac{\cos\theta}{\sin\theta} + \sin\theta = \dfrac{\cos^2\theta}{\sin\theta} + \sin\theta = \dfrac{\cos^2\theta + \sin^2\theta}{\sin\theta} = \dfrac{1}{\sin\theta} = \csc\theta$

25. $\tan x + \cot x = \dfrac{\sin x}{\cos x} + \dfrac{\cos x}{\sin x}$

$\qquad\qquad = \dfrac{\sin^2 x + \cos^2 x}{\cos x \sin x}$

$\qquad\qquad = \dfrac{1}{\cos x \sin x}$

$\qquad\qquad = \sec x \csc x$

29. $\dfrac{\sin x}{1 - \cos x} = \dfrac{\sin x(1 + \cos x)}{(1 - \cos x)(1 + \cos x)}$

$\qquad\qquad = \dfrac{\sin x(1 + \cos x)}{1 - \cos^2 x} = \dfrac{\sin x(1 + \cos x)}{\sin^2 x}$

$\qquad\qquad = \dfrac{1 + \cos x}{\sin x} = \dfrac{1}{\sin x} + \dfrac{\cos x}{\sin x}$

$\qquad\qquad = \csc x + \cot x$

33. $\dfrac{\sec\theta}{\cos\theta} - \dfrac{\tan\theta}{\cot\theta}$

$= \dfrac{1}{\cos\theta}\left(\dfrac{1}{\cos\theta}\right) - \dfrac{\sin\theta}{\cos\theta}\left(\dfrac{\sin\theta}{\cos\theta}\right)$

$= \dfrac{1}{\cos^2\theta} - \dfrac{\sin^2\theta}{\cos^2\theta}$

$= \dfrac{\cos^2\theta}{\cos^2\theta}$

$= 1$

37. $\dfrac{1}{2}\sin\pi t\left(\dfrac{\sin\pi t}{1 - \cos\pi t} + \dfrac{1 - \cos\pi t}{\sin\pi t}\right)$

$= \dfrac{1}{2}\sin\pi t\left(\dfrac{\sin^2\pi t + (1 - \cos\pi t)^2}{\sin\pi t(1 - \cos\pi t)}\right)$

$= \dfrac{1}{2}\left(\dfrac{\sin^2\pi t + 1 - 2\cos\pi t + \cos^2\pi t}{1 - \cos\pi t}\right)$

$= \dfrac{1}{2}\left(\dfrac{(\sin^2\pi t + \cos^2\pi t) + 1 - 2\cos\pi t}{1 - \cos\pi t}\right)$

$= \dfrac{1}{2}\left(\dfrac{1 + 1 - 2\cos\pi t}{1 - \cos\pi t}\right)$

$= \dfrac{2 - 2\cos\pi t}{2 - 2\cos\pi t} = 1$

41. $\dfrac{\tan x \csc^2 x}{1 + \tan^2 x} = \dfrac{\dfrac{\sin x}{\cos x} \cdot \dfrac{1}{\sin^2 x}}{1 + \dfrac{\sin^2 x}{\cos^2 x}}$

$= \dfrac{\dfrac{1}{\sin x \cos x}}{\dfrac{\cos^2 x + \sin^2 x}{\cos^2 x}}$

$= \dfrac{1}{\sin x \cos x} \cdot \dfrac{\cos^2 x}{1}$

$= \dfrac{\cos x}{\sin x} = \cot x$

45. $\dfrac{\tan x + \cot x}{\csc x}$

$= \dfrac{\dfrac{\sin x}{\cos x} + \dfrac{\cos x}{\sin x}}{\dfrac{1}{\sin x}} \cdot \dfrac{\sin x \cos x}{\sin x \cos x}$

$= \dfrac{\sin^2 x + \cos^2 x}{\cos x}$

$= \dfrac{1}{\cos x} = \sec x$

49.

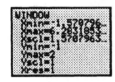  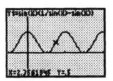 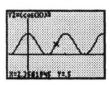

53.

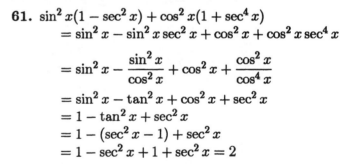

57. $\cos\theta = \cos A \cos B \cos C + \sin A \sin B$;
$\theta = 90°$, $\cos\theta = 0$

$0 = \cos A \cos B \cos C + \sin A \sin B$

$\dfrac{\cos A \cos B}{\cos A \cos B} \cos C = \dfrac{-\sin A \sin B}{\cos A \cos B}$

$\cos C = -\tan A \tan B$

61. $\sin^2 x (1 - \sec^2 x) + \cos^2 x(1 + \sec^4 x)$
$\quad = \sin^2 x - \sin^2 x \sec^2 x + \cos^2 x + \cos^2 x \sec^4 x$

$\quad = \sin^2 x - \dfrac{\sin^2 x}{\cos^2 x} + \cos^2 x + \dfrac{\cos^2 x}{\cos^4 x}$

$\quad = \sin^2 x - \tan^2 x + \cos^2 x + \sec^2 x$
$\quad = 1 - \tan^2 x + \sec^2 x$
$\quad = 1 - (\sec^2 x - 1) + \sec^2 x$
$\quad = 1 - \sec^2 x + 1 + \sec^2 x = 2$

65. $x = \cos\theta$; $\sqrt{1 - x^2} = \sqrt{1 - \cos^2\theta} = \sqrt{\sin^2\theta} = \sin\theta$

Section 8.2
Exercises 21-9, page 583

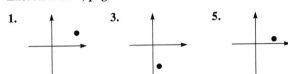

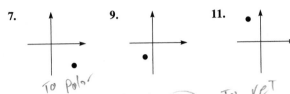

13. $\left(2, \dfrac{\pi}{6}\right)$ 15. $\left(1, \dfrac{7\pi}{6}\right)$ 17. $(-4, -4\sqrt{3})$

19. $(2.76, -1.17)$ 21. $r = 3 \sec \theta$

23. $r = \dfrac{3}{\cos \theta + 2 \sin \theta}$

25. $r = 4 \sin \theta$ 27. $r^2 = \dfrac{4}{1 + 3 \sin^2 \theta}$

29. $x^2 + y^2 - y = 0$, circle   31. $x = 4$, straight line

33. $x - 3y - 2 = 0$, straight line

35. $x^2 + y^2 - 4x - 2y = 0$, circle

37. $x^4 + y^4 - 4x^3 + 2x^2y^2 - 4xy^2 - 4y^2 = 0$

39. $(x^2 + y^2)^2 = 2xy$

41. $B_x = -\dfrac{k \sin \theta}{r}, B_y = \dfrac{k \cos \theta}{r}$

43. $x^4 + y^4 + 2x^2y^2 + 2x^2y + 2y^3 - 9x^2 - 8y^2 = 0$

Section 8.2

21.9 Polar Coordinates

1. $\left(3, \dfrac{\pi}{6}\right)$; $r = 3$, $\theta = \dfrac{\pi}{6}$

5. $\left(-2, \dfrac{7\pi}{6}\right)$; negative r is reversed in direction from positive r.

9. $\left(0.5, -\dfrac{8\pi}{3}\right)$

13. $(\sqrt{3}, 1)$ is (x, y), quadrant I

$\tan \theta = \dfrac{y}{x}$

$\theta = \tan^{-1} \dfrac{y}{x} = \tan^{-1} \dfrac{1}{\sqrt{3}} = \tan^{-1} \dfrac{\sqrt{3}}{3}$;

$\theta = 30° = \dfrac{\pi}{6}$

$r = \sqrt{x^2 + y^2} = \sqrt{(\sqrt{3})^2 + 1^2}$

$\quad = \sqrt{3 + 1} = \sqrt{4} = 2$

(r, θ) is $\left(2, \dfrac{\pi}{6}\right)$

17. (r, θ) is $\left(8, \dfrac{4\pi}{3}\right)$, quadrant III

$x = r \cos \theta = 8 \cos \dfrac{4\pi}{3} = 8\left(-\dfrac{1}{2}\right) = -4$

$y = r \sin \theta = 8\left(-\dfrac{\sqrt{3}}{2}\right) = -4\sqrt{3}$

(x, y) is $\left(-4, -4\sqrt{3}\right)$

21. $x = 3$

$r \cos \theta = x = 3$; $r = \dfrac{3}{\cos \theta} = 3 \sec \theta$

25. $x^2 + (y - 2)^2 = 4$

$x^2 + y^2 - 4y + 4 = 4$

$r^2 - 4 \cdot r \sin \theta = 0$

$r = 4 \sin \theta$

29. $r = \sin \theta$; $r^2 = r \sin \theta$; $r^2 = x^2 + y^2$

$x^2 + y^2 = r^2 = r \sin \theta = y$; $x^2 + y^2 - y = 0$,

circle

33. $r = \dfrac{2}{\cos \theta - 3 \sin \theta}$

$r \cos \theta - 3r \sin \theta = 2$

$x - 3y = 2$, line

37. $r = 2(1 + \cos\theta); \ x = r\cos\theta; \ \dfrac{x}{r} = \cos\theta$

$r^2 = x^2 + y^2; \ r = \sqrt{x^2 + y^2}$

$r = 2(1 + \cos\theta) = 2\left(1 + \dfrac{x}{r}\right) = 2 + \dfrac{2x}{r}; \ r^2 = 2r + 2x$

Multiply through by r.

$x^2 + y^2 = 2\sqrt{x^2 + y^2} + 2x; \ x^2 + y^2 - 2x = 2\sqrt{x^2 + y^2}$
$(x^2 + y^2 - 2x)^2 = 4(x^2 + y^2)$
$x^4 + y^4 - 4x^3 + 2x^2y^2 - 4xy^2 + 4x^2 = 4x^2 + 4y^2$
$x^4 + y^4 - 4x^3 + 2x^2y^2 - 4xy^2 + 4x^2 - 4x^2 - 4y^2 = 0$
$x^4 + y^4 - 4x^3 + 2x^2y^2 - 4xy^2 - 4y^2 = 0$

41. $B_x = \dfrac{-ky}{x^2 + y^2}$

$= -\dfrac{ky}{r^2}$

$= \dfrac{-kr\sin\theta}{r^2}$

$= -\dfrac{k\sin\theta}{r}$

$B_y = \dfrac{kx}{x^2 + y^2}$

$= \dfrac{kx}{r^2}$

$= \dfrac{kr\cos\theta}{r^2}$

$= \dfrac{k\cos\theta}{r}$

PART 9 – APPENDICES

CHAPTER *18* — VARIATION

Experimentation and observation often lead to the discovery of important relationships among related variables. In studying the measured values, it is often possible to see how one changes as the other also changes.

In this chapter we see how such information can be used to set up functional relationships among these variables. Then, using known values, we can set up specific functions that relate the variables for specific situations.

We begin this chapter by reviewing the meanings of *ratio* and *proportion,* which were first introduced in Chapter 1. Then we will see how ratio and proportion lead to *variation* and setting up numerous functional relationships.

Applications of variation are found in all areas of science and technology. It is often used in acoustics, biology, chemistry, computer technology, economics, electronics, environmental technology, hydrodynamics, mechanics, navigation, optics, physics, space technology, thermodynamics, and other fields.

Newton's universal law of gravitation is expressed in the language of variation. In Section 18-2 we discuss a space-age application.

Appendix A.1

18-1 RATIO AND PROPORTION

In Chapter 1 we introduced the terms *ratio* and *proportion* when we first solved equations. Since then we have seen how they are used in the definitions of the trigonometric functions in Chapter 4 and in a few other specific cases. However, only a basic understanding of their meanings has been necessary to this point. In order to develop the meaning of *variation,* we now review and expand our discussion of these important terms.

From Chapter 1 we recall that *the quotient a/b is called the* **ratio** *of a to b.* Therefore, a fraction is a ratio.

Any measurement made is the ratio of the measured magnitude to an accepted unit of measurement. For example, when we say that an object is 5 ft long, we are saying that the length of that object is five times as long as an accepted unit of length, the foot. Other examples of ratios are density (weight/volume), relative density (density of object/density of water), and pressure (force/area). As these examples illustrate, ratios may compare quantities of the same kind, or they may express a division of magnitudes of different quantities (such a ratio is also called a **rate**).

EXAMPLE 1   The approximate airline distance from Chicago to Dallas is 800 mi, and the approximate airline distance from Chicago to Cleveland is 300 mi. The ratio of these distances is

$$\frac{800 \text{ mi}}{300 \text{ mi}} = \frac{8}{3}$$

Since both units are in miles, the resulting ratio is a dimensionless number.

If a jet travels from Chicago to Dallas in 2 h, its average speed is

$$\frac{800 \text{ mi}}{2 \text{ h}} = 400 \text{ mi/h}$$

In this case we must attach the proper units to the resulting ratio. ------—∎

The first jet-propelled airplane was flown in Germany in 1928.

As we noted in Example 1, we must be careful to attach the proper units to the resulting ratio. Generally, the ratio of measurements of the same kind should be expressed as a dimensionless number. Consider the following example.

EXAMPLE 2   The length of a certain room is 24 ft, and the width of the room is 18 ft. Therefore, the ratio of the length to the width is $\frac{24}{18}$, or $\frac{4}{3}$.

If the width of the room is expressed as 6 yd, we have the ratio 24 ft/6 yd = 4 ft/1 yd. However, this does not clearly show the ratio. It is better and more meaningful first to change the units of one of the measurements to the units of the other measurement. Changing the length from 6 yd to 18 ft, we express the ratio as $\frac{4}{3}$, as we saw above. From this ratio we can easily see that the length is $\frac{4}{3}$ as long as the width. ------—∎

Dimensionless ratios are often used in definitions in mathematics and in technology. For example, the irrational number π is the dimensionless ratio of the circumference of a circle to its diameter. The specific gravity of a substance is the ratio of its density to the density of water. Other illustrations are found in the exercises for this section.

From Chapter 1 we also recall that *an equation stating that two ratios are equal is called a* **proportion.** By this definition, a proportion is

$$\frac{a}{b} = \frac{c}{d}$$

(18-1)

Consider the following example.

EXAMPLE 3 On a certain map, 1 in. represents 10 mi. Thus, on this map we have a ratio of 1 in./10 mi. To find the distance represented by 3.5 in., we can set up the proportion

$$\underbrace{\frac{3.5 \text{ in.}}{x} = \frac{1 \text{ in.}}{10 \text{ mi}}}_{\text{land distances}}\ \overset{\text{map distances}}{}$$

$$(10x)\left(\frac{3.5}{x}\right) = 10x\left(\frac{1}{10}\right) \qquad \text{multiply each side by LCD} = 10x$$

$$35 = x \quad \text{or} \quad x = 35 \text{ mi}$$

The ratio 1 in./10 mi is the *scale* of the map and has a special meaning, relating map distances in inches to land distances in miles. In a case like this we should not change either unit to the other, even though they are both units of length. ▪

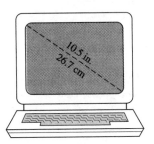

Fig. 18-1

EXAMPLE 4 Given that 1 in. = 2.54 cm, what is the length in centimeters of the diagonal of a rectangular computer screen that is 10.5 in. long? See Fig. 18-1.

If we equate the ratio of known lengths to the ratio of the given length to the required length, we can find the required length by solving the resulting proportion (which is an equation). This gives us

$$\frac{1 \text{ in.}}{2.54 \text{ cm}} = \frac{10.5 \text{ in.}}{x \text{ cm}}$$

$$x = (10.5)(2.54)$$

$$= 26.7 \text{ cm} \qquad \text{rounded off}$$

Therefore, the diagonal of the computer screen is 10.5 in., or 26.7 cm. ▪

In Appendix B there are additional illustrations of changing units. Also, a listing of all the various units used in the text is included.

EXAMPLE 5 The magnitude of an electric field E is the ratio of the force F on a charge q to the magnitude of q. We can write this as $E = F/q$. If we know the force exerted on a particular charge at some point in the field, we can determine the force that would be exerted on another charge placed at the same point. For example, if we know that a force of 10 nN is exerted on a charge of 4.0 nC, we can then determine the force that would be exerted on a charge of 6.0 nC by the proportion

$$\underbrace{\frac{10 \times 10^{-9}}{4.0 \times 10^{-9}} = \frac{F}{6.0 \times 10^{-9}}}_{\text{charges at point}}\ \overset{\text{forces at point}}{}$$

$$F = \frac{(6.0 \times 10^{-9})(10 \times 10^{-9})}{4.0 \times 10^{-9}}$$

$$= 15 \times 10^{-9} = 15 \text{ nN}$$ ▪

SOLVING A WORD PROBLEM   ■**EXAMPLE 6**   A certain alloy is 5 parts tin and 3 parts lead. How many grams of each are there in 40 g of the alloy?

First, we let x = the number of grams of tin in the given amount of the alloy. Next, we note that there are 8 total parts of alloy, of which 5 are tin. Thus, 5 is to 8 as x is to 40. This gives the equation

$$\text{parts tin} \longrightarrow \frac{5}{8} = \frac{x}{40} \longleftarrow \text{grams of tin}$$
$$\text{total parts} \qquad\qquad\qquad \longleftarrow \text{total grams}$$

$$x = 40\left(\frac{5}{8}\right) = 25 \text{ g}$$

Therefore, there are 25 g of tin and 15 g of lead. The ratio 25 to 15 is the same as 5 to 3.   ■

EXERCISES *18-1*

In Exercises 1–8, express the ratios in the simplest form.

1. 18 V to 3 V

2. 27 ft to 18 ft

3. 96 h to 3 days

4. 120 s to 4 min

5. 20 qt to 2.5 gal

6. 6500 cL to 2.6 L

7. 0.14 kg to 3500 mg

8. 2000 μm to 6 mm

In Exercises 9–20, find the required ratios.

9. The *efficiency* of a power amplifier is defined as the ratio of the power output to the power input. Find the efficiency of an amplifier for which the power output is 2.6 W and the power input is 9.6 W.

10. A virus 3.0×10^{-5} cm long appears to be 1.2 cm long through a microscope. What is the *magnification* (ratio of image length to object length) of the microscope?

11. The *coefficient of friction* for two contacting surfaces is the ratio of the frictional force between them to the perpendicular force that presses them together. If it takes 45 N to overcome friction to move a 110-N crate along the floor, what is the coefficient of friction between the crate and the floor? See Fig. 18-2.

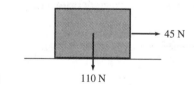

Fig. 18-2

12. The *atomic mass* of an atom of carbon is defined to be 12 u. The ratio of the atomic mass of an atom of oxygen to that of an atom of carbon is $\frac{4}{3}$. What is the atomic mass of an atom of oxygen? (The symbol u represents the *unified atomic mass unit*, where 1 u = 1.66×10^{-27} kg.)

13. An important design feature of an aircraft wing is its *aspect ratio*. It is defined as the ratio of the square of the span of the wing (wingtip to wingtip) to the total area of the wing. If the span of the wing for a certain aircraft is 32.0 ft, and the area is 195 ft^2, find the aspect ratio.

14. For an automobile engine, the ratio of the cylinder volume to compressed volume is the *compression ratio*. If the cylinder volume of 820 cm^3 is compressed to 110 cm^3, find the compression ratio.

15. The *specific gravity* of a substance is the ratio of its density to the density of water. If the density of steel is 487 lb/ft^3 and that of water is 62.4 lb/ft^3, what is the specific gravity of steel?

16. The *percent grade* of a road is the ratio of vertical rise to the horizontal change in distance (expressed in percent). If a highway rises 75 m for each 1200 m along the horizontal, what is the percent grade?

17. The *percent error* in a measurement is the ratio of the error in the measurement to the measurement itself, expressed as a percent. When writing a computer program, the memory remaining is determined as 2450 bytes and then it is correctly found to be 2540 bytes. What is the percent error in the first reading?

18. The electric *current* in a given circuit is the ratio of the voltage to the resistance. What is the current (1 V/1 Ω = 1 A) for a circuit where the voltage is 24.0 V and the resistance is 10.0 Ω?

19. The *mass* of an object is the ratio of its weight to the acceleration g due to gravity. If a space probe weighs 8460 N on earth, where g = 9.80 m/s^2, find its mass. (See Appendix B.)

20. *Power* is defined as the ratio of work done to the time required to do the work. If an engine performs 3650 J of work in 15.0 s, find the power developed by the engine. (See Appendix B.)

In Exercises 21–24, find the required quantities from the given proportions.

21. In an electric instrument called a "Wheatstone bridge," electric resistances are related by

$$\frac{R_1}{R_2} = \frac{R_3}{R_4}$$

Find R_2 if $R_1 = 6.00\ \Omega$, $R_3 = 62.5\ \Omega$, and $R_4 = 15.0\ \Omega$. See Fig. 18-3.

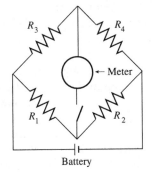

Fig. 18-3

22. For two connected gears, the relation

$$\frac{d_1}{d_2} = \frac{N_1}{N_2}$$

holds, where d is the diameter of the gear and N is the number of teeth. Find N_1 if $d_1 = 2.60$ in., $d_2 = 11.7$ in., and $N_2 = 45$. The ratio N_2/N_1 is called the *gear ratio*. See Fig. 18-4.

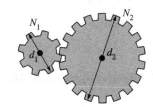

Fig. 18-4

23. According to Boyle's law, the relation

$$\frac{p_1}{p_2} = \frac{V_2}{V_1}$$

holds for pressures p_1 and p_2 and volumes V_1 and V_2 of a gas at constant temperature. Find V_1 if $p_1 = 36.6$ kPa, $p_2 = 84.4$ kPa, and $V_2 = 0.0447\ \text{m}^3$.

24. In a transformer, an electric current in one coil of wire induces a current in a second coil. For a transformer

$$\frac{i_1}{i_2} = \frac{t_2}{t_1}$$

where i is the current and t is the number of windings in each coil. In a neon sign amplifier $i_1 = 1.2$ A, and the *turns ratio* $t_2/t_1 = 160$. Find i_2. See Fig. 18-5.

In Exercises 25–40, answer the given questions by setting up and solving the appropriate proportions.

25. Given that $1.00\ \text{in.}^2 = 6.45\ \text{cm}^2$, what area in square inches is $36.3\ \text{cm}^2$?

26. Given that 1.000 kg $= 2.205$ lb, what mass in kilograms is equivalent to 175.5 lb?

27. Given that 1.00 hp $= 746$ W, what power in horsepower is 250 W?

28. Given that 1.50 L $= 1.59$ qt, what capacity in quarts is 2.75 L?

29. Given that 2.00 km $= 1.24$ mi, what distance in kilometers is 5.00 mi?

30. Given that $10^4\ \text{cm}^2 = 10^6\ \text{mm}^2$, what area in square centimeters is $2.50 \times 10^5\ \text{mm}^2$?

31. How many meters per second are equivalent to 45.0 km/h?

32. How many gallons per hour are equivalent to 540 L/min?

33. A particular type of automobile engine produces $62,500\ \text{cm}^3$ of carbon monoxide in 2.00 min. How much carbon monoxide is produced in 45.0 s?

34. An airplane consumes 36.0 gal of gasoline in flying 425 mi. Under similar conditions, how far can it fly on 52.5 gal?

35. By weight, the ratio of chlorine to sodium in table salt is 35.46 to 23.00. How much sodium is contained in 50.00 kg of salt?

36. Ten clicks on an adjustment screw cause an inlet valve opening to change by 0.035 cm. How many clicks are required for a valve adjustment of 0.049 cm?

37. In testing for quality control, it was found that 17 of every 500 computer chips produced by a company in a day were defective. If a total of 595 defective parts were found, what was the total number of chips produced during that day?

38. An electric current of 0.772 mA passes into two wires in which it is divided into currents in the ratio of 2.83 to 1.09. What are the currents in the two wires?

39. One computer line printer can print 2400 lines/min, and a second can print 2800 lines/min. If they print a total of 9100 lines while printing together, how many lines does each print?

40. Of the earth's water area, the Pacific Ocean covers 46.0% and the Atlantic Ocean covers 23.9%. Together they cover a total of $2.53 \times 10^8\ \text{km}^2$. What is the area of each?

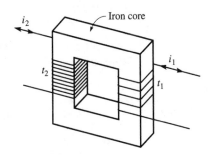

Fig. 18-5

Appendix A.2

18-2 **VARIATION**

Named for the French physicist, Jacques Charles (1746–1823).

Scientific laws are often stated in terms of ratios and proportions. For example, Charles' law can be stated as "for a perfect gas under constant pressure, the ratio of any two volumes this gas may occupy equals the ratio of the absolute temperatures." Symbolically, this could be stated as $V_1/V_2 = T_1/T_2$. Thus, if the ratio of the volumes and one of the values of the temperature are known, we can easily find the other temperature.

By multiplying both sides of the proportion of Charles' law by V_2/T_1, we can change the form of the proportion to $V_1/T_1 = V_2/T_2$. This statement says that the ratio of the volume to the temperature (for constant pressure) is constant. Thus, if any pair of values of volume and temperature is known, this ratio of V_1/T_1 can be calculated. This ratio of V_1/T_1 can be called a constant k, which means that Charles' law can be written as $V/T = k$. We now have the statement that the ratio of the volume to temperature is always constant; or, as it is normally stated, "The volume is proportional to the temperature." Therefore, we write $V = kT$, the clearest and most informative statement of Charles' law.

Thus, *for any two quantities always in the same proportion, we say that one is* **proportional to** (*or* **varies directly as**) *the second. To show that y is proportional to x (or varies directly as x), we write*

DIRECT VARIATION

$$y = kx \qquad \textbf{(18-2)}$$

where k is the **constant of proportionality.** This type of relationship is known as **direct variation.**

EXAMPLE 1   The circumference of a circle is proportional to (varies directly as) the radius r. We write this as $c = 2\pi r$. Since we know that $c = 2\pi r$ for a circle, we know in this case that $k = 2\pi$.

EXAMPLE 2   The fact that the electric resistance R of a wire varies directly as (is proportional to) its length l is written as $R = kl$. As the length of the wire increases (or decreases), this equation tells us that the resistance increases (or decreases) proportionally.

It is very common that, when two quantities are related, the product of the two quantities remains constant. In such a case $yx = k$, or

INVERSE VARIATION

$$y = \frac{k}{x} \qquad \textbf{(18-3)}$$

This is read as "y **varies inversely as** x" or "y **is inversely proportional to** x." This type of relationship is known as **inverse variation.**

Named for the English physicist, Robert Boyle (1627–1691).

EXAMPLE 3   Boyle's law states that "at a given temperature, the pressure p of an ideal gas varies inversely as the volume V." We write this as $p = k/V$. In this case, as the volume of the gas increases, the pressure decreases.

In Fig. 18-6(a) the graph of the equation for direct variation $y = kx$ ($x \geq 0$) is shown. It is a straight line, with slope of k ($k > 0$) and y-intercept of 0. We see that y increases as x increases. In Fig. 18-6(b) the graph of the equation for inverse variation $y = k/x$ ($k > 0, x > 0$) is shown. It is a *hyperbola* (a different form of the equation from that of Example 4 of Section 14-1). As x increases, y decreases.

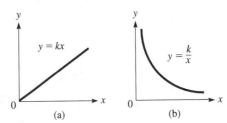

Fig. 18-6

For many relationships, one quantity varies as a specified power of another quantity. The terms *varies directly* and *varies inversely* are used in the following examples with a specified power of the independent variable.

■**EXAMPLE 4** The statement that the volume V of a sphere varies directly as the cube of its radius r is written as $V = kr^3$. In this case we know that $k = 4\pi/3$. We see that as the radius increases, the volume increases much more rapidly. For example, if $r = 2.00$ cm, $V = 33.5$ cm³, and if $r = 3.00$ cm, $V = 113$ cm³. ■

■**EXAMPLE 5** A company finds that the number n of units of a product that are sold is inversely proportional to the square of the price p of the product. This is written as $n = k/p^2$. As the price of the product is raised, the number of units that are sold decreases much more rapidly. ■

One quantity may vary as the product of two or more other quantities. Such variation is called **joint variation.** *We write*

JOINT VARIATION

$$y = kxz \qquad \textbf{(18-4)}$$

to show that y varies jointly as x and z.

■**EXAMPLE 6** The cost C of a piece of sheet metal varies jointly as the area A of the piece and the cost c per unit area. This we write as $C = kAc$. Here, C increases if the *product Ac* increases. ■

Direct, inverse, and joint variations may be combined. A given relationship may be a combination of two or all three of these types of variation.

Formulated by the great English mathematician and physicist, Isaac Newton (1642–1727).

■**EXAMPLE 7** Newton's *universal law of gravitation* can be stated: "The force F of gravitation between two objects varies jointly as the masses m_1 and m_2 of the objects and inversely as the square of the distance r between their centers." We write this as

$$F = \frac{Gm_1m_2}{r^2} \quad \begin{array}{l} \longleftarrow \text{force varies jointly as masses} \\ \longleftarrow \text{and} \\ \longleftarrow \text{inversely as the square of the distance} \end{array}$$

where G is the constant of proportionality.

Note the use of the word *and* in this example. It is used to indicate that F varies

CAUTION ▶ in more than one way, but *it is **not** interpreted as addition.* ■

Calculating the Constant of Proportionality

Once we have used the given statement to set up a general equation in terms of the variables and the constant of proportionality, we may calculate the value of the constant of proportionality if one *complete set of values* of the variables is known. *This value can then be substituted into the general equation to find the specific equation* relating the variables. We can then find the value of any one of the variables for any set of the others.

EXAMPLE 8   If y varies inversely as x, and $x = 15$ when $y = 4$, find the value of y when $x = 12$.

First, we write

$$y = \frac{k}{x} \qquad \text{general equation from statement}$$

to show that y varies inversely as x. Next, we substitute $x = 15$ and $y = 4$ into the equation. This leads to

$$4 = \frac{k}{15} \quad \text{or} \quad k = 60 \qquad \text{evaluate } k$$

Thus, for this problem the constant of proportionality is 60, and this may be substituted into $y = k/x$, giving

$$y = \frac{60}{x} \qquad \text{specific equation relating } y \text{ and } x$$

as the equation between y and x. Now, for any given value of x, we may find the value of y. For $x = 12$, we have

$$y = \frac{60}{12} = 5 \qquad \text{evaluating } y \text{ for } x = 12$$

SOLVING A WORD PROBLEM

```
420/√(1.14)
        393.3660409
Ans*√(3.4)
        725.3311403
```

Fig. 18-7

EXAMPLE 9   The frequency f of vibration of a wire varies directly as the square root of the tension T of the wire. If $f = 420$ Hz when $T = 1.14$ N, find f when $T = 3.40$ N.

The steps in making this evaluation are outlined below.

$$f = k\sqrt{T} \qquad \text{set up general equation: } f \text{ varies directly as } \sqrt{T}$$
$$420 \text{ Hz} = k\sqrt{1.14 \text{ N}} \qquad \text{substitute given set of values and evaluate } k$$
$$k = 393 \text{ Hz/N}^{1/2}$$
$$f = 393\sqrt{T} \qquad \text{substitute value of } k \text{ to get specific equation}$$
$$f = 393\sqrt{3.40} \qquad \text{evaluate } f \text{ for } T = 3.40 \text{ N}$$
$$= 725 \text{ Hz}$$

We note that k has a set of units associated with it, and this usually will be the case in applied situations. As long as we do not change the units that are used for any of the variables, the units for the final variable that is evaluated will remain the same. The calculator screen for this calculation is shown in Fig. 18-7.

EXAMPLE 10 The heat H developed in an electric resistor varies jointly as the time t and the square of the current i in the resistor. If H_0 joules of heat are developed in t_0 seconds with i_0 amperes passing through the resistor, how much heat is developed if both the time and the current are doubled?

$$H = kti^2 \qquad \text{set up general equation}$$

$$H_0 \text{J} = k(t_0 \text{ s})(i_0 \text{ A})^2 \qquad \text{substitute given values and}$$

$$k = \frac{H_0}{t_0 i_0^2} \text{J}/(\text{s} \cdot \text{A}^2) \qquad \text{evaluate } k$$

$$H = \frac{H_0 t i^2}{t_0 i_0^2} \qquad \text{substitute for } k \text{ to get specific equation}$$

We are asked to determine H when both the time and the current are doubled. This means we are to substitute $t = 2t_0$ and $i = 2i_0$. Making this substitution,

$$H = \frac{H_0(2t_0)(2i_0)^2}{t_0 i_0^2} = \frac{8 H_0 t_0 i_0^2}{t_0 i_0^2} = 8 H_0$$

The heat developed is eight times that for the original values of i and t.

See the chapter introduction.

The first landing on the moon was by the crew of the U.S. spacecraft *Apollo 11* in July 1969.

Fig. 18-8

EXAMPLE 11 In Example 7 we stated Newton's universal law of gravitation. This law was formulated in the late 17th century, but it has numerous modern space-age applications. Use this law to solve the following problem.

A spacecraft is traveling from the earth to the moon, which are 240,000 mi apart. The mass of the moon is 0.0123 that of the earth. How far from the earth is the gravitational force of the earth on the spacecraft equal to the gravitational force of the moon on the spacecraft?

From Example 7, we have the gravitational force between two objects as

$$F = \frac{G m_1 m_2}{r^2}$$

where the constant of proportionality G is the same for any two objects. Since we want the force between the earth and the spacecraft to equal the force between the moon and the spacecraft, we have

$$\frac{G m_s m_e}{r^2} = \frac{G m_s m_m}{(240{,}000 - r)^2}$$

where m_s, m_e, and m_m are the masses of the spacecraft, the earth, and the moon, respectively; r is the distance from the earth to the spacecraft; and $240{,}000 - r$ is the distance from the moon to the spacecraft. Since $m_m = 0.0123 m_e$, we have

$$\frac{G m_s m_e}{r^2} = \frac{G m_s (0.0123 m_e)}{(240{,}000 - r)^2}$$

$$\frac{1}{r^2} = \frac{0.0123}{(240{,}000 - r)^2} \qquad \text{divide each side by } G m_s m_e$$

$$(240{,}000 - r)^2 = 0.0123 r^2 \qquad \text{multiply each side by LCD}$$

$$240{,}000 - r = 0.111 r \qquad \text{take square roots}$$

$$1.111 r = 240{,}000$$

$$r = 216{,}000 \text{ mi}$$

Therefore, the spacecraft is 216,000 mi from the earth and 24,000 mi from the moon when the gravitational forces are equal. See Fig. 18-8.

─── EXERCISES *18-2* ───────

In Exercises 1–8, set up the general equations from the given statements.

1. *y* varies directly as *z*.

2. *p* varies inversely as *q*.

3. *s* varies inversely as the square of *t*.

4. *w* is proportional to the cube of *L*.

5. *f* is proportional to the square root of *x*.

6. *n* is inversely proportional to the $\frac{3}{2}$ power of *s*.

7. *w* varies jointly as *x* and the cube of *y*.

8. *q* varies as the square of *r* and inversely as the fourth power of *t*.

(W) *In Exercises 9–12, express the meaning of the given equation in a verbal statement, using the language of variation. (k and π are constants.)*

9. $A = \pi r^2$

10. $s = \dfrac{k}{t^{1.2}}$

11. $n = \dfrac{k\sqrt{t}}{u}$

12. $V = \pi r^2 h$

In Exercises 13–16, give the specific equation relating the variables after evaluating the constant of proportionality for the given set of values.

13. *V* varies directly as the square of *H*, and *V* = 2 when *H* = 64.

14. *n* is inversely proportional to the square of *p*, and $n = \frac{1}{27}$ when *p* = 3.

15. *p* is proportional to *q* and inversely proportional to the cube of *r*, and *p* = 6 when *q* = 3 and *r* = 2.

16. *v* is proportional to *t* and the square of *s*, and *v* = 80 when *s* = 2 and *t* = 5.

In Exercises 17–24, find the required value by setting up the general equation and then evaluating.

17. Find *y* when *x* = 10 if *y* varies directly as *x*, and *y* = 20 when *x* = 8.

18. Find *y* when *x* = 5 if *y* varies directly as the square of *x*, and *y* = 6 when *x* = 8.

19. Find *s* when *t* = 10 if *s* is inversely proportional to *t*, and *s* = 100 when *t* = 5.

20. Find *p* for *q* = 0.8 if *p* is inversely proportional to the square of *q*, and *p* = 18 when *q* = 0.2.

21. Find *y* for *x* = 6 and *z* = 5 if *y* varies directly as *x* and inversely as *z*, and *y* = 60 when *x* = 4 and *z* = 10.

22. Find *r* when *n* = 16 if *r* varies directly as the square root of *n* and *r* = 4 when *n* = 25.

23. Find *f* when *p* = 2 and *c* = 4 if *f* varies jointly as *p* and the cube of *c*, and *f* = 8 when *p* = 4 and *c* = 0.1.

24. Find *v* when *r* = 2, *s* = 3, and *t* = 4 if *v* varies jointly as *r* and *s* and inversely as the square of *t*, and *v* = 8 when *r* = 2, *s* = 6, and *t* = 6.

In Exercises 25–48, solve the given applied problems involving variation.

25. The volume *V* of carbon dioxide (CO_2) that is exhausted from a room in a given time varies directly as the initial volume V_0 that is present. If 75 ft^3 of CO_2 are removed in an hour from a room with an initial volume of 160 ft^3, how much is removed in an hour if the initial volume is 130 ft^3?

26. The amount of heat *H* required to melt ice is proportional to the mass *m* of ice that is melted. If it takes 2.93×10^5 J to melt 875 g of ice, how much heat is required to melt 625 g?

27. In electroplating, the mass *m* of the material deposited varies directly as the time *t* during which the electric current is on. Set up the equation for this relationship if 2.50 g are deposited in 5.25 h.

28. Hooke's law states that the force needed to stretch a spring is proportional to the amount the spring is stretched. If 10.0 lb stretches a certain spring 4.00 in, how much will the spring be stretched by a force of 6.00 lb?

29. The rate *H* of heat removal by an air conditioner is proportional to the electric power input *P*. The constant of proportionality is the *performance coefficient*. Find the performance coefficient of an air conditioner for which *H* = 1800 W and *P* = 720 W.

30. The energy *E* available daily from a solar collector varies directly as the percent *p* that the sun shines during the day. If a collector provides 1200 kJ for 75% sunshine, how much does it provide for a day during which there is 35% sunshine?

31. The time *t* required to empty a wastewater holding tank is inversely proportional to the cross-sectional area *A* of the drainage pipe. If it takes 2.0 h to empty a tank with a drainage pipe for which *A* = 48 in.^{2}, how long will it take to empty the tank if *A* = 68 in.^{2}?

(W)**32.** The time *t* required to make a particular trip is inversely proportional to the average speed *v*. If a jet takes 2.75 h at an average speed of 520 km/h, how long will it take at an average speed of 620 km/h? Explain the meaning of the constant of proportionality.

(W)**33.** In a physics experiment a given force was applied to three objects. The mass *m* and the resulting acceleration *a* were recorded as follows:

m (g)	2.0	3.0	4.0
a (cm/s^2)	30	20	15

(a) Is the relationship *a* = *f*(*m*) one of direct or inverse variation? Explain. (b) Find *a* = *f*(*m*).

(W) **34.** The lift L of each of three model airplane wings of width w was measured and recorded as follows:

w (cm)	20	40	60
L (N)	10	40	90

(a) Is the relationship $L = f(w)$ one of direct or inverse variation? Explain. (b) Find $L = f(w)$.

35. The power P required to propel a ship varies directly as the cube of the speed s of the ship. If 5200 hp will propel a ship at 12.0 mi/h, what power is required to propel it at 15.0 mi/h?

36. The f-number lens setting of a camera varies directly as the square root of the time t that the film is exposed. If the f-number is 8 (written as $f/8$) for $t = 0.0200$ s, find the f-number for $t = 0.0098$ s.

37. The force F on the blade of a wind generator varies jointly as the blade area A and the square of the wind velocity v. Find the equation relating F, A, and v if $F = 19.2$ lb when $A = 3.72$ ft^2 and $v = 31.4$ ft/s.

38. The escape velocity v a spacecraft needs to leave the gravitational field of a planet varies directly as the square root of the product of the planet's radius R and its acceleration due to gravity g. For Mars and earth, $R_M = 0.533R_e$ and $g_M = 0.400g_e$. Find v_M for Mars if $v_e = 11.2$ km/s.

39. The average speed s of oxygen molecules in the air is directly proportional to the square root of the absolute temperature T. If the speed of the molecules is 460 m/s at 273 K, what is the speed at 300 K?

40. The time t required to test a computer memory unit varies directly as the square of the number n of memory cells in the unit. If a unit with 4800 memory cells can be tested in 15.0 s, how long does it take to test a unit with 8400 memory cells?

41. The electric resistance R of a wire varies directly as its length l and inversely as its cross-sectional area A. Find the relation between resistance, length, and area for a wire that has a resistance of 0.200 Ω for a length of 225 ft and cross-sectional area of 0.0500 in.^{2}.

42. The general gas law states that the pressure P of an ideal gas varies directly as the thermodynamic temperature T and inversely as the volume V. If $P = 610$ kPa for $V = 10.0$ cm^3 and $T = 290$ K, find V for $P = 400$ kPa and $T = 400$ K.

43. The power P in an electric circuit varies jointly as the resistance R and the square of the current I. If the power is 10.0 W when the current is 0.500 A and the resistance is 40.0 Ω, find the power if the current is 2.00 A and the resistance is 20.0 Ω.

44. The difference $m_1 - m_2$ in magnitudes (visual brightnesses) of two stars varies directly as the base 10 logarithm of the ratio b_2/b_1 of their actual brightnesses. For two particular stars, if $b_2 = 100b_1$ for $m_1 = 7$ and $m_2 = 2$, find the equation relating m_1, m_2, b_1, and b_2.

45. The power gain G by a parabolic microwave dish varies directly as the square of the diameter d of the opening and inversely as the square of the wavelength λ of the wave carrier. Find the equation relating G, d, and λ if $G = 5.5 \times 10^4$ for $d = 2.9$ m and $\lambda = 0.030$ m.

46. The intensity I of sound varies directly as the power P of the source and inversely as the square of the distance r from the source. Two sound sources are separated by a distance d, and one has twice the power output of the other. Where should an observer be located on a line between them such that the intensity of each sound is the same?

47. The x-component of the acceleration of an object moving around a circle with constant angular velocity ω varies jointly as $\cos \omega t$ and the square of ω. If the x-component of the acceleration is -11.4 ft/s^2 when $t = 1.00$ s for $\omega = 0.524$ rad/s, find the x-component of the acceleration when $t = 2.00$ s.

48. The tangent of the proper banking angle θ of the road for a car making a turn is directly proportional to the square of the car's velocity v and inversely proportional to the radius r of the turn. If 7.75° is the proper banking angle for a car traveling at 20.0 m/s around a turn of radius 300 m, what is the proper banking angle for a car traveling at 30.0 m/s around a turn of radius 250 m? See Fig. 18-9.

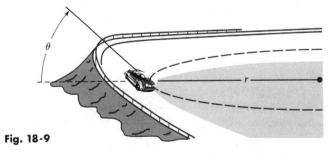

Fig. 18-9

Appendix A.3

▌ CHAPTER EQUATIONS

Proportion	$\dfrac{a}{b} = \dfrac{c}{d}$	**(18-1)**
Direct variation	$y = kx$	**(18-2)**
Inverse variation	$y = \dfrac{k}{x}$	**(18-3)**
Joint variation	$y = kxz$	**(18-4)**

REVIEW EXERCISES

In Exercises 1–8, find the indicated ratios.

1. 4 Mg to 20 kg

2. 300 nm to 6 μm

3. 20 mL to 5 cL

4. 12 ks to 2 h

5. The mechanical advantage of a lever is the ratio of the output force F_0 to the input force F_i. Find the mechanical advantage if $F_0 = 28$ kN and $F_i = 5000$ N.

6. For an automobile, the ratio of the number n_1 of teeth on the ring gear to the number n_2 of teeth on the pinion gear is the *rear axle ratio* of the car. Find this ratio if $n_1 = 64$ and $n_2 = 20$.

7. The pressure p exerted on a surface is the ratio of the force F on the surface to its area A. Find the pressure on a square patch, 2.25 in. on a side, on a tank if the force on the patch is 37.4 lb.

8. The electric resistance R of a resistor is the ratio of the voltage V across the resistor to the current i in the resistor. Find R if $V = 0.632$ V and $i = 2.03$ mA.

In Exercises 9–20, answer the given questions by setting up and solving the appropriate proportions.

9. On a map of Hawaii 1.3 in. represents 20.0 mi. If the distance on the map between Honolulu and Kahului on Maui is 6.0 in., how far is Kahului from Honolulu?

10. Given that 1.000 lb = 453.6 g, what is the weight in pounds of a 14.0-g computer disk?

11. Given that 1.00 Btu = 1060 J, how much heat in joules is produced by a heating element that produces 2660 Btu?

12. Given that 1.00 L = 61.0 in.^{3}, what capacity in liters has a cubical box that is 3.23 in. along an edge?

13. A computer printer can print 3600 characters in 30 s. How many characters can it print in 5.0 min?

14. A solar heater with a collector area of 58.0 m^2 is required to heat 2560 kg of water. Under the same conditions, how much water can be heated by a rectangular solar collector 9.50 m by 8.75 m?

15. The dosage of a certain medicine is 25 mL for each 10 lb of the patient's weight. What is the dosage for a person weighing 56 kg?

16. A woman invests $50,000 and a man invests $20,000 in a partnership. If profits are to be shared in the ratio that each invested in the partnership, how much does each receive from $10,500 in profits?

17. On a certain blueprint, a measurement of 25.0 ft is represented by 2.00 in. What is the actual distance between two points if they are 5.75 in. apart on the blueprint?

18. The chlorine concentration in a water supply is 0.12 part per million. How much chlorine is there in a cylindrical holding tank 4.22 m in radius and 5.82 m high filled from the water supply?

19. One fiber-optic cable carries 60.0% as many messages as another fiber-optic cable. Together they carry 12,000 messages. How many does each carry?

20. Two types of roadbed material, one 50% rock and the other 100% rock, are used in the ratio of 4 to 1 to form a roadbed. If a total of 150 tons are used, how much rock is in the roadbed?

In Exercises 21–24, give the specific equation relating the variables after evaluating the constant of proportionality for the given set of values.

21. y varies directly as the square of x, and $y = 27$ when $x = 3$.

22. f varies inversely as l, and $f = 5$ when $l = 8$.

23. v is directly proportional to x and inversely proportional to the cube of y, and $v = 10$ when $x = 5$ and $y = 4$.

24. r varies jointly as u, v, and the square of w, and $r = 8$ when $u = 2$, $v = 4$, and $w = 3$.

In Exercises 25–52, solve the given applied problems.

25. For a lever balanced at the fulcrum, the relation

$$\frac{F_1}{F_2} = \frac{L_2}{L_1}$$

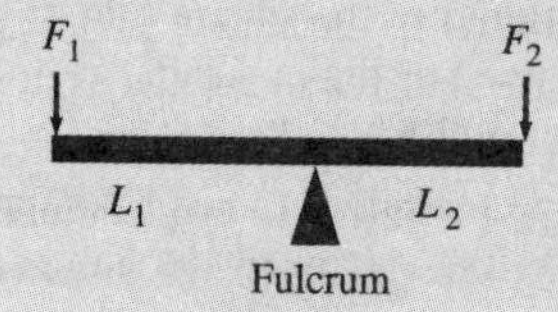

Fig. 18-10

holds, where F_1 and F_2 are forces on opposite sides of the fulcrum at distances L_1 and L_2, respectively. If $F_1 = 4.50$ lb, $F_2 = 6.75$ lb, and $L_1 = 17.5$ in., find L_2. See Fig. 18-10.

26. A company finds that the volume V of sales of a certain item and the price P of the item are related by

$$\frac{P_1}{P_2} = \frac{V_2}{V_1}$$

Find V_2 if $P_1 = \$8.00$, $P_2 = \$6.00$, and $V_1 = 3000$ per week.

27. The charge C on a capacitor varies directly as the voltage V across it. If the charge is 6.3 μC with a voltage of 220 V across a capacitor, what is the charge on it with a voltage of 150 V across it?

28. The amount of natural gas burned is proportional to the amount of oxygen consumed. If 24.0 lb of oxygen is consumed in burning 15.0 lb of natural gas, how much air, which is 23.2% oxygen by weight, is consumed to burn 50.0 lb of natural gas?

29. The power P of a gas engine is proportional to the area A of the piston. If an engine with a piston area of 8.00 in.^{2} can develop 30.0 hp, what power is developed by an engine with a piston area of 6.00 in.^{2}?

30. The decrease in temperature above a region is directly proportional to the altitude above the region. If the temperature T at the base of the rock of Gibraltar is 22.0° and a plane 3.50 km above notes that the temperature is 1.0°C, what is the temperature at the top of Gibraltar, the altitude of which is 430 m? (Assume there are no other temperature effects.)

31. The distance d an object falls under the influence of gravity varies directly as the square of the time t of fall. If an object falls 64.0 ft in 2.00 s, how far will it fall in 3.00 s?

32. The kinetic energy E of a moving object varies jointly as the mass m of the object and the square of its velocity v. If a 5.00-kg object, traveling at 10.0 m/s, has a kinetic energy of 250 J, find the kinetic energy of an 8.00-kg object moving at 50.0 m/s.

33. In a particular computer design, N numbers can be sorted in a time proportional to the square of log N. How many times longer does it take to sort 8000 numbers than to sort 2000 numbers?

34. The velocity v of a jet of fluid flowing from an opening in the side of a container is proportional to the square root of the depth d of the opening. If the velocity of the jet from an opening at a depth of 1.22 m is 4.88 m/s, what is the velocity of a jet from an opening at a depth of 7.62 m? See Fig. 18-11.

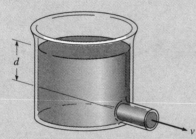

Fig. 18-11

35. In any given electric circuit containing an inductance L and a capacitance C, the resonant frequency f is inversely proportional to the square root of the capacitance. If the resonant frequency in a circuit is 25.0 Hz and the capacitance is 95.0 μF, what is the resonant frequency of this circuit if the capacitance is 25.0 μF?

36. The rate of emission R of radiant energy from the surface of a body is proportional to the fourth power of the thermodynamic temperature T. Given that a 25.0-W (the rate of emission) lamp has an operating temperature of 2500 K, what is the operating temperature of a similar 40.0-W lamp?

37. The frequency f of a radio wave is inversely proportional to its wavelength λ. The constant of proportionality is the velocity of the wave, which equals the speed of light. Find this velocity if an FM radio wave has a frequency of 90.9 MHz and a wavelength of 3.29 m.

38. The acceleration of gravity g on a satellite in orbit around the earth varies inversely as the square of its distance r from the center of the earth. If $g = 8.7$ m/s² for a satellite at an altitude of 400 km above the surface of the earth, find g if it is 1000 km above the surface. The radius of the earth is 6.4×10^6 m.

39. Using *holography* (a method of producing an image without using a lens), an image of concentric circles is formed. The radius r of each circle varies directly as the square root of the wavelength λ of the light used. If $r = 3.56$ cm for $\lambda = 575$ nm, find r if $\lambda = 483$ nm.

40. A metal circular ring has a circular cross section of radius r. If R is the radius of the ring (measured to the middle of the cross section), the volume V of metal in the ring varies directly as R and the square of r. If $V = 2550$ mm³ for $r = 2.32$ mm and $R = 24.0$ mm, find V for $r = 3.50$ mm and $R = 32.0$ mm. See Fig. 18-12.

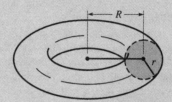

Fig. 18-12

41. The stopping distance d of a car varies directly as the square of the velocity v of the car when the brakes are applied. A car moving at 32 mi/h can stop in 52 ft. What is the stopping distance for the car if it is moving at 55 mi/h?

42. Kepler's third law of planetary motion states that the square of the period of any planet is proportional to the cube of the mean radius (about the sun) of that planet, with the constant of proportionality being the same for all planets. Using the fact that the period of the earth is one year and its mean radius is 93.0 million miles, calculate the mean radius for Venus, given that its period is 7.38 months.

43. The range R of a projectile varies jointly as the square of its initial velocity v_0 and the sine of twice the angle θ from the horizontal at which it is fired. See Fig. 18-13. A bullet for which $v_0 = 850$ m/s and $\theta = 22.0°$ has a range of 5.12×10^4 m. Find the range if $v_0 = 750$ m/s and $\theta = 43.2°$.

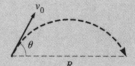

Fig. 18-13

44. The load L that a helical spring can support varies directly as the cube of its wire diameter d and inversely as its coil diameter D. A spring for which $d = 0.120$ in. and $D = 0.953$ in. can support 45.0 lb. What is the coil diameter of a similar spring that supports 78.5 lb and for which $d = 0.156$ in.?

45. The volume rate of flow R of blood through an artery varies directly as the fourth power of the radius r of the artery and inversely as the distance d along the artery. If an operation is successful in effectively increasing the radius of an artery by 25% and decreasing its length by 2%, by how much is the volume rate of flow increased?

46. The safe, uniformly distributed load L on a horizontal beam, supported at both ends, varies jointly as the width w and the square of the depth d and inversely as the distance D between supports. Given that one beam has double the dimensions of another, how many times heavier is the safe load it can support than the first can support?

47. A bank statement exactly 30 years old is discovered. It states, "This 10-year-old account is now worth \$185.03 and pays 4% interest compounded annually." An investment with annual compound interest varies directly as $1 + r$ to the power n, where r is the interest rate expressed as a decimal and n is the number of years of compounding. What was the value of the original investment, and what is it worth now?

48. The distance s that an object falls due to gravity varies jointly as the acceleration g due to gravity and the square of the time t of fall. The acceleration due to gravity on the moon is 0.172 of that on earth. If a rock falls for t_0 seconds on earth, how many times farther would the rock fall on the moon in $3t_0$ seconds?

49. The heat loss L through fiberglass insulation varies directly as the time t and inversely as the thickness d of the fiberglass. If the loss through 8.0 in. of fiberglass is 1200 Btu in 30 min, what is the loss through 6.0 in. in 1 h 30 min?

50. A quantity important in analyzing the rotation of an object is its *moment of inertia I*. For a ball bearing, the moment of inertia varies directly as its mass m and the square of its radius r. Find the general expression for I if $I = 39.9$ g·cm² for $m = 63.8$ g and $r = 1.25$ cm.

51. In the study of polarized light, the intensity I is proportional to the square of the cosine of the angle θ of transmission. If $I = 0.025$ W/m² for $\theta = 12.0°$, find I for $\theta = 20.0°$.

52. The force F that acts on a pendulum bob is proportional to the mass m of the bob and the sine of the angle θ the pendulum makes with the vertical. If $F = 0.120$ N for $m = 0.350$ kg and $\theta = 2.00°$, find F for $m = 0.750$ kg and $\theta = 3.50°$.

Writing Exercise

53. A fruit packing company plans to reduce the size of its fruit juice can (a right circular cylinder) by 10% and keep the price of each can the same (effectively raising the price). The radius and the height of the new can are to be equally proportional to those of the old can. Write one or two paragraphs explaining how to determine the percent decrease in the radius and the height of the old can that is required to make the new can.

PRACTICE TEST

1. Express the ratio of 180 s to 4 min in simplest form.

2. The force F between two parallel wires carrying electric currents is inversely proportional to the distance d between the wires. If a force of 0.750 N exists between wires that are 1.25 cm apart, what is the force between them if they are separated by 1.75 cm?

3. Given that 1.00 in. = 2.54 cm, what length in inches is 7.24 cm?

4. The difference p in pressure in a fluid between that at the surface and that at a point below varies jointly as the density d of the fluid and the depth h of the point. The density of water is 1000 kg/m³, and the density of alcohol is 800 kg/m³. This difference in pressure at a point 0.200 m below the surface of water is 1.96 kPa. What is the difference in pressure at a point 0.300 m below the surface of alcohol? (All data are accurate to three significant digits.)

5. The perimeter of a rectangular solar panel is 210.0 in. The ratio of the length to the width is 7 to 3. What are the dimensions of the panel?

6. The crushing load L of a pillar varies directly as the fourth power of its radius r and inversely as the square of its length l. If one pillar has twice the radius and three times the length of a second pillar, what is the ratio of the crushing load of the first pillar to that of the second pillar?

37. $F = 0.00523Av^2$ **39.** 480 m/s

41. $R = \dfrac{4.44 \times 10^{-5}l}{A}$ **43.** 80.0 W   **45.** $G = \dfrac{5.9d^2}{\lambda^2}$

47. -6.57 ft/s^2

Appendix A.3
Review Exercises for Chapter 18, page 486

1. 200   **3.** $\dfrac{2}{5}$ **5.** 5.6   **7.** 7.39 lb/in.^{2} **9.** 92 mi

11. 2.82×10^6 J $= 2.82$ MJ   **13.** 36,000 characters

15. 310 mL   **17.** 71.9 ft   **19.** 4500, 7500   **21.** $y = 3x^2$

23. $v = \dfrac{128x}{y^3}$ **25.** 11.7 in.   **27.** 4.3 μC   **29.** 22.5 hp

31. 144 ft   **33.** 1.4   **35.** 48.7 Hz   **37.** 2.99×10^8 m/s

39. 3.26 cm   **41.** 150 ft   **43.** 5.73×10^4 m

45. 150%   **47.** \$125.00, \$600.13   **49.** 4800 Btu

51. 0.023 W/m^2

Appendix A.1
Exercises 18-1, page 478

1. 6   **3.** $\dfrac{4}{3}$ **5.** 2   **7.** 40   **9.** $0.27 = 27\%$

11. 0.41   **13.** 5.25   **15.** 7.80   **17.** 3.5%

19. 863 kg   **21.** 1.44 Ω **23.** 0.103 m^3 **25.** 5.63 in.^{2}

27. 0.335 hp   **29.** 8.06 km   **31.** 12.5 m/s

33. 23,400 cm^3 **35.** 19.67 kg   **37.** 17,500 chips

39. 4200 lines, 4900 lines

Appendix A.2
Exercises 18-2, page 484

1. $y = kz$ **3.** $s = \dfrac{k}{t^2}$ **5.** $f = k\sqrt{x}$ **7.** $w = kxy^3$

9. A varies directly as the square of r.

11. n varies as the square root of t and inversely as u.

13. $V = \dfrac{H^2}{2048}$ **15.** $p = \dfrac{16q}{r^3}$ **17.** 25   **19.** 50

21. 180   **23.** 2.56×10^5 **25.** 61 ft^3

27. $m = 0.476t$ **29.** 2.5   **31.** 1.4 h

33. (a) inverse (b) $a = 60/m$ **35.** 10,200 hp

Chapter 18 Appendix A

VARIATION

18.1 Ratio and Proportion
Appendix A.1

1. $\dfrac{18\text{ V}}{3\text{ V}} = 6$

5. $\dfrac{20\text{ qt}}{2.5\text{ gal}} = \dfrac{20\text{ qt}}{10\text{ qt}} = 2$

9. $\dfrac{2.6\text{ W}}{9.6\text{ W}} = 0.27$

13. $R = \dfrac{s^2}{A_w} = \dfrac{32.0^2}{195} = 5.25$

17. $\dfrac{2540 - 2450}{2540} = \dfrac{90}{2540}$
$= 0.035$
$= 3.5\%$

21.
$\dfrac{6.00}{R_2} = \dfrac{62.5}{15.0}$
$62.5R_2 = 90.0;\ R_2 = 1.44\ \Omega$

25. $\dfrac{1.00\text{ in}^2}{6.45\text{ cm}^2} = \dfrac{x}{36.3\text{ cm}^2};\ x = \dfrac{1.00(36.3)}{6.45} = 5.63\text{ in}^2$

29. $\dfrac{2.00\text{ km}}{1.24\text{ mi}} = \dfrac{x}{5.00\text{ mi}};\ 1.24x = 10.0;\ x = 8.06\text{ km}$

33. $\dfrac{62,500}{2.00} = \dfrac{x}{0.75};\ x = \dfrac{62,500(0.75)}{2.00} = 23,400\text{ cm}^3$

37. $\dfrac{17}{595} = \dfrac{500}{x};\ 17x = 297,500;\ x = 17,500\text{ chips}$

Appendix A.2

18.2 Variation

1. $y = kz$

5. $f = k\sqrt{x}$

9. The area varies directly as the square of the radius.

13. $V = kH^2;\ 2 = k \cdot 64^2$
$k = \dfrac{2}{64^2};\ V = \dfrac{2H^2}{64^2} = \dfrac{H^2}{2048}$

17. $y = kx;\ 20 = k(8);\ k = 2.5;\ y = 2.5x$
$y = 2.5(10) = 25$

21. $y = \dfrac{kx}{z};\ 60 = \dfrac{k(4)}{10};\ k = 150;\ y = \dfrac{150x}{z}$
$y = \dfrac{150(6)}{5} = 180$

25. $V = kV_0;\ 75 = k(160);\ k = \dfrac{15}{32};\ V = \dfrac{15}{32}V_0$
$V = \dfrac{15}{32}(130) = 61\text{ ft}^3$

29. $H = kP;\ 1800 = k \cdot 720;\ k = 2.5$

33. (a) a varies inversely with mass.

(b) $a = \dfrac{k}{m};\ 30 = \dfrac{k}{2};\ k = 60\text{ g}\ \cdot\ \text{cm/s}^2$
$a = \dfrac{60}{m}$

37. $F = kAv^2$; $19.2 = k(3.72)(31.4)^2$; $k = 5.23 \times 10^{-3}$ lb $\cdot$ s/ft^3
$F = 5.23 \times 10^{-3} Av^2$

41. $R = \dfrac{kl}{A}$; $0.200 = \dfrac{k(225)}{0.0500}$

$k = 4.44 \times 10^{-5}$ $\Omega \cdot$ in^2/ft

$R = \dfrac{4.44 \times 10^{-5} l}{A}$

45. $G = \dfrac{kd^2}{\lambda^2}$; $5.5 \times 10^4 = \dfrac{k(2.9)^2}{(0.030)^2}$; $k = \dfrac{5.5 \times 10^4 (0.030)^2}{(2.9)^2} = 5.9$

$G = \dfrac{5.9d^2}{\lambda^2}$

Appendix A.3

Chapter 18 Review Exercises

1. $\dfrac{4 \text{ Mg}}{20 \text{ kg}} = \dfrac{4000 \text{ kg}}{20 \text{ kg}} = 200$

5. $\dfrac{28 \text{ kN}}{5000 \text{ N}} = \dfrac{28 \text{ kN}}{5 \text{ kN}} = 5.6$

9. $\dfrac{1.3 \text{ in.}}{20.0 \text{ mi}} = \dfrac{6.0 \text{ in.}}{x}$
$x = 92 \text{ mi}$

13. $\dfrac{3600}{30 \text{ s}} = \dfrac{x}{300 \text{ s}}$ since 5 min $=$ 300 s
$30x = (360)(300)$
$x = 36,000$ characters in 5 min

17. $\dfrac{25.0 \text{ ft}}{2.00 \text{ in.}} = \dfrac{x}{5.75 \text{ in.}}$; $x = 71.9$ ft

21. $y = kx^2$; $27 = k(3^2)$; $k = 3$; $y = 3x^2$

25. $\dfrac{F_1}{F_2} = \dfrac{L_2}{L_1}$; $F_1 = 4.50$ lb, $F_2 = 6.75$ lb, $L_1 = 17.5$ in

$\dfrac{4.50}{6.75} = \dfrac{L_2}{17.5}$

$(6.75)L_2 = (4.50)(17.5)$
$L_2 = 11.7$ in.

29. $p = kA$; $30.0 = k(8.00)$; $k = 3.75 \dfrac{\text{hp}}{\text{in}^2}$.

$p = 3.75A$; $p = 3.75(6.00) = 22.5$ hp

33. $\dfrac{(\log 8000)^2}{(\log 2000)^2} = 1.4$ times longer to sort 8000 numbers.

37. $f = \dfrac{v}{\lambda}$; $v = f\lambda = 90.0 \times 10^6 (3.29) = 299 \times 10^6 = 2.99 \times 10^8$ m/s

41. $d = kv^2$; $52 = k \cdot 32^2$; $d = \dfrac{52}{32^2} \cdot 55^2 = 150$ ft

45. $V = \dfrac{kr^4}{d}$; $V_1 = \dfrac{k(1.25r)^4}{0.98d} = \dfrac{2.44kr^4}{0.98d} = 2.49 \left(\dfrac{kr^4}{d}\right) = 2.49V$

An increase of $V_1 - V = 2.49V - V = 1.49V$ or 149% increase.

49. $L = \dfrac{kt}{d}$; $1200 = \dfrac{k \cdot 30}{8.0}$; $k = 320$ Btu $\cdot$ in/min

$L = \dfrac{320t}{d} = \dfrac{320(90)}{6.0} = 4800$ Btu

53. Let $V_1 = \pi r_1^2 h_1$ be the original volume then the new volume is
$V_2 = \pi r_2^2 h_2 = 0.9\pi r_1^2 h_1$ from which

$\left(\dfrac{r_2}{r_1}\right)^2 \cdot \dfrac{h_2}{h_1} = 0.9$ and since $\dfrac{r_2}{r_1} = \dfrac{h_2}{h_1}$

$\dfrac{r_2^3}{r_1^3} = 0.9$

$r_2 = \sqrt[3]{0.9}\, r_1 = 0.97 r_1$

Reducing the radius and height by 3% will reduce the volume by 10%.

Part 9
Appendix A
Chapter 18

1. $\dfrac{180 \text{ s}}{4 \text{ min}} = \dfrac{180 \text{ s}}{240 \text{ s}} = \dfrac{3}{4}$

2. $F = \dfrac{k}{d}$; $\quad 0.750 = \dfrac{k}{1.25}$, $\quad k = 0.938 \text{ N} \cdot \text{cm}$

   $F = \dfrac{0.938}{d}$; $\quad F = \dfrac{0.938}{1.75} = 0.536 \text{ N}$

3. $\dfrac{1.00 \text{ in.}}{2.54 \text{ cm}} = \dfrac{x}{7.24 \text{ cm}}$

   $x = \dfrac{7.24}{2.54} = 2.85 \text{ in.}$

4. $p = kdh$
   Using values for water,
   $1.96 = k(1000)(0.200)$
   $\quad k = 0.00980 \text{ kPa} \cdot \text{m}^2/\text{kg}$
   For alcohol,
   $p = 0.00980(800)(0.300)$
   $\quad = 2.35 \text{ kPa}$

5. $\quad 2l + 2w = 210.0$
   $\quad\quad\quad l = 105.0 - w$
   $\quad\quad\quad \dfrac{l}{w} = \dfrac{7}{3}$
   $\dfrac{105.0 - w}{w} = \dfrac{7}{3}$
   $315.0 - 3w = 7w$
   $\quad\quad 10w = 315.0$
   $\quad\quad\quad w = 31.5 \text{ in.}$
   $\quad\quad\quad l = 105.0 - 31.5 = 73.5 \text{ in.}$

6. Let $L_1 = $ crushing load of first pillar
   $\quad L_2 = $ crushing load of second pillar

   $L_2 = \dfrac{kr_2^4}{l_2^2} \quad L_1 = \dfrac{k(2r_2)^4}{(3l_2)^2}$

   $\dfrac{L_1}{L_2} = \dfrac{\dfrac{k(2r_2)^4}{(3l_2)^2}}{\dfrac{kr_2^4}{l_2^2}} = \dfrac{16kr_2^4}{9l_2^2} \times \dfrac{l_2^2}{kr_2^4} = \dfrac{16}{9}$

APPENDIX B — UNITS OF MEASUREMENT; THE METRIC SYSTEM

B-1 INTRODUCTION

Most scientific and technical calculations involve numbers that represent a measurement or count of a specific physical quantity. *Such numbers are called* **denominate numbers,** *and associated with these denominate numbers are* **units of measurement.** For calculations and results to be meaningful, we must know these units. For example, if we measure the length of an object to be 12, we must know whether it is being measured in feet, yards, or some other specified unit of length.

Certain universally accepted **base units** *are used to measure fundamental quantities.* The units for numerous other quantities are expressed in terms of the base units. Fundamental quantities for which base units are defined are (1) length, (2) mass or force, depending on the system of units being used, (3) time, (4) electric current, (5) temperature, (6) amount of substance, and (7) luminous intensity. *Other units, referred to as* **derived units,** *are expressible in terms of the units for these quantities.*

Even though all other quantities can be expressed in terms of the fundamental ones, many have units that are given a specified name. This is done primarily for those quantities that are used very commonly, although it is not done for all such quantities. For example, the volt is defined as a meter^2-kilogram/second^3-ampere, which is in terms of (a unit of length)^2(a unit of mass)/(a unit of time)^3(a unit of electric current). The unit for acceleration has no special name and is left in terms of the base units, for example, feet/second^2. For convenience, special symbols are usually used to designate units. The units for acceleration would be written as ft/s^2.

Two basic systems of units, the **SI metric system** and the **United States Customary** system, are in use today. The U.S. Customary system traditionally has been known as the *British system.* (The SI metric system is now used in Great Britain, although many measurements in the traditional British system are also still used.) Nearly every country in the world now uses the SI metric system. In the United States both systems are used, and international trade has led most major U.S. industrial firms to convert their products to the metric system. Also, due to world trade, to further promote conversion to the metric system, the U.S. Congress has passed legislation stating that the metric system is the preferred system and requiring Federal agencies to use the metric system in their business-related activities. It should also be noted that the metric system is used worldwide in nearly all scientific work.

Therefore, for the present, both systems are of importance, although the metric system will eventually be used almost universally. For that reason, where units are used, some of the exercises and examples have metric units and others have U.S. Customary units. Technicians and engineers need to have some knowledge of both systems.

SI METRIC SYSTEM

Although more than one system has been developed in which metric units are used, the system now accepted as the metric system is the **International System of Units (SI).** This was established in 1960 and uses some different definitions for base units from the previously developed metric units. However, the measurement of the base units in the SI system is more accessible, and the differences are very slight. *Therefore, when we refer to the metric system, we are using SI units.*

As we have stated, in each system the base units are specified, and all other units are then expressible in terms of these base units. Table B-1 on the next page lists the fundamental quantities, as well as many other commonly used quantities, along with their symbols and the names of units used to represent each quantity shown.

In the U.S. Customary system, the base unit of length is the *foot,* and that of force is the *pound.* In the metric system, the base unit of length is the *meter,* and that of mass is the *kilogram.* Here, we see a difference in the definition of the systems that causes some difficulty when units are converted from one system to the other. That is, a base unit in the U.S. Customary system is a unit of force, and a base unit in the metric system is a unit of mass.

The distinction between mass and force is very significant in physics, and the weight of an object is the force with which it is attracted to the earth. Weight, which is therefore a force, is different from mass, which is a measure of the inertia an object exhibits. Although they are different quantities, mass and weight are, however, very closely related. In fact, the weight of an object equals its mass multiplied by the acceleration due to gravity. Near the surface of the earth, the acceleration due to gravity is nearly constant, although it decreases as the distance from the earth increases. Therefore, near the surface of the earth, the weight of an object is directly proportional to its mass. However, at great distances from the earth, the weight of an object will be zero, whereas its mass does not change.

Since force and mass are different, it is not strictly correct to convert pounds to kilograms. However, since the pound is the base unit in the U.S. Customary system and the kilogram is the base unit in the metric system, at the earth's surface 1 kg corresponds to 2.21 lb, in the sense that the force of gravity on a 1-kg mass is 2.21 lb.

When designating units for weight, we use pounds in the U.S. Customary system. In the metric system, although kilograms are used for weight, it is preferable to specify the mass of an object in kilograms. The force of gravity on an object is designated in newtons, and the use of the term *weight* is avoided unless its meaning is completely clear.

As for the other fundamental quantities, both systems use the *second* as the base unit of time. In the SI system, the *ampere* is defined as the base unit of electric current, and this can also be used in the U.S. Customary system. As for temperature, *degrees Fahrenheit* is used with the U.S. Customary system, and *degrees Celsius* (formerly centigrade) is used with the metric system (actually, the *kelvin* is defined as the base unit, where the temperature in kelvins is the temperature in degrees Celsius plus 273.16). In the SI system, the base unit for the amount of a substance is the *mole,* and the base unit of luminous intensity is the *candela.* These last two are of limited importance to our use in this text.

The failure to convert units caused the $125 000 000 Mars Climate Orbiter to fly too close to Mars and break up in the Martian atmosphere in September 1999. A spacecraft team submitted force data in pounds, but the mission controllers assumed the data were in newtons. The system for checking data did not note the change in units. (1 lb = 4.448 N)

Table B-1   Quantities and Their Associated Units

Quantity	Quantity Symbol	U.S. Customary Name	U.S. Customary Symbol	Metric (SI) Name	Metric (SI) Symbol	In Terms of Other SI Units
Length	s	foot	ft	**meter**	m	
Mass	m	slug		**kilogram**	kg	
Force	F	pound	lb	newton	N	$m \cdot kg/s^2$
Time	t	second	s	**second**	s	
Area	A		ft²		m²	
Volume	V		ft³		m³	
Capacity	V	gallon	gal	liter	L	$(1\ L = 1\ dm^3)$
Velocity	v		ft/s		m/s	
Acceleration	a		ft/s²		m/s²	
Density	d, ρ		lb/ft³		kg/m³	
Pressure	p		lb/ft²	pascal	Pa	N/m²
Energy, work	E, W		ft·lb	joule	J	$N \cdot m$
Power	P	horsepower	hp	watt	W	J/s
Period	T		s		s	
Frequency	f		1/s	hertz	Hz	1/s
Angle	θ	radian	rad	radian	rad	
Electric current	I, i	ampere	A	**ampere**	A	
Electric charge	q	coulomb	C	coulomb	C	$A \cdot s$
Electric potential	V, E	volt	V	volt	V	$J/(A \cdot s)$
Capacitance	C	farad	F	farad	F	s/Ω
Inductance	L	henry	H	henry	H	$\Omega \cdot s$
Resistance	R	ohm	Ω	ohm	Ω	V/A
Thermodynamic temperature	T			**kelvin**	K	(temp. interval
Temperature	T	degrees Fahrenheit	°F	degrees Celsius	°C	1 °C = 1 K)
Quantity of heat	Q	British thermal unit	Btu	joule	J	
Amount of substance	n			**mole**	mol	
Luminous intensity	I	candlepower	cp	**candela**	cd	

Special Notes:

1. The SI base units are shown in boldface type.

2. The unit symbols shown above are those that are used in the text. Many of them were adopted with the adoption of the SI system. This means, for example, that we use s rather than sec for seconds and A rather than amp for amperes. Also, other units, such as volt, are not spelled out, a common practice in the past. When a given unit is used with both systems, we use the SI symbol for the unit.

3. The liter and degree Celsius are not actually SI units. However, they are recognized for use with the SI system due to their practical importance. Also, the symbol for liter has several variations. Presently L is recognized for use in the United States and Canada, l is recognized by the International Committee of Weights and Measures, and ℓ is also recognized for use in several countries.

4. Other units of time, along with their symbols, which are recognized for use with the SI system and are used in this text, are minute, min; hour, h; day, d.

5. Many additional specialized units are used with the SI system. However, most of those that appear in this text are shown in the table. A few of the specialized units are noted when used in the text. One which is frequently used is that for revolution, r.

6. Other common U.S. units used in the text are inch, in.; yard, yd; mile, mi; ounce, oz.; ton; quart, qt; acre.

7. There are a number of units that were used with the metric system prior to the development of the SI system. However, many of these are not to be used with the SI system. Among those that were commonly used are the dyne, erg, and calorie.

Due to greatly varying sizes of certain quantities, the metric system employs certain prefixes to units to denote different orders of magnitude. These prefixes, with their meanings and symbols, are shown in Table B-2.

Table B-2   Metric Prefixes

Prefix	Factor	Symbol	Prefix	Factor	Symbol
exa	10^{18}	E	deci	10^{-1}	d
peta	10^{15}	P	centi	10^{-2}	c
tera	10^{12}	T	milli	10^{-3}	m
giga	10^{9}	G	micro	10^{-6}	μ
mega	10^{6}	M	nano	10^{-9}	n
kilo	10^{3}	k	pico	10^{-12}	p
hecto	10^{2}	h	femto	10^{-15}	f
deca	10^{1}	da	atto	10^{-18}	a

EXAMPLE 1   Some commonly used units that use prefixes in Table B-2, along with their meanings, are shown below.

Unit	Symbol	Meaning	Unit	Symbol	Meaning
megohm	MΩ	10^{6} ohms	milligram	mg	10^{-3} gram
kilometer	km	10^{3} meters	microfarad	μF	10^{-6} farad
centimeter	cm	10^{-2} meter	nanosecond	ns	10^{-9} second

(Mega is shortened to meg when used with "ohm.")

When designating units of area or volume, where square or cubic units are used, we use exponents in the designation. For example, we use m^2 rather than sq m and $in.^3$ rather than cu in.

B-2 REDUCTIONS AND CONVERSIONS

When using denominate numbers, it may be necessary to change from one set of units to another. *A change within a given system is called a* **reduction,** *and a change from one system to another is called a* **conversion.** Table B-3 gives some basic conversion factors. Some calculators are programmed to do conversions.

Table B-3   Conversion Factors

1 in. = 2.54 cm (exact)	1 ft^3 = 28.32 L	1 lb = 453.6 g	1 Btu = 778.0 ft·lb
1 km = 0.6214 mi	1 L = 1.057 qt	1 kg = 2.205 lb	1 hp = 550 ft·lb/s (exact)
		1 lb = 4.448 N	1 hp = 746.0 W

The advantages of the metric system are evident. Reductions within the system are made by using powers of 10, which amounts to moving the decimal point. Reductions in the U.S. Customary system are made by using many different multiples. Comparisons and changes within the metric system are much simpler.

NOTE ▶ To change a given number of one set of units into another set of units, *we perform algebraic operations with units in the same manner as we do with any algebraic symbol*. Consider the following example.

▌EXAMPLE 1 If we had a number representing feet per second to be multiplied by another number representing seconds per minute, as far as the units are concerned, we have

$$\frac{\text{ft}}{\text{s}} \times \frac{\text{s}}{\text{min}} = \frac{\text{ft} \times \cancel{\text{s}}}{\cancel{\text{s}} \times \text{min}} = \frac{\text{ft}}{\text{min}}$$

This means that the final result would be in feet per minute. ----------▮

In changing a number of one set of units to another set of units, we use reduction and conversion factors and the principle illustrated in Example 1. The convenient way to use the values in the tables is in the form of fractions. Since the given values are equal to each other, their quotient is 1. For example, since 1 in. = 2.54 cm,

NOTE ▶

$$\frac{1 \text{ in.}}{2.54 \text{ cm}} = 1 \quad \text{or} \quad \frac{2.54 \text{ cm}}{1 \text{ in.}} = 1$$

since each represents the division of a certain length by itself. Multiplying a quantity by 1 does not change its value. The following examples illustrate reduction and conversion of units.

▌EXAMPLE 2 Reduce 20 kg to milligrams.

$$20 \text{ kg} = 20 \text{ kg}\left(\frac{10^3 \text{ } \cancel{g}}{1 \text{ kg}}\right)\left(\frac{10^3 \text{ mg}}{1 \text{ } \cancel{g}}\right)$$
$$= 20 \times 10^6 \text{ mg} = 2.0 \times 10^7 \text{ mg}$$

We note that this result is found essentially by moving the decimal point three places when changing from kilograms to grams, and another three places when changing from grams to milligrams. ----------▮

▌EXAMPLE 3 Change 30 mi/h to feet per second.

$$30\frac{\text{mi}}{\text{h}} = \left(30\frac{\cancel{\text{mi}}}{\cancel{\text{h}}}\right)\left(\frac{5280 \text{ ft}}{1 \text{ } \cancel{\text{mi}}}\right)\left(\frac{1 \text{ } \cancel{\text{h}}}{60 \text{ } \cancel{\text{min}}}\right)\left(\frac{1 \text{ } \cancel{\text{min}}}{60 \text{ s}}\right) = \frac{(30)(5280) \text{ ft}}{(60)(60) \text{ s}} = 44\frac{\text{ft}}{\text{s}}$$

The only units remaining after the division are those required. ----------▮

▌EXAMPLE 4 Change 575 g/cm³ to kilograms per cubic meter.

$$575\frac{\text{g}}{\text{cm}^3} = \left(575\frac{\text{g}}{\text{cm}^3}\right)\left(\frac{100 \text{ cm}}{1 \text{ m}}\right)^3\left(\frac{1 \text{ kg}}{1000 \text{ g}}\right)$$
$$= \left(575\frac{\cancel{\text{g}}}{\cancel{\text{cm}^3}}\right)\left(\frac{10^6 \text{ } \cancel{\text{cm}^3}}{1 \text{ m}^3}\right)\left(\frac{1 \text{ kg}}{10^3 \text{ } \cancel{\text{g}}}\right)$$
$$= 575 \times 10^3\frac{\text{kg}}{\text{m}^3} = 5.75 \times 10^5\frac{\text{kg}}{\text{m}^3}$$ ----------▮

EXAMPLE 5 Change 62.8 lb/in.^{2} to newtons per square meter.

$$62.8 \frac{\text{lb}}{\text{in.}^2} = \left(62.8 \frac{\text{lb}}{\text{in.}^2}\right)\left(\frac{4.448 \text{ N}}{1 \text{ lb}}\right)\left(\frac{1 \text{ in.}}{2.54 \text{ cm}}\right)^2\left(\frac{100 \text{ cm}}{1 \text{ m}}\right)^2$$

$$= \left(62.8 \frac{\text{lb}}{\text{in.}^2}\right)\left(\frac{4.448 \text{ N}}{1 \text{ lb}}\right)\left(\frac{1 \text{ in.}^2}{2.54^2 \text{ cm}^2}\right)\left(\frac{10^4 \text{ cm}^2}{1 \text{ m}^2}\right)$$

$$= \frac{(62.8)(4.448)(10^4)}{(2.54)^2} \frac{\text{N}}{\text{m}^2} = 4.33 \times 10^5 \frac{\text{N}}{\text{m}^2}$$

Appendix B.2
EXERCISES FOR APPENDIX *B*

In Exercises 1–4, give the symbol and the meaning for the given unit.

1. megahertz
2. kilowatt
3. millimeter
4. picosecond

In Exercises 5–8, give the name and the meaning for the units whose symbols are given.

5. kV
6. GΩ
7. mA
8. pF

In Exercises 9–44, make the indicated reductions and conversions.

9. Reduce 1 km to centimeters.
10. Reduce 1 kV to millivolts.
11. Reduce 1 mi to inches.
12. Reduce 1 gal to pints.
13. Convert 5.25 in. to centimeters.
14. Convert 6.50 kg to pounds.
15. Convert 15.7 qt to liters.
16. Convert 185 km to miles.
17. Reduce 1 ft^2 to square inches.
18. Reduce 1 yd^3 to cubic feet.
19. Reduce 250 mm^2 to square meters.
20. Reduce 0.125 MΩ to milliohms.
21. Convert 4.50 lb to grams.
22. Convert 0.360 in. to meters.
23. Convert 829 in.^{3} to liters.
24. Convert 0.0680 kL to cubic feet.
25. Convert 2.25 hp to newton centimeters per second.
26. Convert 8.75 Btu to joules.
27. Reduce 25 kW · h to megajoules.
28. Reduce 30 ns to minutes.
29. Convert 75.0 W to horsepower.
30. Convert 326 mL to quarts.
31. A weather satellite orbiting the earth weighs 6500 lb. How many tons is this?

32. An airplane is flying at 37,000 ft. What is its altitude in miles?
33. A car's gasoline tank holds 56 L. Convert this capacity to gallons.
34. A hockey puck has a mass of about 0.160 kg. What is its weight in pounds?
35. The speed of sound is about 1130 ft/s. Change this speed to kilometers per hour.
36. Water flows from a kitchen faucet at the rate of 8.5 gal/min. What is this rate in liters per second?
37. The speedometer of a car is calibrated in kilometers per hour. If the speed of such a car reads 60, how fast in miles per hour is the car moving?
38. The acceleration due to gravity is about 980 cm/s^2. Convert this to feet per squared second.
39. Fifteen grams of a medication are to be dissolved in 0.060 L of water. Express this concentration in milligrams per deciliter.
40. The earth's surface receives energy from the sun at the rate of 1.35 kW/m^2. Reduce this to joules per second square centimeter.
41. At sea level, atmospheric pressure is about 14.7 lb/in.^{2}. Express this in pascals.
42. The density of water is about 62.4 lb/ft^3. Convert this to kilograms per cubic meter.
43. A typical electric current density in a wire is 1.2×10^6 A/m^2. Express this in milliamperes per square centimeter.
44. A certain automobile engine produces a maximum torque of 110 N · m. Convert this to foot pounds.

In Exercises 45–48, use the following information. A commercial jet with 230 passengers on a 2850-km flight from Vancouver to Chicago averaged 765 km/h and used fuel at the rate of 5650 L/h.

45. How many hours long was the flight?
46. How long in seconds did it take to use 1.0 L of fuel?
47. What was the fuel consumption in km/L?
48. What was the fuel consumption in L/passenger?

Appendix B.2

Exercises for Appendix B, page A-9

1. MHz, 1 MHz $= 10^6$ Hz   **3.** mm, 1 mm $= 10^{-3}$ m

5. kilovolt, 1 kV $= 10^3$ V

7. milliampere, 1 mA $= 10^{-3}$ A   **9.** 10^5 cm

11. 63,360 in.   **13.** 13.3 cm   **15.** 14.9 L

17. 144 in.^{2} **19.** 2.50×10^{-4} m^2 **21.** 2040 g

23. 13.6 L   **25.** 1.68×10^5 N $\cdot$ cm/s   **27.** 90 MJ

29. 0.101 hp   **31.** 3.25 tons   **33.** 15 gal

35. 1240 km/h   **37.** 37 mi/h   **39.** 25,000 mg/dL

41. 101,000 Pa   **43.** 1.2×10^5 mA/cm^2

45. 3.73 h   **47.** 0.135 km/L

Appendix C

Trigonometric Functions (Tables)

θ Degrees	θ Radians	sin θ	cos θ	tan θ	cot θ		
0°00'	0.0000	0.0000	1.0000	0.0000	-----	1.5708	90°00'
0°10'	0.0029	0.0029	1.0000	0.0029	343.8	1.5679	89°50'
0°20'	0.0058	0.0058	1.0000	0.0058	171.9	1.5650	89°40'
0°30'	0.0087	0.0087	1.0000	0.0087	114.6	1.5621	89°30'
0°40'	0.0116	0.0116	0.9999	0.0116	85.94	1.5592	89°20'
0°50'	0.0145	0.0145	0.9999	0.0145	68.75	1.5563	89°10'
1°00'	0.0175	0.0175	0.9998	0.0175	57.29	1.5533	89°00'
1°10'	0.0204	0.0204	0.9998	0.0204	49.10	1.5504	88°50'
1°20'	0.0233	0.0233	0.9997	0.0233	42.96	1.5475	88°40'
1°30'	0.0262	0.0262	0.9997	0.0262	38.19	1.5446	88°30'
1°40'	0.0291	0.0291	0.9996	0.0291	34.37	1.5417	88°20'
1°50'	0.0320	0.0320	0.9995	0.0320	31.24	1.5388	88°10'
2°00'	0.0349	0.0349	0.9994	0.0349	28.64	1.5359	88°00'
2°10'	0.0378	0.0378	0.9993	0.0378	26.43	1.5330	87°50'
2°20'	0.0407	0.0407	0.9992	0.0407	24.54	1.5301	87°40'
2°30'	0.0436	0.0436	0.9990	0.0437	22.90	1.5272	87°30'
2°40'	0.0465	0.0465	0.9989	0.0466	21.47	1.5243	87°20'
2°50'	0.0495	0.0494	0.9988	0.0495	20.21	1.5213	87°10'
3°00'	0.0524	0.0523	0.9986	0.0524	19.08	1.5184	87°00'
3°10'	0.0553	0.0552	0.9985	0.0553	18.07	1.5155	86°50'
3°20'	0.0582	0.0581	0.9983	0.0582	17.17	1.5126	86°40'
3°30'	0.0611	0.0610	0.9981	0.0612	16.35	1.5097	86°30'
3°40'	0.0640	0.0640	0.9980	0.0641	15.60	1.5068	86°20'
3°50'	0.0669	0.0669	0.9978	0.0670	14.92	1.5039	86°10'
4°00'	0.0698	0.0698	0.9976	0.0699	14.30	1.5010	86°00'
4°10'	0.0727	0.0727	0.9974	0.0729	13.73	1.4981	85°50'
4°20'	0.0756	0.0756	0.9971	0.0758	13.20	1.4952	85°40'
4°30'	0.0785	0.0785	0.9969	0.0787	12.71	1.4923	85°30'
4°40'	0.0814	0.0814	0.9967	0.0816	12.25	1.4893	85°20'
4°50'	0.0844	0.0843	0.9964	0.0846	11.83	1.4864	85°10'
5°00'	0.0873	0.0872	0.9962	0.0875	11.43	1.4835	85°00'
5°10'	0.0902	0.0901	0.9959	0.0904	11.06	1.4806	84°50'
5°20'	0.0931	0.0929	0.9957	0.0934	10.71	1.4777	84°40'
5°30'	0.0960	0.0958	0.9954	0.0963	10.39	1.4748	84°30'
5°40'	0.0989	0.0987	0.9951	0.0992	10.08	1.4719	84°20'
5°50'	0.1018	0.1016	0.9948	0.1022	9.788	1.4690	84°10'
6°00'	0.1047	0.1045	0.9945	0.1051	9.514	1.4661	84°00'
6°10'	0.1076	0.1074	0.9942	0.1080	9.255	1.4632	83°50'
6°20'	0.1105	0.1103	0.9939	0.1110	9.010	1.4603	83°40'
6°30'	0.1134	0.1132	0.9936	0.1139	8.777	1.4573	83°30'
6°40'	0.1164	0.1161	0.9932	0.1169	8.556	1.4544	83°20'
6°50'	0.1193	0.1190	0.9929	0.1198	8.345	1.4515	83°10'
		cos θ	sin θ	cot θ	tan θ	θ Radians	θ Degrees

θ Degrees	θ Radians	sin θ	cos θ	tan θ	cot θ		
7°00'	**0.1222**	**0.1219**	**0.9925**	**0.1228**	**8.144**	**1.4486**	**83°00'**
7°10'	0.1251	0.1248	0.9922	0.1257	7.953	1.4457	82°50'
7°20'	0.1280	0.1276	0.9918	0.1287	7.770	1.4428	82°40'
7°30'	0.1309	0.1305	0.9914	0.1317	7.596	1.4399	82°30'
7°40'	0.1338	0.1334	0.9911	0.1346	7.429	1.4370	82°20'
7°50'	0.1367	0.1363	0.9907	0.1376	7.269	1.4341	82°10'
8°00'	**0.1396**	**0.1392**	**0.9903**	**0.1405**	**7.115**	**1.4312**	**82°00'**
8°10'	0.1425	0.1421	0.9899	0.1435	6.968	1.4283	81°50'
8°20'	0.1454	0.1449	0.9894	0.1465	6.827	1.4254	81°40'
8°30'	0.1484	0.1478	0.9890	0.1495	6.691	1.4224	81°30'
8°40'	0.1513	0.1507	0.9886	0.1524	6.561	1.4195	81°20'
8°50'	0.1542	0.1536	0.9881	0.1554	6.435	1.4166	81°10'
9°00'	**0.1571**	**0.1564**	**0.9877**	**0.1584**	**6.314**	**1.4137**	**81°00'**
9°10'	0.1600	0.1593	0.9872	0.1614	6.197	1.4108	80°50'
9°20'	0.1629	0.1622	0.9868	0.1644	6.084	1.4079	80°40'
9°30'	0.1658	0.1650	0.9863	0.1673	5.976	1.4050	80°30'
9°40'	0.1687	0.1679	0.9858	0.1703	5.871	1.4021	80°20'
9°50'	0.1716	0.1708	0.9853	0.1733	5.769	1.3992	80°10'
10°00'	**0.1745**	**0.1736**	**0.9848**	**0.1763**	**5.671**	**1.3963**	**80°00'**
10°10'	0.1774	0.1765	0.9843	0.1793	5.576	1.3934	79°50'
10°20'	0.1804	0.1794	0.9838	0.1823	5.485	1.3904	79°40'
10°30'	0.1833	0.1822	0.9833	0.1853	5.396	1.3875	79°30'
10°40'	0.1862	0.1851	0.9827	0.1883	5.309	1.3846	79°20'
10°50'	0.1891	0.1880	0.9822	0.1914	5.226	1.3817	79°10'
11°00'	**0.1920**	**0.1908**	**0.9816**	**0.1944**	**5.145**	**1.3788**	**79°00'**
11°10'	0.1949	0.1937	0.9811	0.1974	5.066	1.3759	78°50'
11°20'	0.1978	0.1965	0.9805	0.2004	4.989	1.3730	78°40'
11°30'	0.2007	0.1994	0.9799	0.2035	4.915	1.3701	78°30'
11°40'	0.2036	0.2022	0.9793	0.2065	4.843	1.3672	78°20'
11°50'	0.2065	0.2051	0.9787	0.2095	4.773	1.3643	78°10'
12°00'	**0.2094**	**0.2079**	**0.9781**	**0.2126**	**4.705**	**1.3614**	**78°00'**
12°10'	0.2123	0.2108	0.9775	0.2156	4.638	1.3584	77°50'
12°20'	0.2153	0.2136	0.9769	0.2186	4.574	1.3555	77°40'
12°30'	0.2182	0.2164	0.9763	0.2217	4.511	1.3526	77°30'
12°40'	0.2211	0.2193	0.9757	0.2247	4.449	1.3497	77°20'
12°50'	0.2240	0.2221	0.9750	0.2278	4.390	1.3468	77°10'
13°00'	**0.2269**	**0.2250**	**0.9744**	**0.2309**	**4.331**	**1.3439**	**77°00'**
13°10'	0.2298	0.2278	0.9737	0.2339	4.275	1.3410	76°50'
13°20'	0.2327	0.2306	0.9730	0.2370	4.219	1.3381	76°40'
13°30'	0.2356	0.2334	0.9724	0.2401	4.165	1.3352	76°30'
13°40'	0.2385	0.2363	0.9717	0.2432	4.113	1.3323	76°20'
13°50'	0.2414	0.2391	0.9710	0.2462	4.061	1.3294	76°10'
		cos θ	sin θ	cot θ	tan θ	θ Radians	θ Degrees